DATE DUE

HANDBOOK OF STRATA-BOUND AND STRATIFORM ORE DEPOSITS

Volume 7
Au, U, Fe, Mn, Hg, Sb, W, AND P DEPOSITS

HANDBOOK OF STRATA-BOUND AND STRATIFORM ORE DEPOSITS

Edited by
K.H. WOLF

I
PRINCIPLES AND GENERAL STUDIES

1. Classifications and Historical Studies

2. Geochemical Studies

3. Supergene and Surficial Ore Deposits ; Textures and Fabrics

4. Tectonics and Metamorphism
   Indexes Volumes 1—4

II
REGIONAL STUDIES AND SPECIFIC DEPOSITS

5. Regional Studies

6. Cu, Zn, Pb, and Ag Deposits

7. Au, U, Fe, Mn, Hg, Sb, W, and P Deposits
   Indexes Volumes 5—7

ELSEVIER SCIENTIFIC PUBLISHING COMPANY
Amsterdam — Oxford — New York   1976

HANDBOOK OF STRATA-BOUND AND STRATIFORM ORE DEPOSITS

II. REGIONAL STUDIES AND SPECIFIC DEPOSITS

Edited by

K.H. WOLF

Volume 7

Au, U, Fe, Mn, Hg, Sb, W, AND P DEPOSITS

INDEXES VOLUMES 5–7

ELSEVIER SCIENTIFIC PUBLISHING COMPANY
Amsterdam – Oxford – New York   1976

ELSEVIER SCIENTIFIC PUBLISHING COMPANY
335 Jan van Galenstraat
P.O. Box 211, Amsterdam, The Netherlands

Distributors for the United States and Canada:

ELSEVIER/NORTH-HOLLAND INC.
52, Vanderbilt Avenue
New York, N.Y. 10017

LIST OF CONTRIBUTORS TO THIS VOLUME

C.J. BOWSER
Department of Geology and Geophysics, University of Wisconsin, Madison, Wisc., U.S.A.

E. CALLENDER
U.S. Department of the Interior, Geological Survey, Reston, Va., U.S.A.

P.J. COOK
Bureau of Mineral Resources, Geology and Geophysics, Canberra City, A.C.T., Australia

E. DIMROTH
Department of Earth Sciences, University of Quebec, Chicoutimi, Que., Canada

J. EICHLER
Department of Geology, Ferteco Mineraçao S.A., Rio de Janeiro, Brazil

G.P. GLASBY
New Zealand Oceanographic Institute, Department of Scientific and Industrial Research, Wellington, New Zealand

A. MAUCHER
Institut für Algemeine und Angewandte Geologie und Mineralogie, University of Munich, Munich, Germany

D.A. PRETORIUS
Economic Geology Research Unit, University of the Witwatersrand, Johannesburg, South Africa

R.I. RACKLEY
AMAX Uranium Corporation, Casper, Wyo., U.S.A.

A.J. READ
Chemistry Division, Department of Scientific and Industrial Research, Lower Hutt, New Zealand

SUPRIYA ROY
Department of Geological Sciences, Jadavpur University, Calcutta, India

H. QUADE
Geological Institute, Technical University, Clausthal-Zellerfeld, Germany

CONTENTS

Chapter 3. ORIGIN OF WESTERN-STATES TYPE URANIUM MINERALIZATION
by R.I. Rackley

Chapter 4. ORIGIN OF THE PRECAMBRIAN BANDED IRON-FORMATIONS
by J. Eichler

Chapter 5. ASPECTS OF THE SEDIMENTARY PETROLOGY OF CHERTY IRON-FORMA-
TION
by E. Dimroth

Chapter 6. GENETIC PROBLEMS AND ENVIRONMENTAL FEATURES OF VOLCANO–
SEDIMENTARY IRON-ORE DEPOSITS OF THE LAHN–DILL TYPE
by H. Quade

Chapter 7. DEEP-SEA MANGANESE NODULES
by G.P. Glasby and A.J. Read

Chapter 1

GOLD IN THE PROTEROZOIC SEDIMENTS OF SOUTH AFRICA: SYSTEMS, PARADIGMS, AND MODELS

D.A. PRETORIUS

INTRODUCTION

The Republic of South Africa is a metal producer of the first rank. Gold is the most important of the metals and up to the end of 1971, U.S.$ 32 billion had been realized from its sale. This figure was equivalent to 80% of the total value of all metals sold. The gold province is located on the Kaapvaal craton which is composed of Precambrian sedimentary-volcanic and granite-greenstone assemblages ranging in age from 1,750 to 3,500 million years. This craton forms the southern part of the Southern African Shield. No significant gold mineralization has yet been found beyond the boundaries of this shield. On the Kaapvaal craton, five Proterozoic sedimentary-volcanic basins lie on an Archean basement. The basins were formed under continental conditions and in only one is there any evidence of a major marine transgression. The gold so far won from the Archean rocks constitutes only 1.77% of the total, with 98.23% coming from the Proterozoic sediments. No gold mineralization has been exploited in the volcanics of the basins. Three types of goldfields exist: those in tectonically and metamorphically reconstituted ultramafics and mafics of the Archean greenstone belts, such as the Barberton-type field in the Swaziland Sequence; those in fluvial fan/lacustrine interface environments, such as the Witwatersrand-type fields in the Pongola, Witwatersrand and Transvaal sequences; and those in delta—open sea interface environments, such as the Transvaal-type fields in the Transvaal Sequence. The Proterozoic host rocks of sedimentary gold deposits are conglomerates, quartzites, shales, silty dolomites, dolomitic argillites and algal mats. A series of conceptual process-response models has been constructed to generalize on times, environments and conditions most favourable to the concentration of gold in Proterozoic sediments. These models refer to source area, transfer system and depository of gold moved in solid state or in solution from greenstone belts into cratonic clastic and nonclastic sediments, and there concentrated by physical, chemical and biological agencies. Various models depict aspects of tectonism, erosion, transportation, stratigraphy, sedimentology, mineralization, biological activity and atmospheric evolution, which interacted to produce the most significant Proterozoic gold mineralization in the world. From the models, a number of generalized conclusions have been drawn which might act as guides to future exploration for further gold deposits in South Africa. (For a regional setting, see Chapter 6, Vol. 5, by Anhaeusser and for details on the geology of the Witwatersrand gold-uranium deposits, a second chapter by Pretorius in this volume.)

GOLD MINERALIZATION IN SOUTH AFRICA

South Africa's place as a mineral producer

The Republic of South Africa covers an area of approximately 472,000 sq. miles. Up to the end of 1971, the total value of mineral production from all recorded mining activity was a little over U.S.$ 49 billion. The exploited value of the crust thus averaged $ 104,500 per sq. mile. The unit regional value of the United States of America up to the same year was $ 266,100 per sq. mile, of Canada $ 17,400 per sq. mile, and of Australia $ 8,700 per sq. mile. These figures show that South Africa ranks very high in the list of great mineral-producing countries of the world. If the total value of all minerals extracted from the crust is broken down according to three broad classifications, it can be seen that fuels have contributed $ 174,000 per sq. mile in the U.S., $ 7,000 per sq. mile in South Africa, $ 5,100 per sq. mile in Canada and $ 2,500 per sq. mile in Australia. The value per sq. mile of non-metallics mined in the U.S. was $ 50,500, in South Africa $ 11,300, in Canada $ 4,500 and in Australia $ 1,000. In the case of metals, the order of importance shows a marked change. The value per sq. mile of metals recovered in South Africa was $ 86,200, in the U.S. $ 41,500, in Canada $ 7,800 and in Australia $ 5,200.[1]

Of course, gold is not distributed equally throughout all segments of the crust in the sub-continent, neither in time nor in space. Except for a very minor porportion, indeed, all the gold so far mined has been found in Precambrian rocks, and, except for a slightly greater fraction, all the gold has come from the northeastern quadrant of South Africa.

Geological eras and mineral production

The history of crustal development and of associated mineralization in South Africa can be fitted into a framework of six eras, each of progressively shorter duration with the passage of time. The Botswanian era extends from the present to 150 million years, the Outeniquian from 150 to 500 m.y., the Bolandian from 500 to 1,000 m.y., the Bushmanian from 1,000 to 1,750 m.y., the Kaapvaalian from 1,750 to 3,000 m.y. and the Barbertonian from 3,000 m.y. to the formation of the earth. Rocks of the Precambrian eras (Barbertonian, Kaapvaalian, Bushmanian and Bolandian) are exposed over a total area of 154,000 sq. miles. From the Precambrian formations, minerals and mineral aggregates to the value of $ 43 billion had been mined up to the end of 1971. The unit regional value of the exposed Precambrian was thus $ 279,700 per sq. mile. Of this Precambrian mineral wealth, 85% had been extracted from sedimentary basins, 9% from igneous complexes, and 6% from metamorphic terranes.

---

[1] See note added in proof, p. 27.

The key words, then, in the distribution of mineral wealth in South Africa are gold, sediments, Precambrian and northeastern part of the country.

Gold in time and space

The Southern African Shield underlies the eastern part of Botswana, the northeastern segment of South Africa, and Rhodesia. It consist of two cratons — the Kaapvaal and the Rhodesian cratons — separated by the Limpopo high-grade metamorphic belt. Significant gold mineralization in Southern Africa is restricted to the two cratons, of which the Kaapvaal crustal fragment is by far the more important contributor. The transition from Archean-type to Proterozoic-type crustal development took place on the Kaapvaal craton at about 3,000 m.y., and on the Rhodesian craton at possibly 2,700 m.y. In Rhodesia, gold mineralization occurs only in the Archean granite-greenstone terrain, whereas, on the Kaapvaal craton, it is found in both the Archean formations and in the Proterozoic sedimentary-volcanic basins. The host rocks to Archean gold deposits are predominantly ultramafic and mafic rocks, many of a cyclic volcanic origin, with intercalated pyroclastics and chemical sediments. Proterozoic gold ore occurs, for the greater part, in clastic and non-clastic sediments. The clastic sediments are both fine- and coarse-grained, but there is a distinct tendency for greater concentrations of gold to occur in, or near, conglomerate horizons. The more important non-clastic host rocks are silty carbonates, transitional between fine-grained clastic sediments and chemical precipitates. The gold has been remobilized in both the Archean and the Proterozoic deposits. In the former case, considerable generation and emplacement of granite, during the terminal phases of the Archean, was the main agent of the remobilization which was more extensive than that developed in the Proterozoic. Reconstitution of gold ores in the sedimentary-volcanic basins was brought about by diagenesis and by subsequent volcanic activity. Gold mineralization in the Archean is primarily igneous in origin, in the Proterozoic primarily sedimentary in origin.

The total value of gold mined in the Kaapvaal craton up to the end of 1970 was $ 32,610 million, of which $ 568 million (1.77%) came from Archean ores and $ 32,042 million (98.23%) from Proterozoic mineralization.

In the Archean, the period between 3,000 and 3,250 m.y. was marked by granitic activity with which little primary gold mineralization was associated. In the classic greenstone area of the Barberton Mountain Land, in the eastern Transvaal, the period between 3,250 and 3,500 m.y. saw the development of the Swaziland Sequence which consists of three major groups — the Onverwacht, at the base of the 25,000 m-thick assemblage, the Fig Tree and the Moodies, at the top of the sequence. The Lower Division of the Onverwacht Group is composed essentially of ultramafics and mafics, with some intercalated pyroclastics and cherts. The Upper Division has significantly lesser amounts of ultramafics, while felsic volcanics are present in addition to the basalts. Pyroclastics and chemical sediments are again present. The Fig Tree Group is constituted by greywackes, shales, cherts and banded ironstones, while the Moodies Group contains conglomerates, quartzites, shales, jaspillites and minor volcanics. The Onverwacht and Fig Tree members were deposited under deep-water marine conditions, whereas the Moodies sediments were laid down in a shallow-water, terrestrial environment.

The bulk of the primary gold mineralization appears to be strata-bound along two particular stratigraphic horizons – the contact between the Lower Onverwacht Group and the Upper Group and the contact between the Upper Onverwacht Group and the Fig Tree Group. Long held to represent typical mesothermal and hypothermal hydrothermal mineralization generated by the intrusive granites of the 3,000–3,250 m.y. period, the gold is now considered to be a product of older volcanic activity in Onverwacht times. The most commonly associated ore minerals are pyrite, arsenopyrite, and stibnite, with smaller amounts of copper, nickel and cobalt minerals.

Five sedimentary-volcanic belts of Proterozoic age are preserved on the Kaapvaal craton: the Pongola Sequence (3,000–2,750 m.y.), the Witwatersrand Sequence (2,750–2,500 m.y.), the Ventersdorp Sequence (2,500–2,250 m.y.), the Transvaal Sequence (2,250–2,000 m.y.) and the Waterberg Sequence (2,000–1,750 m.y.). It would appear that no younger Proterozoic basins were developed on the Kaapvaal craton, and that a very considerable hiatus marks the time between the Waterberg Sequence and the Paleozoic cover of the Karroo Sequence. Each of the basins had a somewhat similar stratigraphic sequence: volcanics at the base and at the top, and fine and coarse clastics in the middle. Banded iron formations are present in the Pongola, Witwatersrand, and Transvaal sequences and substantial dolomite development also occurs in the last-mentioned. The characteristic colour of the Waterberg rocks is reddish-brown, whereas the strata of all four of the other Proterozoic sequences are various hues of grey, white, black, and bluish-green. The general order of thickness of these sequences is 10,000–15,000 m. Ultramafic igneous rocks are absent from the Proterozoic basins and the volcanics are dominantly basalt-andesite, with some felsic components.

The value of gold won up to the end of 1971 from the five Proterozoic basins on the Kaapvaal craton was:

Waterberg Sequence   : nil
Transvaal Sequence   : $ 484 million
Ventersdorp Sequence   : nil
Witwatersrand Sequence : $ 31,557 million
Pongola Sequence   : $ 1 million

In the Pongola rocks, the gold occurs in conglomerates and shales; in the Witwatersrand, in conglomerates, quartzites, shales, and algal mats; in the Transvaal, in conglomerates, shales, silty dolomites and dolomites. The commonly associated ore minerals in the Pongola are pyrite; in the Witwatersrand, pyrite and uraninite; in the Transvaal, pyrite and chalcopyrite. Placer and hydrothermal origins have been advanced for the Witwatersrand ores and hydrothermal processes for the gold in the Pongola and Transvaal rocks. It is now held that all the gold in the three basins is sedimentary in origin, having been transported either as detrital particles to accumulate in the coarser clastics, or in cold solution to be precipitated by the carbonates and the biogenic materials.

On the Kaapvaal craton, gold disappears from the record at the end of the Transvaal times, and is not seen again, to any significant extent, in the remainder of the Proterozoic or in the Phanerozoic. Gold mineralization is thus confined to Barbertonian era and the early and middle periods of the Kaapvaalian era. The same statement can be made for the whole of Southern Africa: gold is of no major economic importance in rocks younger than 2,000 m.y. This time-line also marks an important change in the general nature of ore deposits in the sub-continent. Prior to 2,000 m.y., siderophile mineralization was of much greater significance than deposits of chalcophile elements; subsequent to 2,000 m.y., the reverse is true.

SYSTEMS, PARADIGMS, AND MODELS

With gold mineralization as extensive as it is in the Early Proterozoic and in the Archean of South Africa, it would appear that the styles of crustal development which evolved over a long period of time remained consistently favourable to the concentration of the precious metal. A system of emplacement and redistribution was operative between Archean and Middle Proterozoic times, i.e., for 1,500 m.y. at least, which lends itself to certain generalized statements concerning origin, dispersal and deposition of the gold. Were the occurrences of gold less in number, smaller in volume, more widely distributed in time and place, and located in a greater variety of environments, generalizations would not be possible. The construction of models is an integral part of generalization.

Onions (1959) defined a system as "a set or assemblage of things connected, associated, or interdependent, so as to form a complex unity". In order to generalize about a system — in this case the processes and responses of gold mineralization over 1,500 m.y. in the eastern segment of the Kaapvaal craton — it is necessary to decompose the complexity into a set of relatively simple patterns in which information is organized in a manner that permits understanding and prediction. Process-response models can be regarded as types of filters through which complexity might be transformed into apparent simplicity. Such models are heuristic devices that are useful in deducing a permissive environment for as yet undiscovered ore deposits from an indicative environment in which the characteristics and controls of known mineralization have been established and analysed.

Meadows et al. (1972) stated that: "A model is simply an ordered set of assumptions about a complex system. It is an attempt to understand some aspect of the infinitely varied world by selecting from perceptions and past experience a set of general observations applicable to the problem in hand." Sufficient experience has been gained, over 100 years of exploration and mining, of gold mineralization in South Africa to allow the design of several models which contain both general observations and justifiable assumptions regarding the evolution of the system of processes and environments particularly favourable to the generation of gold deposits in sedimentary assemblages. Information about the system can be structured on four levels: regional, areal, local, and random. The fundamental feature of models, according to Hagget and Chorley (1967), is a highly selective attitude to information, with that on the local and random levels being eliminated, so that a model achieves an overview of the essential characteristics of a domain. Because of this selectivity, models are approximations of reality, bridging the observational and theoretical components of natural phenomena.

The hierarchy of generalization within a system is: (*1*) facts; (*2*) models; (*3*) paradigms (Hagget and Chorley, 1967). Paradigms have been defined as interrelated networks of concepts, on a sufficiently general level, which indicate the nature of the goals of the operation and of the conventional frameworks within which these are pursued. Paradigms can be regarded as large-scale models, not as specifically formulated, within which lower-rank models are set (Hagget and Chorley, 1967). The value of a paradigm lies in the fact that it permits the progressive evolution of an array of models within its general terms, which, themselves, remain essentially unchanged with time.

Conceptual process-response models of Proterozoic basins in South Africa were first employed by Pretorius (1965) in attempting to generalize on the overall pattern of cyclicity in the stratigraphic successions of the Kaapvaalian sequences. Conceptual models for the exploration for further gold mineralization in the Witwatersrand basin were subsequently constructed by Pretorius (1966)[1], these models conforming to Hagget's and Chorley's (1967) definition of devices describing the class of objects or events to be studied, the kinds of measurements to be made, and the properties or attributes of these measurements. The present chapter is an outgrowth of these two earlier attempts at stratigraphic-sedimentological modelling and is an expanded endeavour to emphasize the broad characteristics of a geological system into which gold entered at about 3,500 m.y. and from which it disappeared at about 2,000 m.y. The sedimentary gold deposits are integral parts of the rocks which contain them. To understand the nature of the mineralization, the complex formational history of the Proterozoic sediments has to be simplified through generalizations of the regional and areal variables which determined the optimum depositional milieu for the different types of gold deposits.

PARADIGMS OF SEDIMENTARY GOLD

The gold which has been found in the Pongola, Witwatersrand and Transvaal sequences of the Kaapvaalian era is firmly believed to be of sedimentary origin. Although some of it has been considered to be epigenetic in origin, no substantial evidence has yet been

---

[1] Editor's note: See chapter on models in Vol. 1 for some details.

produced pointing to an acceptable source of magmatic hydrothermal fluids. Perhaps, the most doubt can be attached to the sedimentary origin of the gold in the dolomites and silty non-clastics of the Transvaal Sequence, since many of the features of these deposits can be accommodated in a volcanic fumarolic model. However, the weight of the argument leans well to the syngenetic, sedimentary side for all the Proterozoic gold mineralization in the basins on the Kaapvaal craton.

Under these circumstances, the paradigm (super-model) for such mineralization is that depicted in Fig. 1. For the gold to accumulate in the sediments of a depository, it must have been transported to the depositional site from a source-area, whether this be an Archean greenstone terrane or an earlier Proterozoic sedimentary basin. This paradigm is the fundamental generalization of the genesis of a Proterozoic sedimentary gold deposit in South Africa.

The second paradigm is constructed in Fig. 2. To activate the system shown in Fig. 1, a series of energizers was necessary which produced a range of effects on successive operators. Igneous activity — essentially of an ultramafic-mafic nature, but with felsic magmatism also playing an important role — introduced gold and other metallic minerals into the Archean-type greenstone belts of the Barbertonian era. The gold, in the form in which it first entered the total system, was clearly of magmatic origin. Tectonic adjustment,

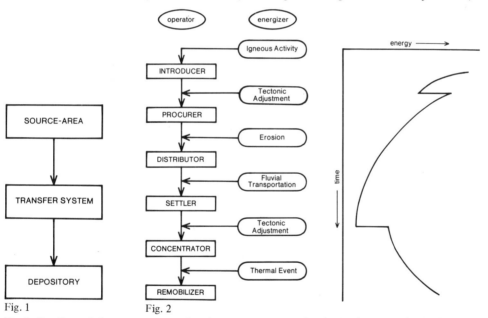

Fig. 1   Fig. 2

Fig. 1. Paradigm of the components and environments necessary for the development of strata-bound, sedimentary gold mineralization in a Proterozoic basin in South Africa.

Fig. 2. Paradigm of the operators and their energizers that combine to produce a Proterozoic sedimentary goldfield in South Africa and of the variations, in time, in the energy level which prevails at different stages in the system.

consequent upon the cessation of igneous activity, uplifted the mineralized greenstones, thus making them vulnerable to processes of physical and chemical degradation, during which the incipient phases of the transfer system could procure the liberated gold from the source rocks. Erosion placed the procured gold within the sphere of influence of the distributor component of the system and fluvial transportation carried the products of erosion into a depository where they settled into a cyclic sequence of sediments. The overall energy within the system showed a progressive decrease from the time of tectonic uplift, which made the source rocks available for erosion, to the time of laying down of the erosional debris in one of the Kaapvaalian yoked basins which developed on the Southern African Shield.

The gold content of the first-stage sediments was too low to be of economic interest and it was necessary to reconstitute the material in order to produce ore. For the physical reworking of the rocks, tectonic adjustment within the basin was necessary for uplift to recycle previously deposited material. Each cycle of reworking contributed to a progressively greater concentration of residual gold and other detrital heavy minerals. For the chemical reconstitution of the gold, an increase in the thermal gradient was required for mobilization of silica, gold, carbonate and, to a lesser extent, other components of the sediments and for the migration of these constituents to zones of lower temperature-pressure or greater chemical reactivity, where precipitation took place. To produce ore from the first-phase sedimentary protore, there was a progressive increase in energy as the basin underwent the tectonism and metamorphism which heralded the conditioning of the crust for the inception of the next basin in the Kaapvaalian sequence.

MODEL OF A SOURCE AREA

The first stage in the Proterozoic gold mineralization system in South Africa was the introduction into higher crustal levels of Archean-type, mantle-derived igneous rocks ranging from ultramafic to felsic. Gold was preferentially contained in the ultramafic and mafic components. Siderophile metals were also more prevalent in these rock types, while chalcophile metals showed a preference for the mafic-felsic members of the magmatic suite. Greater amounts of sulphur appeared to characterize the latter rock types, so that sulphides, particularly pyrite, were present in higher concentrations as the igneous assemblage trended towards the felsic end-point. All these rock types, together with later sediments, constituted the greenstone belts which were subsequently intruded by varieties of granite. The thermal gradient set up by these intrusions was the energizer which caused the remobilization of the gold in the more mafic rocks and the generation of hydrothermal deposits in the Barbertonian era.

Fig. 3 is a model of the variations in mineralization in the source area as a consequence of the changes in the relative volumes of ultramafic, mafic, and acid magmatic rock types. Where ultramafics predominated, siderophile elements were dominant. Where felsics were

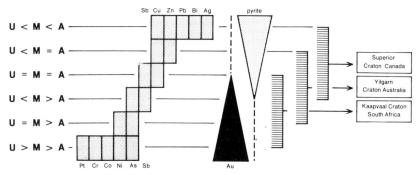

Fig. 3. Conceptual model of the igneous rocks, ore metals and amounts of gold and pyrite in a potential source area for a Proterozoic goldfield. U = relative volume of ultramafic intrusives and extrusives in the igneous components of an Archean-type greenstone belt, M = relative volume of mafic igneous material, A = relative volume of acid igneous material.

present in much greater amounts, chalcophile elements characterized the types of associated mineralization. Where mafic and felsic rocks were approximately equal in proportion, both siderophile and chalcophile metals were in evidence. Gold, being siderophile, was more common in ultramafic and mafic rocks. Where the volume of felsic rocks was equal to, or greater than, the amount of mafic and ultramafic material, gold ceased to be present in any substantial quantities. As gold diminished, so pyrite and other sulphides assumed greater importance. From the model, it follows that the optimum Archean-type source area for Proterozoic sedimentary gold was the one which contained the greater proportions of ultramafic and mafic rock types.

The model also offers a possible explanation for the uniqueness of the Kaapvaal craton as a world-source of gold. In a very generalized manner, the relative proportions of ultramafic, mafic, and felsic material in greenstone belts have been used to characterize three of the major gold-producing Archean cratons in the world. The Kaapvaal craton of South Africa certainly shows a relative paucity of felsic rock types and a minor amount of significant copper-lead-zinc mineralization. The opposite is true of the Superior craton of Canada, where chalcophile ore deposits are a characteristic feature of the Archean greenstone belts. The Yilgarn craton of Australia might be intermediate between the two types. Because the Yilgarn and Superior cratons had lesser volumes of ultramafics, they had lower potentials for providing the amounts of gold which were drawn from the Kaapvaal greenstone belts to feed into the Witwatersrand and other Proterozoic basins.

The variations in relative proportions of rock types in the three cratons might also reflect an age difference for the greenstone belts in South Africa, Australia and Canada. It has been stated earlier that the transition from Archean-type crustal evolution to Proterozoic-type took place in South Africa at about 3,000 m.y. and in Canada at about 2,500 m.y. In Australia, the transition was probably between these two dates. It is possible that, the earlier in earth history a greenstone belt formed, the greater the proportion of its ultramafic constituents. The younger the greenstones, the more significant was the volume of felsic rock types. If such was the case, then the source areas most favourable to the subsequent generation of sedimentary gold deposits would have been those containing the oldest developments of Archean-type ultramafic-mafic greenstone crust.

MODELS OF TRANSFER SYSTEMS

The evidence from all investigations points overwhelmingly to the fact that the erosional debris from the source area was transferred to the depository through the medium of a fluvial system. The Kaapvaalian sedimentary basins were essentially intracratonic in nature and formed under continental conditions, although extensive marine transgression is apparent in at least one instance. It has also been shown that differential subsidence of the depository and uplift of the source area were brought about by tectonic adjustments which had their more important development along the margin of the basin.

A model of the transfer system which was operative into the Proterozoic basins of South Africa is portrayed in Fig. 4. An essentially high-energy system was represented by the short linear fluvial agency, while the long, meandering fluvial processes were associated with a lower-energy regime. A Witwatersrand-type goldfield was the response to the former system, and a Transvaal-type goldfield to the latter. The first system prevailed where intermontane, intracratonic sedimentary basins were formed, while the second characterized the period when the general topography of the crust was subdued and marine transgression developed. The high-energy regime would have its present-day analog in a basin-and-range type of environment, except that far greater quantities of water would be available than is the case, say, in the western United States of America, and the low-energy situation in a continental-shelf type of environment.

The Witwatersrand-type transfer system was best represented during the period 2,500–2,750 m.y. The fluvial fans formed very close to the uplifted source area which consisted essentially of Archean-type granite-greenstone terrane and these fans constituted the interface between the short, relatively linear river systems and the shallow-water lacustrine systems. The rivers debouched from canyons, flowed a comparatively small distance over a piedmont plain and then dispersed, through a braided-stream pattern, into the depository. The gold was transported essentially as detrital particles, and, to a lesser extent, in solution which probably took the form of chloride- or cyanide-complexes. The fluvial-fan type goldfield was a basin-edge phenomenon, with the host rocks comprising conglomerates, sands, silts, shales, and algal mats, the last-mentioned of which developed during periods of relative quiescence in the depositional environment. The concentration of the gold took place physically, through gravity-settling and biologically, through interaction between the dissolved gold and the algal colonies.

The Transvaal-type transfer system was optimally operative during the period 2,000–2,250 m.y. More subdued relief in the source area, marine transgression over the

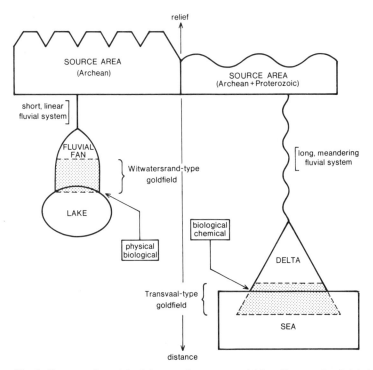

Fig. 4. Conceptual model of the transfer systems which collect erosional debris, including gold in solid state and in solution, in the source area, and transport it to a depository, where it is concentrated by physical and biological agencies to form a Witwatersrand-type goldfield in coarse clastics and algal mats, and by chemical and biological agencies to form a Transvaal-type goldfield in fine clastics and non-clastics.

cratonic area and a more gentle paleoslope, during the middle stages of the Transvaal Sequence, culminated in a long, meandering, fluvial system which developed a delta at some distance out into the basin. A Transvaal-type goldfield was thus not a basin-edge feature, but was formed on the distal side of the depositional axis. The source area consisted of both Barbertonian granite-greenstone rock types and previously deposited Proterozoic sediments and volcanics, belonging mainly to the Witwatersrand and Ventersdorp sequences. The gold was brought into the depository in solution and chemically and biologically precipitated in the delta that formed the interface between the fluvial system and the marine environment. Estuarine conditions were probably the more suitable for the concentration of the gold.

The Witwatersrand-type transfer system operated during regressive conditions, and the Transvaal-type under transgressive conditions. Gold mineralization resulting from the former processes is present in the Pongola, Witwatersrand and Transvaal basins, and has not been found, as yet, in the Ventersdorp and Waterberg sequences. In that the only major marine transgression in the Kaapvaalian era of South Africa took place during

Transvaal times, the deltaic-type goldfield has so far been found only within the confines of the Transvaal basin. The models which have been constructed of the transfer systems require that gold was moved from the source area to the depository by both physical and chemical means. Detrital particles were transported by traction or in suspension, together with the clastic components of the debris of the source area. Gold in solution was apparently more abundant than in present-day surface waters. It is considered that the dissolved gold was in the form of chloride- or cyanide-complexes, which were more prevalent in the Archean and Early Proterozoic periods because of the more primitive composition of the atmosphere, the generally anoxygenic environment and the dominance of reducing conditions. With the evolution of a progressively more oxygenic environment, gold remained in solution for lesser periods of time and was transported over shorter distances.

MODELS OF DEPOSITORIES

Stratigraphic models

The Proterozoic basins of the Kaapvaalian era are characterized by three common features: (*1*) the basin-fill began with a volcanic assemblage and ended with a volcanic assemblage and had the major accumulation of sediments between the two periods of volcanic activity; (*2*) the sedimentation was cyclic in nature; and (*3*) the general lithological successions were repeated from one basin to another. Repetition and cyclicity were typical responses to the processes of basin development. These phenomena led to the attempts by Pretorius (1965) to view the stratigraphy of the Kaapvaalian basins in terms of harmonic patterns.

Basin formation in the Early and Middle Proterozoic, at least, of South Africa had a periodicity of about 250 m.y. (five basins between 1,750 and 3,000 m.y.). This systematic repetition might be regarded as the first harmonic. The next most conspicuous feature of the fill of each basin is the succession of volcanics–sediments–volcanics, which might be considered as a response to a third harmonic of cyclic repetition. Further cycles of sedimentation, of greater and smaller scales, which are numerous in each one of the basin sequences, can be viewed as patterned reflections of fifth, seventh, and still lower-order harmonics. Odd harmonics only are employed, to keep the processes in phase. Each harmonic was interacting with each lower-order harmonic, with the result that the summed response to all the cyclic processes was a gross pattern of superimposed harmonics into which the variations in stratigraphy and lithology could be fitted. It is possible that harmonic analysis could be applied satisfactorily only to basins which developed on a stable craton where the tectonic styles of basin subsidence and source area uplift remained relatively constant over long periods of time. The Proterozoic basins of the Kaapvaal craton in South Africa certainly meet these requirements.

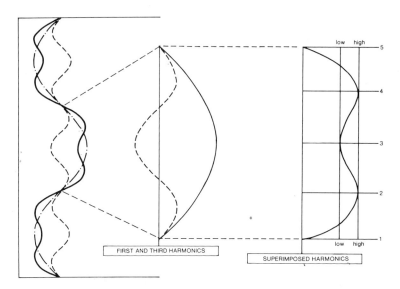

Fig. 5. Model of the pattern resulting from the superimposition of a third harmonic on an in-phase first harmonic. Dromodarian discrete curves are converted into bactrian superimposed curves.

In Fig. 5 is shown the resultant curve of superimposing in-phase first and third harmonics. On the left of the diagram, the primary harmonics are shown in broken lines, and the secondary harmonic, which is the product of the interaction of the two, is drawn in a solid line. The most obvious consequence of the superimposition is the conversion of the dromodarian primary harmonics into a bactrian secondary harmonic. On the right of the diagram, portions of the first and third harmonics and of the resultant superimposed effect are magnified. The point to be stressed in the superimposed harmonics is that, of the three inflexion points, the bottom and the top have the higher amplitude, with a lower magnitude attached to the central point. Rates of change in the resultant curve are highest in segments 1-2 and 4-5, intermediate in segments 2-3 and 3-4 and lowest at the inflexion points 2, 3 and 4.

If the vertical axis of Fig. 5 is made to represent time and the horizontal axis energy, then the stratigraphic model of Fig. 6 can be constructed, which depicts the sequence of lithologies that made up each of the Kaapvaalian Proterozoic sedimentary-volcanic basins. Energy has been scaled according to that prevailing in the depository when non-clastics, fine clastics, coarse clastics, and volcanics were being introduced, it being implied that more energy was required to bring igneous material up from depth and to extrude it into the basin than was needed to form chemical sediments. In Sequence X, Group A would be composed of coarse basal clastics and a substantial volume of volcanics; Group B of coarse clastics, fining upwards; Group C of non-clastics or fine clastics, depending on whether the base-level of energy was lower or higher; Group D of fine clastics, coarsening upwards, and presenting a succession somewhat similar to that of Group B; and Group E

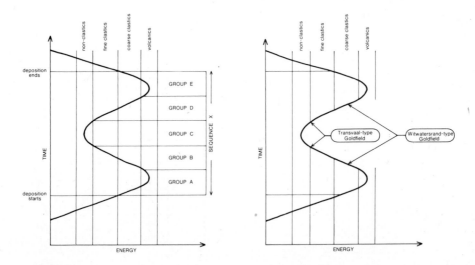

Fig. 6. Conceptual model of the stratigraphic response to harmonic variations in the energy level prevailing in a Proterozoic sedimentary-volcanic basin in South Africa. The first harmonic represents the periodicity of formation of successive basins, and the third harmonic the broad cyclic variations in lithologic response to changes in energy level. The bactrian-model curve requires a mirror-image repetition of the stratigraphic succession from the lower members of the depositional fill into the upper members. Maximum rates of change of energy level occur during the intervals when Groups A and E are formed, and minimum rates of change at the three inflexion points. Intermediate energy-flux prevails during the development of Groups B and D. Because of the mirror-image phenomenon, ideally there are two optimum stratigraphic positions for the formation of an intermediate-energy, Witwatersrand-type goldfield, and two positions for a low-energy, Transvaal-type goldfield.

of terminal volcanics and some coarse sediments. If the energy-base shifted to the right, then the overall energy within the whole system would have been lower, and lesser volcanics and greater non-clastics would have appeared in the stratigraphy, as was the case with the Transvaal Sequence. If the energy-base was displaced to the left, then the depository would have formed under a generally higher energy level, with the result that non-clastics would not have appeared in the stratigraphic assemblage and volcanics and coarse clastics would have become much more prominent, as in the Witwatersrand Basin.

In the Witwatersrand Sequence, Group A would be represented by the Dominion Group, Group B by the Hospital Hill—Government Group, Group C by the Jeppestown Group, Group D by the Main-Bird—Kimberley-Elsburg Group and Group E by the Klip-riviersberg Group. In the Transvaal Sequence, Group A would have its equivalent in the Lower Wolkberg Group, Group B in the Upper Wolkberg—Black Reef Group, Group C in the Malmani Group, Group D in the Pretoria Group and Group E in the Rooiberg Group. The bactrian nature of the superimposed harmonics curve explains the fact that the lithologies of Groups A and B are repeated, in reverse, in Groups D and E, while the lithologies of Group C appear only once in the stratigraphic succession.

In the right side of Fig. 6, the model shows where the various types of goldfields would be placed in the stratigraphic column. The Witwatersrand-type goldfield would occur in Group B or in Group D, in the lower part of the former, where coarse clastics would be more abundant than fine clastics, and in the upper part of the latter, where the same lithofacies would prevail. Some detrital gold would also occur in the coarse clastics of Groups A and E, but would be of much lesser economic significance, due, probably, to the fact that the rate of change of energy would be higher in the initial and terminal groups. Conditions would be too high-energy to favour the settling of large quantities of gold which, in the Proterozoic of South Africa, was always of a very small grain-size. Better conditions for physical concentration of gold would have occurred in the time intervals of intermediate energy-flux, associated with transgression in Group B and regression in Group D. In the Witwatersrand Basin, in particular, coarser clastics laid down under regressive conditions during a period of intermediate rate of energy-change were the optimum sites for the concentration of detrital gold. Group D would have a greater economic potential than Group B, because of the processes of regressive reworking which would characterize the former.

Transvaal-type goldfields would be distributed over a much smaller stratigraphic interval than Witwatersrand-type, because of the fact that Group C-type depositional environments would have developed only once in the broad stratigraphic history of a basin. The Transvaal-type goldfields would be preferentially located where Group B merged into Group C, via a transgressive relationship, and where Group C was transitional into Group D, through the medium of a regression. This type of gold mineralization would be characteristic of an environment where the overall energy level was low and where the rate of change of energy-level, with time, was slow.

In an ideal basin, containing gold-bearing sediments, auriferous horizons of very low economic potential would occur in the basal coarse clastics of Group A; of low potential in the coarse and fine clastics of Group B; of intermediate potential in the intercalated fine clastics and non-clastics of Group C; of high potential in the fine and coarse clastics of Group D; and of intermediate potential in the coarse terminal clastics of Group E. Needless to say, this ideal arrangement has not been found in any one of the Kaapvaalian basins. The Pongola Sequence has its low-rank gold mineralization in the equivalents of Groups B and C; the Witwatersrand Sequence its high-rank mineralization in Groups A, B, C and D; and the Transvaal Sequence its intermediate-rank mineralization in Groups B, C and D. No gold deposits of any importance have thus far been discovered in the Ventersdorp and Waterberg sequences.

Model of a Transvaal-type goldfield

The host rocks of Transvaal-type sedimentary gold deposits are dolomitic shales and silts and silty and argillaceous dolomites that were laid down in the distal facies of a deltaic environment, probably when estuarine conditions prevailed. The rock types are mixtures of deltaic muds and silts and shallow-water shelf carbonates. Algal activity was high episodically during the formation of the fine clastic—non-clastic assemblage of low-energy strata. The protore represented the most distally transported gold entering the depository.

The gold was brought into the basin in solution, from which is was precipitated either chemically or biologically. The precipitants were carbonate material, colloidal particles of clay, and algae, either separately or in combination. The gold in the protore of dolomitic silt was sub-microscopic in size and the rock gave no readily visible sign of being a potential ore of gold. The protore was converted to ore by tectonic and thermal processes. In the former case, bedding-plane slip, associated with concentric-type folding of the strata, which characterizes the style of deformation of the Kaapvaalian basins, produced a pressure differential under which silica, gold and some other metallic constituents migrated, to form conformably-disposed gold—quartz veins. The thermal energy for the redistribution of the gold into cross-cutting quartz veins was provided by the intrusion of large numbers of dykes and sills acting as feeders to the terminal volcanic stage of the succession. The exploitable gold was thus the product of lateral and vertical secretion of selected constituents of the original distal deltaic silts, muds, and carbonates.

No diagrammatic model has been constructed to illustrate the generalizations on the formation of a Transvaal-type goldfield. The main components have been depicted in Fig. 4, 6, and 10, the last-mentioned of which will be discussed under the model of gold distribution through Kaapvaalian time.

Model of a Witwatersrand-type goldfield

A Witwatersrand-type sedimentary goldfield is, in most of its general features, the antithesis of a Transvaal-type goldfield. It was the response to a high-energy environment on the edge of a regressing basin, and the host rocks to the mineralization were essentially coarse clastics, although fine clastics also assumed considerable importance. Non-clastics found no place in the model of a Witwatersrand-type goldfield, and chemical precipitation of gold played a very minor role. The goldfields took the form of fluvial fans, or fan deltas, as opposed to the true deltas of the Transvaal-type goldfields, and developed relatively close to the source area, so that the distance of fluvial transportation was comparatively short. Such goldfields were located on the proximal side of the depositional axis of a lacustrine environment.

Fig. 7 is a generalized representation of the main elements of a typical Witwatersrand-type goldfield. The fluvial fan had its apex along a tectonically unstable basin-edge, where repeated uplift of the source area side of the depository took place along longitudinal faults. Movement along such dislocations served two purposes: the fanhead section of an earlier fan was subjected to uplift and reworking into a later fan, and the midfan and fanbase sections were structurally depressed, ensuring optimum preservation. Downward displacement of the lower two-thirds of the fan also contributed to the transgression of

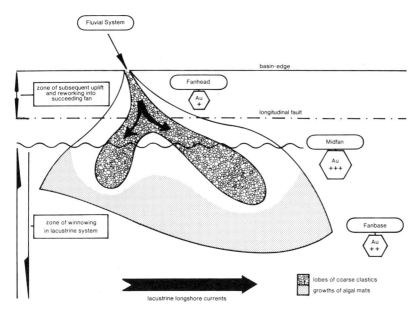

Fig. 7. Conceptual model of a Witwatersrand-type goldfield. The fluvial system brings from the source-area unsorted erosional debris which undergoes soting on the fluvial fan in accordance with a hydrodynamic regime radially decreasing in energy away from the apex of the fan. Because of the small grain-size of the gold particles, they are unable to settle, to any marked extent, in the fanhead facies. Optimum conditions for settling occur in the midfan facies. The energy level becomes too low to move detrital particles in any quantity to the fanbase environment. However, gold in solution is precipitated by the algae which grow preferentially in the non-turbulent conditions along the margins and base of the fan.

the lake waters over the fan, during which winnowing of the sediments took place, resulting in the removal of the fines and the development of residual concentrations of heavy minerals as lag accumulations. Longshore currents in the lake moved the finer sediments farther from the entry point of the clastic material, and thus helped form the asymmetrical shape of the fans. The evidence to date suggests that the movement of water in the Proterozoic depositories on the Kaapvaal craton was in a clockwise direction for at least the greater part of the 1,250 m.y.-long history of basin development.

The fluvial fan was typically composed of two main lobes, each containing a greater concentration of braided stream channels, thicker accumulations of coarser sediments, including gravels, and high concentrations of gold and other heavy minerals. The angle between the two lobes was between 60° and 120° and the material between the lobes was of the same lower-energy character as the sands, silts, and muds which were deposited along the fan margins and the fanbase. In these same segments of the fan, conditions, on occasion, favoured the development of algal growths which took the form of thin, inter-woven mats. In the channels on the lobes of the fan, detrital gold accumulated by gravity settling. For the small grain-size of the gold particles, the energy conditions in the fanhead section were too high to permit any substantial quantities of gold concentrating, with the result that this facies of the fan sediments normally had the lowest gold content. The highest amounts of gold were usually in the midfan section. In the fanbase section, the energy level was too low to support the transportation of significant amounts of detrital gold beyond the midfan environment. However, gold in solution reacted with the algal material in the fanbase area and the quantities of this absorbed gold often made the fanbase sediments hosts to important mineralization.

The build-up of a fan was accomplished in a series of pulses of sedimentation, which started with progradation during regression, proceeded through aggradation during transgression and ended with degradation during stillstand. Such a combination of pulses constituted a cycle. Fig. 8 has been constructed to portray the evolving pattern of sedimentation during the cyclic accumulation of coarse and fine material on a fluvial fan. A new cycle was initiated through tectonic adjustment along the longitudinal faults bounding the source area. This adjustment produced a steepening of the gradient of the paleoslope, with the result that the increased competency of the fluvial system brought greater amounts of coarser debris onto the fan. The prevailing higher energy level also caused the fan to prograde out into the depository, thus establishing a regressive relationship between the end sediments of the previous cycle and the initial clastics of the new cycle. The coarser material took the form of an openwork gravel. The matrix, of sand size, was

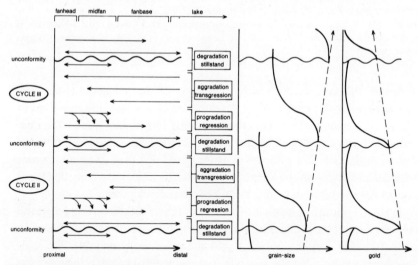

Fig. 8. Conceptual model of the evolution of a depositional cycle on a fan, from progradation during regression consequent upon tectonic uplift along the basin-edge, through aggradation during transgression, to degradation during stillstand when the energy level of the transporting currents is too low to bring erosional debris from the source area onto the fan. Maximum winnowing by transgressive lake waters takes place during stillstand, to produce residual concentrations of lag gold. The second pulse of sedimentation during progradation brings in gold-bearing sand which infiltrates downwards into the openwork gravel of the higher-energy preceding pulse.

introduced during the next pulse of regressive sedimentation. The sand infiltrated the gravels, so that there was a continuum between the matrix of the conglomerates and what became the hanging-wall quartzites. Heavy minerals, including gold, were transported with the sand, and by gravity settling and subsequent jigging and winnowing, were concentrated between the pebbles. As the energy level fell, finer and finer material was deposited on the fan, and transgressive conditions took over from the regressive environment which favoured the formation of a basal gravel at the beginning of the cycle. At the end of the cycle, no more clastics were introduced by the fluvial system, and sediment accumulation gave way to degradation. The amount of winnowing increased with time, with the consequent greater concentration of residual heavy minerals on the erosion surface. Incipient tectonic activity caused tilting of the surface, in which process originated the unconformable relationship between the two cycles of sedimentation. On this tilted surface, degradation was enhanced, winnowing was intensified and lag concentrations of heavy minerals were brought to an optimum. The continued tectonic adjustment then culminated in the prograding sedimentation which marked the beginning of the next cycle. The gravels, washing in under somewhat turbulent conditions, broke up their depositional floor, in some instances, and incorporated into their bed the thin streaks of lag gold lying on the unconformity. Thus, the gold, under ideal circumstances, was introduced into the gravels in two processes: pick-up from the footwall sediments and downward infiltration from the sand pulse that succeeded the deposition of the pebbles.

The right side of Fig. 8 models the variations in grain size of sediment from cycle to cycle and in gold content in the basal and terminal phases of each cycle. Because tectonic uplift along the basin-edge caused erosion and reworking of the fanhead sections of previous cycles, relatively greater volumes of coarser material were deposited in successive cycles, so that, where tectonic activity was sufficiently intense, there was a general increase in grain size stratigraphically upwards. This trend was also a response to the overall regressive nature of sedimentation in a shrinking basin. Since, in the model, each successively higher cycle represented a relatively more proximal facies than the underlying accumulation of sediments, there was a closer and closer approach to a fanhead facies stratigraphically upwards. As a result, the tenor of gold showed a generally diminishing trend from earlier to later cycles, because the energy level in a fanhead section was usually too high to permit optimum conditions for the concentration of gold. The model also shows the distinctly enhanced intensity of the mineralization along the unconformity between cycles, both immediately below and immediately above the plane of discontinuity separating the cycles.

In that the Witwatersrand basin is postulated to have been filled by the erosional debris from an Archean granite-greenstone terrane, it follows that the lithologies of the Witwatersrand Sequence should reflect the order in which the various formations of the greenstone belt were stripped off the source area, entered the transfer system, and were brought into the depository. The best-known of the greenstone belts on the Kaapvaal craton is the Barberton Mountain Land and the model devised for the development of this belt has been successfully used to interpret the stratigraphic successions and depositional histories of other greenstone belts of the Barbertonian era. The Swaziland Sequence of the Barberton Mountain Land is comprised of four groups of rocks and each of these has three formations as constituent members. The Lower Onverwacht Group is dominated by ultramafic and mafic igneous rocks; the Upper Onverwacht Group has less ultramafic and more felsic components; the Fig Tree Group consists essentially of a turbidite assemblage of greywackes and argillites, with an important iron formation near the top; and the Moodies Group represents the first continental-type sediments, with quartzites and shales most prominent. The greater part of the gold mineralization is in strata-bound orebodies along the contacts between the Lower and Upper Onverwacht groups and between the Upper Onverwacht and the Fig Tree groups.

The Witwatersrand Sequence consists of five groups of rocks: the Dominion Group at the base, in which mafic and acid volcanics are the major members; the Hospital Hill Group, of quartzites and shales, with a conspicuous iron formation in the upper sections; the Government Group, of quartzites and shales, mainly; the Jeppestown Group, of predominantly shales; the Main-Bird Group, of conglomerates, quartzites and shales; the Kimberley-Elsburg Group, of conglomerates and quartzites; and the Klipriviersberg Group of mafic and acid volcanics and sediments. The Hospital Hill, Government, and Jeppestown groups are locally referred to as the Lower Division of the Witwatersrand Sequence and the Main-Bird and Kimberley-Elsburg groups as the Upper Division.

The Witwatersrand Sequence formed in a yoked basin, with an active, fault-bounded margin along the northwestern rim of the depository, and a more passive, downwarping, southeastern edge. The main source area lay to the northwest and the Witwatersrand-type transfer system operated from northwest to southeast. The erosional remnants of Swaziland Sequence rocks on the northwestern side of the basin are members of the Lower Onverwacht assemblage, and no rock types of stratigraphically higher groups have been observed. On the southeastern side of the basin, the whole succession, up to and including the Moodies Group, has been preserved, in places, supporting the contention that the southeastern limits of the Witwatersrand depository suffered a far lesser degree of tectonic uplift than the northwestern, source area region. Significantly, an attenuated stratigraphic column, consisting of lower-energy sediments, characterizes the southeastern side of the basin. More pronounced preservation of the Swaziland succession indicates that erosion did not reach down to the gold-bearing horizons at the bases of the Fig Tree and of the Upper Onverwacht groups, with the result that there are no significant Witwatersrand goldfields in the southeastern edge of the depository.

On the northwestern rim of the basin, the erosional level of the Swaziland Sequence lies below the gold-bearing horizons of the greenstone assemblage, and the Witwatersrand goldfields are all located along this edge of the depository. The Witwatersrand succession of this portion of the basin can be correlated with the stratigraphy of the Swaziland Sequence through the inverted stratigraphy model which is portrayed in Fig. 9. The topmost members of the Swaziland Sequence contributed to material which formed the

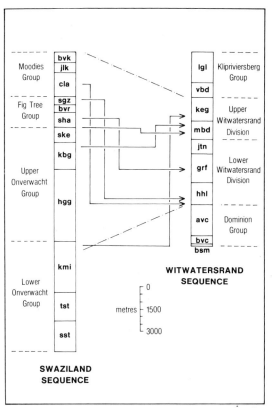

Fig. 9. An inverted stratigraphy model showing the influence of the later lithologies of the source area on the early lithologies of the Witwatersrand Sequence, and vice-versa. Swaziland Sequence: *bvk* = Baviaanskop Formation; *jlk* = Joe's Luck Formation; *cla* = Clutha Formation; *sgz* = Schoongezicht Formation; *bvr* = Belvue Road Formation; *sha* = Sheba Formation; *ske* = Swartkoppie Formation; *kbg* = Kromberg Formation; *hgg* = Hooggenoeg Formation; *kmi* = Komati Formation; *tst* = Theespruit Formation; *sst* = Sandspruit Formation. Witwatersrand Sequence: *lgl* = Langgeleven Formation; *vbd* = Vaal Bend Formation; *keg* = Kimberley-Elsburg Group; *mbd* = Main-Bird Group; *jtn* = Jeppestown Group; *grf* = Government Group; *hhl* = Hospitial Hill Group; *avc* = Acid Volcanic Formation; *bvc* = Basic Volcanic Formation; *bsm* = Basal Sedimentary Formation. The main gold-bearing horizons in the Swaziland Sequence are at the top of the Upper Onverwacht Group and the top of the Lower Onverwacht Group; in the Witwatersrand Sequence, in the Kimberley-Elsburg Group and the Main-Bird Group.

basal section of the Lower Witwatersrand Division. Since the Moodies Group contained quartzites, the recycling of these clastics produced the clean, arenaceous members of the Hospital Hill Group, which are the only true quartzites in the Witwatersrand succession. As the greywackes and argillites of the Fig Tree Group were stripped from the source area, so were the subgreywackes of the Government and Jeppestown groups formed. In the Upper Division, coarse clastic sediments were originally feldspathic quartzites, derived from the mafic and felsic volcanics of the Upper Onverwacht Group and from the ever-increasing volumes of granites that were eroded as more and more of the greenstone belt was stripped away. The lower members of the Swaziland Sequence thus constituted the source material for the upper section of the Witwatersrand Sequence.

The iron formations of the Witwatersrand Sequence lie towards the top of the Hospital Hill Group, in the lower segment of the stratigraphic column. The iron formations in the Swaziland Sequence are located at the top of the Fig Tree Group, in the upper portion of the greenstone-belt column. They would have been the next source rocks to have been eroded after the Moodies Group. The Moodies arenaceous strata went to form the Hospital Hill quartzites, while the Fig Tree iron formations, underlying the former, contributed to the development of the Hospital Hill iron horizons, above the latter. The major accumulation of shales in the stratigraphically higher Jeppestown Group points to a possible derivation from the argillites and greywackes of the Fig Tree Group, which underlie the iron formations.

The gold mineralization along the contact between the Fig Tree and the Upper Onverwacht groups was, by far, the more important of the two strata-bound sources of gold in the Swaziland Sequence. This mineralization was the first to be eroded, and was transferred to the sediments of the Main-Bird Group, in which is located the major proportion of the Witwatersrand gold deposits. When the stratigraphically lower mineralization, along the contact between the Upper and Lower Onverwacht groups, was eroded and transported into the Witwatersrand Basin, it went into the auriferous beds of the Kimberley-Elsburg Group, which lie above the Main-Bird horizons and have a distinctly lower economic potential than the stratigraphically lower gold-bearing horizons.

MODELS OF GOLD IN TIME

Tectonic elevation model

The tectonics of the Precambrian crust on the Kaapvaal craton reflect a broad cyclical pattern of alternating higher and lower structural elevation with the passage of time, from the Barbertonian era to the end of the Kaapvaalian era. The Lower and Upper Onverwacht extrusive and intrusive rocks were probably emplaced under deep-water marine conditions. As emergence started to take place, the Fig Tree turbidites were formed in a somewhat shallower, but still deep-water, environment. The depositional floor rose above sea-level in Moodies times, so that the end of the Barbertonian era marked the transition from marine to continental conditions. Emergence continued, with the craton rising higher and higher above sea-level during Pongola, Witwatersrand, and Ventersdorp times. The rate of tectonic elevation was relatively slow. The continental land-mass probably stood at its highest during the period when the great volumes of Ventersdorp mafic and intermediate volcanics were sub-aerially extruded. Following this episode of significant igneous activity, there was a period of relatively rapid tectonic subsidence which culminated in the only extensive marine transgression during the evolution of the Kaapvaal craton. The Malmani shelf-carbonates of the Transvaal Sequence were the products of a

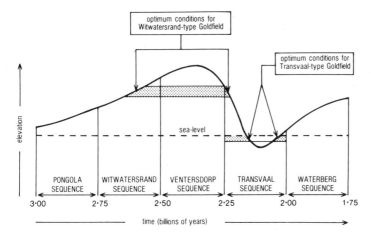

Fig. 10. Conceptual model of the variation, with Proterozoic time, in the tectonic elevation above sea-level of the Kaapvaal craton in South Africa. Conditions for the development of a Witwatersrand-type goldfield are at an optimum when the elevation is near, but not at, a maximum, and for a Transvaal-type goldfield when the elevation is near, but not at, a minimum.

time of minimum tectonic elevation. Emergence started during the middle of the Transvaal period, and continued to increase into Waterberg times. At the close of Waterberg deposition, Proterozoic sedimentary deposition ceased on the Kaapvaal craton, and moved to regions lying to the northwest, southwest, and southeast. The next sedimentation on the craton was in Late Paleozoic times.

Fig. 10 depicts a model which has been constructed to show the variations in tectonic level with time, and the periods of essentially continental and mainly marine deposition. The time positions of the main stratigraphic horizons hosting gold mineralization have been indicated. Witwatersrand-type goldfields, which are best developed in the upper portion of the Witwatersrand Sequence and the lower section of the Transvaal Sequence, were preferentially formed when the craton was at near-maximum tectonic elevation. Under such conditions, the depositories took the form of intermontane, yoked basins in which the fluvial fan—lacustrine environment was dominant. Transvaal-type goldfields, which are restricted to the middle portions of the Transvaal Sequence, originated when the craton was at near-minimum tectonic elevation during the Proterozoic. Marine transgression characterized such conditions, in which the delta—open sea environment was optimally developed.

Algal activity model

The oldest evidence of biological activity yet recorded has come from the Archean rocks of the Swaziland Sequence on the Kaapvaal craton. Bacteria and filamentous algae probably started developing about 3,300 m.y. ago, and went through cycles of evolution, which attained their acme during the marine transgression of the Transvaal Period. The visible evidence of biological activity became more pronounced with time, as the size and frequency of the algal colonies increased. The first readily discernible remnants of algae are present in the Witwatersrand rocks. In the Swaziland Sequence, the evidence is on a microscopic scale, while no signs have as yet been noted of algal activity in the Pongola strata. Stromatolitic structures made their first appearance in the Ventersdorp sediments and became most conspicuous in the Transvaal dolomites. The Waterberg Sequence has not yet produced any indications of algal activity. Empirically, it would appear that there might exist some degree of correlation between the presence of algal material in a sedimentary sequence and the presence of gold.

Fig. 11 models the variations in the intensity of gold mineralization with time and in the apparent abundance of algae. It is not suggested that there is a one-to-one correlation, since the greatest amounts of gold, by far, were in the Witwatersrand Sequence, but algal activity was much more prolific in the Transvaal period. There was, nevertheless, a peak in algal development where there was a peak in degree of gold mineralization. The distribution of gold through the stratigraphic column shows that alternating sequences were impoverished and enriched in the amount of the metal present in the sediments. The Swaziland, Witwatersrand and Transvaal strata acted as hosts to important ore deposits,

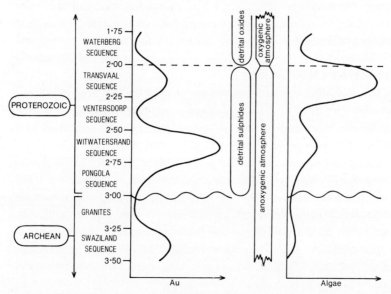

Fig. 11. Conceptual model of the variation, with Archean and Proterozoic time, in the degree of gold mineralization and in the intensity of algal activity. Alternating sequences show greater and lesser amounts of mineralization and of evidence of algal development. A significant change from an anoxygenic to an oxygenic atmosphere took place at 2,000 m.y., following on the great bloom of algal activity during the Middle Proterozoic. Detrital sulphides and sedimentary gold mineralization disappear from the South African stratigraphic column at this time, and detrital oxides and sedimentary copper-lead-zinc start appearing.

while the Pongola, Ventersdorp and Waterberg sequences were comparatively deficient in gold. The evidence, to date, of algal activity shows the same pattern. It might be concluded from the model that, where the environment favoured the development of algae, the physical-chemical-biological conditions were also such that gold settled out from traction or suspension, or was precipitated. This points to the river-depository interface as the optimum environment for the formation of stratiform gold mineralization in the evolution of the Proterozoic crust on the Kaapvaal craton in South Africa. Whether the interface was a fluvial-lacustrine product or a fluvial-open sea condition, it also favoured the maximum growth of algae.

The model shows two other features that record important environmental changes in the evolution of the sedimentary basins. The Pongola, Witwatersrand, Ventersdorp and Transvaal sediments contain detrital sulphides, predominantly in the form of pyrite, but also as arsenopyrite and cobaltite. These particles are in hydraulic equilibrium with unequivocal detrital minerals that constitute the conglomerates and quartzites, and were transported, deposited, and preserved as sulphides. The abundance of these water-worn sulphide particles, plus the universal black, grey, blue, green and white colours of the strata that compose the four sequences, point strongly to the fact that reducing conditions were prevalent at all times in the history of Proterozoic basin formation between 3,000 and 2,000 m.y. For such conditions to have been consistently present, it is likely that an anoxygenic atmosphere prevailed. This would help explain the apparent ease with which gold went into solution during the major part of the Kaapvaalian era, since chloride- and cyanide-complexes could have survived. Such solutions would have been short-lived where oxygen was freely available.

The first great bloom of Proterozoic algal activity took place at about 2,000 m.y. It probably contributed significantly, through photosynthesis, to increasing the amount of oxygen in the atmosphere. Thereafter, the detrital sulphides disappeared, and their place was taken by detrital oxides. Red beds were developed. Both of these features are well illustrated in the Waterberg Sequence. Exploration over the years has established that, at that time, sedimentary gold also disappeared from the stratigraphic record of South Africa. Major gold mineralization in sedimentary environments is thus restricted to the first cycle of continental emergence — the 1,250 million years between the end of Fig Tree times and the middle of Transvaal times. Subsequent cycles of emergence generated sediments in which copper, lead, zinc, and other chalcophile mineralization was developed, but not gold.

GROUND-RULES FOR GOLD PROSPECTING

The purpose of the models constructed has been to permit generalizations to be made about the distribution patterns in time and space of gold mineralization in the Proterozoic sediments of South Africa. The use to which the models might be put is to allow

predictions to be made as to the locations of maximum likelihood for further mineralization. Employing the models as predictive devices, the following conclusions have been
drawn as guides to prospecting for new, permissive environments:

(*1*) Regions should be selected where the rocks are older than 2,000 m.y., no matter
whether they belong to Proterozoic-type, sedimentary-volcanic, cratonic basins or to
Archean-type, granite-greenstone terranes.

(*2*) Preference should be given to regions where the rocks were emplaced during the
period of time when the primitive atmosphere was anoxygenic; hence, where the colours
of the strata are blacks, greys, blues, greens and whites; where red beds are absent; where
detrital sulphides are present in the sediments; and where detrital iron oxides are absent
(the parochial nature of the ground-rules can be seen in the fact that the important
gold-bearing conglomerates of Ghana contain detrital iron oxides).

(*3*) Regions should be investigated where the preserved sediments were laid down
during the first cycle of continental emergence after the formation of the Archean-type
crust.

(*4*) In Archean-type strata, greater importance should be attached to the ultramafics
and mafics which formed during the earlier stages of development of a greenstone belt,
especially where such rocks show an extrusive origin, and where they have been reconstituted by metamorphic and tectonic processes; preference should be shown for the belts
of greater age, which contain relatively larger volumes of ultramafic rocks, rather than for
the younger greenstone belts which house comparatively more significant volumes of
felsic volcanics.

(*5*) In Proterozoic basins,

(*a*) the geological periods should be selected when the tectonic elevation of the craton
was near, but not at, its maximum and when it was near, but not at, its minimum;

(*b*) the geological periods should be considered when algal activity was relatively more
intense;

(*c*) the areas should be investigated where the greenstone belts in the source area
contained greater amounts of ultramafics, with the mafics, and lesser amounts of felsics,
and where such greenstone belts have been eroded down to the lowermost members of
the stratigraphic succession;

(*d*) the regions should be looked at where intermontane, cratonic, yoked basins developed (for Witwatersrand-type goldfields), and where marine transgressions occurred over
the cratonic edge (for Transvaal-type goldfields);

(*e*) the stratigraphic zones should be examined where intermediate ranges of energy-
flux prevailed in the lower and upper halves of the stratigraphic record, and where
minimal energy-flux occurred in the middle of the column;

(*f*) the areas on the proximal side, relative to source area, of the depositional axis of
the basin should be investigated for fluvial fan—lacustrine interfaces, and the areas on the
distal side for delta—open sea interfaces; on the Kaapvaal craton, these areas would be on
the northwestern and southeastern sides, respectively, with the fluvial fan—lacustrine envi-

ronment possibly containing a Witwatersrand-type goldfield and the delta—open sea environment possibly a Transvaal-type goldfield;

(g) localities should be preferred where the fluvial fans show a regressive attitude upwards, indicating a shrinking basin with time and more favourable conditions for reworking of earlier fans into later fans;

(h) localities should be selected where midfan and fanbase facies are preserved;

(i) localities should be given a higher priority where unconformities are present in low-energy sediments which were laid down at the end of a depositional cycle; where conglomerates are developed above the unconformity; and where algal mats, not stromatolites, are preserved on the plane of unconformity; and

(j) localities should be investigated where silts and muds are interstratified with dirty carbonates; and where bedding-plane slip and dyke intrusion are well developed in such silty dolomites and dolomitic argillites.

NOTE ADDED IN PROOF (Cf. p. 2)

The importance of South Africa as a mineral producer clearly lies in the concentration of metals and, of these metals, gold has been the most substantial contributor, by far. Up to the end of 1971, the total value of gold produced stood at more than $ 32 billion, so that the unit regional valve of the precious metal was of the order of $ 69,100 per sq. mile, equivalent to 80% of the unit regional value for all metals.

REFERENCES

Hagget, P. and Chorley, R.J., 1967. Models, paradigms and the new geography. In: R.J. Chorley and P. Hagget (Editors), *Integrated Models in Geography*. University Paperbacks, Methuen, London, pp. 19—41.

Meadows, D.H., Meadows, D.L., Randers, J. and Behrens, W.W., 1972. *The Limits to Growth*. Potomac Associates, London, 205 pp.

Onions, C.T. (Editor), 1959. *The Shorter Oxford English Dictionary on Historical Principles*. Clarendon Press, Oxford, 3rd ed., 2515 pp.

Pretorius, D.A., 1965. The evolution of Precambrian basins in South Africa: a conceptual stratigraphic process-response model (abstract). *Geol. Soc. S. Afr., Synopses Papers 8th Ann. Congr., Johannesburg*, pp. 28—30.

Pretorius, D.A., 1966. Conceptual geological models in the exploration for gold mineralization in the Witwatersrand Basin. In: *Symposium on Mathematical Statistics and Computer Applications in Ore Valuation*. South African Institute of Mining and Metallurgy, Johannesburg, pp. 225—266.

Chapter 2

THE NATURE OF THE WITWATERSRAND GOLD-URANIUM DEPOSITS

D.A. PRETORIUS

INTRODUCTION

The Witwatersrand Basin was filled with 13,900 m of sediments and volcanics in the period between 2500 and 2750 million years ago. The depository took the form of a yoked basin, with a fault-bounded, active, northwestern edge, and a gently downwarping, more passive, southeastern edge. The basin was enclosed, and had dimensions of at least 350 km, in a northeasterly direction, and 200 km, in a northwesterly direction. Six major goldfields and several smaller mineralized areas have been discovered since 1886. Of the order of 150 mines have been operative at one time or another, and from these 2.8 billion tons of ore have been mined up to the end of 1972. The total gold recovered amounted to 28,722 metric tons, valued at a little under US $ 34 billion, and the total uranium to 76,012 metric tons, valued at more than $ 2 billion. The average gold content of the ore mined to the end of 1972 was 10 p.p.m. and the average uranium tenor 280 p.p.m. The distribution of goldfields is intimately related to the pattern of interference folding that produced structural depressions and culminations, the latter in the form of domes of basement granite. The folds are accentuated by major faults parallel to the axial plane traces of the folds. The same interference pattern controlled the morphology of the floor of the basin, influenced the nature and distribution of the sedimentation, and deformed the strata after they had been laid down. The goldfields are all located in the downwarps between the domes, and all take the form of fluvial fans, or fan deltas, which preferentially developed on the northwestern edge of the basin, at the interface between a fluvial system bringing sediments from the source area and a lacustrine, or inland-sea, system which distributed the material in the basin. The depository, as a whole, had a regressive history, shrinking with time and displacing the apices of successive fans farther and farther into the basin. Uplift of the source area along the basin-edge was a continual process in the mechanism of sedimentation, with the result that the fanhead sections of early fans were subjected to elevation, erosion, and reworking into later fans. This repeated reworking resulted in the development of economic concentrations of gold and/or uranium on at least sixteen different horizons in the stratigraphic column. Each of these horizons straddled a plane of unconformity which separated the terminal phases of one cycle from the initial stages of a succeeding cycle of sedimentation. The top members of the earlier cycle were fine sands, silts, or muds, frequently with algal mats, that settled in a delta-flat or estuarine environment as a transgressive sequence of sedimentation started giving way to a regressive phase. Gold, uranium, and other heavy minerals were concentrated on the unconformity. The bottom members of the later cycle were generally conglomerates, formed as openwork gravels into which auriferous sands subsequently washed, as the depositional energy-level decreased. In many instances, the conglomerates also incorporated into their matrices gold and uranium concentrated on the underlying finer sediments or in the filaments of the algal mats. The source of the gold was in ultramafic and mafic igneous rocks of Archean greenstone belts older than 3250 m.y., while the uranium was drawn from the granites which intruded the greenstones between 3050 and 3200 m.y. ago. The mineralization is unequivocally the response to sedimentary processes.

THE ECONOMIC SIGNIFICANCE OF THE WITWATERSRAND BASIN

The Witwatersrand Basin ranks as one of the greatest mining fields the world has ever known. It has been estimated that, of all gold mined in all countries in all parts of the world, over the whole span of recorded history, about 55% has come from the auriferous sediments of the Witwatersrand sequence of rocks. Gold-bearing conglomerates were first discovered in March 1886, near where the city of Johannesburg is now located, and, in the 88 years that have elapsed since then, no less than about 150 mines, of varying size and importance, have exploited the sedimentary concentrations of heavy minerals. In 1953, recovery started of the associated uranium mineralization. A very high level of mining activity still prevails within the confines of the basin, and it has been calculated that the depository contains the world's largest reserves of gold-bearing ore and among the world's largest reserves of low-grade uranium ore. Current projections indicate that mining operations will still be in progress at the end of the century.

The basin is located in the northeastern part of the Republic of South Africa, within the provinces of the Transvaal and the Orange Free State. The approximate centre of the presently known basin is at 27°E and 27°S. The area underlain by Witwatersrand strata has a roughly ovoidal shape, with a long axis stretching 350 km in a northeasterly direction, and a short axis 200 km in a northwesterly direction. The northwestern rim of the basin, to which the mining activity is restricted, runs for a distance of 500 km from near the town of Evander in the northeast to near the town of Welkom in the southwest. Mining operations have reached a maximum depth of 3600 m below surface, and core-drilling has penetrated to a maximum depth of 4600 m. In certain sections of the basin, particular stratigraphic horizons have been mined out completely for 70 continuous km along strike and for 8 km down dip.

From all the boreholes that have been drilled, shafts that have been sunk, tunnels that have been excavated, and stopes that have been mined, a volume of data has been

TABLE I

Gold production and sales of gold in South Africa, 1964–1973

Year	Gold recovered (kg)	Sales value (billions $)	$/kg
1973	852,325	2.563	3007
1972	908,725	1.633	1797
1971	976,297	1.259	1289
1970	1,000,417	1.164	1163
1969	972,956	1.126	1158
1968	967,146	1.099	1136
1967	949,679	1.075	1132
1966	960,466	1.087	1131
1965	950,332	1.073	1129
1964	905,470	1.023	1129

gathered over the 88 years that is staggering in its dimensions. A single, large-sized, deep-level mine, at the end of its life, will have been sampled at certainly no less than 10 million points, at each of which at least the metal content, the thickness of the mineralized horizon, and the number of bands comprising the horizon will have been measured. At many of these points, other geological information will also have been recorded. It is probably correct to say that from no other Precambrian sedimentary basin in the world has so much information been gathered with respect to the inter-relationships between stratiform mineralization, structure, stratigraphy, and sedimentology.

The production of gold from South Africa during the past ten years and the total value of sales of such gold are shown in Table I. Of the annual amount of gold won in the country, approximately 98% comes from the Witwatersrand Basin, the main source of the

TABLE II

Estimated world gold production: 1972

Country	Kg gold	Percentage
South Africa	908,700	66.43
U.S.S.R.	186,000	13.60
Canada	64,700	4.73
U.S.A.	45,900	3.36
Australia	30,000	2.19
Ghana	22,700	1.66
Philippines	18,200	1.33
Rhodesia	15,500	1.13
Japan	7,500	0.55
Colombia	5,700	0.42
Elsewhere	63,000	4.60
Total	1,367,900	100

balance being mineralization in the Archean greenstone belts. Peak production was realized in 1970, when just over 1000 metric tons of gold were mined, and US$ 1.164 billion were realized from sales. The quantity of gold extracted each year since then has been declining steadily, but the value of sales has increased substantially, due to the rising price of gold on the free market. In 1973, revenue from gold sales amounted to $ 2,563 billion.

The place which South Africa occupies in the ranks of the world's gold-producing countries can be seen in Table II, which was compiled for the year 1972. The contribution from the U.S.S.R. is an estimate only. Of a total output of almost 1368 tons, South Africa's share was a little under two-thirds. It is truly remarkable that one sedimentary basin can so dominate the pattern of distribution of a particular metal in the earth's crust.

THE WITWATERSRAND BASIN IN TIME AND SPACE

Age of the Witwatersrand strata

Except for the very basal members of the succession, no age measurements have been obtained on any of the strata that compose the Witwatersrand sequence. Lavas in the lowermost section of the stratigraphic column have been dated at 2820 ± 55 million years, by the Rb/Sr method, and at 2800 ± 60 m.y., by the U/Pb method. The Witwatersrand rocks rest on Archean basement granites which have yielded two ages – 2900 ± 50 m.y., by the Rb/Sr method, and 3100 ± 100 m.y., by the U/Pb method. Stratigraphically well above the top of the Witwatersrand succession, lavas belonging to the Ventersdorp sequence have been dated at 2300 ± 100 m.y.

Uraninite grains in the mineralized arenaceous horizons have given an age of 3040 ± 100 m.y., and monazite grains one of 3160 ± 100 m.y. Both of these ages are older than that of the lowermost members of the Witwatersrand succession, pointing to the fact that these minerals are of a detrital origin, and are not the products of epigenetic mineralization of the sediments. These ages provide valuable evidence in the old placer-hydrothermal controversy regarding the origin of the gold and uranium mineralization.

From such meagre data, it has been put forward that the age of the Witwatersrand sequence is between 2500 and 2750 m.y. These rocks rest on a granitic basement which has a probable age of 3050–3200 m.y. From this basement was derived the detrital uraninite which forms a characteristic constituent of some of the economically exploitable horizons within the Witwatersrand succession. There is a suggestion that a later granite (2800–2950 m.y.) intruded into this basement. A conspicuous lead loss in the uranium minerals has been dated at 2000–2100 m.y., a period which is believed to mark the beginnings of magmatic activity associated with the emplacement of the Bushveld Igneous Complex. An earlier metamorphic overprint on the Witwatersrand strata is thought to be a product of Ventersdorp volcanic activity which probably took place between 2250 and 2500 m.y. ago.

Proterozoic basins and the pattern of crustal evolution

The Southern African sub-continent is built about two ancient Archean nuclei which are located in the eastern part of the region. One of these is located between Lesotho, northern Natal, and the eastern Transvaal, and the other in Rhodesia. These nuclei are constituted by granite-greenstone terranes which have different ages for the last periods of regional metamorphism. The older nucleus is contained within the Kaapvaal craton, in the northeastern part of South Africa, which suffered its last major metamorphic event between 3000 and 3250 m.y. ago. The younger nucleus forms the basement of the Rhodesian craton which reached a stable state possibly 2750–3000 m.y. ago.

Most of the Archean formations on the Kaapvaal craton were deposited under marine conditions. The topmost members of the Archean stratigraphy — the Moodies clastic sediments and intercalated non-clastics and volcanics — represent the emergence from below sea level, and the first indications of continental-type sedimentation can be seen at a time somewhere round 3250 m.y. From then on, supracrustal development in the Proterozoic took the form of shallow-water basin formation, with no indications of deep marine conditions having played any role. The strata were laid down in fluvial, deltaic, and shelf environments. Crustal instability is reflected in the volcanic members that are associated with all the Proterozoic sediments that were laid down on the Kaapvaal craton.

Between 3250 and 1750 m.y. ago, five separate Proterozoic basins were formed on the Kaapvaal craton. The locations of the depositional axes of each of these are shown in Fig. 1. The Pongola Sequence is the oldest of the basins, but the Moodies rocks, assigned to the Archean, have many of the characteristics of the later basins. The age of the Pongola rocks has been considered to be between 2750 and 3000 m.y., but there are indications that the lower limit might lie between 3100 and 3200 m.y. The Pongola Sequence is succeeded by Witwatersrand strata (2500–2750 m.y.), Ventersdorp rocks (2250–2500 m.y.), Transvaal formations (2000–2250 m.y.), and Watersberg strata (1750–2000 m.y.). There is no preserved record of further Proterozoic sedimentation on the Kaapvaal craton, and the next sequence of strata, covering all the above-mentioned rocks, belongs to the upper half of the Paleozoic.

It would appear that the five Proterozoic basins all have the general geometry of yoked basins. The depositional axes were originally oriented east-northeastwards, and the fault-bounded, more unstable side of the depositories was always to the northwest of the depositional axes. The southeastern margins of the basins were much less active, and downwarping, rather than downfaulting, was the preferred mode of tectonic adjustment. It can be seen in Fig. 1 that there is a migration of the basin axes northwestwards with time, and that there is a younging of Proterozoic depositories from the Caledon gravity low in the southeast to the Limpopo gravity high in the northwest. The northwestern active side of each basin was buried beneath the more passive edge of the succeeding basin.

The transition from Archean to Proterozoic style of crustal evolution took place on

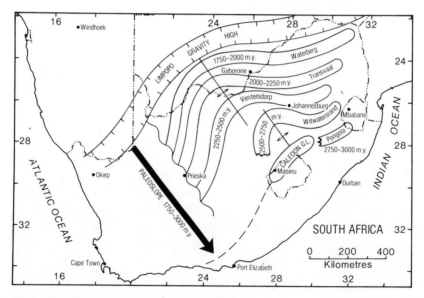

Fig. 1. The relative positions of the depositional axes of progressively younger Proterozoic sedimentary basins on the Kaapvaal craton in the northeastern part of South Africa. The basins young up the regional paleoslope from the Caledon gravity low towards the Limpopo gravity high. The full extensions of the Pongola and Witwatersrand basins still remain to be determined beneath the Phanerozoic cover.

the Kaapvaal craton at between 3000 and 3250 m.y. ago. On other shield areas of the world, the age of the transition has been dated at about 2500 m.y. Continental conditions thus started to prevail in Southern Africa about 500 m.y. before they became apparent elsewhere. The Witwatersrand Sequence was deposited during these 500 m.y., and it is thought that this is one of the major factors contributing to the uniqueness of the Witwatersrand Basin and its contained gold and uranium mineralization. Greenstone environments were still to the fore elsewhere in the world when optimum conditions for Witwatersrand, continental-type sedimentation were operative on the Kaapvaal craton.

THE ARCHITECTURE OF THE WITWATERSRAND BASIN

Structure and components

The Witwatersrand Basin is filled with approximately 14,000 m of sediments and volcanics which have been folded into an asymmetrical synclinorium. The dips of the strata on each limb, but particularly the northwestern one, decrease stratigraphically upwards. Very steep dips, and even overturning, might be present in the lowermost members of the succession, while the beds at the top might be inclined at angles of less

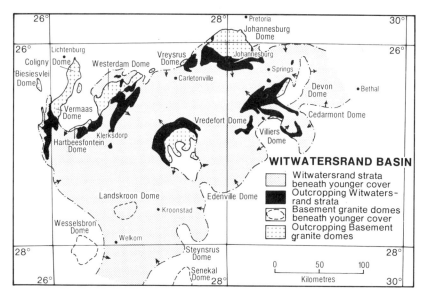

Fig. 2. The outcrop pattern of Witwatersrand strata and basement granite domes. The position of the outcrop and sub-outcrop of the base of the Witwatersrand Sequence has been determined by surface mapping, by magnetometric and gravimetric geophysical surveys, and by coredrilling.

than 20°. Two main directions of deformation have resulted in the present configuration of the basin, as portrayed in Fig. 1: folding about axial plane traces which trend between northwest and north-northwest and traces which lie between northeast and east-north-east. Superimposition of the two trends has resulted in an interference pattern, the regional manifestation of which can be seen in the broad arcuation of the Witwatersrand and other Proterozoic basins along a northwesterly-trending continental arch.

By far the greater proportion of the Witwatersrand rocks lies beneath a younger cover of Proterozoic and Phanerozoic formations, as can be seen in Fig. 2. Overlying strata can be either conformable or uncorformable on the Witwatersrand Sequence, which, in turn, rests on the Archean basement with a sedimentary contact along a grand unconformity representing a hiatus of up to 500 m.y. The best exposures of Witwatersrand rocks lie along the flanks of the various basement granite domes which have their optimum outcrop along the northwestern rim of the basin and in the northeastern section of the depository. Considerable tectonic movement has taken place along the contacts between the Witwatersrand formations and the granite domes, and, on some of the latter, the basement has been remobilized to give the appearance of being later than the Witwatersrand rocks. The most conspicuous example of this is on the Vredefort dome where the younger strata have suffered high-grade metamorphism and intense structural deformation.

Within the basin are six major goldfields, the positions of which are indicated in Fig. 3. The presence of three of these fields — Klerksdorp, West Rand, and East Rand — was

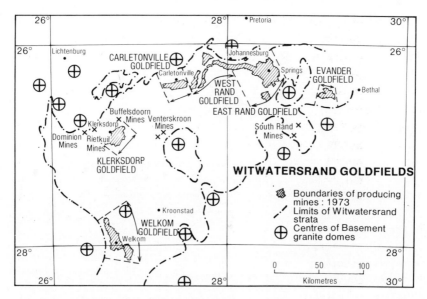

Fig. 3. The location of the major goldfields and the minor mineralized areas in the Witwatersrand Basin. The boundaries of current mining activities within each goldfield are shown, as well as the locations of the goldfields in synclinal downwarps between basement granite domes.

indicated by outcrops of the auriferous horizons. The other three goldfields — Welkom, Carletonville, and Evander — have no surface representation, and were located beneath a younger cover of up to 3000 m by gravimetric and magnetometric geophysical prospecting and by deep coredrilling. In earlier Witwatersrand literature, the Welkom goldfield is referred to as the Orange Free State field, the Carletonville goldfield as the Far West Rand field or the West Wits Line. The Central Rand field, in which the gold-bearing strata were first discovered, and which is located about the city of Johannesburg, is now taken to be a geographic term used for the area of common overlap of the West Rand and East Rand goldfields.

In addition to the six major goldfields, there are five smaller areas where limited amounts of gold have been won in the past. The Dominion mines, Rietkuil mines, and Buffelsdoorn mines, shown in Fig. 3, can be regarded as subsidiary sections of the Klerksdorp goldfield. The defunct Venterskroon mines are located on the northwestern flank of the Vredefort dome, and proved to be of the same limited economic significance as the South Rand mines. This latter group of old workings can be regarded, in some respects, as the extreme southeastern portion of the East Rand goldfield.

The centres of the basement granite domes have been plotted in Fig. 3 in relation to the various goldfields. It is apparent that each of the six fields is situated in a downwarped segment of the basin between the domes. The Welkom goldfield is positioned between the Wesselsbron, Landskroon, and Senekal domes; the Klerksdorp goldfield between the Hartbeesfontein, Westerdam, and Vredefort domes; the Carletonville goldfield between the Westerdam, Vreysrus, and Vredefort domes; the West Rand goldfield between the Vreysrus and Johannesburg domes; the East Rand goldfield between the Johannesburg and Devon domes; and the Evander goldfield between the Devon and Cedarmont domes.

Pattern of folding

The main fold components of the Witwatersrand Basin and surrounding country are shown in Fig. 4. The northwesterly-trending flexures have retained a relatively straight disposition, whereas the northeasterly traces reflect considerable bending about the former. It would appear from this relationship that the northwesterly folds are younger than the northeasterly, but there is abundant evidence that both fold directions were active before, during, and after Witwatersrand sedimentation, and they have been mutually interactive throughout all phases of the structural history of the basin. The northeasterly folds, which are longitudinally parallel to the depositional axes of the Proterozoic sedimentary basins, belong to the Vaal trend; the transverse, northwesterly folds are members of the Orange trend. The interaction of these two trends has produced the Vosfi Pattern: the Vaal-Orange Superimposed Fold Interference Pattern. The geometries of deposition, preservation, and exposure of all the Proterozoic rocks, not only those of the Witwatersrand Basin, on the Kaapvaal craton are the responses to deformational processes which acted within the framework of this interference pattern.

In Fig. 4, only the first-order regional folds have been shown. These now form subcontinental arches and downwarps. Conspicuous arcuation, concave to the southeast, is developed along the Koppies anticline, of the Orange trend, while a lesser intensity of arcuation, concave to the northwest, is apparent along the Palala syncline. The regional plunge on these transverse folds is obviously to the northwest, in the same direction as the younging of the Proterozoic basins.

The five dominant anticlines of the longitudinal Vaal trend — the Morokweng, Lichtenburg, Rand, Senekal, and Van Reenen folds — show a progressively greater tightness of their hinge-zones from northwest to southeast. This increasing constriction of the cores of the Vaal folds along the transverse Koppies arch culminates in the severe deformation and metamorphism of the Archean and Proterozoic rocks of the Vredefort dome.

On a lower order of interference, the Vosfi Pattern has given rise to the many structural culminations — where anticlinal traces intersect anticlinal traces — and structural depressions — where syncline intersects syncline — which are apparent in Fig. 2 and 3. The most obvious examples of the synclinal downwarps between the lines of domes can be seen in the northwards protuberance of Witwatersrand rocks southwest of the Vermaas dome and in the southwards embayment between the Villiers and Cedarmont domes. The periodicity of the transverse folds in measurable in the following distances between the traces of anticlines running through the domes: between Wesselsbron and Senekal-Landskroon-Hartbeesfontein-Vermaas-Biesiesvlei, 55 km; between Senekal-Biesiesvlei and

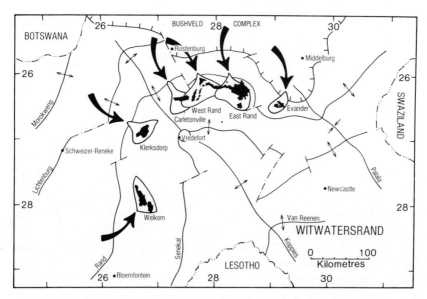

Fig. 4. The relationship between goldfields, fluvial fans, and major fold axes in the Witwatersrand Basin. The arcuate shape of the basin is the result of the two superimposed directions of folding, and has been formed about the northwesterly-trending Koppies continental arch. The arrows indicate the direction of transportation of sediment from the source area in the northwest to the basin.

Steynsrus-Southwest Westerdam-Coligny, 40 km; between Steynsrus-Coligny and Edenville-Vredefort-Northeast Westerdam, 50 km; between Edenville-Northeast Westerdam and Vreysrus, 50 km; between Vreysrus and Villiers-Johannesburg, 45 km; and between Villiers-Johannesburg and Cedarmont-Devon, 45 km. The wavelengths of the longitudinal anticlines are as follows: between Biesiesvlei and Vermaas-Coligny, 40 km; between Vermaas-Coligny and Hartbeesfontein-Westerdam, 50 km; between Westerdam and south of Potchefstroom, 45 km; between south of Potchefstroom and Vredefort, 45 km; between Vredefort and south of Koppies, 50 km; and between south of Koppies and Edenville, 50 km.

   This second-order fold pattern, which controls the distribution of basement domes and major goldfields, has average periodicities of 40—50 km for both the longitudinal and the transverse folds. The transverse continental arches have wavelengths of between 400 and 500 km. Detailed structural investigations in the South Rand area (Pretorius, 1964) have shown that smaller-scale sedimentological and tectonic features have periodicities of 4—5 km; 1.5—2.5 km; and 0.5—0.8 km. The overall regional frequencies of folds are affected by the size of, and amount of vertical movement on, the granite domes which form on the structural culminations. Where large domes are formed, as in the Vredefort and Johannesburg instances, more lower-order, tighter folds are developed as the dome is approached. These smaller-scale folds often have a marked influence on localized sedimentological features, such as the formation of fluvial channels and the concentration of heavy minerals.

The locations of the existing goldfields are intimately related to the larger-scale structures, as depicted in Fig. 4. With the exception of the Evander field, all the goldfields are located immediately southeast of the axial plane trace of the Rand anticline. The original basin was contained between the Lichtenburg and Van Reenen anticlines, and by far the greater part of the presently preserved strata is to be found between the Rand and Senekal anticlines. There is repeated evidence pointing to the fact that the post-depositional regional structures, which account for the pattern of present preservation, are reactivations of the same structures that controlled the geometry of sedimentation during Witwatersrand times, and of the same structures that moulded the morphology of the pre-Witwatersrand surface.

Pattern of faulting

Faulting is very closely associated with folding. The most important of the array of faults that affect the strata are the strike faults which run parallel to the depositional axis of the basin and to the longitudinal, Vaal trend of folds. This type of fault is well illustrated in the Klerksdorp goldfield (Fig. 5). The Buffelsdoorn, Kromdraai, and East Buffelsfontein faults follow the same trend as the edge of the basin and the syncline

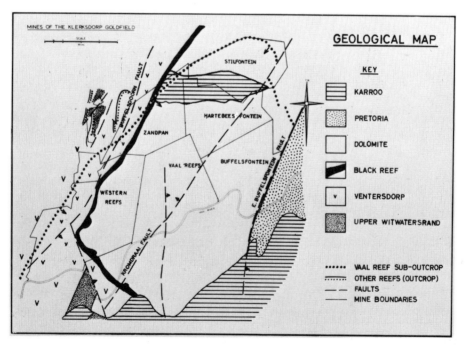

Fig. 5. The structure of the Klerksdorp goldfield (after Minter, 1972). The basin-edge strike faults can be seen to run parallel to the axial plane traces of the folds. Grabens contain synclinal downwarps and horsts anticlinal upwarps. The boundaries of the main deep-level mines are shown.

which has a closure on Stilfontein mine. A graben is developed between the Buffelsdoorn and Kromdraai faults and a horst between the Kromdraai and East Buffelsfontein faults. A syncline and an anticline, respectively, lie between these same faults, giving an example of a structural feature that is the rule within the Witwatersrand Basin, viz., blocks of elevated ground are generally horst-anticline structures, while downwarped blocks are usually graben-syncline structures.

The major strike faults are typically normal faults, with the downthrown side towards the depositional axis of the basin. The amount of vertical displacement on these faults is of the order of 1000–2000 m, but a displacement of almost 5000 m has been recorded. The strike faults are invariably accompanied by parallel, anthithetic, normal faults which dip towards the plane of the major strike faults. The result of this association is that the strata are disposed in elongated blocks of varying width, which are wedge-shaped in a vertical section.

The pattern of strike faults is shown in Fig. 6, which portrays the more important structural elements of the South Rand area. The Sugarbush fault is an example of the normal strike fault. A short distance south of it is another persistent strike fault, and then, farther to the south, are several parallel faults, of shorter length, which dip towards the Sugarbush fault. This arrangement is repeated in a group of faults south of Deneys-

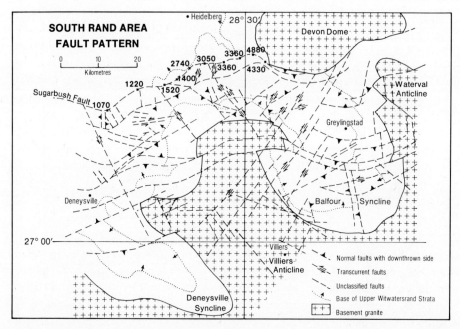

Fig. 6. The complex pattern of folding and faulting along the southeastern margin of the basin in the South Rand area. The northwesterly-trending folds are well displayed. The major east-west faults are coupled with antithetic, parallel faults. The vertical displacements on the Sugarbush fault are given in metres.

TABLE III

Types and frequency of 95 faults in the South Rand area

Strike of fault	Type of fault	Perc. of total
N75W	normal	8
N60W	normal	6
N30W	left-lateral	18
N10W	reverse	19
N10E	right-lateral	4
N40E	right-lateral	12
N60E	reverse	13
N80E	left-lateral	6
N80E	normal	14

ville-Greylingstad. The area also serves the purpose of illustrating the overall complexity of faulting which is ubiquitous in the Witwatersrand Basin, and also the outcrop pattern resulting from the interplay of the fault regime and the series of alternating folds from the Deneysville syncline, through the Villiers anticline and the Balfour syncline, to the Waterval anticline. The types and the frequency of each among the total of 95 observed displacements in the area have been analysed in Table III, which can be considered representative of the nature of faulting to be found throughout the Witwatersrand Basin.

That vertical tectonics, associated with the rising of the granite domes, has played a significant part in the deformation of the basin can be detected in the variations in vertical displacement along the Sugarbush fault. The northern side is the downthrown side. The displacement is 1070 m at the western extremity of the portion of the disloca-tion shown in Fig. 6, and this increases progressively to a maximum of 4880 m adjacent to the Devon dome. This differential uplift of 3810 m takes place over a distance of 40 km. There is also a less impressive indication of the effects of vertical tectonics on the nose of the Villiers anticline, where this appears in the base of the Upper Witwatersrand strata, just north of the Sugarbush fault. On the axial plane trace, the amount of displace-ment is 1520 m, whereas the movements on either side of the hinge of the fold are 1220 and 1400 m.

The long history of deformation in the basin and the changes in the stress fields can be discerned in the imprints of different movements on the same fault plane. The strike faults are believed to have been the planes of weakness along which the crust foundered to form the yoked basin that subsequently filled with Witwatersrand sediments and lavas. Differential movement between the uplifted edges of the depository and the subsiding floor continued, spasmodically, down these faults for the entire period of basin forma-tion. As subsidence of the basin, as a whole, progressed and a space problem was created in a vertical sense, stratigraphically higher strata started to ride upwards and outwards along bedding planes, in compliance with adjustment according to the tenets of concentric folding. At the same time, some of the strike faults, which had been acting as normal, gravity faults, were reactivated as high-angled reverse dislocations to assist in the upward movement of material from the inner sections of the basin. With the rising of the granite domes, a further space problem was created, with lateral as well as vertical over-tones. Strata squeezed between adjacent domes adjusted by horizontal movement along the strike faults, so that, after having served as normal and reverse faults, these disloca-tions suffered a third reactivation as transcurrent or wrench faults. With the onset of the succeeding period of basin development, the strike faults again moved according to a normal gravity pattern. Related to the folding of the beds, many of the earlier fault planes were also flexured, so that sinuous fault traces are characteristic of most of the longitudinal dislocations.

SOURCE OF WEALTH IN THE WITWATERSRAND BASIN

In 1971, South Africa celebrated the centenary of its mining industry, and the oppor-tunity was taken to assess the total value of minerals or mineral aggregates that had been recovered from each of the geological formations which constitute the total stratigraphic spectrum of the country. The Witwatersrand Basin witnessed its first sustained mining in 1886, so that Table IV is an evaluation of the first 85 years of exploitation of the contained mineral deposits.

Up to the end of 1971, almost 69% of the gross value of all minerals produced in South Africa had come from the Witwatersrand Basin. Of a grand total of a little under $ 34 billion, gold had been responsible for 93% of the output of mined products from the basin. Uranium recovery, which had been in operation for only eighteen years, accounted

TABLE IV

Total value of mineral production from Witwatersrand Basin, 1871–1971

Product	Sales value (millions $)
Gold	31,557.492
Uranium	2,183.777
Silver	109.856
Pyrite	79.149
Platinoids	11.402
Building stones	6.300
Diamonds	0.019
Total	33,947.995
% of South Africa's production, 1871–1971	68.78

for $ 2 billion. The balance of the realized mineral wealth came from silver, pyrite, platinoids, building stones, and diamonds.

With the exception of the building stones, the source of the revenue came from a limited number of narrow stratigraphic horizons, called reefs, distributed erratically through the 14,000 m of the succession. These reefs are in no way analogous to those encountered in carbonate sedimentology. They represent mining terminology for any bed or portion of a bed in the Witwatersrand Sequence, which carries gold and/or uranium mineralization that can be economically exploited. The understanding of the nature of these reefs and the environments in which they formed is the objective of most geological work undertaken in the Witwatersrand Basin.

STRATIGRAPHY AND LITHOLOGY

Succession and thickness

The full succession of members comprising the Witwatersrand Sequence is not present in any one locality in the basin. One or more groups are missing either completely or partially, due to depositional onlapping or erosional removal. Table V, therefore, repre-

TABLE V

Composite stratigraphical thickness and ratios of Witwatersrand Sequence from type areas of development

Group	Total (m)	Volcanics (m)	Quartzites (m)	Shales (m)	Sand/shale ratio	Volcanics/ sediments ratio
Klipriviersberg	3,050	2,740	130	180	0.7	8.8
Kimberley-Elsburg	1,670	0	1,640	30	54.7	0.0
Main-Bird	1,490	300	1,010	180	5.6	0.3
Jeppestown	1,380	420	410	550	0.8	0.4
Government	1,970	0	1,240	730	1.7	0.0
Hospital Hill	1,620	0	610	1,010	0.6	0.0
Dominion	2,720	2,650	60	10	6.0	37.9
Klipriviersberg	3,050	2,740	130	180	0.7	8.8
Upper Witwatersrand	3,160	300	2,650	210	12.6	0.1
Lower Witwatersrand	4,970	420	2,260	2,290	1.0	0.1
Dominion	2,720	2,650	60	10	6.0	37.9
Witwatersrand	13,900	6,100	5,100	2,690	1.9	0.8

sents a composite stratigraphic assemblage of all the groups that are present at various localities. The Dominion Group, for instance, can be found only around the Vredefort dome and from the Klerksdorp goldfield westwards. Only the lower part of the Klipriviersberg Group is present in the northeastern portion of the presently known basin. All members of the Lower Witwatersrand succession have not been found in the Evander goldfield and surrounding area. Controversy still exists as to whether the Dominion Group is the basal member of the Witwatersrand Sequence or whether it belongs to an older succession of rocks, and as to where the uppermost Witwatersrand volcanics end and the basal lavas of the succeeding Ventersdorp Sequence begin. Many of the boundaries between groups comprising the Lower and Upper Witwatersrand divisions are quite arbitrary, and have not been related to specific episodes in the sedimentological history of basin development. Despite all that is known, there is still ample room for revision of the stratigraphic classification of the Witwatersrand Sequence.

The ratio of volcanics/sediments is a pointer to the general order of infilling of all the Proterozoic basins on the Kaapvaal craton in South Africa. The Witwatersrand Basin had an initial period of high crustal instability in which most of the material entering the basin was drawn from the simatic lithosphere, with only limited quantities of sediments being mixed with the volcanics. The middle stages of basin development were almost devoid of volcanic activity, and continental, shallow-water sedimentation dominated the scene. The terminal phase of the depository was marked by a recurrence of crustal instability and associated volcanism. Sedimentation during this period was also relatively minimal. In the middle period of intensive sedimentation, the ratio of sand/shale increased markedly with time. Higher-energy conditions are believed to have existed in the depository during the laying down of the Upper Witwatersrand sediments than during the accumulation of the muds, silts, sands, and chemical sediments of the Lower Division.

Of the 13,900 m that comprise the stratigraphic column, there are 5100 m of arenaceous sediments, 2690 m of argillaceous sediments, and 6110 m of volcanic products. The sand/shale ratio is 1.9, and the volcanics/sediments ratio 0.8. The relatively low overall percentage of fine-grained sediments is an indicator of the generally high level of energy that prevailed in the basin during the whole period of its formation, a factor which is of importance in defining the conditions that were uniquely favourable to the generation of the Witwatersrand mineralization.

Nature of components

The volcanic rocks in the Witwatersrand succession have been described by Whiteside (1970b). The Dominion Group consists of a lower, basic formation (610 m thick) and an upper, acid volcanic formation (2040 m thick). The basic volcanics are underlain by 40 m of conglomerate, sericitic quartzites, and shaly quartzites, and contain a layer of quartzites, 30 m thick, near their base. The basic volcanics are composed of andesites, tuffs, tuffaceous breccias, and quartz-feldspar porphyries. The acid volcanics consist of rhyolites, which predominate, and subordinate amounts of andesite, tuff, and volcanic ash. No sediments are present in these upper volcanics.

Two volcanic episodes occurred during the middle period of the development of the Witwatersrand Basin. The Jeppe Amygdaloid occurs within the Jeppestown Group, and is present over almost the whole of the basin, being absent only in the Johannesburg and Evander areas. The horizon consists of andesites, agglomerates, and tuffs, with intercalated quartzites. A maximum thickness of 450 m has been recorded, but the volcanics are usually between 30 and 100 m thick. The Bird Amygdaloid is located near the top of the Main-Bird Group, and has been found only in the portion of the basin stretching from the East Rand goldfield to the Evander goldfield. The main rock-type is a diabase which is considered to represent an altered basalt. Shales and quartzites occur with the volcanics. The maximum thickness is 300 m, with the normal thickness being of the order of 40–110 m.

The Klipriviersberg Group consists of the Vaal Bend Formation at the base, 915 m of andesites, pyroclastics, quartz-feldspar porphyries, with associated conglomerates, quartzites, and shales. The upper part of the group is represented by the Langgeleven Formation which is 2135 m thick, and is composed of andesites, agglomerates, and tuffs, with minor amounts of sediments. In general, tuffs and agglomerates are more commonly developed in the southwestern half of the basin.

The three end-points in a triangular plot of the composition of the sediments in the Witwatersrand Sequence can be represented by conglomerates, quartzites, and shales. Chemical sediments, in the form of banded ironstones, occur only in the Hospital Hill Group. They represent the products of the lowest-energy conditions in the basin's history, although, in places, carbonate-bearing shales have been reported from the Jeppestown Group.

The shales are usually composed of varying amounts of quartz, kaolinite, pyrophyllite, sericite, chlorite, and chloritoid. Certain shale horizons have a distinctive mineralogical assemblage, and there are also facies variations in the same horizon, which are indicated by variations in the ratios of the different phyllosilicates present. The Kimberley Shales at the top of the Main-Bird Group are frequently very high in magnesium, while the shales of the Lower Witwatersrand Division are unusual in that their sodium content is greater than that of potassium.

Quartzite is a misnomer for the arenaceous rocks which occur throughout the stratigraphic column. Fuller (1958) found that true quartzites occur only in the Hospital Hill Group. The supposed quartzites of the Government and Jeppestown groups are, in fact, sub-greywackes consisting of quartz and chlorite, with small amounts of muscovite and, in several horizons, fine-grained, disseminated magnetite. The quartzites of the Main-Bird and Kimberley-Elsburg groups are, more correctly, hydrothermally altered feldspathic quartzites. Quartz constitutes 70–90% of the minerals, with the balance consisting of muscovite, pyrophyllite, chlorite, chloritoid, and chert. The Main-Bird quartzites are 10–15% higher in silica than those of the other groups. Recrystallized quartz is present only in the Main-Bird quartzites.

TABLE VI

Ages and types of dykes and sills intrusive into Witwatersrand strata

Ventersdorp	post-Ventersdorp	post-Transvaal	post-Karroo
Epidiorite	dolerite	carbonatite	kimberlite
Diabase	quartz dolerite	porphyritic diabase	lamprophyre
Amygdaloidal diabase	quartz porphyry	Pilanesberg dolerite	dolerite
Quartz diabase	quartz diorite	syenite	
Ilmenite diabase	granophyre	elaeolite syenite	
	norite	quartz keratophyre	
	gabbro	diorite	
	pyroxenite		

Dykes and sills

The whole of the Witwatersrand Basin is perforated with dykes and sills, and, by volume, they occupy at least 5–10% of the space in which the basin is set. At least four different ages have been recognized. The Ventersdorp Sequence which follows on the Witwatersrand rocks is characterized by a substantial volume of volcanics, and it is believed that most of the older dykes in the Witwatersrand Basin acted as feeders to the Ventersdorp lavas. The bulk of the post-Ventersdorp dykes and sills are thought to have been emplaced during the igneous activity associated with the Bushveld Complex at about 1950 m.y. The post-Transvaal intrusions are considered to be contemporaneous with the Pilanesberg period of activity at between 1250 and 1350 m.y. The post-Karroo dolerites are Jurassic in age, and belong to the time of great outpouring of basaltic lava as the continents began to break up. The kimberlite dykes are possibly Cretaceous in age.

The various types of dykes and their age-groupings have been summarized in Table VI.

SEDIMENTOLOGY

Depositional isopachs

Attempts have been made to reconstruct the Witwatersrand Basin at the time of deposition, in order to learn how extensive the basin originally was, and whether there remains room for undiscovered goldfields to be present. Earlier efforts did not take into consideration the manner in which the strata have been deformed about the transverses arches. Since this information became available, it has been possible to extrapolate to the original basin edges with a fair degree of confidence. However, in a basin where unconformities abound, and where extensive reworking of sediments has taken place from one

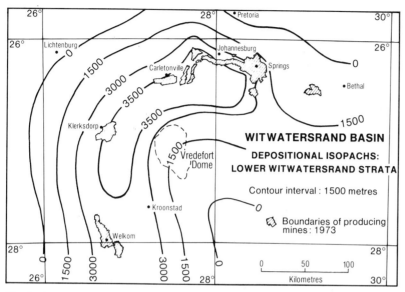

Fig. 7. The extrapolated depositional isopachs (metres) of the Lower Witwatersrand Division (Hospital Hill, Government, and Jeppestown groups). The locations of the current mining areas with reference to the isopach contours are shown. The isopachs illustrate the arcuate nature of the basin geometry. The Vredefort dome can be seen to be located well to the southeast of the depositional axis, and not in the centre of the basin, as has been suggested previously.

cycle of sedimentation to the next, there is no reliable way of determining precisely how much material has been eroded from each of the units, the preserved thicknesses of which have been used for the extrapolation.

Fig. 7 portrays the postulated depositional isopachs of the Lower Witwatersrand Division, composed of the Hospital Hill, Government, and Jeppestown groups. The maximum thickness of this division was 3500–4500 m. The deepest part of the basin appears to have been between the Vredefort and Johannesburg domes. The depositional axis lay on the northwestern side of the Vredefort dome, contrary to previous conclusions that the dome has been punched up in the very centre of the basin. The contours reflect the arcuation of the whole basin about the Koppies continental arch.

The distance between the northwestern zero-isopach and the depositional axis was 110 km, and the distance between the axis and the southeastern zero-isopach 130 km. Of the original total width of 240 km, there is preserved at present 170 km. On the northwestern side, about 50 km have been eroded away, while on the southeastern side only 20 km have been removed. These figures serve to show the original asymmetry of the yoked basin, and the greater amount of erosion on the more active northwestern edge.

The projected depositional isopachs are depicted in Fig. 8 of the Upper Witwatersrand Division, comprising the Main-Bird Group and the Kimberley-Elsburg Group. The maximum thickness of the strata was 3000–3500 m. The comments made concerning the

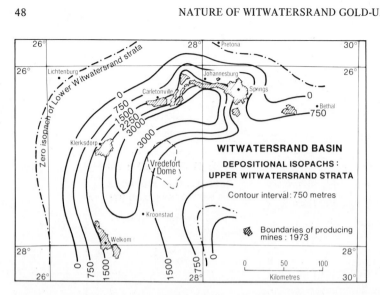

Fig. 8. The extrapolated depositional isopachs (metres) of the Upper Witwatersrand Division (Main-Bird and Kimberley-Elsburg groups). The generally regressive mechanism of basin development can be seen in the distance that the zero isopach has moved towards the centre of the depository between Lower and Upper Witwatersrand times. The mines are located between the 1500- and 2250-m isopachs, indicating that the mineralized fluvial fans are regressive protuberances into the basin.

location of the depositional axis with respect to the Vredefort dome, the deepest part of the depository, the shape of the basin, and the arcuation of the Lower Witwatersrand rocks also apply to the Upper Division strata.

On the northwestern side, the distance from the zero isopach to the depositional axis was 70 km, while, on the southeastern side, it was 140 km. There now remain about 130 km of the original width of 210 km. About 40 km have been eroded on the northwestern side, and about the same amount on the southeastern side.

The isopachs clearly show that the basin was a shrinking depository with time. Between the beginnings of Lower Witwatersrand and Upper Witwatersrand times, the edge of the basin moved southeastwards by about 60 km. The depositional axis moved in the same direction by about 10 km. On the southeastern side of the depository, the Upper Witwatersrand strata onlapped on to the Lower Division. All four features mentioned are characteristic of the mechanism of development of a yoked basin, with one very active fault-bounded side — the northwestern edge in the case of the Witwatersrand Basin — and a more passive, slowly subsiding opposite side. In this type of depository, continual uplift on the yoked margin causes previously deposited material to be repeatedly available for reworking into younger beds. It is probable that the major proportion of the missing widths of 40—50 km on the northwestern side was represented by sediments that were laid down, uplifted, reworked, and re-deposited during the development of the Witwatersrand Basin, and that only a small fraction was lost due to post-depositional erosion. On the southeastern side, it is likely that the bulk of the missing sediment was removed in post-Witwatersrand times.

The asymmetry of the depository can also be seen in the gradients of the paleoslopes. During Lower Witwatersrand sedimentation, the slope was 1 : 25 on the northwestern side, and 1 : 30 on the southeastern side. In Upper Witwatersrand times, the gradients changed to 1 : 20 and 1 : 40, respectively. The steeper paleoslope on the northwestern side during Upper Division sedimentation was a contributing factor to the higher-energy conditions that prevailed to give a sand/shale ratio of 12.6 for the Upper Division, compared to 1.0 for the Lower Division.

The contours of the depositional isopachs for each division show that the basin is open to both the south and the east-northeast. The original extent of the depository still remains to be determined, and the full economic potential to be realized.

Fluvial fans

From numerous studies carried out, in all of the goldfields, of the areal geometry of various stratigraphic horizons, of the patterns of facies variations, of trends in the changes of the grain size of sediments, of directions and patterns of paleoflow, of the nature of environmental indicators, and of the distribution of heavy minerals, including gold and uranium, it has become apparent that a goldfield represents a fluvial fan, or fan delta. The properties of the sediments constituting the goldfield are transitional between those characteristic of an alluvial fan and of those of the classical delta. Far greater amounts of water were active in the goldfields than are associated with typical alluvial fans, and the energy level on a goldfield was higher than that which can be recognized in the conventional delta of the Mississippi- or Nile-type. A goldfield is interpreted as having formed at the interface between a fluvial system and a shallow-water, lacustrine, or inland-sea, environment. The provenance area was close to the edge of the depository, the fluvial system was relatively short, the rivers debouched through canyons that remained fixed in their positions for very long periods of time, and the depository was an enclosed continental basin, with no connection to an open sea having yet been found.

From Fig. 4 it can be seen that the fluvial fans were all formed on the northwestern, fault-bounded edge of the depository. No large, well-developed fans have yet been found on the southeastern rim of the basin, which was tectonically more passive, and which responded to stress more by downwarping than by downfaulting. The paleocurrent directions indicate that the rivers flowed from the northwest, out of a source area that now lies buried, for the most part, under the Middle Proterozoic Bushveld Complex.

The fans which have so far been discovered along the northwestern basin-edge are located at the following distances from each other, as measured along the periphery of the depository: Welkom to Klerksdorp, 150 km; Klerksdorp to Carletonville, 120 km; Carletonville to West Rand, 50 km; West Rand to East Rand, 70 km; and East Rand to Evander, 100 km. The irregular distances highlight the overlaps and suggest possible gaps that still remain to be filled. The Carletonville, West Rand, and East Rand fans coalesce in their more distal parts, so that a false impression has been created of great continuity along strike of particular horizons within the stratigraphy. The extensive sheets of gravel that are referred to in earlier accounts of the Witwatersrand Sequence are, in fact, more limited beds of conglomerate that have merged into one another where separate fans have overlapped. The distances between the Welkom, Klerksdorp, and Carletonville goldfields, particularly, indicate possible gaps in the systematic distribution of fluvial fans.

The fans generally have an asymmetrical shape, with the left-hand section, looking from the basin-edge towards the depositional axis, longer and larger than the right-hand section. Each fan usually consists of two broad lobes, representing areas of greater channel development, which run down the marginal sections of the fan, separated by a central section with less robust development of coarser sediments. The East Rand fan extends for 40 km down the central section from the apex of the fan to the base of the fan where it merges with sediments deposited in the main lacustrine environment. The midfan portion is 50 km wide and the fanbase section 90 km wide. The western lobe is 45 km long, and the eastern lobe 60 km. In the Welkom fan, the northern lobe is 50 km long, and the eastern lobe 20 km. The East Rand fan is the largest of the six goldfield areas, and the Welkom fan is of intermediate size, the smallest being the Carletonville and Evander fans.

The coarser sediments of the fan exhibit a typical braided stream pattern. The channels are usually filled with the coarsest fraction of the material, but, in some instances, the channel fillings is of a finer grain-size than the adjacent sediments. Bars of gravel are well developed in some of the larger channels, while the interfluve areas are composed of finer-grained overbank material. The channels are usually shallow, with a relatively high width/depth channel index. Minter (1972) has reported that the Vaal Reef conglomerate horizon of the Klerksdorp goldfield is up to 2 m thick and covers an area of 250 km². Estuarine-like braided channels abound, which are up to 1.5 m deep and 150 m wide. Generally, the channels are less than 0.7 m deep. The largest channels so far recorded occur in the East Rand fan. In the western lobe, two channels have been cut, which are parallel to each other for the greater parts of their lengths, and which have been filled with heavily pyritic sand and only minor amounts of gravel. The one channel has a maximum width of 1000 m and a maximum depth of 35 m, while the other channel is up to 750 m wide and 85 m deep. Both channels have been traced for distances of over 8 km in the mine workings.

The arenaceous sediments comprising each fan are typically cross-bedded. Planar, tangential, and trough cross-bedding occur in various parts of the fan, indicating the different energy levels which prevailed at the time of transportation and deposition of the sand. Sims (1969) and Minter (1972) gathered the data summarized in Table VII, which give an indication of the thickness of the cross-bedded units and the inclination of the foresets. The units normally vary between 5 and 100 cm in thickness, and the foresets generally dip at between 18° and 25°. The characteristics of the cross-bedding point strongly to a fluvial environment in which the sand was deposited. Distribution of cross-bedding vectors is commonly bimodal, with a large angular difference between the two modes. One of the modes has been interpreted as having been produced by transporting currents

TABLE VII

Thicknesses of cross-bedded units and angles of dip of foresets

Fluvial fan	Reef group	Reef horizon	Thk*	Dip**
Welkom	Elsburg	Upper	–	22°
Welkom	Kimberley	A	–	18°
Welkom	Bird	Leader	14	20°
Welkom	Bird	Basal	8	23°
Welkom	Main	Livingstone	24	24°
Klerksdorp	Bird	Vaal	8	18°
Klerksdorp	Bird	Basal Grit	8	23°
West Rand	Klipriviersberg	Ventersdorp	–	19°
West Rand	Main	Livingstone	–	19°

*Thk = average thickness (cm); **dip = average angle of dip.

moving down the paleoslope and bringing the material from the source-area to, and beyond, the fluvial fans. The second mode is believed to be representative of the distributing currents within the basin, probably longshore drift movement, which washed the sediment parallel to the paleoslope. Sand waves, with an amplitude of up to one metre, were produced by the distributing currents. These latter currents swept the finer material along the shoreline, giving rise to the asymmetry of the fluvial fans. In all the goldfields, the distributing currents have been observed to have moved in a clockwise direction within the basin.

Each fan is composed of a large number of cycles of sedimentation, with the boundaries between cycles usually represented by unconformities of varying magnitude. The plane of unconformity marked a transition from a transgressive condition, at the end of the preceding cycle, to a regressive process at the beginning of the succeeding cycle. Each cycle started with a coarse phase, frequently gravel or grit, and fined upwards, with numerous breaks in continuity of deposition, reflecting different pulses of sediment inwashing. The basal gravels were formed in interlacing channels and bars, and, laterally, were the least continuous of the beds comprising the cycle. The finer material was distributed in sheets of sand which continued beyond the limits of the fan and intermingled with the offshore lacustrine sediments. The terminal phase of a cycle was generally marked by fine-grained sand, but in several instances the depositional energy dropped low enough to permit the deposition of silts and clays. The end-phase sediments were frequently subaerially exposed and scoured by erosional processes that were dominant between the cycles of sedimentation. The planes of inter-cycle unconformity are of considerable economic importance, since all exploitable reefs occur on, or immediately adjacent to, the unconformities.

The evidence points to the cycles building up the fan as being the products of tectonic adjustments along the bounding strike faults which separated the source area from the depository. The fans, being basin-edge phenomena, often straddled these faults. Relative uplift of the source area resulted in a regression basinwards of the fanhead environment. The change in the gradient of the paleoslope, brought about by the uplift of the basin-edge, produced a higher energy level on the fan, and coarser and heavier material was washed in and deposited. A progressive return to a state of equilibrium caused finer and finer sediment to be brought in. Finally, the amount of material being washed in was reduced to a minimum, and the fan was then subjected to optimum winnowing conditions by both the transporting currents down the fan and the longshore currents along the midfan and fanbase. Movement along the bounding faults commonly resulted in the fanhead facies of the previous cycle being uplifted and reworked into the basal members of the next cycle.

Minter (1972), from his study of the Vaal Reef in the Klerksdorp goldfield, has calculated that, at the time of the deposition of the basal gravel, the depth of water on the fan was of the order of 40–50 cm. As the cycle proceeded, the depth of water increased, so that, during the laying down of the finer-grained hangingwall sands, the depth reached between 110 and 120 cm.

Vertical distribution of mineralized horizons

By far the greater proportion of gold and uranium mineralization occurs in, or immediately adjacent to, bands of conglomerate which are preferentially developed at, or near, the base of each cycle of sedimentation. Within the Lower and Upper Witwatersrand Divisions in the Johannesburg area, the conglomerates occupy about 8% of the total thickness of sedimentary strata. On the opposite side of the basin, in the Vredefort area, the conglomerate horizons constitute 1% of the stratigraphy. Only a small proportion of the conglomerate horizons contains economically exploitable concentration of gold and uranium, with the maximum number being present in the West Rand fan, where their aggregate thickness amounts to about 2% of the total thickness of conglomerate development. Over the whole thickness of sediments on the northwestern side of the basin, the exploited conglomerate horizons constitute less than 0.2%.

From Table VIII, it can be seen that the main concentration of payable reefs is within the Main-Bird Group of the Upper Witwatersrand Division. The Dominion Group has only one series of reefs, while the Lower Witwatersrand Division has only two series. In the Main-Bird Group of the Upper Witwatersrand Division, there are nine series of reefs that have been exploited, and in the Kimberley-Elsburg Group three series, so that the total number of mineralized horizons which has been worked in the Upper Witwatersrand Division amounts to twelve, or 75% of the overall number of exploited horizons within the basin. The Black Reef belongs to the younger Transvaal Sequence, and was formed where the latter sediments onlapped over the gold-bearing Witwatersrand reefs.

The number of reefs that have been mined in a particular fan vary from a minimum of

TABLE VIII

Number of major mines which have worked different reef horizons in main fluvial fans

Reef	WKM	KDP	CTV	WRD	ERD	EVD	Total
Black	–	4	2	4	7	–	17
Ventersdorp	–	1	–	9	–	–	10
Elsburg	1	1	–	3	–	–	5
Kimberley	2	1	–	7	7	4	21
Bird	12	7	–	7	–	–	26
Livingstone	–	–	–	2	4	–	6
Johnstone	–	–	–	1	3	–	4
South	–	1	–	9	3	–	13
M.R. Leader	–	–	–	–	37	–	37
Pyritic Quartzites	–	–	–	–	10	–	10
Main	–	1	–	12	7	–	20
North	–	–	–	1	3	–	4
Carbon Leader	–	–	5	–	–	–	5
Jeppestown	–	2	–	–	–	–	2
Government	–	4	–	–	–	–	4
Dominion	–	2	–	–	–	–	2

WKM = Welkom fluvial fan; KDP = Klerksdorp fluvial fan; CTV = Carletonville fluvial fan; WRD = West Rand fluvial fan; ERD = East Rand fluvial fan; EVD = Evander fluvial fan.

1, in the Evander goldfield, to a maximum of 10 in the Klerksdorp and West Rand goldfields. The average per fluvial fan is between 5 and 6. In that the areas of fan formation have remained more or less constant on the rim of the basin during the whole of Witwatersrand sedimentation, it can be appreciated how very infrequently, during the infilling of the depository, conditions were favourable for the concentration of the exploitable heavy minerals.

An approximate guide can be gained to the relative economic importance of each reef through the number of mines which have exploited it. Fig. 9 is a representation of the frequency of mining on each mineralized horizon. The size of the different mines is highly variable; therefore, the number of mines is not directly proportional to the quantity of gold and/or uranium that has been extracted. The Carbon Leader, worked on five very large, deep-level mines, has contributed appreciably greater amounts of gold than the Black Reef which has been mined on seventeen much smaller, shallow-level mines. Nevertheless, it is apparent that there are six peaks among the mineralized horizons of the Witwatersrand Sequence: the Government reefs of the Klerksdorp fan, the Carbon Leader (Main-Bird Group) of the Carletonville fan, the Main Reef (Main-Bird Group) of the West Rand and East Rand fans, the Main Reef Leader (Main-Bird Group) of the East Rand fan, the Bird Reefs (Main-Bird Group) of the Welkom, Klerksdorp, and West Rand fans, and the Ventersdorp Contact Reef (Kimberley-Elsburg Group) of the West Rand fan. The

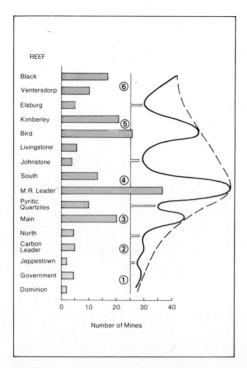

Fig. 9. The relative importance of the sixteen different stratigraphic horizons in which economic gold and uranium mineralization occurs, as indicated by the number of mines which have exploited each horizon. The representation is purely diagrammatic, since there is great variation in the sizes of the individual mines. The Main Reef Leader is the most important economic horizon. Of the sixteen reefs, twelve are members of the Upper Witwatersrand Division, emphasizing the stratigraphic centre of gravity of the gold and uranium mineralization.

smoothed profile indicates that there is a comparatively rapid build-up in economic importance from the Dominion Reef to the Main Reef Leader, and then a much slower decrease in importance from the latter reef to the Black Reef. Conditions favourable to the deposition of gold reached their acme in Main Reef Leader times, and this mineralized horizon represents the pivotal point in the stratigraphic distribution of mineral wealth in the Witwatersrand Basin.

The stratigraphic distances between the reef horizons above the Main Reef Leader are much smaller than those between the reefs lying above the base of the Witwatersrand Sequence and below the Main Reef Leader. The more closely spaced development of reefs in the Upper Witwatersrand Division was probably the result of more frequent tectonic adjustment and more intense reworking of previously deposited material, which processes followed after the basin started shrinking early in Main-Bird times. The gold in the apices and upper midfan sections of the Main Reef, Main Reef Leader, and South Reef was probably recycled a number of times before the last reef horizon was formed in Black Reef times.

TABLE IX

Thickness of Upper Witwatersrand reef groups at Johannesburg

Reef group	Thickness (m)
Elsburg	400
Kimberley	210
Bird	70
Leader-South	40
North-Main	30

The overall regressive nature of sedimentation in the Upper Witwatersrand Division is reflected in the progressively greater thickness of the conglomerate groups stratigraphically upwards. In Table IX are shown the variations in the zone thicknesses over which the bands of conglomerates are concentrated. In the normal geometry of a fluvial fan, more gravels are deposited in the fanhead and upper midfan sections, while lesser quantities of pebbles, of small size, are transported to the fanbase section. The thicknesses in Table IX, plus other sedimentological features, indicate that the North-Main, the Leader-South, and the Bird groups of conglomerates were formed in lower midfan environments, the Kimberley series of reefs in upper midfan sections, and the Elsburg conglomerates in fanhead environments. This continuous superimposition of more proximal facies over more distal facies is indicative of a shrinking basin, with a progressive advance of the apices of younger fans from the basin-edge towards the depositional axis. Comparing Table IX with Table VIII and Fig. 9 reveals that optimum conditions for the concentration of heavy minerals in the conglomerates prevailed in the lower midfan environments. The hydraulic regime became less and less favourable for the deposition of detrital particles, as the fanhead and the fanbase were approached from the midfan sections.

THE NATURE OF THE MINERALIZATION

Production of gold and uranium

The amount of gold won from mining operations in the Witwatersrand Basin between 1887 and 1972 is shown in Table X. This is a minimum figure, since early production figures are not necessarily complete. From 112 mines that have been operative at one time or another, almost 3 billion metric tons of ore have been extracted. From this ore, 28,722 metric tons of gold have been won. The average grade of the ore treated has been a little over 10 p.p.m. gold, with a range per goldfield of 7–21 p.p.m. The relative contributions of each goldfield have been summarized in Table XI. The East Rand fluvial fan, in addition to being the oldest producer, has also been the main contributor of tonnage and gold, but at the expense of having the second lowest average yield per ton.

TABLE X

Gold production from the Witwatersrand goldfields, 1887–1972

Goldfield	Year of first production	Total number of mines	Ore treated (mill. tons)	Gold recovered (kg)	Average grade (g/ton)
Welkom	1951	14	302.447	4,659,557	15.41
Klerksdorp	1941	7	172.818	2,299,301	13.30
Carletonville	1942	5	123.012	2,632,255	21.40
West Rand	1888	20	451.150	3,121,803	6.92
East Rand	1887	62	1737.680	15,412,216	8.87
Evander	1958	4	53.032	597,219	11.26
Total	1887	112	2840.139	28,722,351	10.11

Total sales value of Witwatersrand gold, 1887–1972: $33,896,713,000

The Carletonville goldfield has proved twice as rich as the average for the basin as a whole. The second richest field is the Welkom group of mines, while the lowest yields have come from the West Rand goldfield.

Uranium was first recovered in 1953 from the same ores as have yielded the gold. In the 20 years of production till the end of 1972, approximately, 76,012 metric tons of uranium oxide were won from 271 million tons of rock, at an average recovery grade of 280 p.p.m. The yield of uranium oxide is thus 28 times that of gold, and, by weight, uranium is a more important constituent of the ore than gold, but not by value. Table XII shows that the West Rand goldfield, which has the lowest yield per ton of gold, has, by far, the richest ores of uranium. This inverse relationship does not apply to the rest of the fields, and there is no general correlation between gold and uranium values. The lowest average recovery grade has been recorded in the Welkom goldfield, but no uranium at all has been won from the Evander mines.

TABLE XI

Gold production from the Witwatersrand goldfields, 1887–1972

Goldfield	Perc. of total tonnage	Perc. of total gold	Years in production	Ratio grade/ mean grade
Welkom	10.65	16.22	22	1.52
Klerksdorp	6.08	8.02	32	1.32
Carletonville	4.34	9.16	31	2.17
West Rand	15.88	10.87	85	0.68
East Rand	61.18	53.64	86	0.88
Evander	1.87	2.09	15	1.11
	100	100	86	1.00

TABLE XII

Production of uranium oxide from Witwatersrand Basin, 1953–1972

Reef	Goldfield	No. of producers	U_3O_8 (kg)	U_3O_8 (g/ton)
Elsburg	Welkom	1	328,533	117
Kimberley	East Rand	2	3,005,335	205
Bird	Welkom	7	12,909,704	196
Bird	Klerksdorp	6	29,558,598	258
Bird	West Rand	4	21,761,004	628
Main	Klerksdorp	2	561,273	154
Carbon Leader	Carletonville	4	9,204,809	248
Jeppestown	Klerksdorp	2	690,310	274
Dominion	Klerksdorp	1	1,882,841	510
All	Welkom	8	13,238,237	193
All	Klerksdorp	11	32,633,022	262
All	Carletonville	4	9,204,809	248
All	West Rand	4	21,761,004	628
All	East Rand	2	3,005,335	205
All	Evander	0	–	–
All	all	29	76,011,992	280

A comparison of Table XII, Table VIII, and Fig. 9 reveals that maximum gold concentration occurs at a different stratigraphic position than does the richest uranium mineralization. The most significant gold reefs occur in the lower (or Main) section of the Main-Bird Group, while the more important uranium horizons are located in the upper (or Bird) section of the same group. The richest carriers of both gold and uranium are the Carbon Leader (Main strata) of the Carletonville goldfield and the Basal and Vaal reefs (both in the Bird strata) of the Welkom and Klerksdorp fields, respectively. The Dominion Reef is generally richer in uranium than in gold, as are the Bird reefs over much of their area of development. Whiteside (1970a) has reported that the horizons between, and including, the North and South reefs contain no economic concentrations of uranium, except to a very limited extent in a small area of the Klerksdorp field. The conglomerates at the very top of the succession — the Elsburg Reefs and the Ventersdorp Contact Reef — are also poor in uranium. The Black Reef of the Transvaal Sequence does not carry significant amounts of uranium.

Types of reefs

The conglomerates have long been regarded as the typical gold- and uranium-bearing horizons of the Witwatersrand Basin. It is certainly true that most of the gold and uranium so far won has come from the conglomerates, but other types of mineralization have become progressively more important as newer goldfields have been opened up. It has also become apparent that, in many cases, the gold and uranium in the matrix of the conglomerates were not deposited at the same time as the original gravels were laid down. This does not imply an epigenetic origin for the mineralization, as was put forward in the hydrothermal theory, favoured by a minority of earlier investigators. It means that the gold was incorporated into the conglomerate by the reworking of previously deposited sediments, or was introduced into the gravels during the washing over of later sands. The gold and uranium now exploited occur in five forms:

(*1*) in the matrix of conglomerates;

(*2*) in heavily pyritic sands which usually fill erosion channels, the gold, uranium, and pyrite particles lying on the foresets of the cross-bedded sands;

(*3*) on sand along the planes of unconformities that separate two cycles of sedimentation;

(*4*) on mud along the planes of unconformity that separate succeeding cycles of sedimentation; and

(*5*) in carbon seams that are developed on, or immediately adjacent to, planes of unconformity.

In the ideal case, where the full spectrum of reefs is present, types 3, 4 and 5 would be the result of processes active during the terminal phase of a preceding cycle of sedimentation, and types 1 and 2 the responses in the initial stage of the succeeding cycle. Depending upon the degree of turbulence and the prevailing depositional energy level at the beginning of the succeeding cycle, the heavy minerals deposited at the end of the preceding cycle either would be buried, undisturbed, beneath the later sands, or be picked up and incorporated into the matrix of the overlying gravels.

In that coarser material, frequently in the form of conglomerates, marks the beginning of many of the cycles in the Upper Witwatersrand Division, gold and uranium, whether belonging to the preceding or the succeeding cycle, are closely associated with conglomerate horizons. The conglomerates are the main exploration targets, even where the gold is located a short distance below, on the unconformity which marks the end of the earlier cycle of sedimentation. In a number of instances, the energy level of the succeeding cycle was not high enough to bring in gravels, and only sand and silt washed over the unconformity, so that mineralized bands can occur along the interface between sand and sand or mud and sand, without any conglomerate being present in the immediate vicinity.

The carbon seams that have considerable economic importance on the horizons of the Carbon Leader of the Carletonville goldfield, the Vaal Reef of the Klerksdorp goldfield, and the Basal Reef of the Welkom goldfield, but which also assume local importance elsewhere in the stratigraphy, would now appear to be the remains of very primitive plant-life. In its present form, the carbon is either thucholite, a mixture of hydrocarbon and uraninite, with varying amounts of gold and sulphides, or a substance resembling bituminous coal. Many interpretations have been put forward for the origin of this material, the most strongly argued of the earlier ideas being that it represented the product of polymerization of methane gas by radioactive minerals in the sediments. The most recent work by Hallbauer (1972) presents persuasive evidence that the carbon was originally blue-green filamentous algae, with a suggestion that material resembling fungal spores might also be present. It would seem that the plant remains are parts of old algal mats that developed in quiet-water conditions on the margins of the fluvial fans or along the fanbase sections, at the end of certain cycles of deposition. Depending upon the coarseness of the sediments of the succeeding cycle, the carbon can be preserved intact, in which case it forms the carbon-seam type of reef, or it can be broken up and then mixed with the succeeding material, in which it takes the form of small particles, called fly-speck carbon, 0.5—1.0 mm in diameter, often clustered as three or more pieces.

Hallbauer and Joughin (1972) have reported that 85% of the gold recovered from the Witwatersrand mines comes from reefs less than 1 m thick, and that a very large fraction of this amount occurs in reefs less than 0.1 m thick. Over strike and dip sections of the reefs, the gold is patchily distributed in zones of general enrichment or impoverishment, which run for distances from a few tens of centimetres up to a few metres. These patches have a typical dimension of about 1 m. The gold particles themselves are distributed according to five different patterns within the reefs, none of the patterns being consistent over large areas (Hallbauer, 1972):

(1) particles which are dispersed throughout the matrix of the reef, in a somewhat even manner, with the individual particles spaced a few millimetres apart;

(2) discrete particles separated from each other by distances of up to 100 mm;

(3) isolated clusters, very rich in gold particles, inside a few cubic centimetres of matrix; 200 grains of gold might be present in a patch measuring 0.4 X 0.7 mm;

(4) thin streaks on either the hangingwall or the footwall contact; and

(5) very rich, isolated clusters occupying a few cubic centimetres and spaced 50 mm or more apart.

In many of the reefs, there is a very marked concentration of gold on the bottom contact. Minter (1972) found that, in the Vaal Reef of the Klerksdorp field, the average grade over the whole thickness of the reef was of the order of 15 p.p.m. but that concentrations of up to 1500 p.p.m. on the basal contact were not rare. In the past, it was assumed that the basal concentration indicated gravity settling of heavy minerals to the bottom of the gravel bed. Where the reef was originally an openwork gravel, over and into which sand washed during a succeeding pulse of sedimentation, this mechanism might well have been operative. However, in reefs which have a less well-developed conglomerate, it is now thought that the gold was concentrated on the top of the previous cycle, with the later pebbles being deposited on a very thin layer of precious metal. The supposed basal enrichment would then represent concentration by winnowing during the terminal stages of the preceding cycle, and not concentration by gravity settling of heavy detrital particles during the early stages of the succeeding cycle. In such cases, the key to the distribution patterns of gold mineralization lies in the sedimentology of the end-phase of one cycle of sedimentation and, to a much lesser extent, in the processes active in the initial phases of the next cycle.

The gold in the carbon seams occurs either as very small, discrete particles on top of, or within, the seams or as coatings and replacements of the algal filaments. The particles are believed to be of detrital origin, representing micro-nuggets that were physically entrapped in the network of filaments. The coatings and replacements probably formed from gold in solution. It is possible that, in the primitive, anoxygenic atmosphere that prevailed at the time the Witwatersrand deposits formed, gold could have been dissolved in cyanide- or chlorine-rich solutions. The algae, reacting with the mineralized waters in which they developed, absorbed the gold from solution, to build up protective coatings round the filaments or to replace the fibres. It is also possible that streaks of gold were already present on the sandy or muddy surface that formed during the terminal stages of a cycle of sedimentation, and that the algae grew subsequently on the gold-streaked unconformity, the base of the algal mats being anchored in the gold and other heavy minerals. By direct contact, without any intervening stage of solution, the gold could have been absorbed into the plant structure.

In the Klerksdorp goldfield, at least, the gold/uranium ratio is greater in the conglomerates than in the carbon seams (Minter, 1972). In general, the maximum concentrations of uranium are more towards the depositional axis of the basin than are the greater enrichments of gold. In any one particular horizon on a fan, the reef tends to have a higher gold tenor relatively closer to the fanhead and a greater uranium grade relatively closer to the fanbase.

Composition of conglomerates

A normal conglomerate consists of 80%, by weight, of pebbles, set in a matrix composed of recrystallized quartz, a phyllosilicate mixture of sericite, chlorite, and sometimes pyrophyllite, and sulphides and heavy minerals (Liebenberg, 1973). In addition to the presence of pebbles, the conglomerate is generally distinguishable from overlying and underlying quartzites by its cleaner nature, a larger percentage of phyllosilicates having been removed that from the adjacent sands. The quartz pebbles are barren. Only infrequent veinlets and dust-like inclusions of sulphides, gold, and hydrocarbon might be present in them, the products of remobilization after the deposition of the pebbles. The hangingwall and footwall quartzites typically consist of a mosaic of quartz grains, with lesser amounts of fine-grained micaceous constituents, and still smaller amounts of chromite, zircon, and pyrite. Gold and uranium normally do not occur in the matrix of the ordinary type of quartzite. An example of the difference between the matrix of a conglomerate horizon and the overlying quartzites can be seen in Table XIII, taken from Minter (1972).

The types of pebbles which can be found in the conglomerates are listed in Table XIV, which was prepared from observations made by Sims (1969) in a number of different reefs in the Main-Bird and Kimberley-Elsburg groups in the central part of the Welkom fluvial fan. The relative percentages of some of these pebble-types are set out in Table XV

TABLE XIII

Percentage mineral composition of conglomerate and quartzite in Klerksdorp fluvial fan

Mineral	Vaal Reef matrix	MB.4 quartzite
Quartz	95	62
Rock fragments	1	4
Sericite	3	26
Chlorite	1	8

TABLE XIV

Composition of pebbles in Upper Witwatersrand strata in Welkom fluvial fan

Durable pebbles	Non-durable pebbles
White quartz	yellow silicified shale
Smoky quartz	grey silicified shale
Opalescent blue quartz	grey quartzite
Dark grey massive chert	yellow quartzite
Grey banded chert	green quartzite
Green banded chert	quartz porphyry
Red banded chert	serpentinite
	talc schist
	chlorite schist

TABLE XV

Variations in composition and size of pebbles in different reefs in Western Holdings mine, Welkom fluvial fan

Pebbles	1	2	3	4	5	6
Quartz (%)	3	50	45	47	10	10
Green chert (%)	5	0	0	0	60	50
Yellow chert (%)	85	2	14	40	11	10
Black chert (%)	2	46	32	5	15	20
Quartzite (%)	5	2	7	3	1	5
Quartz porphyry (%)	0	0	2	5	3	5
Quartz (mm)	30	30	15	135	210	150
Green chert (mm)	15	—	—	—	90	50
Yellow chert (mm)	40	—	10	75	15	40
Black chert (mm)	15	15	15	10	25	75
Quartzite (mm)	40	—	10	10	—	150
Quartz porphyry (mm)	—	—	—	100	150	135

1 = UF-2 Reef, Livingstone Group; 2 = Middle Reef, Bird Group; 3 = Leader Reef, Bird Group; 4 = B Reef, Kimberley Group; 5 = Lower Reef, Elsburg Group; 6 = Upper Reef, Elsburg Group.

(after McKinney, 1964). It can be seen that the pebble assemblages vary widely from reef to reef, and in a number of instances the particular reef horizon can be accurately identified from the composition of the contained pebbles.

The lithology of the pebble frequently determines its mean size. The average diameters of pebbles vary between reefs, as can be seen in Table XV, where the pebbles of the Kimberley-Elsburg Group are appreciably greater in size than those of the underlying Main-Bird Group. Larger pebbles are normally indicative of a higher-energy regime that typically prevails in the fanhead and upper midfan sections of the depository. In that gold and uranium are generally concentrated in the midfan section, it is often, but not necessarily, the case that lower concentrations of the two are found where larger-pebble conglomerates are developed. In addition to the size of the pebbles decreasing down the fluvial fan into the lacustrine environment, the ratio of durable to non-durable pebbles increases substantially. Sims (1969) observed that, in the Welkom fan, the percentage of non-durable pebbles in the B Reef diminishes from 77 to 34% from the upper midfan to the lower midfan sections, and, in the Big Pebble Reef, from 27 to 9%. In general, where a conglomerate is characterized by a high proportion of non-durable pebbles, the gold and uranium values are low.

Table XVI gives an indication of the pebbles which are present in various conglomerates of the Klerksdorp fan (Minter, 1972). The highest percentage of quartz and the lowest percentage of quartzite pebbles are present in the Vaal Reef, a feature which is usually observed in conglomerates with economic concentrations of gold. The mean pebble-size of the Vaal Reef is 22 mm and the mean grain-size of quartz in the matrix 0.54 mm. The Trask sorting coefficient of the pebbles in the Vaal Reef is 1.29−1.34, and they could be regarded as being part of well-sorted marine gravels, if it were assumed that they had gone through one cycle of sorting only. The pebbles are roller- or muffin-shaped, and have a high degree of rounding. Modified dreikanter pebbles have been

TABLE XVI

Average size and composition of pebbles in Main-Bird strata of Klerksdorp fluvial fan

Pebbles	Basal Grit	Vaal Reef	Zandpan Marker	Upper MB. 4 Grit
Average size (mm)	−	22	30	30
Quartz (%)	70	85	78	52
Chert (%)	17	12	13	8
Quartzite (%)	7	3	5	10
Quartz porphyry (%)	6	< 1	4	21
Yellow shale (%)	< 1	< 1	< 1	−
Black shale (%)	−	< 1	< 1	−
Chloritic schist (%)	<.1	< 1	−	9
Serpentinite (%)	< 1	−	< 1	−

TABLE XVII

Thicknesses, compositions, and uranium/gold ratios of selected reef horizons

Reef Group	Reef Horizon	Fluvial fan	TN	SZ	QU	CT	QT	OS	U/Au
Bird	Zone 2	West Rand	62	21	77	7	16	–	769
Bird	Monarch	West Rand	99	18	82	6	11	–	435
Bird	White	West Rand	35	12	85	8	3	4	40
Bird	Vaal	Klerksdorp	15	22	85	12	3	–	11
Bird	Basal	Welkom	36	20	60	23	5	12	18
Main	Livingstone	West Rand	50	35	–	–	–	–	11
Main	South	West Rand	10	17	86	7	7	–	14
Main	Main	West Rand	110	37	84	6	10	–	9
Main	North	West Rand	50	30	83	6	11	–	--

TN = average thickness (cm); SZ = average size of 10 largest pebbles (mm); QU = percentage vein quartz pebbles; CT = percentage chert pebbles; QT = percentage quartzite pebbles; OS = percentage other types of pebbles; U/Au = ratio of uranium content to gold content.

found, indicating fluvial reworking of pebbles abraded by wind in the source area. The pebbles constitute 20% of the volume of the Vaal Reef, which low figure would suggest that this reef is not a typical conglomerate.

Whereas the gold has a tendency to be concentrated near the base of a conglomerate band, uranium can occur throughout the thickness of the horizon. From this it follows that thicker reefs often have greater concentrations of uranium. Table XVII has been compiled from Minter's (1972) data to show that, if uranium mineralization is present, the uranium/gold ratio is considerably enhanced where thicker reefs are developed. Uranium is not a characteristic feature of the Main group of reefs anywhere in the basin, and there is no apparent relationship between reef thickness and gold/uranium ratios. However, in the Bird reefs, which are the best uranium carriers in the stratigraphic column, there is a clear indication that much more uranium is present where the reef is thicker.

Thick conglomerates are not the product of one single pulse of sedimentation. They are normally built up of three or four inwashings of gravel, with intervening periods of sand deposition. Heavy minerals, even if they do tend to form basal concentrations, can therefore occur in several bands through the total thickness of conglomerate, each band being at the bottom of an individual pulse of gravel.

Mineralogy of the reefs

Table XVIII has been prepared to show the full range of minerals that have so far been observed in the various types of gold- and uranium-bearing reefs within the Witwatersrand Basin. The economic minerals are those that have been commercially exploited: the ores

TABLE XVIII

Minerals present in Witwatersrand auriferous horizons

Economic minerals	Sulphides	Oxides	Silicates	Others
Gold	pyrrhotite	quartz	muscovite	calcite
Tellurium	leucopyrite		sericite	dolomite
	loellingite	cassiterite	pyrophyllite	
Silver	marcasite		chlorite	zenotime
Stromeyerite		chromite	chloritoid	monazite
Proustite	chalcopyrite		biotite	
Dyscrasite	chalcopyrrhotite	columbite		diamond
	cubanite		kaolinite	graphite
Platinum	chalcocite	corundum		
Platiniridium	neodigenite		epidote	
Osmiridium	covellite	magnetite		
Iridosmine	bornite	hematite	tourmaline	
Sperrylite	tennantite	goethite		
Braggite			garnet	
Cooperite	galena	rutile		
		leucoxene	zircon	
Uraninite	sphalerite	ilmeno-rutile		
Thucholite		ilmenite	sphene	
Brannerite	molybdenite	anatase		
Uranothorite	bismuthinite	brookite		
Pyrite				
	arsenopyrite			
	skutterudite			
	cobaltite			
	glaucodot			
	linnaeite			
	safflorite			
	gersdorffite			
	niccolite			
	millerite			
	pentlandite			
	bravoite			
	mackinawite			

of gold, platinum, and uranium, and pyrite which has been used in the manufacture of sulphuric acid. The list contains primary, secondary, and even some tertiary minerals, the latter two groups of which are the products of the metamorphism and remobilization which have affected the mineralized horizons. The fact that the economic minerals and the sulphides have been reconstituted, for the most part, has given rise in the past to the arguments in favour of the mineralization being of epigenetic origin. Although remobilization did not cause the secondary products to move more than a few millimetres from the primary sources, the change in morphology of many of the minerals gives the appearance of crystallization in situ and of a hydrothermal sequence of replacement — the evidence used by the hydrothermalists in their dispute with the placerists.

The bulk of the gold occurs in the free state, and only a small portion is locked in the sulphides. Hallbauer and Joughin (1973) stated that the gold occurs in three forms: with quartz or silicates; with thucholite; or as a coating on pyrite. Liebenberg (1973) found that most of the gold is confined to the matrix of the conglomerates, where it is associated with quartz, chlorite, and sericite, and only rarely with muscovite, chloritoid, tourmaline, zircon, or iridosmine. Sometimes, the gold is associated with chromite. The gold frequently is present in cracks and pits in uraninite grains, these stringers of gold varying in width between 0.005 and 0.25 mm. Secondary sulphides, such as galena, pyrrhotite, chalcopyrite, pentlandite, and sphalerite, often accompany the gold when it is in the uraninite.

The gold that is found with thucholite, in addition to encrusting or replacing the algal filaments, takes the form of veinlets, specks, and patches in phyllosilicates that are wedged in cracks and cavities in the columnar thucholite (Liebenberg, 1973). Such gold has a thickness of 0.001—0.03 mm. Associated with the thucholite may be pyrite, pyrrhotite, chalcopyrite, pentlandite, sphalerite, cobaltite, linnaeite, galena, arsenopyrite, all of which may be replaced by gold. According to Hallbauer (1972), the columns, 0.2 mm in diameter and 0.5—1.0 mm long, of the columnar carbon or thucholite, consist of a tissue-like outer shell with a distinctly fibrous structure in longitudinal section. Inside the columns is a network of irregular fibres, individuals of which have a diameter of about one micron. Gold occurs in a fibre-like form between the columns and parallel to the long axis, or as a replacement or encrustation on the network of filaments within the columns.

Only a few pyrite grains contain included gold, but the precious metal is often present in particles of pyrrhotite, chalcopyrite, galena, pentlandite, sphalerite, arsenopyrite, linnaeite, and cobaltite (Liebenberg, 1973). Gold in the banded pyritic quartzites replaces pyrite, pyrrhotite, sphalerite, chalcopyrite, arsenopyrite, quartz, chlorite, and sericite. In such reefs, most of the gold is a replacement of buckshot pyrite which has a diameter of 0.002—0.18 mm. Gold in the Dominion Reef is relatively rare, and, when it does occur, it has a preferential association with leucoxene, and replaces pyrite, chlorite, and quartz. In the Ventersdorp Contact Reef, gold replaces quartz and chlorite, and, to a lesser extent, chalcopyrite and pyrite. In this reef, pyrrhotite is a very common associate of gold. In the Black Reef, gold replaces quartz. Much of the metal is associated with pyrite, and where other sulphides are present, the gold has a greater affinity for sphalerite than for chalcopyrite or pyrrhotite (Liebenberg, 1973).

The platinoids are present in only very low concentrations in the reefs. Cousins (1973) has stated that 3.5 mg of platinoids per ton has been the average recovery grade in the basin. One part of the platinum group of metals has been won for every 2000 parts of gold.

In the typical conglomerate, pyrite forms 3% of the total reef, and about 15% of the matrix alone. Pyrite constitutes about 90% of the sulphides present (Saager and Esselaar, 1969). It occurs predominantly as rounded, waterworn, detrital grains which are accompanied by pyrite pseudomorphs, concretions, and subhedral crystals. Secondary pyrite forms either fracture fillings in other components of the matrix or overgrowths on older detrital pyrite. Of the other sulphides present, only cobaltite, linnaeite, and arsenopyrite have morphologies that are indicative of detrital, water-transported materials. The heaviest concentrations of pyrite are in the banded pyritic quartzites, where this sulphide can comprise 25% of the total rock. The pyrite grains are in hydraulic equilibrium with unequivocal detrital particles, and generally rest on the foresets of cross-bedded units. Sedimentary partings, representing breaks in sedimentation, are very frequently layered with pyrite.

The quantitative mineralogy of two different types of reefs is shown in Table XIX, compiled from data provided by Liebenberg (1973). Despite the fact that the two reefs were formed in different environments, the Vaal Reef being a lower midfan development, and the Ventersdorp Contact Reef an upper midfan to fanhead sediment, the mineralogical composition shows significant differences only in the contents of chlorite, sericite, and sulphides. The higher chlorite content of the Ventersdorp Contact Reef has been produced, in part, by the fact that the reef shows an intermingling with volcanic material that was laid down at the base of the immediately overlying Klipriviersberg Group.

The three most persistent and abundant heavy minerals in the matrix of the conglomerate are chromite, zircon, and leucoxene, the last-mentioned being a secondary alteration product of primary titanium minerals. The relative percentages of these three minerals in the succession of reefs is depicted in Table XX, which represents a summation of data taken from Coetzee (1965). The relative percentages vary widely from reef to reef, and

TABLE XIX

Mineralogical composition of two auriferous conglomerates

Component	Vaal	Ventersdorp
Gold (p.p.m.)	50	44
Silver (p.p.m.)	8	5
Urianium oxide (p.p.m.)	870	290
Quartz (%)	88.3	88.9
Chlorite (%)	0.8	4.9
Muscovite (sericite) (%)	4.4	3.0
Pyrophylite (%)	0.1	0.2
Zircon (%)	0.1	0.2
Chromite (%)	0.2	0.1
Titanium minerals (%)	0.1	0.1
Sulphide minerals (%)	6.0	2.6

Vaal: Vaal Reef, Hartebeesfontein Mine, Klerksdorp fluvial fan.
Ventersdorp: Ventersdorp Contact Reef, Venters Mine, West Rand fluvial fan.

TABLE XX

Relative percentages of chromite, zircon, and leucoxene in major Witwatersrand reefs

Reef horizon	Chromite	Zircon	Leucoxene	Chromite/Zircon ratio
Black	58	14	28	4.14
Ventersdorp	34	25	41	1.36
Elsburg	64	34	2	1.88
Kimberley	59	26	15	2.27
Bird	38	36	26	1.06
South	6	7	87	0.86
Leader	11	12	77	0.92
Main	14	8	78	1.75
Carbon Leader	34	39	27	0.87
Dominion	13	9	78	1.44

many of the mineralized horizons can be distinguished one from the other on triangular plots of these heavy mineral assemblages. The origin of the titanium minerals could be either in basic or acid igneous rocks, with the result that leucoxene cannot be reliably employed to gain an idea of the source rocks that were supplying the depository at the time that any one particular reef was being laid down. However, it can be taken that the chromite would be preferentially drawn from ultrabasic to possibly basic rocks, while the zircon would come from acid rocks. The chromite/zircon ratio is, therefore, some measure of the mix of material being eroded in the source area.

In reefs which are sufficiently close to each other stratigraphically to be considered as belonging to one major and relatively continuous episode of sedimentation, such as the Main-Leader-South and the Kimberley-Elsburg-Ventersdorp groups, it would appear that the chromite/zircon ratio decreases upwards. An increase in chromite heralds the onset of a major episode of sedimentation. From this it can be concluded that first-order tectonic adjustment in the source-area exposed more ultramafic material for erosion, and that, as conditions tended towards a state of equilibrium, less and less ultramafic rocks were available, and more and more acidic rocks provided the erosional debris. In Table XX, the times of relatively greater exposure of ultramafic rocks in the source area are indicated at the Dominion, Main, Bird, Kimberley, and Black horizons.

Chemistry of the reefs

A succession of reefs lying stratigraphically one above the other in the Upper Witwatersrand Division on the West Rand Consolidated Mine in the West Rand fluvial fan was analysed to produce the results depicted in Table XXI. It is apparent that the chemistry very closely reflects the mineralogy, with quartz and phyllosilicates being responsible for the very high silica content. The figures support Fuller's (1958) contention that higher silica is a characteristic of the rocks in the Main Reef group, in that the

TABLE XXI

Chemical analyses (%) of auriferous conglomerates in the West Rand Consolidated Mine, West Rand fluvial fan

	NR	MR	BPQ	SR	LLR	ULR	WR	BR
SiO_2	89.26	93.14	62.08	94.06	86.38	88.18	87.19	88.32
Al_2O_3	2.31	1.69	1.92	2.51	5.13	4.42	3.97	1.77
Fe_2O_3	1.01	0.48	10.72	0.30	1.63	1.03	1.11	3.01
FeO	3.05	1.36	2.07	0.79	0.78	1.07	0.87	0.79
FeS_2	1.26	1.24	14.88	0.73	1.98	1.72	1.16	3.60
MgO	0.45	< 0.02	1.07	< 0.02	< 0.02	< 0.02	0.05	< 0.02
CaO	< 0.02	< 0.02	< 0.02	< 0.02	0.03	< 0.02	0.02	< 0.02
Na_2O	0.04	0.03	0.02	0.10	0.61	0.12	0.04	0.10
K_2O	0.01	0.02	0.01	0.12	0.35	0.14	0.27	0.18
TiO_2	0.10	0.12	0.25	0.15	0.53	0.28	0.22	0.09
P_2O_5	0.03	0.04	0.02	0.03	0.03	0.02	0.04	0.02
MnO	0.02	0.01	0.03	0.02	0.02	0.01	0.02	0.01
Loss	1.43	1.07	6.36	0.99	1.91	2.15	2.15	2.27
Th*	< 5	223	12	15	14	23	228	8
La*	5	38	18	8	38	23	26	15
Cl*	137	179	67	78	124	83	84	56
Total	98.98	99.24	99.44	99.81	99.40	99.15	97.14	99.17

NR = North Reef; MR = Main Reef; BPQ = Banded Pyritic Quartzites; SR = South Reef; LLR = Livingstone Reef (Lower Band); ULR = Livingstone Reef (Upper Band); WR = White Reef, BR = Boulder Reef; Loss = corrected loss on ignition; * in p.p.m.

Main Reef and the South Reef have silica contents in excess of 93%. The silica content of the conglomerates is greater than 86% in all cases, whereas silica drops to below 63% in the banded pyritic quartzites, illustrating a point that has been mentioned previously to the effect that the phyllosilicate content of the adjacent quartzites is always higher than that of the enclosed conglomerates, and that the coarser clastics are cleaner than the finer sands. The appreciably higher pyrite content of the banded pyritic quartzites is also readily apparent.

Some trace elements are shown in Table XXI, but more comprehensive studies have been carried out by Sellschop et al. (1973) and by Rasmussen and Fesq (1973). The results of their analyses are summarized in Table XXII and Table XXIII, respectively. There are distinct differences between the trace element patterns for shales and quartzites, but it would appear from Table XXIII that, in the case of the Kimberley reefs of the West Rand fan, at least, the matrix of the conglomerates is not readily distinguishable chemically from the overlying and underlying quartzites. This probably reflects the fact that much of the sand which infiltrated into the openwork gravels was associated with the series of pulses which brought large quantities of finer arenaceous material into the basin

TABLE XXII

Trace-element content of Witwatersrand strata in the East Rand Proprietary Mine, East Rand fluvial fan

	Na (%)	Sc (p.p.m.)	Co (p.p.m.)	Rb (p.p.m.)	Cs (p.p.m.)	Ba (p.p.m.)	La (p.p.m.)	Ce (p.p.m.)	Eu (p.p.m.)	Yb (p.p.m.)	Lu (p.p.m.)	Hf (p.p.m.)	Ta (p.p.m.)
Kimberley Shale	0.14	26.53	59.00	117	2.88	719	8.20	53.60	1.23	0.94	0.13	1.90	–
Bird Quartzite	0.03	3.10	6.00	–	0.66	–	6.93	25.70	0.56	0.42	0.05	1.34	0.26
Livingstone Quartzite	0.02	6.56	10.80	–	–	–	11.13	51.70	0.80	0.51	0.08	2.42	0.70
South Quartzite	0.05	6.35	32.90	62	0.90	309	9.01	38.50	0.76	0.46	0.10	2.53	0.59
Jeppestown Shale	0.53	19.00	50.30	103	2.38	389	17.49	56.50	0.91	2.16	0.54	3.55	0.75
Jeppestown Shale	0.56	18.48	48.80	–	1.70	362	20.39	64.70	1.55	2.32	0.56	4.62	1.32
Jeppestown Quartzite	0.11	12.40	25.30	71	1.45	335	21.03	48.10	1.18	1.92	0.32	3.61	0.63

TABLE XXIII

Trace-element content of Kimberley strata in the Durban Roodepoort Deep Mine, West Rand fluvial fan

Element		Conglomerates	Quartzites
Gold	p.p.m.	1.00	0.03
Uranium	p.p.m.	10	6
Thorium	p.p.m.	7	5
Sodium	%	0.04	0.05
Potassium	%	0.08	0.10
Barium	p.p.m.	60	50
Rubidium	p.p.m.	10	7
Caesium	p.p.m	0.60	0.50
Lanthanum	p.p.m.	15	15
Cerium	p.p.m.	35	30
Neodymium	p.p.m.	20	10
Europium	p.p.m.	0.50	0.50
Terbium	p.p.m.	0.20	0.20
Ytterbium	p.p.m.	1.20	1.00
Lutetium	p.p.m.	0.20	0.10
Titanium	%	0.15	0.08
Zirconium	p.p.m.	160	130
Hafnium	p.p.m.	3.50	3.50
Tantalum	p.p.m.	0.50	0.50
Tungsten	%	0.50	0.60
Gallium	p.p.m.	5	5
Iron	%	1.30	0.20
Scandium	p.p.m.	4	3
Chromium	p.p.m.	90	90
Cobalt	p.p.m.	30	6
Nickel	p.p.m.	45	25
Arsenic	p.p.m.	30	30
Antimony	p.p.m.	0.30	0.30

during the intermediate stages of the cycle of sedimentation, after the initial high-energy phase that deposited the pebbles, and before the terminal phase which transported the very fine sands, silts, or muds.

The carbon seams, identified as the remains of plant colonies, have given the analytical results shown in Table XXIV (De Kock, 1964). From the relative percentages of the organic components, the carbon could be classified as a bituminous coal. The sulphur content is influenced to a great extent by the volumes of pyrite and other sulphides that are present in the carbon. A striking feature is the very high gold content of the carbon — Carbon Leader and Main Reef Leader — in the bottom half of the Main-Bird Group, and the very low gold content of the carbon in the Bird Reef in the upper part of the same group.

The gold which is recovered from the various reefs produces a bullion which is com-

TABLE XXIV

Composition of carbon seams in Upper Witwatersrand strata

	A	B	C	D	E
Specific gravity	1.35	1.51	< 1.30	< 1.63	< 1.63
Moisture (%)	0.88	3.70	3.84	1.28	4.00
Volatiles (%)	18.41	22.65	16.82	12.34	18.76
Fixed carbon (%)	66.45	52.35	61.84	61.05	65.34
Ash (%)	14.26	21.30	17.50	25.33	11.90
Sulphur (%)	2.77	1.04	2.32	1.91	2.50
Gold (p.p.m.)	2397	9103	32	–	1073
Silver (p.p.m.)	220	768	10	–	80
Gold/Silver	10.89	11.86	3.29	–	13.39

A = Carbon Leader Reef, Doornfontein Mine, Carletonville fluvial fan; B = Carbon Leader Reef, West Driefontein Mine, Carletonville fluvial fan; C = Bird Monarch Reef, Luipaards Vlei Mine, West Rand fluvial fan; D = Kimberley May Reef, Vogelstruisbult Mine, East Rand fluvial fan; E = Main Reef Leader Reef, Vogelstruisbult Mine, East Rand fluvial fan.

posed of 88–90% gold and 7–11% silver. Other metals which are present in the bullion are mainly copper, lead, zinc, and iron, together with traces of the platinum group of metals, notably osmiridium. The gold itself contains silver, copper, nickel, and mercury (Liebenberg, 1973).

Relationships between components

The gold content of the reefs is highly variable from point to point, both laterally and vertically within the mineralized horizon, and there have been many attempts to find other components of the reefs, which have a much lower variability but a high correlation with the general tenor of gold mineralization. Saager and Esselaar (1969) carried out an

TABLE XXV

Metal content of Basal Reef in the Free State Geduld Mine, Welkom fluvial fan

Metal	p.p.m.	High correlation
Gold	375	Au + Ag
Silver	36	Au + U
Uranium	937	U + Ag
Nickel	253	U + Pb
Cobalt	156	Ni + Co
Copper	212	
Lead	448	
Zinc	99	
Sulphur	6.3%	

TABLE XXVI

Correlation (by chemical analysis) of major components of conglomerate reefs

Components	Correlation
Gold/silver	very close
Gold/silver/uranium	close
Gold/zirconium	significant
Gold/chromium	significant
Uranium/zirconium	significant
Uranium/chromium	significant
Gold/titanium/iron	inconclusive
Gold/uranium/potassium	none

extensive investigation of the Basal Reef in the Welkom goldfield, employing factor analysis, and obtained the results which are presented in Table XXV. A high correlation was found to exist only between gold and uranium and between gold and silver. In that the silver is alloyed with the gold, its variability within and between samples is as high as that for the gold. Liebenberg (1973) studied a larger number of reefs, and found the same relationship between gold and silver and between gold and uranium. The correlation he found between gold and some of the heavy and light minerals of the conglomerate horizons is listed in Table XXVI.

The silver which is intimately related to the gold is present to the extent of 8.9—12.3% of the gold, with an average content of 10%. The composition of the gold that is closely associated with the carbon seams shows a different pattern of silver content to that of the bulk of the gold present in the conglomerates. The spread is narrower, ranging between 7.7 and 11.0%. There is a stratigraphic variation in the silver content of the gold, as indicated in Table XXVII, prepared from data supplied by Liebenberg (1973). It has also been shown that, more often than not, the silver content of gold in the proximal portions of the fans is higher than that of gold in the more distal facies. In hydrothermal deposits, there is generally an increase in silver content of the ores with depth. Thus, the increase in silver content of stratigraphically higher reefs in the Witwatersrand Basin might be due to

TABLE XXVII

Stratigraphic variation in silver content of gold

Reef horizon	Perc. silver
Black	16
Ventersdorp	12
Elsburg	10
Bird	11
Main	5

TABLE XXVIII

Gold/pyrite relationships on the Village Main Reef Mine in the East Rand fluvial fan

Gold grade (p.p.m.)	Weight percentage of pyrite		
	Banded Pyritic Quartzites	Main Reef Leader	South Reef
0– 10	7.0	0.5	1.4
10– 25	18.0	3.6	1.8
25– 70	21.6	3.3	3.0
70–170	30.5	4.5	3.6
> 170	51.2	6.2	3.9

the preferential recycling of the fanheads of previously deposited gold-bearing strata, or to the tapping of deeper gold with the progressive erosion of mineralization in the source area.

The high correlation between gold and uranium is of a local nature within the reef. Over the whole of the fan, as mentioned previously, the greater concentrations of gold are upstream from the more pronounced uranium mineralization, so that the most payable gold-bearing areas do not coincide with the portions of the fan containing the maximum development of uranium ore. The higher amounts of gold are more likely to be in the conglomerate facies, while greater quantities of uranium are more probable in the pebbly quartzite facies (Minter, 1972).

The most conspicuous constituent of the reefs, after quartz, is pyrite, and many studies have been carried out in an attempt to correlate the amount of gold present and the volume of pyrite. Although Liebenberg (1973) has shown that there is a significant correlation between gold, uranium, chromium, and zirconium, all four elements are present in very small quantities, and neither of the last-mentioned two can be employed as a readily visible indicator of the degree of concentration of the first two. In certain sections of certain reefs, there is a definite correlation between the contents of gold and pyrite, as can be seen in Table XXVIII, prepared for three reef horizons in the Village Main Reef

TABLE XXIX

Variations in gold/pyrite relationships stratigraphically upwards in the East Rand fluvial fan

Reef Group	% pyrite/p.p.m. gold
Black	3.12
Kimberley	0.66
South	0.18
Main Reef Leader	0.36
Banded Pyritic Quartzites	1.80
Main	0.49

TABLE XXX

Average percentage composition of platinoids in Witwatersrand reefs

Goldfield	Iridium	Osmium	Ruthenium	Platinum	Rhodium	Palladium	p.p.b.
Welkom	33.1	40.1	13.0	11.9	1.2	tr.	4.7
Klerksdorp	38.5	44.3	12.3	7.1	0.8	tr.	1.9
Carletonville	35.8	36.6	15.0	11.4	0.8	tr.	8.9
West Rand	36.0	39.9	13.7	9.8	0.8	tr.	2.4
East Rand	35.8	38.0	15.1	10.4	0.8	tr.	4.3
Evander	33.7	37.3	13.5	15.3	1.2	tr.	93.0
Average	35.3	39.2	13.7	10.9	0.9	tr.	11.8

Mine near Johannesburg. The correlation is strongest in the Banded Pyritic Quartzites. However, when the whole range of reefs is considered, there is no constant relationship between the pyrite and gold contents. Table XXIX was compiled for a succession of mineralized horizons in the East Rand fluvial fan, and shows clearly that the ratio between pyrite and gold varies between very wide limits. The lack of constancy in the relationship mitigates against the visual employment of pyrite as a pointer to the amount of gold that might be present in any horizon, except under localized conditions.

Cousins (1973) commented on the surprisingly uniform composition of the platinoids in the Witwatersrand reefs. Table XXX has been compiled from his data for the average composition of the platinoids in the various goldfields. The conspicuous feature about the relationships among the various metals is that iridium and osmium are much in excess of ruthenium, platinum, and rhodium, and that palladium is absent or in trace quantities only. It has been found that mature alluvial deposits contain osmium and iridium as the major platinoids, and that immature alluvials have predominantly platinum. Richer ores are generally the less mature ores. Cousins (1973) interpreted the ratios of platinoids in the Witwatersrand reefs as indicating that the waters of the basin were sufficiently chemically active to leach the platinum and the ruthenium, and that very mature platinoid deposits were formed.

The very low tenor of the platinoid mineralization is seen in the fact that the average content for all the goldfields is less than twelve parts per billion. The Klerksdorp field is impoverished in the platinoids, whereas the Evander field has a markedly higher concentration of the metals. The Kimberley reefs of the latter goldfield thus contain the maximum amounts of platinoids, but the Black Reef of the much younger Transvaal Sequence, where it occurs in the Witwatersrand Basin, is also rich in the platinum-group metals. The Black Reef is distinctive in having a higher pyrite content, a higher platinoid content, and a higher proportion of silver in the gold than most of the Witwatersrand reefs.

Grain size of gold, uranium, and platinoids

The gold particles are present as thin platelets, sponge-like grains, crystalline octa-hedra, and irregular specks (Hallbauer, 1972). Most of the particles show sings of meta-morphism and recrystallization. The flat, plate-like particles are the most widespread. Liebenberg (1973) reported that, where primary gold particles are seen, they are round, oval, or cylindrical in shape. The secondary grains are hackly, with serated outlines.

Hallbauer and Joughin (1973) undertook a grain-size frequency distribution study of gold particles in various reefs from various fluvial fans, the results of which are shown in Table XXXI. It is apparent that in many of the reefs mobilized gold has been re-deposited on pyrite grains from which it is not readily detachable. All the gold that is larger than 1 mm in size was found to be attached to the large pyrite crystals. All gold less than 0.15 mm occurred as free gold. Particles in the carbon seams were seen to be nugget-shaped in many instances, their size being in the 0.05–2.00 mm range. Extremely fine-grained gold, less than 0.001 mm in diameter, occurs as thin fibres within the structure of the individ-ual carbon columns.

The normal range in size of the gold particles is 0.005–0.5 mm (Hallbauer, 1972). The weight of these particles is between a few and 500 micrograms, but heavier grains of up to 60,000 micrograms have also been observed.

A comparison has been made between the sizes of the gold, uraninite, and platinoid particles from information provided by Coetzee (1965) and De Kock (1964), and this has been depicted in Table XXXII. The average size of the gold grains is 0.035 mm, of the uraninite grains 0.065 mm, and of the platinoid grains 0.055 mm. All these figures illustrate the extremely small size of the minerals of economic importance in the reefs.

TABLE XXXI

Grain-size frequency distribution (percentage) of gold particles in various Witwatersrand auriferous horizons

Reef	Fluvial fan	< 0.075 mm	0.075 – 0.15 mm	0.15 – 0.30 mm	0.30 – 1.00 mm	Attached to coarse pyrite	Attached to thucho-lite
Ventersdorp	West Rand	20	7	30	19	24	0
B	Welkom	30	17	10	7	3	33
Kimberley	Evander	51	11	23	7	8	0
Basal	Welkom	21	15	14	22	13	15
Vaal	Klerksdorp	25	22	18	15	5	15
Monarch	West Rand	31	4	20	40	0	5
South	West Rand	19	17	31	3	0	30
Carbon Leader	Carletonville	18	17	14	9	0	42

TABLE XXXII

Grain-size frequency distribution of gold, uraninite, and platinoid particles in some Witwatersrand reefs

Fluvial fan	Reef	Mineral	Percentage frequency						
			0.000–0.015 mm	0.015–0.030 mm	0.030–0.060 mm	0.060–0.090 mm	0.090–0.120 mm	0.120–0.250 mm	> 0.250 mm
East Rand	Kimberley	uraninite	3	37	46	11	2	1	0
Welkom	Basal	uraninite	4	16	31	28	19	2	0
West Rand	Main	gold	46	20	13	10	7	2	1
Carletonville	Carbon Leader	gold	4	13	34	23	15	10	1
Carletonville	Carbon Leader	platinoids	13	19	38	25	4	1	0

No medium- to large-sized nuggets have been found during mining operations, and it can be concluded that, in regard to gold-particle size, the detrital deposits of the Witwatersrand are not comparable with modern-day placers.

THE CHARACTERISTICS OF A GOLDFIELD

Processes of development

The weight of the evidence which has been gathered to date indicates that a goldfield is a fluvial fan, or fan delta, that developed where a major river, flowing from a source-area to the northwest, discharged into a shallow-water lake or inland sea. The depository took the form of a yoked basin, fault-bounded on the northwestern edge, which was shrinking progressively with time. Repeated tectonic adjustment took place along the active northwestern margin of the basin, with the source area and earlier basin-edge deposits being uplifted relative to the downward-moving asymmetrical basin. Such uplift produced frequent steepening of the gradient of the paleoslope, which was accompanied by a regression of the apices of the fans from the shoreline towards the centre of the basin. The uplift of basin-edge material led to many cycles of reworking of previously deposited sediments, and this recycling was an important factor in the gradual concentration of gold and uranium until these components accumulated in economically exploitable amounts in the later stages of the life of the basin.

The fans are built up of cycle upon cycle of arenaceous and argillaceous material which was laid down on the interface between fluvial and lacustrine environments. Each cycle started with a high-energy pulse of sedimentation, consequent upon tectonic adjustment along the basin-edge, with succeeding pulses represented by lower and lower energy levels, until conditions of non-deposition prevailed at the end of the cycle. The base of a cycle is thus marked by a regression, and the remainder of the cycle by transgressive conditions. The tectonic responses between cycles produced an unconformity, the sediments below which were laid down at the end of a transgression and the sediments above the unconformity at the beginning of a regression. Economic concentrations of gold, uranium, and other heavy minerals are optimally located along the more important of such unconformities, either on the plane of the unconformity itself or in the immediately overlying conglomerates.

The material was brought from the source area on to the fan and distributed over its surface by a system of braided-stream channels. Interlacing of the channels often gives the impression of continuous sheets of gravel. Payshoots of higher gold and uranium values typically occur in the channels. However, greater amounts of heavy minerals also accumulated in interfluve areas, as the result of the winnowing of lighter components from the sands in which the gold was brought from the source area to the fan. This winnowing was produced by either the braided streams themselves or by longshore currents active in the more proximal parts of the depository.

The longshore currents played a progressively more important role in the distribution of sediments on the fan and in the lake, as the transgression proceeded. Transgressive conditions probably reached their maximum in the penultimate stage of the cycle. In the time interval before the onset of the next regression, there was probably a period of stillstand, when incipient tectonic adjustment caused gentle tilting of the strata and when degrading conditions were prevalent, rather than the normally dominant aggrading processes. Estuarine or deltaic mud- or sand-flat conditions assumed major importance on the margins of the fan and along the lower midfan and fanbase sections. The environment was then at its optimum for the growth of algal mats. The degrading processes were also particularly favourable for the winnowing out of light material and the consequent formation of residual concentrations of heavy minerals including gold and uranium. It is envisaged that the overall processes that were in operation during this terminal stage of a sedimentary cycle — incipient tectonic tilting, degrading hydraulic regimes, fluvio-deltaic-estuarine environments, maximum winnowing of earlier sediments, and optimum algal development — were some of the essential factors responsible for the genesis of the Witwatersrand goldfields.

Final responses to processes

The best-developed fan that has so far been recorded in the Witwatersrand Basin is that of the East Rand. It is the largest known, and the one that has been mined most extensively. Fig. 10 illustrates the main components of this typical gold- and uranium-bearing fluvial fan. The apex was located in a synclinal downwarp between two granite domes. The fan as a whole was also contained between domes of basement granite which were in existence before the fan was deposited, which continued to rise during sedimentation, thereby influencing the geometry of the fan and the lithofacies, and which were still active after the cessation of sedimentation, causing the faulting and folding which were responsible for the present morphology of the fan.

Two main lobes were formed, with an intervening central portion of lower-energy sedimentation and attentuated stratigraphy. The fan was typically asymmetrical with the left-hand lobe (looking towards the basin centre) much larger than the right-hand lobe. Possibly, the main cause of the asymmetry was the direction of clockwise flow of the longshore currents, which tended to sweep the material brought on to the fan farther out in a southeasterly direction. On each lobe numerous channels formed (only those on the left-hand lobe are shown in Fig. 10), which assumed a braided pattern radiating out from the apex of the fan. Clusters of channels generated second-order lobes on the major lobes, and three of these are present in the eastern section of the fan. The channels contain higher concentrations of heavy minerals, and constitute the payshoots which are preferentially mined.

The gross characteristics of the western, left-hand lobe are presented in Fig. 11. The stratigraphic horizon on which the Main Reef Leader was formed has been studied in

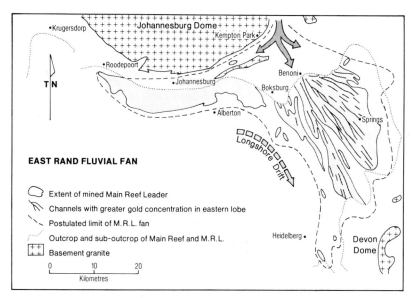

Fig. 10. The main components of a typical fluvial fan in which optimum mineralization is found. The western lobe forms part of the Central Rand goldfield and the eastern lobe the whole of the East Rand goldfield. The original fan covered at least 1300 km². The asymmetry of the fan is typical, with the left-hand lobe always larger than the right-hand, due to the influence of clockwise longshore currents.

detail. The isopachs of the preserved thickness of the conglomerate reef are at their maximum down the centre of the lobe, with two smaller protuberances down the paleo-slope off the main channel. The average recovery grade of gold reaches its highest values in the main channel; the ounces of osmiridium recovered per million ounces of gold also do so. The percentage silver in the bullion is lowest in the centre of the lobe, as would be expected in a typical alluvial deposit where more pronounced movement of water down the main channel would have tended to leach out greater amounts of silver. Even down the subsidiary channels there is an impoverishment in silver. The contours of the mean grain-size of zircon in the matrix of the Main Reef Leader conglomerate clearly reflect the overall geometry of the western lobe, and show a close correlation with the thickness of the reef. Bigger zircon grains are present in the main channel and the two subsidiary channels. The gold values can also be correlated with the zircon grain-sizes, the limit of payability being demarcated by the 0.20 mm contour line.

The properties of the reef described above point strongly to the intimate relationship between sedimentary processes and the mineralization of the conglomerate horizon. The gold and uranium were concentrated to varying degrees in different localities, in response to variations in the hydraulic regime that prevailed at a particular period of time during

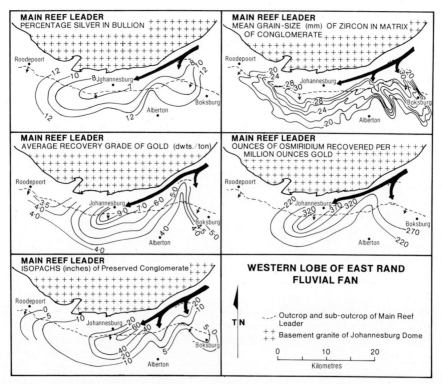

Fig. 11. Some of the characteristics of the western lobe of the East Rand fluvial fan. Away from the centre of the main channel, the thickness of the preserved conglomerate decreases, the gold values drop off, the concentration of platinoids diminishes, the percentage of silver in the gold increases, and the grain size of zircon in the matrix of the conglomerate becomes smaller. Similar patterns can be seen in subsidiary channels forming down the paleoslope from the main channel.

the infilling of the Witwatersrand Basin. The processes of ore formation came into operation on less than twenty occasions during the laying down of more than 8000 m of sediments, the deposition of which could have occupied 100–250 m.y. The generation of auriferous and uraniferous syngenetic sedimentary ore-bodies was a rare phenomenon.

A detailed study of the facies variations down the lobe of a fluvial fan has been carried out by Sims (1969) for the Basal Reef in the Welkom goldfield. These changes have been summarized in Table XXXIII, in which it can be seen that all the gradations in properties are in accord with those that would be produced in a fluvial system in which the competency of the streams diminished down the paleoslope, and the energy level of the hydraulic regime decreased from the proximal to the distal portion of the fan that was being built into the depository by the streams.

TABLE XXXIII

Variations between proximal and distal facies of Basal Reef in the southern part of the Welkom fluvial fan

	Massive Southern Reef	Multiple, Late-Channel Reef	Central, Double Reef	Northern, Single Reef
Zone thickness (m)	1.5	4.5	1.8	0.9
Conglomerate % of zone	65	45	25	25
Nature of conglomerate	massive	6 bands	2 bands	1 band
Pebble size	largest	smaller	still smaller	smallest
Composition of conglomerate	polymictic	polymictic	oligomictic	oligomictic
Lower boundary surface	very irregular	devoid of pebbles	largest pebbles	carbon seams
Cleanness of quartzites	very dirty	dirty	clean	very clean
Grain size of quartzites	coarse	coarse	medium	fine
Cross-bedding	obscure	well-developed	well-developed	abundant
Pyrite content	abundant, large	abundant, medium	minor, small	minimal, small
Carbon specks	very rare	occasional	plentiful	plentiful
Carbon seams	absent	absent	present	frequent
Distribution of gold	throughout	internal bands	bottom contact	bottom contact
Uranium values	very low	very low	higher	highest

Sequential development of adjacent fans

Where fans were relatively close to each other, the processes of sedimentation inter-
acted, and the margin of one fan merged, almost imperceptibly, into the margin of the
other. The best example of this is seen in the West Rand and East Rand fans. The western
lobe of the East Rand fan overlapped the eastern lobe of the West Rand fan, in the
vicinity of Johannesburg, to give the appearance of a single environment of continuous

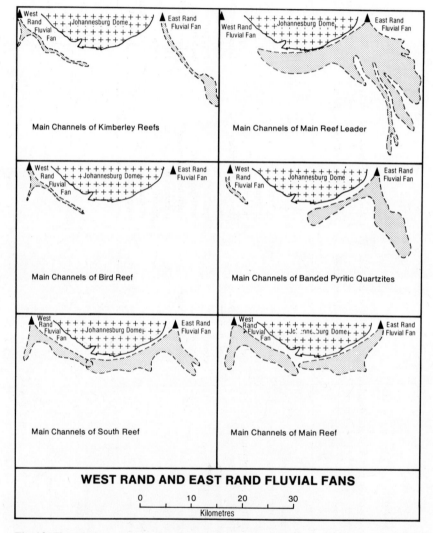

Fig. 12. The relative amounts of coarser sediments deposited at particular times on the adjacent West
Rand and East Rand fluvial fans. The main channels are portrayed that were formed during Main Reef,
Banded Pyritic Quartzites, Main Reef Leader, South Reef, Bird Reef, and Kimberley Reef times.

deposition. The area of intermingling of the two lobes is known as the Central Rand goldfield, which now can be regarded as a geographic term only, and not the expression of a discrete fluvial fan.

Fig. 12 has been prepared to show the relative degrees of activity at any one particular period of time on the two adjacent fans. The sizes of the main channels of Main Reef deposition are about the same for the West Rand and East Rand fans. Both lobes were forming in the West Rand, but only the western lobe of the East Rand was active. When the Banded Pyritic Quartzites were being formed, the East Rand was subjected to more intense sedimentation, with both lobes being constructed. Only one lobe of the West Rand fan, however, was receiving material. During Main Reef Leader times, all activity was focused on the East Rand fan, with both lobes building out to a very marked extent. The West Rand fluvial system does not seem to have been in operation. When the South Reef was being deposited, the East Rand fan was much less active than in Main Reef Leader times, and the West Rand depositional processes were once again operative. The East Rand fan appears to have received no auriferous sediments during Bird Reef times, and the West Rand fan only a relatively small volume. In Kimberley times, the East Rand fan was reactivated, and sedimentation on it was of greater importance than on the West Rand fan.

The variations in relative activity of the two fans are diagrammatically depicted in Fig. 13. The East Rand fan received a greater amount of sediment overall, a fact which is reflected in the greater amounts of gold which have been won from mines in this fan. The periods of active sedimentation in each fan seem to have had a see-sawing relationship, as can be seen in the peaks and depressions in the curves drawn through the bars of the diagram. Whenever abundant sediment, carrying gold and uranium, was brought down to one fan, the transportation and depositional system on the other fan was markedly diminished in importance. The cause of this phenomenon probably lay in relative differ-

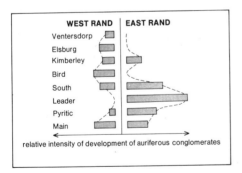

Fig. 13. A diagrammatic representation of the waxing and waning in the intensity of auriferous conglomerate development on the West Rand and East Rand fluvial fans. The diagram has been prepared from the information in Fig. 11. There is an antipathetic relationship apparent, so that appreciable development of conglomerate on one fan is contemporaneous with minimal deposition on the adjacent fan.

ences in response to non-uniform tectonic disturbances in the uplifted source-area. Wherever fault-blocks of source material were lifted higher, the drainage system off those blocks received greater amounts of erosional debris, and the fan into which the particular system ultimately discharged was consequently subjected to more intense sedimentation than the adjacent fan that was served by a source area in which uplift had been relatively slight.

Progressive development of a goldfield

A goldfield is a basin-edge feature. Over the whole history of the basin, its dimensions diminished, so that the basin-edge, in a broad context, was a regressing feature. This would imply that each stratigraphically higher fan would have been located farther out towards the depositional axis of the basin. Because the basin-edge was an active fault-environment, the more proximal portions of earlier fans would have been subjected to uplift, erosion, and recycling into later fans. Cannibalization was an integral process in the formation of auriferous fans.

The full sequence of events in the history of development of a goldfield is best seen in the Klerksdorp field, and has been illustrated in Fig. 14. The same fluvial system moving down the paleoslope from the northwest, and confined between uplifted granite domes,

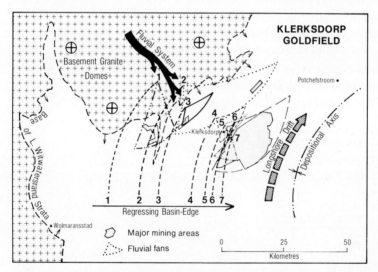

Fig. 14. The regressive nature of the basin-edge in the Klerksdorp goldfield. The apices of successive fans move from the basin-edge towards the depositional axis. *1* = Dominion Reef; *2* = Government Reefs; *3* = Jeppestown Reefs; *4* = Main Reef; *5* = Livingstone Reef; *6* = Bird Reef; *7* = Kimberley Reefs. The consistent position of the fluvial system between granite domes over a long period of time is apparent. Increasing structural instability is indicated by the more frequent development of fans in the Upper Witwatersrand Division (4,5,6,7). Left-handed asymmetry of the fans, due to clockwise longshore drift, is also discernible.

formed a series of fans, starting with the Dominion Reef and ending with the Kimberley Reefs. The positions of the apices of the fans changed from time to time, but generally remained within a relatively narrow zone. The apex of the oldest fan is fartherest to the northwest, and the apex of the youngest fan closest to the centre of the basin. The larger fans show the asymmetrical geometry produced by the interaction of the transporting fluvial system and the distributing lacustrine system.

Increasing structural instability with time is apparent in the greater number of fans developed during Upper Witwatersrand sedimentation than during the formation of the Lower Witwatersrand Division. The apices of the Upper Witwatersrand fans were also closer to each other than were those of the Lower Witwatersrand period. The formation of a fan was the response to tectonic adjustment across the fault boundaries of the yoked basin, and the more frequently major movement took place, the more frequently were fans formed.

THE SOURCE OF THE GOLD AND URANIUM

The six goldfields which have thus far been found in the Witwatersrand Basin are all located along the northwestern edge of the depository. The paleocurrent directions support the gross sedimentological indications that the source area of the detrital material, including heavy minerals, was to the northwest of the region now occupied by the portion of the basin which has been preserved from erosion. Material was introduced from the southwestern edge of the basin, but the volumes were smaller, the energy levels lower, argillaceous components more abundant than arenaceous, and only uneconomic amounts of gold and uranium introduced, for the most part. The evidence thus points to the fact that the source of the gold and uranium lay to the northwest of the basin.

It is believed that the pre-Witwatersrand rocks which, on erosion, gave rise to the sediments that filled the basin were members of a typical Archean assemblage of a granite-greenstone terrane. Most of the postulated source area is presently covered by younger Proterozoic sequences of impressive dimensions, such as the Ventersdorp lavas, the Transvaal sediments, and the Bushveld Complex. Consequently, there are only a few windows on to the pre-Witwatersrand rocks, but all of these show only Archean strata and no other pre-Witwatersrand sequences. The rock types that have been observed are similar to those found in the classic area of the Barberton Mountain Land, where a full succession of very early granite-greenstone rocks has been preserved. The topmost members of the succession are the Moodies sediments which were deposited in a continental environment; the middle members are the Fig Tree greywacke-turbidite sediments, formed under marine conditions; and the lowermost members are the ultramafic, mafic, and acid members of the Onverwacht group of igneous rocks which were extruded in a marine environment. The Onverwacht Group consists of a lower division, where ultramafic rocks are abundant, mafic rocks very well-developed, and acid rocks present to a very limited extent. In the upper division, the ratio of mafic to ultramafic rocks increases substantially, and there is a greater volume of acid material than in the lower division. Most of the gold mineralization is located along two stratigraphic horizons, the unconformities between the Lower Onverwacht and the Upper Onverwacht and between the Upper Onverwacht and the Fig Tree. No uranium mineralization has yet been found in any of the greenstone belts of the Kaapvaal craton.

According to Liebenberg (1973), 30—86% of the gold in the Barberton Mountain Land occurs in a free form, while 14—70% is intimately associated with sulphides, mainly pyrite and arsenopyrite. The average size of the grains of gold is 0.005—0.05 mm, with the free particles generally larger than those in the sulphides. Pink gold is occasionally present in the Barberton mines, the pinkness resulting from the gold being alloyed with nickel. The only other place where such gold has been found in South Africa is in the Dominion Reef, at the base of the Witwatersrand succession.

The gold content of the ultramafic and metabasaltic rocks of the Barberton Mountain Land varies between 0.005 and 0.01 p.p.m. Where the rocks have been weathered and recycled, the gold content rises to 0.075 p.p.m. The tenor of gold in the associated granites is less than 0.005 p.p.m. The average recovery grade of the Witwatersrand reefs is two orders of magnitude greater than the gold content of the reconstituted lavas of the Onverwacht Group.

The nature of the heavy minerals in the Witwatersrand reefs is a pointer to the composition of the source rocks from which the mineralization was drawn. The diagnostic minerals can be placed in at least two groups. The platinoids, chromite, diamonds, and cobalt and nickel sulphides were probably in ultramafic rocks originally. The uraninite, zircon, cassiterite, garnet, and quartz were probably drawn from granitic members of the pre-Witwatersrand basement. It is possible that some, at least, of the pyrite and copper sulphides were originally in the acid volcanics of the Upper Onverwacht Division.

The age of detrital uraninite in the basal members of the Witwatersrand sequence has been determined at 3040 ± 100 m.y., and of detrital monazite at 3160 ± 100 m.y. Both of these ages are younger than the topmost rocks of the Archean greenstone sequence in the Barberton Mountain Land, which are older than 3250 m.y. The age of the granitic basement which underlies the Witwatersrand rocks is 3050—3200 m.y., younger than the Moodies rocks, and the uranium-thorium mineralization is probably a product of the processes involved in the emplacement of the granitic basement.

Köppel and Saager (1973) reported that the isotopic composition of the lead in some of the detrital sulphides in the Witwatersrand reefs is similar to that of lead in galena from certain mines in the Barberton Mountain Land.

The conclusion is that the minerals of economic importance in the Witwatersrand Basin were drawn from two different populations of mineralized rocks in the Archean granite-greenstone terrane which lay to the northwest of the depository. The gold came from the ultramafics and mafics of the greenstone belts, while the uranium came from the younger granites which enveloped the belt. Depending upon the relative volumes of the two different source rocks, that were being eroded at any particular time, and upon the overall status of the hydraulic regime which denuded, transported, and deposited the weathered material, varying quantities of gold and uranium, relative to each other, were concentrated in the sediments at different stratigraphic horizons.

The transition from Archean-type crustal evolution to Proterozoic-type took place in South Africa between 3000 and 3250 m.y. ago, 500 m.y. earlier than on the Canadian Shield where the first continental sedimentation commenced at about 2500 m.y. In addition to this time difference, there are also major dissimilarities between the gross compositions of the greenstone belts of Canada and South Africa. Those of Canada contain substantially greater volumes of acid volcanics, while those of South Africa are dominated by ultramafics. The Canadian belts are hosts to gold, copper, and zinc mineralization; the South African belts are devoid of copper and zinc, and the most important sulphide ores are those of antimony. The South African greenstones are hosts to essentially siderophile mineralization, while those of Canada have both siderophile and chalcophile ore deposits. Since it is believed that the source of the Witwatersrand gold was in the ultramafics and mafics of the greenstone belts, the much greater volumes of such rock types in South Africa, compared to the Canadian Shield, might offer an explanation. in addition to that of the greater age of Proterozoic sedimentation, for the uniqueness of the Witwatersrand gold mineralization.

REFERENCES

Coetzee, F., 1965. Distribution and grain-size of gold, uraninite, pyrite, and certain other heavy minerals in gold-bearing reefs of the Witwatersrand Basin. *Geol. Soc. S. Afr., Trans.,* 68: 61–88.

Cousins, C.A., 1973. Platinoids in the Witwatersrand System. *S. Afr. Inst. Mining Metall., J.,* 73: 184–199.

De Kock, W.P., 1964. The geology and economic significance of the West Wits Line. In: S.H. Haughton (Editor), *The Geology of Some Ore Deposits in Southern Africa, 1.* Geological Society of South Africa, Johannesburg, pp. 323–391.

Fuller, A.O., 1958. A contribution to the petrology of the Witwatersrand System. *Geol. Soc. S. Afr., Trans.,* 61: 19–50.

Hallbauer, D.K., 1972. Distribution and size of gold particles in reefs. *Chamber Mines S. Afr., Ann. Rep.,* 10: 24–29.

Hallbauer, D.K. and Joughin, N.C., 1972. Distribution and size of gold particles in the Witwatersrand reefs and their effects on sampling procedures. *Inst. Mining Metall., Bull.,* 788: A133–142.

Hallbauer, D.K. and Joughin, N.C., 1973. The size distribution and morphology of gold particles in Witwatersrand reefs and their crushed products. *S. Afr. Inst. Mining Metall., J.,* 73: 395–405.

Köppel, V.H. and Saager, R., 1973. Lead isotope evidence for the detrital origin of Witwatersrand pyrites and its bearing on the provenance of the Witwatersrand gold. *Econ. Geol. Res. Unit, Inf. Circ.,* 79: 1–17.

Liebenberg, W.L., 1973. Mineralogical features of gold ores in South Africa. In: R.J. Adamson (Editor), *Gold Metallurgy in South Africa.* Chamber of Mines of South Africa, Johannesburg, pp. 352–446.

McKinney, J.S., 1964. Geology of the Anglo American group of mines in the Welkom area, Orange Free State Goldfield. In: S.H. Haughton (Editor), *The Geology of Some Ore Deposits in Southern Africa, 1.* Geological Society of South Africa, Johannesburg, pp. 451–506.

Minter, W.E., 1972. *Sedimentology of the Vaal Reef in the Klerksdorp Area.* Thesis, University of the Witwatersrand, Johannesburg, 170 pp. (unpublished).

Pretorius, D.A., 1964. The geology of the South Rand goldfield. In: S.H. Haughton (Editor), *The Geology of Some Ore Deposits in Southern Africa, 1.* Geological Society of South Africa, Johannesburg, pp. 219–282.

Rasmussen, S.E. and Fesq, H.W., 1973. Neutron activation analysis of samples from the Kimberley Reef conglomerate. *Natl. Inst. Metall., Rep.,* 1563: 1–241.

Saager, R. and Esselaar, P.A., 1969. Factor analysis of geochemical data from the Basal Reef, Orange Free State goldfield, South Africa. *Econ. Geol.,* 64: 445–451.

Sellschop, J.P., Rasmussen, S.E. and Fesq, H.W., 1973. Distribution of trace and minor elements in Durban Roodepoort Deep Mine rock samples. *Nucl. Phys. Res. Unit, Rep.,* C87/69: 1–79.

Sims, J.F., 1969. *The Stratigraphy and Paleocurrent History of the Upper Division of the Witwatersrand System on President Steyn Mine and Adjacent Areas in the Orange Free State Goldfield, with Specific Reference to the Origin of the Auriferous Reefs.* Thesis, University of the Witwatersrand, Johannesburg, 181 pp. (unpublished).

Whiteside, H.C., 1970a. Uraniferous Precambrian conglomerates of South Africa. In: *Uranium Exploration Geology.* International Atomic Energy Agency, Vienna, pp. 49–75.

Whiteside, H.C., 1970b. Volcanic rocks of the Witwatersrand triad. In: T.N. Clifford and I.G. Gass (Editors), *African Magmatism and Tectonics.* Oliver and Boyd, Edinburgh, pp. 73–87.

Chapter 3

ORIGIN OF WESTERN-STATES TYPE URANIUM MINERALIZATION

RUFFIN I. RACKLEY

INTRODUCTION

The Colorado Plateau is the "home" of the uranium industry in the United States. Many uranium—vanadium deposits in sandstone occur there and these occurrences constitute a geologic type of ore deposit recognized in other areas of the world. The uranium deposits in the Wyoming basins are geologically similar to those of the Colorado Plateau in tectonic history and source-rock type, sedimentation, sedimentary environment, paleoclimate, mineralization, and alteration. This type of uranium deposit has been referred to as carnotite type, sandstone type, or western-states type. Because the bulk of reserves are non-carnotite and other types of uranium occurrences can also occur in sandstone, the use of the term western-states type is preferred for area and type recognition. The uranium occurrences in Cretaceous formations of the Black Hills of Wyoming and South Dakota are of this type (Renfro, 1969). Uranium occurrences in the Permian sandstones of Europe also demonstrate many similarities (Barthel, 1974). The Texas uranium deposits are similar in ore-body configuration and in some of the elements present, but differ in sedimentary environment and in some aspects of uranium source (Eargle and Weeks, 1973).

While there is and probably will continue to be differences of opinion concerning the similarities and differences, there is an increasing awareness that the similarities in the sedimentology and ore-forming processes far outweigh the differences in details of shape, size and elements present (Gruner, 1956a and Fischer, 1970 and 1974). These deposits have provided over 90% of the United States domestic production of uranium and vanadium and will continue to be the principal source of domestic uranium for some time to come. The importance of this type in the U.S. production and reserve picture indicates it constitutes approximately one fourth of the free-world reserves. This type of deposit possibly contributes a much higher portion of the total world supply, depending on the east-European and USSR reserves. No major uranium deposits of other types are known in the United States. Fig. 1 is a location map of the principal uranium-producing districts. Grutt (1972) provides an excellent review of the U.S. uranium occurrences.

The uranium deposits are epigenetic in the sense that they were formed in their present position after the enclosing sediment was deposited. How much later than the

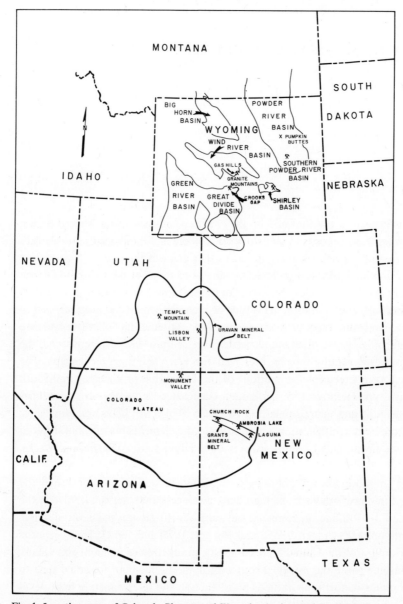

Fig. 1. Location map of Colorado Plateau and Wyoming basin uranium districts.

deposition of the host is one question yet to be answered. The deposits are also epigenetic in the sense used by Perel'man (1967) to indicate geological processes originating at or near the surface of the earth at low temperatures and pressures. In many respects, the ore deposits are similar to strata-bound supergene enrichments but have horizontal scales measured in miles. This implies that the metals were present in the sediment in small quantities, but in readily leachable form. Some geologists will not admit this possibility and some contradictory evidence has been presented. While more knowledge is being accumulated, this intrinsic source should be considered at least as a possible alternative because it requires the simplest process. These uranium deposits are considered to be the product of a physical—chemical trap, such as the hydrogen sulfide, reducing geochemical barrier for V, Fe, Cu, Co, As, Se, Ag, Ni, Zn, Cd, Hg, Pb, and U (Perel'man, 1967), which precipitates ore minerals from solutions on the basis of their concentration in solution, their sensitivity to changes in Eh and pH and their affinity for sulfur.

The most significant fact in the geological mobilization, transportation and deposition of uranium is that uranium has two naturally occurring valence states. In the hexavalent oxidized state, uranium can be taken into solution by acidic, neutral or basic water and transported infinitely. In the tetravalent reduced state uranium is practically insoluble. Therefore, the uplift and erosion of any provenance will take place under conditions favorable for the oxidation and mobilization of its uranium content. The accumulation of uranium from this or any other source can only take place in sediment in an environment in which reducing conditions are sufficiently developed to reduce it to the tetravalent state and precipitate it.

The typical ore body represents an addition of less than 1%, which is accommodated in the pore space. The physical habit of ore minerals in deposits of this type is thin coatings on detrital grains which may fill the pore spaces in high-grade deposits. The dissemination and microscopic size of the minerals increases the susceptibility to subsequent oxidation and remobilization by both alteration and weathering. The end result is an ore body formed by a mineralizing process which has little effect on the host rock, other than the addition of or an increase in the epigenetic minerals. The ore bodies are adjacent to moderately to strongly oxidized zones, which may show marked changes in color and epigenetic mineral content.

The metals known to occur in these deposits in significant quantities are: uranium, vanadium, copper, silver, selenium, and molybdenum. Other metals also known to be present include chromium, lead, zinc, arsenic, cobalt, and nickel, none of which are known to be commercially important. A deposit may be composed of any one or more metals in almost any combination, except copper and vanadium, which tend to be mutually exclusive. The reason for the latter phenomenon is not definitely known, but vanadium is deposited on the basis of reduction while copper is precipitated by hydrogen sulfide regardless of its redox state (Perel'man, 1967). The metals present always have a definite relationship to each other and to the overall geometry of the deposit. These minerals provide the principal limitations on the character of the process. Throughout this chapter the deposits will be referred to as uranium deposits although other metals may be commercially important.

Like "beauty is in the eye of the beholder", the "differences" between the Colorado Plateau and the Wyoming uranium deposits with respect to host rock depositional environment, diagenesis, epigenetic alteration, and mineralization are largely in the eyes of the observer and in the observer's interpretation. The present cycle of erosion with the attendant oxidation of outcrops has caused confusion concerning the initial conditions of deposition and diagenesis. This, in turn, further adds to the confusion concerning the nature of the alteration and mineralizing process (Fischer, 1970 and 1974 and Adler, 1970 and 1974).

The present state of knowledge is conclusive that sedimentation and syndiagenesis of fluvial pyritic carbonaceous green, gray or black sand and mud produce these colors in the sediment almost immediately on entering the depositional basin, where vegetation is abundant in waterlogged sediment. The iron-oxide minerals staining the oxidized sediments are quickly converted to the reduced state and, if hydrogen sulfide is being generated, pyrite forms as discussed by Love (1964) and Berner (1973). Coleman (1971) reports pyrite forming on rootlets of living cypress trees along the lower Mississippi River at depths of 30 cm. Perel'man (1967) describes a reduced sediment (gley) at the bottom of streams and rivers in the USSR. One only has to venture into any marsh or swamp to examine the reduction of sediment taking place at the surface. It is possible to oxidize these sediments and thereby convert them to a red color but it is not possible to emplace carbonized logs, detrital carbonaceous material or bacterial residue into sediment deposited and brought into equilibrium as red beds.

The occurrence of uranium in sequences containing red beds is similar in some respects to the copper occurrences in fluvial sediment. References have been made to these red-bed copper deposits of the southwest United States, but from the author's examination of many of these deposits, it can be safely stated that none of these "red-bed" copper occurrences are actually in red sediment (Fischer, 1937; Soule, 1956; Ham and Johnson, 1964 and Woodward et al., 1974). The copper mineralization occurs in local bleached reduction centers within the red beds or in light-green or gray, white or medium-gray siltstone or claystone beds or sandstone channel deposits interbedded with or in the case of channels cut into red sediments. There is undoubtedly a genetic connection between the oxidizing environment in which copper and uranium are mobile and the reduced sediments in which hydrogen sulfide precipitates the copper as sulfide minerals, principally chalcocite, and uranium is precipitated by reduction, principally as uraninite.

The adoption of terminology for forms of an entire ore deposit or for geometrically similar segments has emphasized unnecessarily the "differences" between deposits in the various districts of the Colorado Plateau and Wyoming basins (Shawe et al., 1959; Fischer, 1960 and Gould et al., 1963). The variation of metals present from district to district also tend to emphasize the "differences", especially when weathered deposits are included. However, a roll, trend, wing, solution front, roll front, stack, limb, tube, or blanket can all be produced by a common process described below. The sizes, forms, or the metals present in the system, are not critical to the development or explanation of the process but are of primary economic concern.

There is a tendency to classify or characterize uranium deposits and the sediment in which they occur by some of their properties. Unless these characteristics are based on interpretations of the basic sciences and observations of modern processes, there can be little progress toward unraveling the mysteries of their origin. The true differences reflect local variations, which are understandable and predictable if the overall process is known.

Although the uranium deposits of the Colorado Plateau and Wyoming occur in sediment ranging in age from Triasssic to Eocene, there are a number of features common to most, if not all, of the deposits. These features, listed in Table I, fall into four major divisions: (a) tectonic conditions; (b) sedimentation; (c) sedimentary environment, paleoclimate and diagenesis; and (d) mineralization and alteration. A discussion of these features could become a discussion of the origin of the uranium deposits, but since these are largely products of a series of conditions which occurred in each district, the conditions will be discussed rather than the products.

TABLE I

Common features of western-states type uranium deposits

Tectonic conditions

1. Host rock is part of a thick, extensive continental sequence, much of which may be red beds
2. Host rock is feldspathic to arkosic, micaceous or cherty sandstone
3. Volcanic material is present in or overlying the host rock
4. Upstream erosion of host rock
5. Burial and preservation

Sedimentation
1. Sedimentation by stream flow of braided or meandering streams on local or regional unconformities
2. Sandstones and conglomerates tend to be lenticular and relatively restricted
3. Siltstone and mudstone are interbedded with and in erosional relationship to sandstones and conglomerates
4. Mudstone clasts are common constituents of sandstone and conglomerates

Sedimentary environment, paleoclimate and diagenesis
1. Light gray or green to dark gray sandstones with gray and green mudstone, all commonly pyritic; pink or red mudstones present but minor in amount
2. Gypsum crystals in mudstones
3. Reptilian fauna
4. Bioturbation
5. Vegetal carbonaceous material from logs, stumps and roots in place, detrital fragments to bacterial residue and/or asphaltic material

Mineralization and alteration
1. Uraninite and coffinite are principal uranium minerals, in non-weathered deposits
2. Mineralization is both discordant and concordant with sedimentation
3. Mineralization occurs in sharp contact with carbonaceous-free or oxidized zones
4. Epigenetic minerals occur in same relative spatial positions when present
5. Mineralization is most common in thicker sandstone-facies belts where mudstone facies make up 20–50% of the sequence

---

TABLE II

Development phases of western-states type uranium deposits

Source area	Depositional area
1. Strong positive, erosion removes sedimentary cover, sediment supply very large and easily eroded, stream volume low to moderate; volcanic centers develop	weak positive to neutral, extensive accumulation of continental sediments; alluvial fans-bajadas, sand dunes, vegetation sparse to moderate, sediment dominantly oxidized; red beds and gypsum
2. Moderate positive, erosion of mountain cores; rainfall increases, sediment supply large and easily eroded, stream volume moderate to high; volcanic centers active	relatively limited accumulation of sand on alluvial fans or meanderbelts; rainfall increases or natural irrigation, vegetation abundant, swamps; sand — organic rich, pyritic, light to dark gray; clay — light- to medium-gray or green, pyritic, some carbonaceous clay or lignite; local high areas subaerially oxidized
3. Weak positive, erosion; stream gradient lowered, sediment supply moderate but difficult to erode, stream volume moderate; volcanic center inactive	sediment increasingly clay, sand deposited as point and braid bars, organic rich, light- to dark-gray; clay light- to medium-gray or green, swamps increase, vegetation very abundant, lignite and carbonaceous clay form
4. Weak positive, erosion; stream gradient low, stream volume moderate, sediment supply moderate but difficult to erode	sedimentation ceases, extensive basin erosion or erosion of basin margin, geochemical cells develop if oxygenated water invades host rock
5. Weak positive to neutral, erosion	host rock buried by new depositonal environment, geochemical cells expand if oxygen supply continues
6. Collapse	basin uplifted, faulted, erosion of basin begins; geochemical cell develops and reaches maximum expansion if not initiated previously
7.	weathering and erosion of host rock, oxidation of ore bodies, some loss with erosion, some enrichment of unoxidized ores

In the series of events from the initial uplift of a positive area to the accumulation of a uranium ore body, the sequence is rather consistently repeated in the Triassic and Jurassic of the Colorado Plateau and the Tertiary of the Wyoming basins. All of the producing districts have been subjected to seven more or less distinct episodes or phases in the development of their present conditions. All phases in all districts are not developed to the same degree, but all are recognizable in every district. The seven development phases are outlined in Table II. These phases have unique combinations of tectonic conditions, erosion, sedimentation, sedimentary environment, paleoclimate, diagenesis and hydraulics, which have produced uranium concentrations of commercial importance.

The host formations of the uranium deposits discussed in this chapter contain or have produced approximately 90% of the known United States uranium (U.S. A.E.C., 1974). Since the United States has approximately 29% of the uranium reserves of the free world, these deposits constitute over 26% of the free-world reserves (Nininger, 1973). In the Triassic, the Chinle Formation is the principal uranium host formation. The Jurassic Morrison Formation is the host of the largest known uranium deposits in the United States. In the Wyoming basins the Paleocene Fort Union Formation and the Eocene Wasatch Formation, or equivalent formations, are host to the important uranium deposits.

TECTONIC CONDITIONS

The Wyoming basins are all intermountain basins developed on the platform well removed from the continental margin. These basins developed in Paleocene time as a result of the Laramide orogeny, ending Cretaceous sedimentation in the Wyoming area. The entire area was uplifted, but the Granite Mountains area was thrust up into a prominent range of mountains in Paleocene and Early Eocene time. From the Granite Mountains coarse sediment spread into the adjacent basins (lower areas on and between mountains) in a series of pulses.

The Colorado Plateau is also on the platform well removed from the continental margin. The entire Paleozoic and Mesozoic sedimentary section is of shallow water or continental clastic sediment with very small amounts of volcanics. The area can be considered a miogeosyncline filled with molasses-type sediment (Mitchell and Reading, 1969). The sediment was derived from the ancestral Rockies east of the Colorado Plateau from Permian through Early Triassic, but from Late Triassic through Jurassic the primary source of sediment was to the west. The development of this new source area reflects the westward movement of the North American plate and the development of the Mesocordilleran geanticline with its attendant acidic intrusive bodies near the continental margin (Dietz and Holden, 1970).

The sequence which produced each of the uranium provinces began with the uplift of a positive area from which large quantities of detritus was supplied to adjacent negative, or at least less positive areas. At the end of the first phase the erosion of the positive area and the filling of the depositional basin approach equilibrium. While the source area remains moderately positive, the relationship of sediment supply, stream volume, and gradient to the depositional area reaches a condition where sedimentation is greatly reduced.

The tectonic conditions of the source and depositional area are shown in Fig. 2 in graphic form for the seven development phases. Figs. 3, 4, and 5 should be referred to for

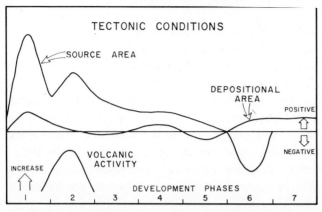

Fig. 2. Tectonic conditions in the principal source area and in the depositional area in which uranium deposits occur in sandstone during the seven development phases of uranium deposits.

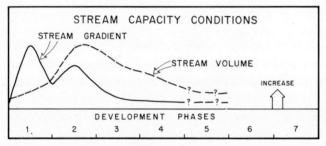

Fig. 3. Stream capacity conditions from the source area into the depositional basin during the first four development phases.

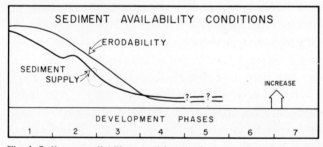

Fig. 4. Sediment availability conditions in the source area during the first four development phases.

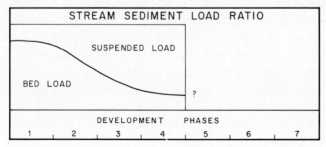

Fig. 5. Stream sediment load ratio of the stream during the first four development phases.

the complementing conditions of sediment availability, erodability, stream capacity and bed-load/suspended-load ratio. Since the sediment of interest is a product of phases 2 and 3, interpretation of conditions other than tectonics are limited to about the end of phase 4.

The initiation of the second phase can be produced by renewed uplift of the source area or an increase in precipitation or most likely a combination of both. With the mountain core exposed, the sediment is largely derived from granitic rock which may have an anomalous uranium content. In contrast to the thick accumulations of red or variegated sediment of the first phase, the second phase produces a relatively limited amount of sediment deposited under conditions which give rise to a reducing environment. The increase in water supply causes the growth of abundant vegetation in the depositional area. The decay of vegetation growing in and buried with the sediment consumes the available oxygen and permits the development of a reducing environment in which sulfides might form. Weathering conditions in the source area would permit the oxidation and solution of uranium present. The reducing conditions in the depositional area would permit the reduction of hexavalent uranium carried in solution and cause its deposition in a tetravalent form. Volcanic centers become active and may contribute to the depositional basin directly through ash-fall or indirectly through stream-transported detritus.

The third phase may simply be a tectonically stable time during which the erosion and deposition during the second phase caused a reduction in the gradient of the streams. There is also the probability that the orographic rainfall may diminish as the mountains are reduced in height. Weathering of the source area becomes more intense and deeper, which increases the breakdown of both rocks and minerals and increases the availability of metals mobilized by an oxidizing environment. In the depositional area, the lower gradient reduced the rate of sedimentation and increased the residence time of water and contained metals and the probability of those metals being reduced and deposited.

The fourth phase is a critical stage, because the depositional area in continental sedimentation may become subject to erosion as slowly reduced stream gradients cut into sediment deposited by high energy, steeper-gradient streams. If erosion continues, the potential host may be partially or completely destroyed, and the probabilities are great that more have been destroyed than preserved. In the Jurassic and Tertiary host rock a few tens to a few hundreds of meters of sediment were deposited over the favorable host sandstone to provide a confining as well as a protective cover before the basin was subjected to erosion. Preservation of the favorable host during this phase is paramount, but the subjection of the basin or at least the basin margins to erosion may be almost as important. During this period of erosion, the surface water would tend to retain its oxygen because the reducing environments have been destroyed or restricted in size. The introduction of oxygenated water into the favorable host rock during this period would begin to destroy the carbonaceous material and the reducing conditions in the sediment. When conditions of oxygen input are adequate an invading oxidizing zone or geochemical cell is initiated. The period between the beginning of erosion and the final burial may be sufficient to initiate and complete the mineralizing process or the process may be initiated during this time but completed much later. This period of erosion presents the first opportunity for the initiation of geochemical cells and possibly the only opportunity for the mineralization of some of the erosional remnants of channels enclosed by fine-grained sediment.

After the sediment, deposited during the second and third phases, has successfully survived the erosion of the fourth phase, negative tectonic conditions of the depositional area cause renewed sedimentation to bury the potential host rock in the fifth phase. The sedimentary environment of the covering sediment may be considerably different than that of the host rock. The role of the source area becomes less important as its positive tectonic condition continues to diminish in the fifth phase.

The time the host rock remains buried varies with the age of the enclosing sediment, because all of the districts under consideration in this chapter entered the sixth phase of uplift and erosion at about the same general period of time.

The search for uranium deposits has been directed to those areas which have been subjected to the fifth and sixth and most commonly seventh phases of development. The search for uranium deposits presently in the process of formation could be most easily identified in the second, third or fourth phases. The fifth phase may be very long compared to the length of the others. Much of the earth's uranium resources may be in deposits which have reached this fifth phase but which have no surface expression. These deposits can be identified through evaluation of tectonic history and the processes of sedimentation.

The character of the streams, the supply of sediment and the sediment load are shown in Figs. 3, 4, and 5. The stream gradient was high in phase 1, but the stream volume was low and the sediment supply was dominantly older sediment on the uplift. As the second positive tectonic pulse began in phase 2, increased stream volume combined with increased stream gradient from renewed uplift to produce a flood of sediment from the erosion of the weathered mountain core. The sediment supply and erodability were both high in phases 1 and 2, but diminished thereafter. Stream volume decreased from its peak in the second phase. Sediment load diminished from the peak in phase 2 and the bedload/suspended-load ratio decreased, resulting in a progressively higher percentage of silt and clay deposition as the end of phase 3 approached.

SEDIMENTATION

Sedimentation of the formations containing uranium has been largely, if not exclusively, by the process of stream flow. No debris flow is known to be present, but mud flows have been suspected in two Wyoming uranium districts close to the source area. The basic physics of fluids and sediment movement govern the process of stream-flow erosion, transport and deposition, a discussion of which is beyond the scope of this chapter. Wolman and Miller (1960), Doeglas (1962), Ore (1963), Coleman (1969), Williams and Rust (1969) and Allen (1970) have presented excellent work on this subject to which the reader is directed for more information. However, those factors which influence the erosion and dispersal of sediment as a part of the process which forms uranium deposits require some comment.

Streams draining the rising positive area at the beginning of a tectonic cycle have a large supply of debris available in the source area. However, unless there is sufficient stream volume to transport the sediment, the amount of sediment deposited in the depositional area is relatively small. The gradient of the streams is also a factor in determining the capacity of the streams to transport sediment. The conditions prevailing in the early phases of the development of a uranium host rock are shown in Fig. 3. Disaggregation of a deeply weathered granite mass provides a large supply of easily eroded material, as indicated by Fig. 4. The amount of bed load is high in the early phases, but gradually decreases as the gradient of the stream decreases, as indicated in Fig. 5. The amount of suspended load may decrease as well as the bed load, but the ratio will shift to a higher suspended load as the energy of the stream decreases. Where these streams enter the adjacent depositional areas, the gradients abruptly decrease and alluvial fans and aprons or bajadas develop. If the streams have sufficient volume, boulders will be deposited on the apex of the fan, gravel and sand will be deposited on a lower gradient further down slope, fine sand and silt will be deposited on the lower flatter parts of the fan, and mud will be deposited if the water reaches flats or lakes where settling can take place. Permanent streams on alluvial fans will have a braided pattern, because the cohesionless sediment of the upper fan is easily eroded with increase in stream volume. An aggrading braided stream tends to be shallow, further increases in stream volume cause the stream to spread over its banks and disperse sediment over much of the fan. The accretion of sediment takes place on the braid bars as the stream volume diminishes. Further diminution of stream volume causes successive levels of bars to form or emerge as the stream adjusts itself to reducing volumes.

Meandering stream patterns develop in areas where the bank material is cohesive and the bank is eroded by undercutting and slumping. The principal deposit in meandering streams is point-bar accretion. Clay clasts and blocks of considerable size accumulate with the point-bar sand from the slumping-bank material. Because of the decrease in gradients on alluvial fans and the increase of cohesive bank materials at the lower edge of fans, braided streams may change to meander patterns as the streams leave the fan. Both types of aggrading streams will be influenced by pre-existing topography, but neither have power to erode an obstacle and remove it. An easier alternative is to deposit the bed load and bury the obstacle or change directions.

From the preceding discussion of the development phases of uranium deposits, the changes in tectonic setting and climate interact to produce changes in stream volume and gradient, sediment supply and erodability which in turn determines the sediment load.

Fluvial systems, like other complex systems, are affected by changes in the variables. Since a wide variety of conditions are possible, it is necessary to relate to the genetic factors of process and environment for proper interpretation. The genetic approach provides a means whereby the complex variables can be estimated. Stratigraphic models based on process and environment of the fluvial systems have recently been synthesized by Fisher and Brown (1972), from work by Ore (1963), Bernard and Major (1963), Smith (1970). McGown and Garner (1970), Bernard et al. (1970), and excellent diagrams presented in Brown (1973). The terrigenous clastic fluvial depositional systems have three end members of the spectrum which are important in the sedimentation of the known uranium-producing districts. These are the braided system, the coarse-grained meander-belt system and the fine-grained meanderbelt system. These systems are summarized briefly below from the above authors with comments relating the depositional models to the uranium-producing areas.

Braided-stream fluvial system

The braided-stream deposits are composites and remnants of lens-shaped channel fills and braid-bar accretions. The composition and texture of higher-energy streams are a mixture of grain sizes from cobbles to coarse sand and from pebbles to medium sand in moderate-energy streams. Silt or clay beds are normally not present, although clay clasts are present in the sand and conglomerate. Internal structures become increasingly less conspicuous as the grain size increases and the sorting decreases. Coleman (1969) found internal structures to be abundant in the fine sand of the Brahmaputra River where large-scale bed forms have been observed (by sonar) to migrate rapidly when the river is at flood stage. The beds of braided-stream deposits range from a fraction of a meter to a few meters in thickness, but the aggregate thickness of braided-stream sediment may reach hundreds of meters (Allen, 1970). Fig. 6 is a block diagram of an idealized fluvial system developed by Brown (1973).

The characteristics of the braided-stream system have been described by Fisher and Brown (1972) from which the following summary is largely taken. Braided streams are best developed where slope is relatively high and bed load is very high. These streams deposit under low flash—discharge conditions and dominate sedimentation on humid area alluvial fans. Geometry of the channel units are essentially flatbedded, discontinuous, tabular and lenticular bodies deposited as longitudinal and transverse bars. Structures are predominantly parallel bedding and tabular cross-beds with minor trough cross-beds and ripple cross-lamination. Composition is invariably coarse-grained with few fines or top-stratum deposits. Texture is poorly to moderately sorted, except longitudinal bar deposits fine and become better sorted downstream. Scouring is slight and commonly marginal to longitudinal bar as it becomes emergent. Individual channels can be delineated only by textural differences or discontinuities in structural trends. The braided streams produce multilateral sand facies as shown in Fig. 6. Braided streams have no levees and no in situ organics accumulate with the sediment.

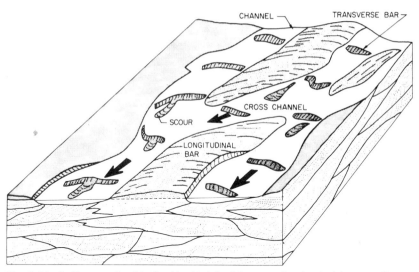

Fig. 6. Block diagram of an idealized braided fluvial system showing bed forms, sedimentary structure, and multilateral sand geometry. Brown (1973), with permission, modified from Ore (1963, 1965), Smith (1970); described by Fisher and Brown (1972).

The distribution of braided-stream sediment in typical aggradational periods is that of an alluvial fan. Figs. 11 and 12 (pp. 109, 110) show a simplified example from the Morrison of the Colorado Plateau. In the beginning of tectonic cycles, such as the early development phases of uranium deposits, the alluvial fan may be modified by prominent topographic features. The Gas Hills uranium deposits (Wyoming) occur in an alluvial fan, which was deposited over and around topographic features high enough to protrude through the fan during the period when the host sand was deposited, as shown in Fig. 7. The known ore bodies are along the margin of the fan where the sediment onlaps the preexisting topography (Rackley, 1972). The central Gas Hills trend is on the south extension of the west flank of the Dutton basin anticline near the center of the figure. Other ore trends are present on the opposite side of the fan from the central trend and on the margins of the fan segment east of the Gas Hills topographic features (Dutton basin anticline). The northern portion of the Crooks Gap area of central Wyoming is braided-stream facies on alluvial fans. The western portion of the Grants mineral belt of northwest New Mexico is also in the braided-stream facies. In the vicinity of Ambrosia Lake near the center of the Grants mineral belt the structure and geometry of the stream deposits indicate deposition under slightly different conditions (those found in a coarse-grained meanderbelt). Still further downstream in the Grants mineral belt (southeast) conditions change more to those of a fine-grained meanderbelt. The uranium deposits at Laguna are in the remnant of channel sands deposited in a fine-grained meanderbelt.

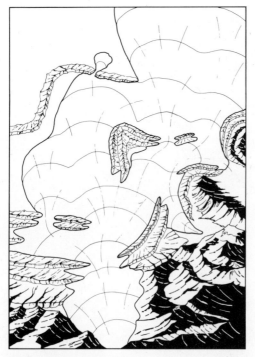

Fig. 7. Pattern of braided-stream sediment distribution on alluvial fan in Gas Hills, Wyoming. Modified from Rackley (1972).

Coarse-grained meanderbelt

Since the most important uranium deposits of the western-states type are in sandstones deposited in a coarse-grained meanderbelt fluvial system, a summary of this system is appropriate here. Fig. 8 is a depositional model of this system from Brown (1973). The block diagram in Fig. 8A shows the bedforms, sedimentary structures, and multilateral-sand geometry. Fig. 8B is a cross-section of a point-bar deposit of this system. The characteristics of the coarse-grained meanderbelt fluvial system have been described by Fisher and Brown (1972) and Brown (1973) from which the following summary is largely taken. These systems occur in the lower part of moderate to high bed-load streams under lower to moderate discharge and intermediate gradient. Sand bodies are a multilateral complex of partly preserved channel and other meanderbelt units. Larger sand units are built up of superposed and adjacent meanderbelt sand bodies. Internal structures include moderate- to large-scale trough cross-beds and wedge sets, some tabular cross-beds, and small-scale trough cross-beds, and few horizontal or ripple cross-laminations. Composition is mainly fine to dominantly coarse-grained sand with common granule to fine-pebble gravel. Mud and silt are minor constituents. Depositional units are laterally accreting

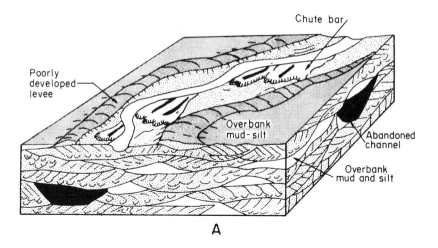

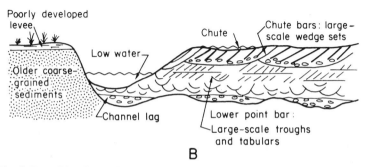

Fig. 8. Depositional model of an idealized coarse-grained meanderbelt fluvial system. A. Block diagram showing bed forms, sedimentary structures, and multilateral sand geometry. B. Schematic cross-section of coarse-grained point-bar deposits. Brown (1973), with permission, after McGowen and Garner; described by Fisher and Brown (1972).

coarse-grained point bars and vertically accreting chute channel-lag gravels and chute bars that develop on point bars during floods.

Fine-grained meanderbelt

The fine-grained meanderbelt system was active in the deposition of host-rock sequences of the Shirley basin and Powder River basin uranium districts of Wyoming as well as the Laguna district of the Grants mineral belt, New Mexico. This depositional system occurs under conditions of low gradient, moderately high discharge, mixed-load streams on aggrading alluvial plains (Fisher and Brown, 1972). Fig. 9 is a depositional model of an idealized fine-grained meanderbelt fluvial system from Brown (1973).

Fig. 9A is a block diagram showing bedforms, sedimentary structures and the multistory geometry of the channel sands. Included with the overbank mud in this diagram are

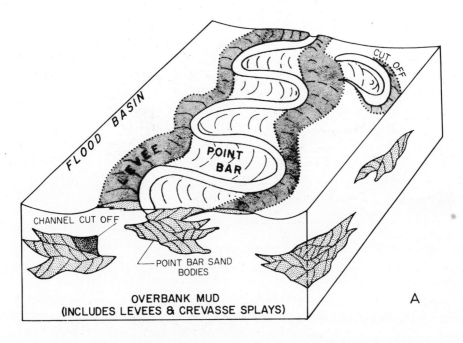

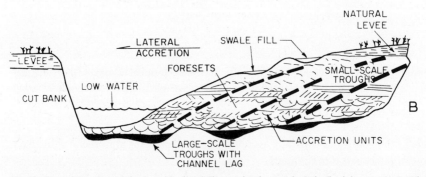

Fig. 9. Depositional model of an idealized fine-grained meanderbelt fluvial system. A. Block diagram showing bedforms, sedimentary structures, and multistory geometry. B. Schematic cross section of fine-grained point-bar deposits. From Brown (1973), with permission, after Bernard and others (1963); described by Fisher and Brown (1972).

sand bodies deposited as levees and crevasse splays and there may also be deposits of other smaller streams which are commonly present on the flood basin of the larger stream. Fig. 9B is a schematic cross-section of fine-grained point-bar deposits which are the typical host to the uranium deposits in contrast to the levee, crevasse splay and small flood basin stream sand bodies which are not normally mineralized except in proximity to the larger point-bar sand bodies. The geometry of the channel units are multistoried and asymmetric. The base and cut-bank side of the channel are erosively bounded. Point-bar deposits of the channel are transitional at the top with levee and overbank deposits. Moderate- to large-scale trough cross-beds, a few tabular cross-beds, some small-scale trough and tabular cross-beds and a variety of ripple cross-laminations are the sedimentary structures. The deposits of this system are chiefly fine-grained sand, ranging from gravel at the base to mud at the top in an upward fining of textures. Clay-pellets and plant debris are prominent in the upper point bar. Deposition of point bars is by accretion on the sedimentation side during flood stage. The meanderbelt sand body is enclosed in topstratum or overbank muds in well-developed systems (Fisher and Brown, 1972).

When streams shift by avulsion to more advantageous gradients, multistorying of meanderbelt sands occur. The Fort Union Formation, host to the uranium deposits of the southern Powder River basin, has three fairly distinct stories of meanderbelt sands in a stratigraphic interval of 360 m. Each of the stories occupies significantly different portions of the basin overlapping only locally. Equally important from an exploration standpoint are the areas in which none of the meanderbelt sands are present. The entire interval is topstratum or overbank mud with coal and carbonaceous shale.

In addition to silt and mud accumulations on flood plains, carbonaceous shales and lignites are common if the climate is temperate to warm and humid (Allen, 1970). In contrast to the thick sand wedges deposited by braided streams, the sand bodies of meandering streams tend to be linear bodies. Soft-sediment deformation occurs when uneven sand loading above clay causes the clay to deform resulting in spectacular contemporary faulting and folding.

In Wyoming the sediment of the Gas Hills area of the Wind River basin, the northern margin of the Great Divide basin which includes the Crooks Gap area, and the western part of the Shirley basin, were deposited as alluvial fans formed where the gradient of the streams entering the basins decreased abruptly. Downstream the deposits pass into normal flood-plain sediment where coarse material was deposited by meandering streams, and silt and clay were deposited in flood basins. Flood-plain deposits occur throughout the Fort Union and Wasatch Formations of the Powder River basin, the Battle Spring Formation farther south in the Great Divide basin, and the Wind River Formation in the eastern Shirley basin (Rackley, 1972, p. 758). The Morrison Formation of the Colorado Plateau is dominated by an alluvial fan with its apex in the southwest portion of the plateau. From the apex braided streams fanned out across the plateau eventually reaching gradients where the fan merged with flood-plain deposits and the stream pattern changed from braided to meandering in a manner similar to that shown in Fig. 13 (see p. 111) and described by Brown (1973) in the series of depositional models which change from a braided system to a coarse-grained system and, finally, to a fine-grained system laterally down the slope of the fan and vertically upward as the gradient diminished.

Streams supplying sediment to all the uranium-bearing basins of Wyoming headed in the Sweetwater arch. The headwater of the stream, building the alluvial fan of the Morrison Formation of the Colorado Plateau, was in the vicinity of western Arizona. The evidence suggests the size of the stream at normal flow was no greater than about 100 m wide; however, flood stages were an entirely different matter.

From a regional study of the transmissive character of the sedimentary rocks of the Colorado Plateau, Jobin (1962) found the uranium deposits to occur in formations of intermediate transmissivity between the thick porous eolian sequences and the thick low permeable shales. This general statement still holds true on a formation basis, but on the basis of the fluvial systems within a formation, the uranium ore bodies occur on the lateral margins of a moderate to highly transmissive central zone of alluvial fans and meanderbelts where the central zone intertongues with finer flood-plain sediment or other fluvial or eolian systems.

SEDIMENTARY ENVIRONMENT, PALEOCLIMATE AND DIAGENESIS

Sedimentation of a sequence of fluvial conglomerates, sandstones and shales is, like most other sedimentary sequences, a process which acts on the sediment many times between the time a particle is torn from its parent rock and deposited in the new sequence.

This repetitive process may bring the sediment closely into equilibrium with its environment well before it reaches its final position. The sorting of grain sizes by running water is offset by slumping of the banks as mud is remixed with sand. The freshly buried plant material begins to decay and is partially carbonized, when it is eroded and disaggregated, only to be redeposited with new plant material and clastic particles. Consequently, diagenesis may begin as soon as the sediment enters the depositional basin and may be almost completed by the time the sediment reaches its final position. Climate, environment of deposition, sedimentation, and diagenesis are so intimately related in the formation of fluvial deposits that it is impractical to consider them as separate steps in the development of a sedimentary rock.

The paleoclimate of the areas in which the host sediment of the uranium deposits accumulated was warm subtropical to tropical. The amount and distribution of the precipitation is not so easily determined. Crocodiles, alligators and turtles were common in the Wyoming basins, and terrestrial reptiles were near their peak in Morrison time on the Colorado Plateau. These cold-blooded reptiles would suggest year round frost-free conditions.

In the Mesozoic breakup of Pangaea, the position of the North American continental plate during Late Triassic Chinle time would have placed the Colorado Plateau in the vicinity of $15°N$ (Seyfert and Sirkin, 1973, p. 328). The Pacific Ocean was present on the southwest margin of the Colorado Plateau, where its influence would dominate the climate during the summer when the equatorial maritime air mass migrates northward producing a hot wet season. The dry season is characterized by dry dusty northeasterly tradewinds. The paleoclimate was similar to the present Nigeria climate. Alternatively, the proximity of the ocean and a large land mass may have produced a monsoon climate with its typical hot, wet summers and dry winters. In the winter, when the northeast trade-wind belt migrates southward, hot dry winds from the continent would produce no precipitation. As the North American plate continued to drift northwestward during the Jurassic Period the Colorado Plateau occupied an area in the vicinity of 20–30°N and 50–60°W, a position north and east of modern Puerto Rico (Dietz and Holden, 1970, p. 108). By Morrison time, the area began to leave the dominating influence of the trade-wind belt and to come under the seasonal influence of the cyclonic storms of the westerly wind belt, which migrate southward during the winter. This produced dry summers and wet winters. The climate of the Colorado Plateau was also effected by the Mesocordille-ran geanticline immediately to the west, which supplied sediment and probably caused orographic rainfall to naturally irrigate the depositional area of the Morrison during the dry summers (Seyfert and Sirkin, 1973, pp. 326–332).

The depositional environment and systems of the Morrison Formation are used as an example of the conditions in which sediments favorable to the deposition of uranium host rock occur. The terrigenous clastic depositional systems evolved in an area of relative continental stability and include eolian, fluvial and lake systems which evolved through a progressive change in climate from arid to seasonally moist. Figs. 10–13 show the progressive development of the Morrison and attempt to show the distribution of the major facies units. The terrigenous depositional systems of the Morrison are not unique to the Morrison on the Colorado Plateau. The eolian system has been a dominant factor in deposition of sediment on the Colorado Plateau throughout the Late Triassic and Early Jurassic. Mixed with the eolian sand dunes are interbeds of fluvial sediments described by Glennie (1970) as wadi environment. The eolian system is best represented on the Colorado Plateau by the Triassic Navajo Sandstone, but the system continues through the overlying Entrada, Bluff, and Cow Springs. Contemporaneously with the eolian system was a low-energy fluvial system dominated by fine sands, silts and clay. This sediment was deposited in the basin during the early arid phase and was gradually restricted to higher slopes of the fan as a more plentiful supply of water irrigated its lower portions. This system is best represented by the Recapture Member of the Morrison Formation, although the system prograded into the basin as the Todilto Limestone and gypsum system ended as the basin once again rose above the level of the sea. Fig. 10 shows the distribution of the depositional systems at the maximum development of the Recapture Member of the Morrison Formation. The positive nature of the southwestern part of the Colorado Plateau was emphasized by the retreat of the Todilto Sea as alluvial fans fed by intermittent streams covered the depositional area. The preexisting eolian system continued along the southwest margin of the basin and new eolian systems may have developed from the deflation of the alluvial fans. Towards the end of this depositional period, as the climate became increasingly humid, small lakes developed as evidenced by the local distribution of green silty zones with sparse lime nodules. With the exception of the lakes deposition, sedimentation during this period was in a strongly oxidizing subaerial environment in

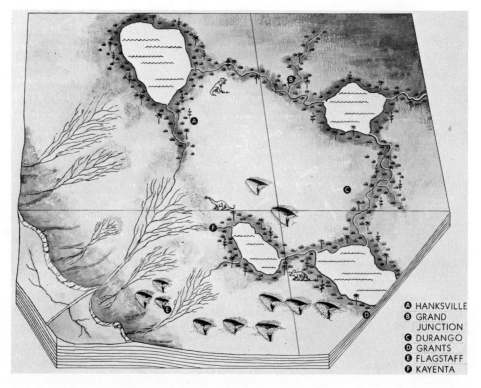

Fig. 10. Summerville–recapture depositional environment.

which dark-red is the dominant color. The major exception to the dark-red color is the white gypsiferous zones which occur in the lower part of the sequence (Summerville Formation).

Continued uplift to the southwest of the depositional basin, in combination with an increase in precipitation, caused the development of a major fluvial system fed by perennial streams, as shown in Fig. 11. Sand dunes continued to be prominent in this scene. Local intermittent streams continued to deposit under the same conditions as before, but the addition of significantly greater amounts of water produced some major changes in the environment of deposition. Fig. 11 represents the facies distribution of the fluvial system which deposited the Salt Wash Formation, the lower of the two important uranium-bearing members of the Morrison Formation. Along with the development of permanent streams came the substantial increase in vegetation. As the water spread over the previous red mud flats, vegetation developed these flats into marshes with shallow temporary lakes. The combination of waterlogged sediment and abundant vegetation created reducing conditions in the sand facies, as well as in the mud in the extensive marshes. The overbank flood stage deposits higher on and between the Salt Wash alluvial fans remained in an oxidizing environment to cause the Summerville–Recapture environment

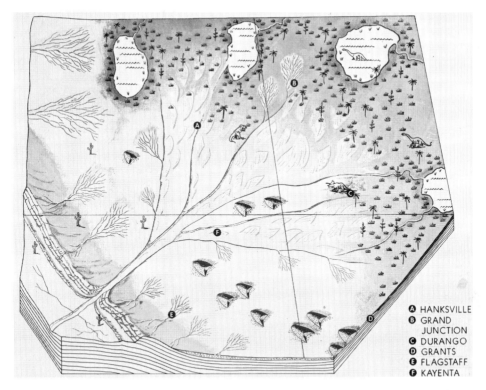

Fig. 11. Salt Wash Member of Morrison Formation distribution and depositional environment.

to persist contemporaneously with the development of blue-green mud and silt, commonly referred to as the Brushy Basin Member of the Morrison. From the period represented
by Fig. 11 throughout the remainder of Morrison time, the Recapture diminishes as the
Brushy Basin environment increases. In the development of the Salt Wash alluvial fans
came an increase in the amount of vegetation and the rise of the water table to permit the
preservation of the organic material in the sands. These reducing conditions probably
developed earliest on the mud flats and gradually moved up the fan as the water table
intersected the surface of the fan at progressively higher levels. Thus, conditions favorable
for the deposition of uranium could occur in the lower portions of the fan while conditions higher in the system may not have been permissive.

In the further development of the coarse fluvial system of the Morrison, the major
stream draining the rising source area to the southwest shifted from a northeasterly
course to a southeasterly course at the apex of the fan, as shown in Fig. 12. This diagram
represents the early phases of deposition of the Westwater Member of the Morrison, the
uppermost and most significant of the uranium-producing members. The reason for this
southeasterly shift may have. been a simple avulsion or it may have been a slight shifting
of the basin axis. The cause may also have been the result of the addition of large

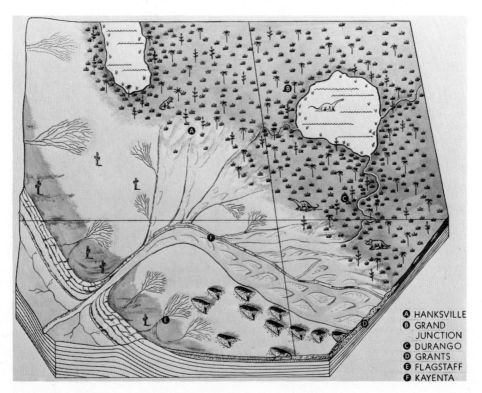

A HANKSVILLE
B GRAND
   JUNCTION
C DURANGO
D GRANTS
E FLAGSTAFF
F KAYENTA

Fig. 12. Early Westwater and Brushy Basin Members of Morrison Formation distribution and depositional environments.

quantities of fine-grained material in the center of the basin, possibly as a result of an ash fall. In this case, the fluvial system could best accommodate itself by lapping against the eolian system which bordered it on the southwest. Thus, we have the coarse fluvial facies intertonguing with the fine-grained, blue-green sediment of the mud flat on one side and onlapping onto the eolian system on the other.

The final phase of the coarse fluvial Morrison sand deposition is represented in Fig. 13. The blue-green mud flat environment encroaches higher onto the alluvial fan causing the stream to adapt to a meandering pattern as it encounters the difficult-to-erode cohesive banks of the mud-flat environment. As the major stream meanders across thick sequences of the waterlogged blue-green mud, differential loading causes the sand to subside into the mud to produce trough-shaped bodies of sands similar to that in the Laguna area to the east of this diagram. In both Figs. 12 and 13, vegetation was extensive over the coarse fluvial facies of the Morrison, as well as on the adjacent mud flats.

An environmental analysis of the Morrison Formation of the Colorado Plateau has not been published prior to this oversimplified version and is a subject which is deserving of considerably more study.

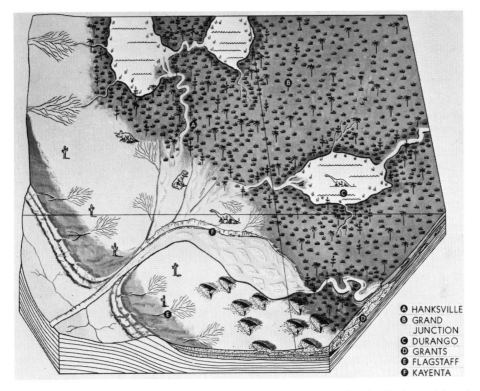

Fig. 13. Late Westwater and Brushy Basin Members of Morrison Fórmation distribution and depositional environments.

The climate of the Wyoming basins was warm enough to permit alligators, crocodiles and turtles to survive even though the drift of the North American plate was near its present latitude in Paleocene and Eocene time (Dietz and Holden, 1970, p. 109). The elevation was lower than at present and a warming trend between the Paleocene and Eocene interrupted the worldwide cooling that began in the Late Cretaceous (Seyfert and Sirkin, 1973, p. 418). Orographic rainfall on the rising Sweetwater arch provided ample water, either directly as rainfall or indirectly as natural irrigation, to maintain abundant vegetation and a high groundwater level in the uranium host sediment similar to the conditions in Figs. 12 and 13.

The combination of warm temperatures, rainy seasons and natural irrigation during dry seasons is adequate to support abundant vegetation. However, vegetation is abundant under other climatic conditions, particularly in tropical rain forest and humid continental climates which indicates the amount of vegetation growing on the surface is not critical, once a certain minimum level is reached. The critical factor in the development of a favorable uranium host rock is the mixing of the vegetation with the sediment in large enough quantities to shift the decay of the vegetation from aerobic to anaerobic conditions. Decay of vegetation begins under aerobic environments through the oxidation by bacteria and fungi, but if the oxygen available is insufficient to complete the process, an anaerobic environment develops. In anaerobic environments, the vegetation is initially decomposed by fermentation, and the organic products of fermentation are further oxidized by anaerobic respiration, provided nitrate, sulfate or CO_2 are present as hydrogen acceptors in a manner similar to that shown on the left side of Fig. 16 (see p. 116; see also Stanier et al., 1963 and Chapter 6 of Vol. 3 by Trudinger). Vegetation decaying on the surface and buried or burrowed in the sediment combined with warm, organic-rich oxygen-deficient surface water would permit anaerobic conditions to exist near the surface of the sediment. The decomposition begins almost as soon as life ends and continues at a rate dependent on availability of suitable nutrients. The rate of decomposition of organic matter is greatest in the earliest stages, because a greater variety of decomposable materials are available to a broader spectrum of organisms. It can be reasonably concluded that reducing conditions are established in a sedimentary environment while sedimentation is still in progress and not at some later time (Love, 1964 and 1967; Perel'man, 1967 and Coleman, 1971). This is demonstrated by the common occurrence of plant debris in the sediment which has been partially carbonized or decomposed, then reworked with the sediment, disaggregated into segments, blocks and flakes to be redeposited with the clastic sediment, typically concentrating on cross-stratification surfaces. Fig. 14 shows carbonized wood flakes and blocks up to 1 cm long deposited with coarse

Fig. 14. Detrital carbonized wood flakes in coarse cross-bedded arkose (sketch from photograph).

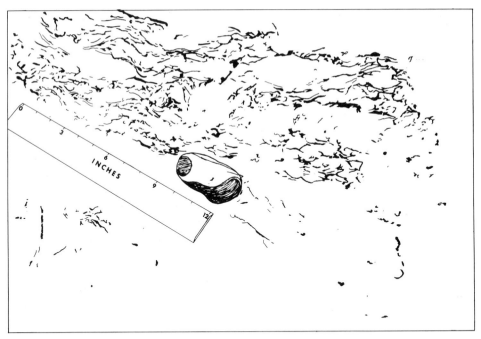

Fig. 15. Water-worn carbonized wood "cobble" 5 cm in diameter adjacent to carbonaceous films of leaves not disturbed after initial burial in coarse unstratified arkose (sketch from photograph).

arkose. Fig. 15 illustrates contorted carbonaceous films of leaves and related plant fragments "rolled" into the sediment with the inorganic detrital components and a water-worn "cobble" of carbonized wood. The carbonized films have not been disturbed since initial burial as recently fallen or living leaves.

Among the by-products of the anaerobic decomposition of the vegetation are carbon dioxide, methane, hydrogen, and hydrogen sulfide. Iron in the system reacts with the hydrogen sulfide to form pyrite and marcasite. Excess hydrogen sulfide may escape to the surface water or atmosphere, where it oxidizes to sulfate and may contribute to gypsum formation (Hem, 1970, p. 162). Gypsum may also accumulate from evaporation and transpiration of plants during dry seasons. Carbon dioxide increases the solubility of calcium carbonate and essentially prohibits its formation in this environment.

The environment at the time of deposition had a slightly alkaline pH and a strongly reducing Eh. These conditions are favorable for the reduction and deposition of uranium which enters the system. Uranium, released in the weathering of the granitic terrane of the source area and moved into the depositional area in solution, has a reasonable probability of entering the system where reduction and deposition would occur. Other metals stable in a reducing environment and those with an affinity for sulfur may also accumulate.

Coexisting with the abundant vegetation, which produces a reducing environment, is bioturbation caused by root-burrowing, animal burrows and the trampling of the sediment by large animals. This bioturbation destroys the stratification in the silt and clay which are typically light-gray to light-green in color and commonly contain very small euhedral pyrite crystals. Leaf impressions are present in some clays. Carbonaceous clays and lignite are also present. Some mottled medium-gray sandy zones are extensively root-burrowed and commonly contain abundant pyrite and carbonized roots in place. The color of reduced sandstones ranges from very light-gray, indicating reducing conditions but little carbon content, to medium- or dark-gray with 1—5% carbonaceous matter. The carbonaceous material normally consists of flakes and small fragments of carbonized wood well disseminated through the sandstone, except for a greater concentration on cross-stratification surfaces. Large segments of logs and stumps are present, but quantitatively are less important than the disseminated carbon. These large woody pieces commonly have major pyrite replacements, typically at the core. The detrital character of much of the carbonaceous debris and the content of bacterial residue indicates the woody material can be partially carbonized before final deposition. Undoubtedly, some continuation of the carbonization of the organic material takes place after burial, but it is essentially complete within weeks or months and in the case of large trees and stumps within a century or two.

The general absence of oxidized zones within the fluvial system indicates that the surface was poorly drained and well supplied with moisture to maintain the reducing environment. Oxidized zones that are present are thin and discontinuous beds or oxidized clay pebbles in the sandstones.

The process described above produces most of the conditions present in the uranium host rock. The major exceptions are compaction and those changes related to mineralization which will be described below. The changes which convert sediment entering a depositional basin into a uranium host rock begin while the sediment is still in transit and are almost complete when it reaches its final resting place; hence, the term most fitting to the process is syndiagenesis. The principal post-depositional change in the sediment is compaction of the sand and dewatering of the clays. The relative lack of cementing typical of uranium host rock, causes poor mining conditions. The clays are normally moderately to strongly sensitive to water which causes sloughing of the clays in mining and in drilling. In general, uranium host rock has greater lithification with age, but rock deposited under other conditions younger than the youngest uranium host may be more lithified than the oldest uranium-bearing rock.

MINERALIZATION AND ALTERATION

Uraninite, UO_2, and coffinite $U(SiO_4)_{1-X}(OH)_{4X}$, are the principal uranium minerals in non-weathered deposits of the Colorado Plateau and Wyoming. These minerals are of

exceedingly low solubilities, yet they are clearly epigenetic in that they have been introduced into their present location since the deposition of the sediment. The host rocks
show no evidence of alteration by hydrothermal solutions, nor do they show evidence of
the extreme pH conditions necessary to mobilize and transport the reduced uranium
minerals. It was stated in the "Introduction" that uranium has two naturally occurring
valence states which is most significant in its geological mobilization, transportation, and
deposition. In the reduced or tetravalent state, uranium minerals are practically insoluble,
while in the oxidized or hexavalent state uranium minerals can be taken into solution at
low temperature by acidic, neutral, or basic water and transported infinitely. The basic
problems concerning the origin of uranium deposits are: (1) what are the processes which
mobilize uranium, transport it for distances of miles and redeposit it with little change in
the rock through which it passes; (2) what is the source of uranium; (3) when was it
deposited; and (4) why do the ore bodies commonly have both discordant and concordant relationships to the enclosing sediments.

The kinds of processes were identified by Gruner (1956b) as oxidation—solution—
migration—precipitation and reduction. The manner in which these processes operated,
however, and the source of their energy was not well defined. The mineralizing processes
have minor effects on the host rock, namely, principally the destruction of the carbonaceous material and the conversion of iron sulfides to iron oxides.

The source of uranium is difficult to identify.* There are two popular ideas regarding
the source: (1) the granite from which the sediment is derived is considered by many to
be the source either directly or indirectly through transfer to the sediment, followed by
remobilization and then concentration into ore bodies; and (2) the second popular idea
concerning the source is the volcanic debris which overlies the host sandstone or is
interbedded with it.

The time of ore-body emplacement has received considerable attention through age
dating. The age dates have not been conclusive, partially because the deposits may have
migrated either intermittently or continuously over a long period of time. It is not
unreasonable that some of the deposits are migrating now. The relationship of the orebody shape and position within the sediment is the result of an invasion of the sediment
by oxidizing and mineralizing water along zones of greatest permeability. The ore bodies
conform to the external configuration of the invading zone.

Vickers (1957) recognized that the small ore bodies of the northern Black Hills, South
Dakota, were at the margin of altered pink (oxidized) sandstones in buff to gray carbonaceous—pyritic sandstones within the same stratigraphic unit. He also recognized there was
a genetic relationship between the oxidized zones and the ores in the adjacent reduced,
laterally equivalent zones. These relationships were not tested in other areas, and since
these deposits were not commercially important, the significance of Vicker's findings
were not immediately recognized by the industry.

---

* Editor's note: see the chapter on conceptual models, Vol. 1, Chapter 2.

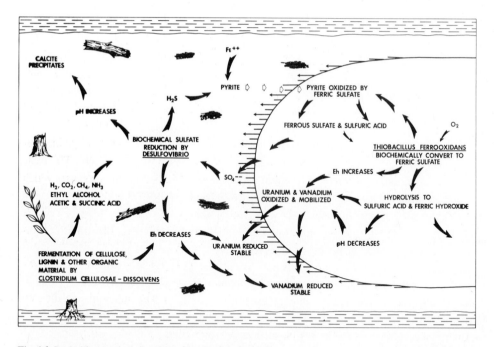

Fig. 16. Probable reactions in advancing geochemical cell.

In 1960 Philip N. Shockey independently recognized that uranium ore bodies in the Shirley Basin district of Wyoming were on the margin of an extensive body of sandstone which was oxidized in varying degrees, but the ore bodies and the adjacent and equivalent sandstone were carbonaceous and pyritic, a situation illustrated in Fig. 16 and described by Germanov (1960), Kashirtseva (1964), Lisitsyn and Kuznetsova (1967), Rackley et al. (1968) and Shockey et al. (1968). The oxidized sandstone had anomalous radioactivity at its upper and lower surfaces and occupied most of the sandstone, except an area adjacent to the ore body where the sandstone onlapped a paleoridge. The oxidized zone thinned at a greater rate than the enclosing sandstone, forming a blunt, wedge-shaped body which was strongly mineralized on its lateral margin and moderately to well mineralized on irregularities of its upper and lower surfaces. The uranium "roll" has long been known to uranium producers, but this was the first recognition that the "roll" had a genetic relation to the epigenetically oxidized sandstones within a reduced fluvial sequence (Rackley, 1972, p. 761). This provided an important guide for exploration and mining in the Shirley Basin and its validity was soon successfully tested in the Gas Hills mines. The successful use of this relationship did not provide answers to the questions of origin, but it did provide an empirically based concept or framework on which to build a hypothesis for the origin of the uranium deposits. Shockey et al. (1968, pp. 3—4) introduced the term "geochemical cell" for the processes occurring as oxygenated water invaded the reduced, carbonaceous, and pyritic sandstones, the resulting alteration of the sandstones, and the ore bodies on the margins of the altered zones.

Geochemical-cell concept

The geochemical cell originates at the outcrop or at any place where oxygenated water has access to the previously reduced sediment and expands to form a continuous, three-dimensional, finite body. The cell is a dynamic system of advancing oxidizing fronts which causes changes in Eh, pH, mineralogy, chemistry and microorganisms. The shape of the cell and the position of the related ore bodies is determined chiefly by gross permeability and by the concentration of oxidizable constituents. A geochemical cell in sediment deposited in the meander belt of a meandering stream is an elongated tongue-shaped body pointing down the hydrostatic gradient, typically downstream and/or downdip. The lateral edges of the cell are irregular due to the physical variations in sand deposition along the margins of the sand body and the chemical variations due to organic carbon and pyrite accumulations associated with the physical environment. Ideally, the fronts are convex outward in vertical section with the overall edge of the cell in the shape of a compressed crescent, the shape expected from the velocity of flow through a uniform sandstone layer (Germanov, 1960, p. 69). Fig. 16 is a typical shape of a roll, but the overall wedge shape of the margin of a geochemical cell has been vertically expanded for drafting considerations. Figs. 21B—21E and 22B—22D (pp. 132—135) are more realistic shapes.[1]

The cells have dimensions comparable to those of the sand bodies in which they occur. Known lateral dimensions are measured in miles and thicknesses in hundreds of feet. Irregularities in sedimentation cause the cell to take complex shapes which are reflected in the size and shapes of related ore bodies. The size of the cell is very large compared with the size of the mineralized fronts along the edge and on the irregularities on the upper and lower surfaces. The contrast between the character of the original reduced sediment and the altered sediment inside the cell are important guides in exploration for the mineralized margins.

Since the recognition of the genetic relation between the mineralized margins of the geochemical cell — the "rolls" — and the altered interior of the cell, research has been directed toward a knowledge of the processes which take place at the margins of the cell. This research has demonstrated that the processes are very complex and difficult to identify. The close spatial location of some reactions, such as oxidation and dissolution, to the opposite reactions of reduction and deposition along with the transitory nature of those reaction zones, increases the difficulty in identifying the processes. The process of uranium migration, oxidation, dissolution, transportation, reduction and deposition, involve both physical and chemical reactions all of which may be taking place within an overall distance of a few centimeters. The proximity of the reactions suggests that there are additional factors which exert controlling influences to produce microenvironments. The intimate association of these reactions with organic carbon further suggests that the reactions and the microenvironments are controlled by biological processes. Some of the

---

[1] See Notes added in proof, (1), p. 151.

biologically important elements undergo cyclic changes in their state of oxidation (valence) as a result of the activities of living organisms. These cyclic changes are characteristic of carbon, oxygen, nitrogen, sulfur and, on a minor scale, hydrogen and iron (Stanier et al., 1963). All of these elements are present in the margins of geochemical cells and some of these cyclic changes in states of oxidation could produce conditions for the oxidation and dissolution of uranium and for its reduction and deposition on either micro- or macro-scales.

No natural sedimentary process can take place in a sterile environment because some microorganisms will be active. Only those that are favored by the local and temporary environment reproduce, and their growth ceases when they have changed their environment. However, a few cells of each type of microorganism persist to initiate a new burst of growth when conditions again become favorable for their development. The importance of microorganisms in the mineralization process, i.e., conversion of living organisms into inorganic forms, is caused by their ubiquity, their high rates of growth and metabolism, and their ability to attack all naturally occurring organic compounds (Stanier et al., 1963).

The role of microorganisms in the formation of uranium deposits has been investigated through traditional bacteriological methods by Lisitsyn and Kuznetsova (1967) and by Douros (1967; see also Chapter 6, Vol. 2). Both investigations revealed the presence of a wide variety of bacteria. Douros worked with rock samples from the mineralized areas while Lisitsyn and Kuznetsova worked with water samples from artesian wells which produce from the mineralized strata covering a broad area from the vicinity of the recharge area across the mineralized reduction barrier into the center of the artesian basin. Another line of investigation had been the work on sulfur isotopes as a measure of bacteria fractionation by sulfate reducing bacteria (Jensen, 1958; Jones and Starkey, 1962; Jensen, 1963 and Cheney and Jensen, 1966). A general concensus has developed that bacteria are important in the development of the environment in which uranium deposits occur. There is much less agreement on the role of bacteria in the actual formation of the ore deposits. Rackley et al. (1968) proposed that bacteria control the chemical and physical conditions which form the ore deposits. Austin (1970) presented a status report on the distribution of sulfur isotopes in uranium deposits and concluded that the roll structure contained a population of bacteria which reduced and fractionated sulfur to produce H_2S, with the process culminating at or near the solution front. Grutt (1972) also supports the thesis that bacteria played a part in the formation of the uranium deposits. Granger and Warren (1969 and 1974) and Warren (1971) proposed an abiological chemical process to produce a reduction barrier to which Cheney and Trammel (1973) and Dahl and Hagmaier (1974) lend their support. This is a subject deserving of much additional research in both the laboratory and in the field where actual ore occurrences can be related to the laboratory and theoretical findings. There is further treatment of the conflicting views on this subject in the "Discussion" section of this chapter.

The pattern of ore distribution and the positions of the major altered areas were reasonably well established in the Shirley Basin and in the Gas Hills by the late 1960's. By this time continued mining and exploration had also produced much detailed information on some of the ore bodies in both districts. The association of carbonaceous material with uranium and vanadium deposits has been a common thread in the geologic literature from the early workers like Coffin (1921), Hess (1933), and Fischer (1937, 1942) continuing through the period of intensive research by the U.S. Atomic Energy Commission (Everhart, 1951a and b; McKelvey et al., 1955; Wright, 1955; Shawe et al., 1959; Gruner, 1956a and b; Laverty et al., 1963 and Young, 1964) to recent papers (Grutt, 1972; Haji-Vassilious and Kerr, 1973; Adler, 1974; Barthel, 1974; Mittempergher, 1974 and Woodward et al., 1974). The work of Jensen (1958 and 1963) and Cheney and Jensen (1966) on bacterial fractionation of sulfur isotopes combined with the finding of Lisitsyn and Kuznetsova (1967) and Douros (1967) on the bacterial populations associated with mineralized areas, suggested a direct relationship between the ore deposits, the bacteria and carbonaceous material which serves as an energy source for the bacteria. Further study on the activities of microorganisms (Stanier et al., 1963) and their relationship to geologic processes (Kuznetsov et al., 1963 and Silverman, 1967) provided a basis for numerous discussions of the possible role of bacteria in the ore-forming process with biologist Dr. Gail Zimmerman. From these seemingly diverse lines of evidence, a hypothesis was developed to relate the known associations of geochemical cells and uranium deposits with probable reactions and conditions (Rackley et al., 1968, p. 120).

Geochemical-cell reaction

Many reactions probably take place in the advancing edge of a cell, but those that can be identified as important are shown in Fig. 16. The reactions shown in this figure and discussed more fully below, are biologic activities and biochemically controlled changes in physical and chemical conditions. The right side of the figure, inside the curved line is the oxidizing zone, and the left side is the reducing zone. The arrows indicate product or conditions created by one reaction affecting or entering some other reaction. Pyrite and reduced ore minerals are not mobile; the cell migrates from right to left bringing a previously reduced area under the influence of the encroaching oxidizing environment.

The bacteria discussed in the following processes have not been identified by the writer, but bacteria of these types have been identified by Lisitsyn and Kuznetsova (1967, fig. 1, table 3) in a study of the bacterial population from flowing water-well samples taken from a Russian basin. The samples were taken from the recharge area of a mineralized formation basinward across the edge of the geochemical cell (reduction barrier). The U.S. Atomic Energy Commission had studies made in which some of these bacteria were identified (Douros, 1967, pp. 43–49). In geology, however, we are more compelled than most investigators to use the extrapolative technique of identifying bacteria by their effects, a method used in bacteriology and medicine.

Reducing environment. Several reactions occur in the reducing side of the cell just ahead of the oxidizing zone. The increases in the amount of organic material and pyrite compared to the sediment beyond the influence of the cell (King and Austin, 1965, p. 32 and Rubin, 1970, pp. 5–8) indicate an increase in activity in that area. Other evidence of increased reactions in this zone is the change in the carbonaceous material from vitreous, carbonized plant fragments retaining much of their original woody character in the area just outside the influence of the cell, to sooty, incoherent but distinct masses near the interface with the oxidized zone, and finally complete obliteration of these masses. These changes indicate the carbonaceous material is being acted upon and utilized by the bacterial population as the cell encroaches.

The microorganisms present in the reducing environment of a geochemical cell are characterized by a group of organisms, the strict anaerobes, to which oxygen is harmful. Oxygen-free conditions in nature are best developed in media of low oxidation–reduction potential. In this anaerobic environment, organic compounds are initially decomposed by fermentation. The organic products of fermentation are then further oxidized by other bacteria in anaerobic respiration if nitrate, sulfate or carbon dioxide are present (Stanier et al., 1963).

The fermentation of the cellulose and other organic material by the anaerobic spore-formers, *Clostridium cellulosae–dissolvens* and similar bacteria produce ethyl alcohol, acetic and succinic acids, carbon dioxide, and hydrogen as the principal end products (Stanier et al., 1963). The hydrogen tends to lower the oxidation–reduction potential and the other products of fermentation are utilized by other bacteria such as the sulfate-reducing genus, *Desulfovibrio*, in anaerobic respiration. Almost any form of organic-matter cellulose, lignin, or sewage can be utilized by ubiquitous sulfate-reducing microbes (Zajic, 1969; see also Chapter 6 by Trudinger, Vol. 2).

The sulfate-reducing genus, *Desulfovibrio*, utilizes the inorganic sulfate and carbon dioxide with decomposable organic matter in the following types of reactions (Berner, 1973):

For carbohydrates:
$$2CH_2O + SO_4^{2-} \rightarrow H_2S + 2HCO_3^-$$

For amino acid: $4CH_2NH_4COOH + 4H_2O + 3SO_3^{2-} \rightarrow H_2S + 2HS^- + 8HCO_3^- + 4NH_4^+.$

Methane-forming bacteria are present in the reducing environment of a geochemical cell (Cheney and Jensen, 1966 and Lisitsyn and Kuznetsova, 1967). They are strict anaerobes and obtain the energy for growth by anaerobic oxidation of specific inorganic or simple organic compounds coupled with a reduction of CO_2 to methane (CH_4), a reaction which requires relatively large amounts of CO_2 (Stanier et al., 1963).

All these bacteria are extremely strict anaerobes in that oxygen is toxic to them and their activity is inhibited by selenates (Baas Becking and Moore, 1961, p. 263). *Desulfovibrio* create an environment of pH = 7.8–8.4 (Jones and Starkey, 1962, p. 65) and $E_h \approx$ −200 mV (Germanov, 1958), but are capable of an Eh = −500 mV (Baas Becking and

Moore, 1961, p. 262). These bacteria convert the organic constituents of the original sediment into energy-producing products and create an environment which physically reduces and precipitates the uranium and associated minerals. Sulfate-reducing bacteria normally do not select and precipitate specific metals, but they act as generators of H_2S which reacts with metals to precipitate sulfide minerals (Zajic, 1969, p. 85). The formation of pyrite in uranium deposits, as well as most reduced sediment, is not a direct one-step process. At neutral pH and low temperatures, the first formed iron sulfides resulting from the reaction of H_2S with either iron minerals or dissolved Fe^{2+} or Fe^{3+}, are always iron monosulfides such as mackinawite (FeS) and greigite (Fe_3S_4) and never pyrite (Berner, 1973). Iron is reduced and monosulfides formed by the following reactions:

$$2HFeO_2 + 3H_2S \rightarrow 2FeS + S^0 \quad + 4H_2O$$

$$2Fe_2O_3 \cdot H_2O + 6H_2S \rightarrow \quad FeS + Fe_3S_4 + S^0 + 8H_2O$$

The transformation reactions from monosulfides to pyrite entails oxidation and the addition of sulfur by the following reactions (Berner, 1973):

$$FeS + H_2S \rightarrow \quad FeS_2 + 2H^+ + 2e$$

$$Fe_3S_4 + H_2S \rightarrow 3FeS_2 + 4H^+ + 4e$$

$$FeS + \quad S^0 \rightarrow FeS_2$$

$$Fe_3S_4 + \quad 2S \rightarrow 3FeS_2$$

Pyrite, FeS_2, is stable and can form only at low oxidation—reduction potentials in the absence of dissolved oxygen. In addition, the anaerobic waters must be sufficiently high in dissolved H_2S so that pyrite is stabilized relative to other reduced iron compounds. If total dissolved sulfide is too low, siderite, magnetite, pyrrhotite, hematite and probably glauconite are stable relative to pyrite (Berner, 1973). The fact that pyrite is stable relative to other reduced iron minerals in high concentrations of dissolved H_2S probably accounts for the general low magnetite content of most uranium host rock and the leaching of iron from ilmenite in the New Mexico deposits, as described by Adams et al. (1974). Because sulfate is mobile and able to diffuse into sediment undergoing sulfate reduction, the limiting factor in sulfate reduction is usable organic matter while the limiting factor on pyrite formation may be the concentration of reactive iron (Berner, 1973).

The iron monosulfides are black and this coloration combined with the carbonized organic material is responsible for the gray to black color of reduced sediment.

Under certain conditions, some sulfate-reducing microorganisms produce a bituminous oil-like substance (Zajic, 1969, p. 83) which may be the source of the asphaltic material in some uranium districts.

Oxidizing environment. In the altered, oxidizing part of the cell, shown inside the curving line on the right of Fig. 16, a distinctly different group of bacteria and conditions are present. The contact zone separating the oxidizing environment from the reducing environment is commonly 1–8 cm wide. In the oxidizing environment *Thiobacillus ferrooxidans* and related bacteria are the most active populations (Lisitsyn and Kuznetsova, 1967). *Thiobacillus ferrooxidans* belong to a group of bacteria that can use CO_2 as their sole source of carbon and can develop in environments that are entirely free of organic matter. This group of bacteria are able to use molecular hydrogen, nitrogen compounds, sulfur compounds and iron as their only and specific source of energy and are unable to utilize organic compounds (Stanier et al., 1963).

Thiobacillus can oxidize several reduced forms of sulfur (H_2S, S, thiosulfate) with the formation of sulfate as the end product and are adapted to growth in an acid environment. In well-aerated laboratory conditions, the oxidation–reduction potential increased to +715 mV with increasing oxidation of ferrous iron and accumulation of ferric iron (Kuznetsov et al., 1963). While this level of Eh is not likely to be achieved in the oxidizing portion of a geochemical cell, it does indicate the potential for geochemical change of these microorganisms. They create pH as low as 1.8 and can survive in a pH of zero. The optimum pH is from 2 to 4 and with a pH of over 4.5 activity is greatly reduced (Kuznetsov et al., 1963).

Thiobacillus ferroxidans are found in nature wherever sulfides are found in an oxidizing environment (Kuznetsov et al., 1963). These bacteria are the cause of the acidity of coal-mine waters and are used in the recovery of copper from mine dumps. The oxidation of pyrite by *Thiobacillus* is approximately 200 times faster than by atmospheric oxygen alone. Along with the oxidation of pyrite, sulfuric acid is produced. The work of Silverman (1967) indicated that ferric iron is a participant in the bacterial oxidation of pyrite which is also a product of *Thiobacillus ferrooxidans* (Kuznetsov et al., 1963) by the following reaction:

$$4FeSO_4 + 2H_2SO_4 + O_2 \rightarrow 2Fe_2(SO_4)_3 + 2H_2O$$

Silverman (1967) indicates that the bacterial oxidation of pyrite with the participation of ferric iron follows the following pattern:

$$FeS_2 + Fe_2(SO_4)_3 \rightarrow 3FeSO_4 + 2S$$

$$2S + 6Fe_2(SO_4)_3 + 8H_2O \rightarrow 12FeSO_4 + 8H_2SO_4$$

$$\overline{} +$$

$$FeS_2 + 7Fe_2(SO_4)_3 + 8H_2O \rightarrow 15 FeSO_4 + 8H_2SO_4$$

The ferrous sulfate may be recycled by the bacteria or pass into the reducing area of the cell where the anaerobic bacteria utilize it to produce H_2S to form new pyrite. The ferric sulfate may hydrolize according to the following reaction and be removed from the system, but produce more sulfuric acid (Kuznetsov et al., 1963):

$$2Fe_2(SO_4)_3 + 12H_2O \rightarrow 2Fe_2(OH)_6 + 6H_2SO_4$$

The addition of carbon dioxide from the reduced portion of the cell and oxygen from the invading water are all that are required to carry forward the oxidizing reactions. The addition of sulfate from the oxidizing zone may be the only requirement to carry forward the reducing reactions.

Physical and chemical conditions

There are large contrasts in both pH and Eh on the leading edge of a geochemical cell. The mildly alkaline but strongly reducing environment of *Clostridium* and *Desulfovibrio*, both strict anaerobes, is hostile for the growth of *Thiobacillus* while the low pH and high Eh of *Thiobacillus* aerobic environment in incompatible for the growth of the other two bacteria. The oxidizing *Thiobacillus* zone is a mobile environment a few centimeters to a few meters in cross-section width, controlled by the availability of nutrients and by conditions unfavorable for this bacteria. This mobile zone of oxidizing acidic conditions created temporary conditions favorable for the oxidation and mobilization of uranium, vanadium and other elements unstable under these conditions. Once mobilized these metals move, in solution, into the reducing part of the cell where they again encounter conditions favorable for their precipitation by reduction or reaction with hydrogen sulfide. The reducing conditions are inherent in the sediment from the time of sedimentation and diagenesis, but the bacteria are inactive until the advance of the oxidizing zone begins to contribute nutrients for their activation and growth. The two bacterial populations have a dependent relation initiated or terminated by the introduction or discontinuation of a supply of oxygenated water.

The amount of pyrite and carbonaceous material appears to be the controlling factor in determining the nature of the reaction zones and the gradients in pH and Eh between them. Typically, there are sharp contacts between the altered and mineralized zones, but in the Powder River basin of Wyoming there is a zone of incomplete oxidation of varied thickness and width between the completely oxidized and the mineralized zones (Davis, 1969, pl. 4 and Rubin, 1970, p. 8). This incompletely oxidized zone is a pale yellowish-green and contains some remnants of carbonaceous debris, pyrite, minor limonite and hematite stains, and some uranium. This appears to be the result of a lower Eh gradient across the front which is also reflected in somewhat broader and thicker but lower-grade mineralized zones.

Character of alteration

Although alteration has a different connotation to almost everyone, it is a good term for the alteration in the interior of a geochemical cell. While the general processes of geochemical cells are essentially the same, the differences in alteration are considerable from district to district, particularly as reflected in color. Some of these colors are characteristic of sediments which are unrelated to uranium mineralization or secondary alteration, and therefore it is essential to determine that the suspected alteration is in fact in the same sandstone body as unaltered carbonaceous pyritic sediment. Oxidation— reduction potentials of an environment can be evaluated by means of mineral-indicators. Because of their bright coloring, iron minerals are the most diagnostic. The trivalent iron minerals hematite, goethite and limonite are red, yellow, and brown while bivalent iron minerals siderite, vivianite, or the high-iron clay mineral, nontronite, are white, blue or greenish (Perel'man, 1967). The bivalent ferrous monosulfides, i.e., mackinawite and greigite, produce a black coloration but pyrite adds no color to the sediment. However, the monosulfides are not likely to be present in alteration zones. In addition to the oxidation—reduction potential, the pH and the concentration of dissolved sulfide deter- mines the iron minerals present in a particular environment (Berner, 1973). Any of the iron minerals in the altered zone are subject to further oxidation and maturation. The color changes associated with alteration described in Adler (1970) are not those found in actual conditions except in limited areas, a situation he partially corrected in subsequent work (Adler, 1974).

Some areas have readily recognizable alteration while others have very subtle differ- ences between the altered and unaltered portions of the geochemical cell. There are some criteria which can be used to verify areas that are altered. The altered zone is invariably more oxidized than the unaltered. This can be identified by the absence of carbonaceous material if good samples are available. Pyrite may be present in areas of alteration, but it is much less abundant than in the unaltered portions of the host sandstone. Yellowish- green, buff or pink from iron-staining of the clay and thin coatings on larger clastic grains make alteration easily recognizable to the careful observer. The pink to brick-red hema- tite staining is so obvious that untrained observers can see the change, even if they do not appreciate its meaning.

Recognition of alteration in outcrop may be especially difficult if not impossible. Weathering of altered sediment has little effect on the color of the outcrop but weather- ing of pyritic carbonaceous, unaltered strata tends toward the yellow and brown colors on and near the outcrops and along major fault zones. This subject is worthy of more investigation.

There is generally very little cementation in the host rock of uranium deposits and this is especially true of the altered zone. In the vicinity of ore, the alteration will have low radioactivity but the upper and lower margins of the altered zone are commonly accom- panied by thin sharp radioactive anomalies.

Mineral zoning

The Eh and pH gradients at the edge of a geochemical cell determine which minerals are deposited and their positions in the cell. One of the peculiarities of the geochemical cell is the minerals which are concentrated by it and the characteristic order in which they occur. The cells in the Tertiary sediments are very simple, containing principally uranium with minor amounts of molybdenum and minor to moderate amounts of selenium, but vanadium is present in some areas. In cells in other districts of the Rocky Mountains, the metals copper, silver, chromium and lead occur in significant amounts. It normally is not possible to identify minerals directly by their characteristics because of the low concentrations and extremely small size of the mineral grains or coatings. Color of the minerals will indicate their presence, particularly the oxidation products. The zones are best identified by detailed analysis and actually show the distribution of the elements which can be related to the mineralogy of the geochemical cell. Since selenium, silver and copper are the only elements concentrated by geochemical cells which are likely to occur in the metallic state, mineral zoning is the preferred term rather than metal or element zoning.

Mineral zones like roll fronts, have been known for several years. Shawe (1956) showed the mineral zoning in figures of ore bodies in the Salt Wash Member of the Morrison Formation of the Colorado Plateau. Garrels et al. (1959) reported on detailed analysis of the suite of samples taken across a roll front of the Mineral Joe Mine in the Uravan mineral belt. Botinelly and Fischer (1959) and Fischer (1960) described the mineral zones in the Rifle Mine. Harshman (1966, 1970 and 1972) reported the zoning of the Shirley basin roll fronts and recently extended this phase of roll-front studies to other districts (Harshman, 1974). Granger et al. (1961) showed the mineral zoning in the Ambrosia Lake area of New Mexico. Rosholt et al. (1964) described an isotopic fractionation between ^{234}U and ^{235}U and ^{238}U across roll features in the Shirley Basin, and Dooley et al. (1966) reported similar fractionation across ore boundaries in Ambrosia Lake. King and Austin (1965) did considerable work on the mineral zones of the Gas Hills, Wyoming. Kashirtseva (1964) reported mineral zones in uranium deposits of the USSR. Typically these studies have been restricted to a single linear suite of samples which goes from the interior altered zone across the ore body into the barren fresh or unaltered. Rackley and Johnson (1971) reported detailed analysis of a cored profile across the nose of a Powder River basin roll front to emphasize the three-dimensional nature of the mineral zoning.

Figs. 17 and 18 show the characteristic positions or uranium, vanadium, selenium, molybdenum and calcite. Fig. 19 shows the uranium-grade distribution and the distribution of radiometric disequilibrium. In these figures, the limits of uranium and the calcite cemented areas are shown for reference for the other elements.

Since the knowledge of these three-dimensional relationships can be very useful in exploration and exploitation of these ore bodies, Figs. 17, 18 and 19 are shown as block

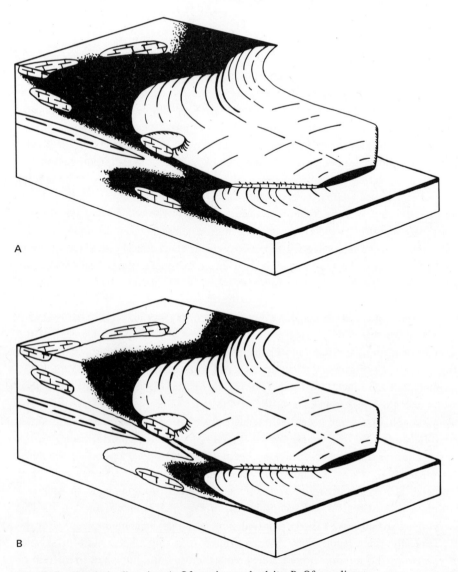

Fig. 17. Geochemical-cell zoning. A. Of uranium and calcite. B. Of vanadium.

diagrams of the lower portion of a segment of a geochemical cell. Since a roll front is commonly much more complex than the typical C-shape, a small incomplete or subsidiary roll is shown on the lower limb of the major roll to further emphasize the three-dimensional nature of the mineral zoning. While the mineral zoning is generally best developed across the nose of a front where it may be many meters wide, it also occurs above and below the altered zone commonly compressed to a few centimeters in thickness. This compressed zoning may extend from a few meters to as much as a kilometer on

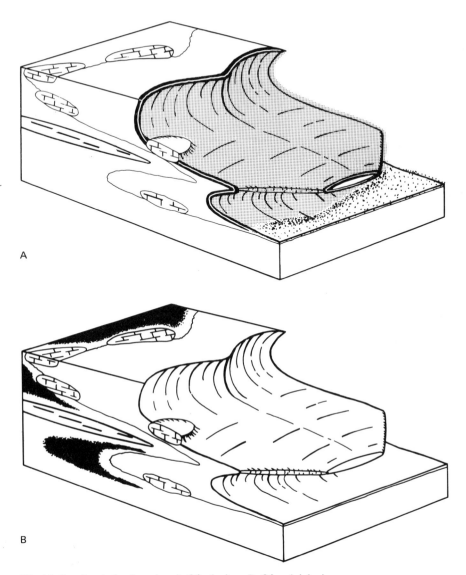

Fig. 18. Geochemical-cell zoning. A. Of selenium. B. Of molybdenium.

the upper and lower surfaces of the altered zone from the roll front. This zone of residual minerals, commonly at the contact between a mineralized sand and the bounding shales above and below, produce weak radioactive anomalies at these points which is commonly characteristic of the altered sands. The incomplete upper limb of the lower or subsidiary roll in the block diagram is a common and significant feature. If it is caused by a finer-grained carbonaceous zone, which is commonly the case, this kind of feature may extend a considerable distance into the altered zone. With alteration both above and

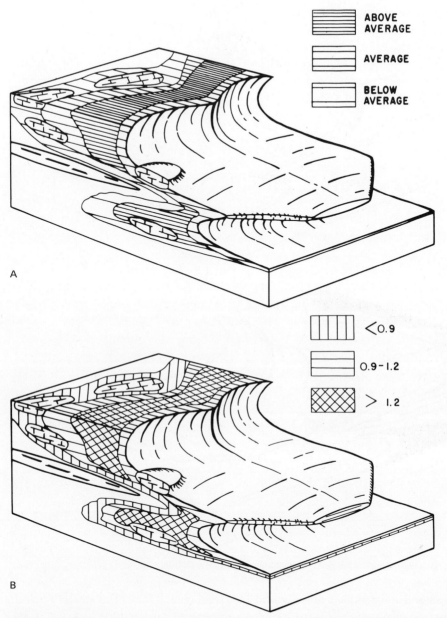

Fig. 19. Geochemical cell. A. Zoning of uranium grade distribution. B. Radiometric disequilibrium ratio of a geochemical cell.

below, the mineral zoning will be symmetrical in an otherwise asymmetrical zoning pattern. Granger et al. (1961), by sampling of the trend ore bodies in New Mexico, demonstrated this symmetrical pattern in which selenium and lead, followed by uranium were symmetrical from the upper and lower boundaries of the mineralized body to the interior.

In the simple cells uranium occurs on the reduced side of the contact, as shown in Fig. 17A, diminishing gradually away from it. Uranium also occurs in the margin of the altered zone adjacent to the contact, but this uranium is actively being oxidized and leached (Harshman, 1966, p. C172). However, if vanadium is also present, vanadium minerals will occur adjacent to the contact, as shown in Fig. 17B, and this zone may or may not contain uranium. If the uranium is separated from the vanadium, vanadium occurs at the contact and uranium occurs adjacent to the vanadium.

Selenium occurs in trace amounts in the altered zone, increasing in concentration towards the contact with the unaltered zone. The visible presence of selenium has been noted only at the contact zone with the selenium on both sides of the contact, as shown in Fig. 18A. Lead occurs with selenium in the contact zone of some districts. Molybdenum occurs furthest form the contact as indicated in Fig. 18B and may be completely separate from the uranium zone. The oxidation of the molybdenum to ilsemannite causes a deep-blue bloom to form as a halo around the dark uranium ore.

Calcite-cemented lenses and concretions occur in the outer margins of the reaction zones approximately in the outer margins of the uranium zone, as shown in Fig. 17A. The calcite is resistant and commonly the contact moves past a calcite-rich zone and un-commonly forms a ghost roll in the altered zone.

The distribution of uranium values within the uranium zone is illustrated in Fig. 19A. The highest values are commonly a few centimeters to as much as a meter from the altered contact. Carbonaceous debris within the zone shown as above-average grade may be enriched in uranium five to twenty times the average. From this zone of the above average grade, the values diminish further into the unaltered until the typical host-rock values are reached. The actual grades are relative with the high-grade zone ranging from 0.20% to 2.00% U_3O_8. The size is also relative, a zone such as Fig. 19A may be as little as two meters or more than 100 m across.

Uranium and its gamma-ray emitting daughter products tend to become separated within an ore body. Part of this separation appears to be related to the movement of the cell and part is related to the grade. The disequilibrium ratio is uranium over equivalent uranium. The equivalent uranium is the amount of gamma-ray emissions from a sample in which uranium and all the daughter products are in equilibrium. In the unoxidized deposits, there is a tendency for grades of less than 0.08% to have a disequilibrium ratio of less than one, while grades above 0.08% tend to have a ratio greater than one. The ratio increases as the grade increases, with very high-grade samples attaining ratios of three to five. The typical distribution of disequilibrium ratios in a geochemical cell is shown in Fig. 19B. When uranium deposits of this type are subjected to weathering near the surface, the disequilibrium ratios attain ranges from almost zero to near infinity as the uranium is oxidized and leached leaving the gamma-ray emitting products behind. If the uranium is redeposited below the oxidizing zone, it may have little gamma-ray emissions and hence a very high disequilibrium ratio.

Cell growth and shape

The cells originate at the basin margins or on a structure which permits groundwater recharge of the host sediment with oxygenated water. The water is capable of transporting hexavalent uranium and probably has a uranium content ranging from a few tens parts per billion to a few parts per million. The water also has the capacity to initiate the biological reactions to leach and concentrate the very low concentration of uranium (5–50 ppm) already in the host rock. The uranium introduced into the cell by the groundwater recharge is held in solution until it reaches the roll front, where it accumulates by accretion from both sources. From the points of origin in the recharge area the small oxidized areas expand down the hydrostatic gradient, growing like smouldering fires and ultimately coalescing to occupy the more permeable portion of the recharge area. With passage of time, erosion of the overlying formations would enlarge the surface area exposed to recharge and accelerate growth of the cell. Within the deposits of a specific paleo-stream system the cell originates essentially at a point and expands to form a continuous three-dimensional, finite body.

Referring again to the Colorado Plateau as an example, Fig. 20 illustrates the distribution of altered zones of the Morrison Formation based on Fig. 11 which illustrates the distribution of the Salt Wash Member and Fig. 13 which refers to the Westwater Member. This figure is a very simplified example and is not intended to encompass all the altered and mineralized areas of Colorado Plateau. The Salt Wash fan, extending northeastward into the basin, was deposited during a period of gradually increasing rainfall on the fan and in the drainage basin (headwaters) of the Salt Wash streams. Consequently, the upper segment of the fan, which consists of very thick sandstone units, did not accumulate sufficient organic material to lower the oxidation–reduction potential to a reducing environment. On the lower-gradient portions of the fan, surface or near-surface water would increase the vegetation and also permit the development of reducing environments. In the case of the Salt Wash sandstones, the geochemical cell(s) may not have developed except in the lower portions of the fan. Fig. 20 depicts in a simple way the alteration (stippling) and mineralization distribution, the thickened areas on the margin of the alteration, of the Uravan mineral belt, the Green River district (Utah); the Henry Mountain district (Utah); the Lukachucki district (Arizona); and projects undiscovered districts in the San Juan basin of northwest New Mexico.

The Westwater Member was deposited to the east and southeast of the apex of the fan (Figs. 12 and 13) along the southwest margin of the basin. In this instance, the alteration in the Westwater originated in two areas. One altered area is in the Arizona portion of the Westwater facies, which was essentially a downdip development from the apex of the fan. This alteration extends into the structural low between the Fort Defiance uplift in eastern Arizona and the Zuni uplift east of Gallup, New Mexico. The Westwater is removed by erosion from most of its initial depositional distribution in eastern Arizona, but the well-developed facies extends into the San Juan basin of northwest New Mexico from the

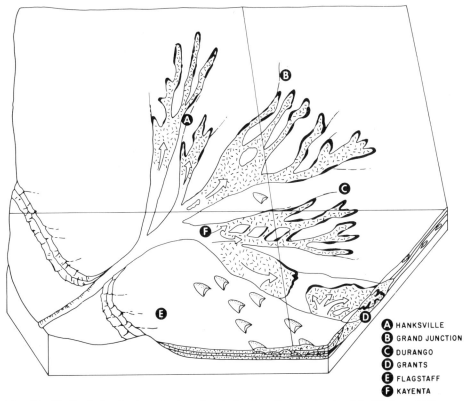

Fig. 20. Idealized distribution of alteration and mineralization in the Salt Wash and Westwater Members of the Morrison Formation of the Colorado Plateau.

well-altered outcrops on the west margin of the basin. The extent of the facies and the associated alteration is unknown. The other altered area encompasses the Grants mineral belt from Grants to a point northeast of Gallup. The alteration of this area has unusual access to the favorable Westwater facies in that the hydraulic gradient was developed on the Zuni uplift and the oxygenated water migrated through the eolian system into the fluvial Westwater system. In the area from the north end of the Zuni uplift eastward for about 20 miles (about 32 km) the Westwater sands are in direct contact with the eolian Cow Springs sands. Eastward from this point the hydraulic continuity is partially or completely interrupted by silts and clay of the Recapture facies. From the area of access on the north of the Zuni uplift alteration spread, as indicated by the arrows in Fig. 20, northward to the Church Rock mineralized area and southeastward into the Ambrosia Lake area (how much further to the southeast is still not fully known). Parts of the Grants mineral belt alteration and its associated mineralization is poorly known, because depths from the surface to the Westwater targets range from 2,000 to 4,000 ft (about 300–600 m). The next few years will see these areas explored and hopefully many new ore bodies will be defined on this important geochemical cell.

Returning to the model of the growth and shape of a geochemical cell, once oxygen-ated water establishes oxidizing conditions in the host sediment the cell continues to grow as long as oxygen is supplied. As the cell moves through the host, the ore bodies on its margin increase in size and grade. It migrates around shale partings which intertongue with the main sand system and divide the cell into lobes, still maintaining its finite, three-dimensional shape.

A series of five drawings is shown in Fig. 21 to show in a simple manner the growth and shape of a generalized geochemical cell in an average fluvial sequence. This sequence was deposited by a meandering stream on a regional unconformity. Downstream and downdip are perpendicular to the figure and the central portion of its meander belt is on the left with the right side of the belt beyond the right side of the drawings. Fig. 21A is

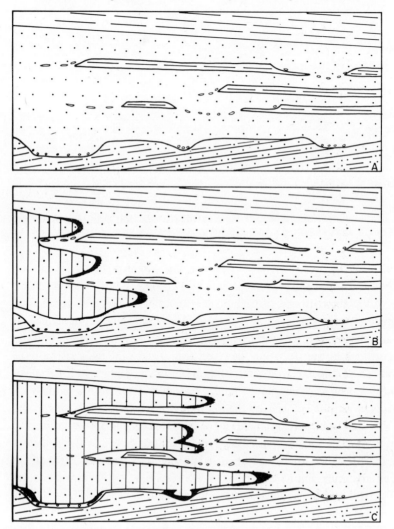

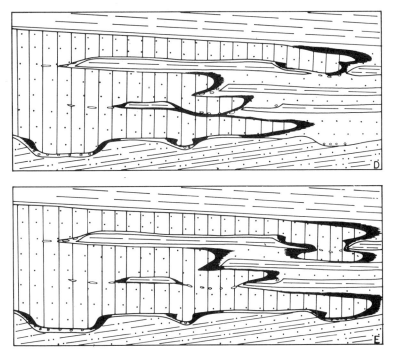

Fig. 21. Growth of a geochemical cell. A. Prior to invasion the sands are gray carbonaceous and pyritic interbedded with green to gray shale resting on a regional unconformity. B–E. Successive periods of advance. The oxidized area is indicated by vertical lines and the mineralization is indicated by the shading on the margin of the oxidized zone.

prior to invasion by the cell and the sediment contains the disseminated pyrite and carbon originally present when the sediment reached diagenetic equilibrium shortly after deposition. In Fig. 21B, the cell has invaded from the left occupying the central portion of the sand because of the greater gross permeability in that area and mineralization accumulates on the margins. The invaded or altered area is indicated by vertical lines. The shale has a retarding effect and tends to divide the cell into lobes. Further invasion in Fig. 21C had divided the cell into three distinct lobes and has produced ore bodies adjacent to the cut banks on the old erosion surface. The middle lobe is beginning to divide into an upper and lower lobe because of the influence of the shale to the right. In Fig. 21D the altered zone on the left side continues to expand against the margins of the sand, ultimately reaching the shale. The cell continues to migrate to the right and the size of the ore bodies also increases. The shale lag blocks are completely enveloped by alteration.

In Fig. 21E the cell has reached a typical development in which the central sand of the meander belt is completely altered while the ore bodies accumulate in the thinner sands along the margins and on irregularities on the erosion surface. These conditions satisfy the statistical determination that ore bodies most commonly occur in areas where shales make up 20–50% of the host rock. The observation that ore bodies most commonly occur where the sand bodies thin to less than 10 m in thickness is also related to the growth pattern of a geochemical cell (Wright, 1955).

The expansion of the upper lobe through an erosional perforation in the underlying shale into the sand below is a common occurrence. These situations produce donut-shaped ore bodies below and around small perforations. Moderate-size perforations tend to have altered areas comparable in shape to that of the perforation. Vertical migration of the cell through major areas of erosion or shale pinch-out are common. The cell can also migrate downward into deeply eroded areas or into areas of subsidence due to displacement of soft mud by differential loading of channel sand.

Modification of geochemical-cell development

Ore bodies, such as those in the Laguna district at the southeast end of the Grants mineral belt, New Mexico, and many in the Chinle of Arizona and Utah, have conditions common to those of geochemical-cell ore bodies but have other conditions which prohibit the development of a geochemical cell in the conventional manner, namely isolation of the host sand into discrete bodies not connected hydraulically to each other or to an outcrop from the time of burial until the present cycle of erosion. With slight modifications of cell shape, manner of development, and a precise fixing of the time of mineralization these ore bodies conform to the overall geochemical-cell concept.

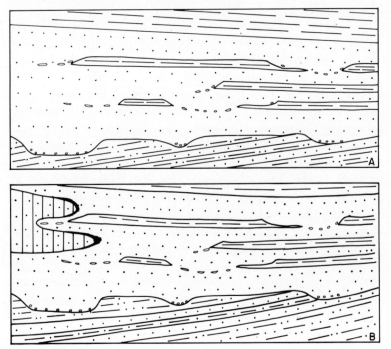

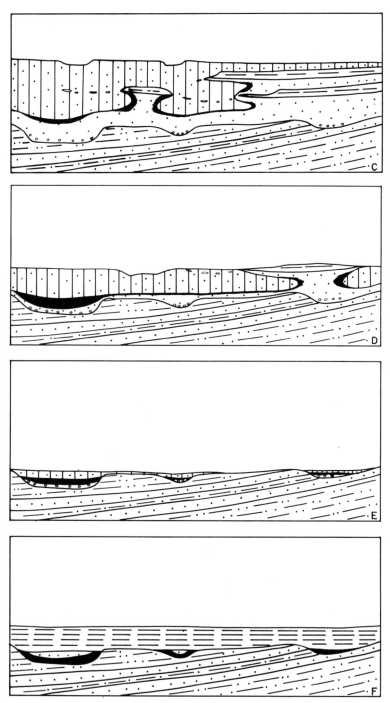

Fig. 22. Growth of a modified geochemical cell. A. It begins with the same conditions as Fig. 21, but B–E moves principally vertically rather than horizontally. F. Remnants of the cell are covered and preserved. The oxidized area is indicated by vertical lines and the mineralization is indicated by the shading on the margin of the oxidized zone.

The modifications of a cell to produce ore bodies in discrete sand bodies are shown in the series of drawings in Fig. 22. The series begins with the same condition as the beginning of a conventional cell in Fig. 21, which was formed by horizontally flowing fluids, and its initial development may be essentially the same as indicated by Figs. 21A and 22A. There is one major difference in the two cases: the protective cover is stripped away by wide-spread erosion as shown in Fig. 22C. This allows the direct (i.e., vertical) access of rainfall into the host formation, as well as other oxygenated surface water. This period of erosion occurs in the fourth development phase, as discussed under tectonic conditions. Although there are no known cases where both the conventional and the modified cells have developed in the same basin, there is no reason why both could not occur simultaneously, either in separate horizons or in separate areas. The depositional areas may have a weak positive tectonic tendency to cause the erosion or they may simply be the result of a stream which slowly reduces its gradient headward and cuts into the sediment it deposited under higher-energy, steeper-gradient conditions. Figs. 3, 4, and 5 indicate this phase would be characterized by moderate stream volume, but the erodability and sediment supply from the source area were low and the load was dominantly suspended sediment. These conditions combine to enhance the probability of erosion rather than continued sedimentation in the depositional area. The development of oxidizing conditions on the surface would occur quickly in the hot seasonally dry areas once the water table is lowered by the down-cutting of the streams. Seasonal rains would accelerate the leaching and oxidation process once the water table subsided, the amount of vegetation decreased, and aerobic decomposition of organic material became dominant again. The geochemical-cell reactions, once initiated, should continue without regard to direction as long as the supply of nutrients (oxygen and carbonaceous material) were available. The leachable minerals in the near-surface sediment would be available for concentration in the reducing zone below. Possibly more important is deep leaching of the source area and the best opportunity during the entire cycle to introduce the metal content from that leaching directly into the geochemical cell.

Fig. 22D shows a continuation of erosion and advance of the cell. Since remnants of the uranium host rock survive this period of erosion, the rate of downward migration of the cell and the rate of erosion diminish as indicated in Fig. 22E. As the conditions for the deposition of reduced sediment over the remnants of the host formation are being developed, the altered portion of the cell may be bleached. Fig. 22F shows the final stage in which clay and silt cover the remnants and their contained ore, isolating them from other opportunities for subsequent mineralization.

There are two other possible interpretations. One is that the cell developed in the conventional manner and was eroded subsequently and destroyed, the other that the host sediment was exposed at the surface, similar to Fig. 22C, when erosion began and oxidation migrated downward over the entire depositional area.[1]

---

[1] See Notes added in proof, (2), p. 152.

Time of mineralization

A knowledge of the time of mineralization in either absolute age or in relative terms in relation to other geologic conditions would assist immeasurably in establishing limiting conditions for theories of origin of the ores. There has been a reasonable amount of work concerned with determining the absolute age of uranium deposits (Miller and Kulp, 1963; Harshman, 1972 and Dooley et al., 1974). Their results have shown wide ranges of age for samples in the same formation and within the same deposit. The success (?) of each worker tends to be determined by the assumption and techniques used to obtain the results. Harshman (1972, p. 73) used selected high-grade samples to date the Shirley Basin deposits (Wyoming) obtaining a range just over 10 million years to nearly 40 million years in sediment considered to be 50 million years old. He concluded 18 million years, Late Miocene, is a reasonable age. More recent work by Dooley et al. (1974) on massive uraninite samples from Gas Hills and Shirley Basin ores indicates an age of 22 million years, plus or minus 3 million years, for both deposits to establish an Early Miocene age. Miller and Kulp (1963) used polished sections, when necessary to obtain pure minerals, from which they obtained mineralization-age ranges from Triassic rock of 22 to 220 million years and from Jurassic rock of 65 to 175 million years. They concluded from their work that there were two periods of mineralization, one about 110 million years ago and one about 210 million years ago for ore of the Colorado Plateau, but recognized that remobilization and redeposition could have occurred throughout the history of the Colorado Plateau. Miller and Kulp (1963, p. 621) also concluded that initial uranium deposition may have occurred soon after or during the formation of the sedimentary rock at temperatures less than $90°C$ in the presence of biogenic hydrogen sulfide (reducing condition).

There is one inherent problem in age-dating using either the isotopic or total lead/ uranium ratios. Lead and uranium have different chemical characteristics. Lead has only one valence state and is less affected by oxidation—reduction potential than it is by the concentration of selenate or sulfides in solution in the media, while uranium is strongly dependent upon oxidation—reduction potential for its activity or stability. Therefore, it is unlikely they will be mobilized, transported and redeposited together. Some spatial separation is, consequently, likely to occur if all the lead and uranium migrate with the cell. Rosholt et al. (1964) found there was even a fractionation of the ^{234}U isotope from the ^{235}U and ^{238}U isotopes across the contact from the altered to the unaltered, i.e., ore-bearing, areas of the roll in the Shirley Basin, and Dooley et al. (1966) found a similar relationship on the contacts of Ambrosia Lake ores.

It is even more likely that one will be more completely leached than the other. The concept of uranium—lead age dating is that radiogenic lead accumulates at a fixed rate from the time of uranium deposition until the present. The ratio of uranium/lead should indicate the length of time since the formation of the uranium minerals. Translated into typical uranium ore concentrations a 10 million year old uranium deposit of 0.20% U_3O_8

would have a radiogenic lead content of 0.00025% or 2.5 ppm Pb provided there were no losses or additions of uranium daughter products or of lead. It is hardly conceivable that uranium at 2,000 ppm would be leached, transported, and redeposited with the same efficiency as lead at 2.5 ppm.

When lead has been identified as either galena (PbS) or clausthalite (PbSe) in geo-chemical-cell occurrences, it is concentrated at the alteration boundary with selenium. This would indicate that lead and uranium both migrate in a geochemical cell and also that a geochemical cell can concentrate lead, crustal as well as radiogenic. They do not concentrate in the same zones of the cell, which makes this method of age-dating highly suspect. A large bulk sample representative of the entire ore body might come closest to giving the correct age since the commencement of mineralization. A sample taken from the zone of highest uranium values a short distance from the front may be sufficiently separated from the lead—selenium zone to permit the initial formation of uranium min-erals without contamination by radiogenic lead. This may be the case with the samples collected by Dooley et al. (1974), and would represent the true age of the mineral or the minimum age of the geochemical cell. Evidence indicates the geochemical-cell ore bodies, or segments of them, have changed or moved in the recent past and may be moving at present. Any sample can be expected to indicate the time of its formation only if no lead has been added to that sample from external sources before, during, or after uranium precipitation. True age dates are most likely to come from deposits, such as the Triassic Chinle areas, which probably were formed in one mineralizing episode and immediately isolated from conditions which would cause subsequent migration.

As discussed under "Tectonic conditions", all the western-states type uranium districts were subjected to either basin margin or basin-wide erosion in the fourth phase of devel-opment soon after sedimentation of the host rocks. The Chinle was subjected to basin-wide erosion which removed an unknown thickness of sediment before accumulation of the Upper Chinle halted the erosion and buried the remnants of channels under a blanket of mud and silt. For the Chinle uranium occurrences, this period of erosion offered the only opportunity for mineralization from non-hydrothermal sources.

The Morrison was subjected to a period of erosion prior to the advance of the Creta-ceous sea depositing the Dakota Formation. The latter rests directly on the Jackpile eroding it to a level which isolates this sand body from other channel sands of the Morrison. The Dakota rests directly on the Westwater on the north end of the Zuni uplift where the Cow Springs and Westwater also have good hydraulic continuity. The apex of the Salt Wash fan was truncated by this period of erosion. Since some or all of the Grants mineral belt host sediment was derived from a stream emanating from the vicinity of the apex of the Salt Wash fans, this pre-Dakota erosional truncation also removed the up-stream portion of the Westwater.

In the Wyoming basins, moderate folding and erosion took place between the Fort Union and Wasatch in the Powder River basin and between the Lower and Upper Battle Springs on the northern margin of the Great Divide basin. The Gas Hills and Shirley Basin districts were deeply eroded between the end of Upper Eocene sedimentation and prior to the deposition, in Oligocene, of the White River. The Wasatch in the Powder River basin also had some upstream erosion prior to White River time.

These periods of erosion soon after sedimentation of the host formation offer the best opportunity for the introduction of oxygenated water into the formation and for the introduction of elements from external sources into the cell, because the formations are exposed. The reason for the erosion could be either an increase or a decrease in stream-load capacity. In the event of an increase due to renewed uplift, the host sediment most likely would not survive. The decrease in stream-load capacity is most probable and further suggests a period of slow physical degradation and deep chemical weathering. The weathering of the granitic provenance would ultimately make the uranium and other elements mobile in an oxidizing environment available to water draining from it. The position of the recharge area of the host rock would provide direct access for the oxygenated mineral-bearing water into the geochemical cell. Under these conditions, it is unlikely that reducing conditions along the stream would be extensive or persist for long. Rainfall on the exposed host rock would supplement oxygenated water from the streams to initiate an invading oxidizing zone or geochemical cell. Harshman's (1972) genetic model of the mechanism and timing of mineralization in the Shirley Basin is similar to the ideas presented here with the major difference in time from Miocene to pre-Oligocene and thickness of cover difference of 600–100 m.[1]

From the evidence and reasoning above, it has been concluded that the period of ore-body formation was associated with the period of erosion shortly after deposition of the host rock. For some ore bodies, such as those in the Chinle and in the Laguna area, this was the only opportunity for mineralization because they were sealed from further access of oxygenated or mineralizing water and the means of further migration and ore accumulation ended until the present cycle or erosion. For most other deposits of the Colorado Plateau and Wyoming, subsequent periods of ore concentrations and migration have occurred. It can be reasonably expected that when hydrodynamic conditions permitted oxygenated water to be supplied to the geochemical cells, they responded with the redevelopment of the original processes. The present cycle of erosion is the latest period of cell migration and certainly some has taken place in recent time.

Source of mineralization

Clear identification of the source of the uranium and other metals associated with it in sandstone occurrences in Wyoming and the Colorado Plateau remains elusive.* From the uranium mining industry's experience of the last twenty years, it can be reasonably concluded that the oxidized uranium minerals are remnants of previously reduced minerals. It can also be extrapolated that no significant uranium occurrence in fluvial sandstone

---

[1] See Notes added in proof, (3), p. 152.

* Editor's note: see the chapter on conceptual models, Vol. 1, Chapter 2.

originated in the oxidized hexavalent state. These deposits are in the process of being destroyed. From this experience, it has also been learned that uranium is mobilized quite readily under the present weathering conditions. No extraordinary conditions are needed on a macroscale to accomplish the oxidation and remobilization of uranium minerals. The reprecipitation of the mobilized uranium is quite readily accomplished by reduction to the tetravalent state which can be accomplished by the reducing environment so characteristic of uranium host rock. With the exception of a period around 1950, most thought concerning the deposition of uranium has been based on these simple basic facts.

Workers prior to 1930 considered the uranium to have been precipitated with, or introduced into, the sands at the time of sedimentation. Hess (1933) postulated that distinct metalliferous provinces, containing a particular suite of metals, weathered and contributed those metals in a soluble form into local basins where subtropical vegetation was decaying slowly in warm, wet sediment. The metals accumulated in and around the plant remains by reduction of soluble ions to stable minerals as a result of reducing conditions caused by decaying vegetation.

The possibility of hydrothermal sources is ever present, but this possibility is relied upon less and less since the early 1950's. The geochemistry of uranium was so poorly known that D'Arcy George (1949) stated that uranous oxide (UO_2) is the stable oxide under high-temperature reducing conditions and uranous salts are highly unstable, being rapidly oxidized to the uranyl form and consequently not found in nature. He also stated UO_2 was an original constituent in all hypogene uranium minerals, although, as now found, most of the uranium in these minerals has been oxidized.

In a review of the geology of uranium, Everhart (1951a) described three types of uranium occurrences in sandstone: carnotite, copper–uranium, and uranium-bearing asphalt. All deposits were similar structurally and lithologically, and were in sandstone channels. Everhart (1951b) concluded that the carnotite ore bodies were formed by slight chemical change in the groundwater moving through the channel sandstone shortly after sedimentation. He attributed the other two types of occurrences, with sulfide minerals, to igneous hydrothermal solutions moving through the permeable channel sandstones.

Kerr's (1958) extensive study of mineral associations, relationships of uranium ore bodies and volcanic or other igneous activity and the alteration of the sediment, led him to the conclusion that temperatures were above those attributed to even deeply buried groundwater (hence hydrothermal solutions were the source of the uranium). The reasoning that, because a group of elements are associated in a vein or clearly igneous-related deposit, they are hypogene when found in any deposit, is not necessarily acceptable today. The alteration of bright-colored sediment to gray is now fairly well accepted as being a product of the sedimentary environment. Not even the vertical bleaching along faults and fractures is necessarily hydrothermal, because hydrogen sulfide and other natural gas can produce the bleaching. Kerr's recent work (Haji-Vassilious and Kerr, 1973) indicated that he no longer holds to the hydrothermal source for the extensive bedded deposits of the Colorado Plateau. Instead, the deposits are attributed to low-temperature (groundwater) solutions whose migration was dominantly lateral.

Gabelman (1970) considers the mineralizing fluids to be connate or groundwater or water of crystallization. This water has been heated by deformation and mobilized by differential tectonic pressures in addition to temperature gradients. The increase in temperature increases the corrosive power and ability of the water to leach mobile elements. If compression is sufficiently intense the water enters the magmatic–hydrothermal cycle, but if there is no magmatism the fluids may be termed tectonic–hydrothermal. The elements are mobilized in reverse paragenetic sequence and move down the metallo-tectonic temperatures gradients to new zones of stability. The more mobile, lower-temperature elements, such as sandstone uranium, copper, and vanadium, are flushed from the hinterland (Gabelman, 1970). Gabelman (1971) also considers the ore occurrences of the Colorado Plateau and Wyoming to be unrelated to regional paleogeographic, sedimentational, and tectonic features present at the time of sedimentation. This conclusion is diametrically opposed to the thesis of this chapter. While tectonic features may generate some or all of the conditions he proposes, these same features can generate other conditions which bear more directly on the formation of ore deposits. These other possible conditions produced by tectonic features are: increased stream gradient; increased stream volume due to orographic rainfall; changes in climate in the provenance and depositional area. The principal reason why uranium deposits are zoned about tectonic features is that the climate and depositional conditions conducive to producing a favorable uranium host rock are most likely to occur simultaneously in adjacent areas or reoccur more frequently in areas where they have previously occurred. In which case preservation of the favorable host-rock sequence commonly preserves several of these potential host rocks rather than all being eroded and destroyed together, which is the more common fate of continental sediment.

A non-hydrothermal source was proposed for the uranium in the lignites of the Dakotas. Love (1952) indicates that Denson, Bachman, and Zeller originated the theory that the uranium in the South Dakota lignites migrated downward from radioactive tuffs in the overlying White River and Arikaree Formations. Love also believes that the Powder River basin uranium deposits were formed in a similar manner. Since these tuffaceous sediments covered most of Wyoming, as well as the northern great plains, they were a potential source for the uranium deposits in the Wyoming basins. Waters and Granger (1953) determined that volcanic debris was also present in the Morrison and Chinle sediment of the Colorado Plateau. They concluded that the simple leaching of ash and precipitation of the leached uranium and vanadium by organic matter is inadequate to explain the genesis of the sandstone-type ores of the Colorado Plateau. They suggested the possibility that some and possibly most of the uranium and vanadium may have been supplied by the devitrification of volcanic ash, then reconcentrated into ore bodies by groundwater circulation caused by igneous invasion, hydrothermal activity or uplift.

Davis (1969) suggests that the bulk of the uranium in the Powder River basin deposits was derived from tuffaceous sediment with some enrichment from the arkosic host sediment as the solution passed through them in the formation of the ore deposits. Davis offers the evidence that the analysis of cores ahead of the front are only 2 ppm U, while those in altered rock several thousand feet back of the front are 6 ppm U. He also questioned the adequacy of the arkosic sediment actually traversed by the solutions (geochemical cell) to supply the known uranium.

The granitic provenance supplying the clastic material which accumulated as arkose, feldspathic, or micaceous sandstone uranium host rock is considered by some to be the source of the uranium. There is no doubt that the average granite contains sufficient uranium to provide an adequate source. The average granite contains 4 ppm uranium, which is equivalent to 40,000 tons of uranium metal (Gruner, 1956b) or 96,000,000 pounds of U_3O_8 per cubic mile. Some granites contain several times the average abundance of uranium and one of those granites is in the Granite Mountains or Sweetwater arch of central Wyoming. Masursky (1962) found 20–30 ppm uranium in these granites. Harshman (1972) indicated the eastern end of the Sweetwater arch, which supplied sediment to the Shirley Basin, contains granites with a uranium content of several ppm. Rosholt and Bartel (1969) found uranium concentrations in Granite Mountain samples ranged from 2.4 to 7.09 ppm for seven of eight samples and the eighth had 402 ppm U.

The availability of the uranium in the granites to leaching solutions is well established. Gruner (1956b) indicated that the uranium in granite was readily leachable and Harshman (1972) demonstrated that almost 1% of the uranium in granite samples was leached in a ten-hour period by a leach solvent similar to present-day Shirley Basin groundwater. The work by Szalay and Samsoni (1973) found the uranium content of granite and rhyolite is far more leachable than that of gabbro, andesite or basalt. They also found the concentration of uranium in the water attains within four to five hours an equilibrium value, due to an absorption equilibrium between the rock surface and water. Replacement of the leaching water at four-hour intervals produced repeatedly a new equilibrium. The new equilibrium concentration decreased somewhat, but the leachable uranium was not exhausted. The work of Rosholt and Bartel (1969) indicated uranium has been leached from the near-surface rock of the Granite Mountains, thus providing a major source for uranium deposits.

There are two variations of the granite-leach source idea. One is that the uranium was transported along with the sediment, probably in solution, to form a protore (Gruner, 1956b and Shockey et al., 1968). This protore has been described by Shockey as the original granitic source prepared and mixed with the other necessary ingredients (pyrite and carbonaceous material). The other variation is that the uranium was leached from the granite and introduced into the host rock either a little later or much later than the deposition of the sediment. Hess (1933), Wright (1955), Hilpert (1969), and Houston (1969) have indicated their acceptance of the granite as the direct source without being specific as to the time or the means of transportation.

However, Harshman (1972) proposes a much later time when the host rock is buried and subsequent uplift produced a change in hydraulic gradient. This change in gradient was necessary to induce the circulation of the uranium-bearing groundwater downward to the host sands where it moved laterally through the permeable zones. Erosion of the uplifted area may have subsequently permitted easier, more direct access for the mineralizing water which may have derived its uranium from both the granite and the overlying tuffaceous sediment.

These two variations constitute the "granite leach" school, but most likely there is a combination of the two variations from almost one extreme to the other. From the standpoint of simplicity, the conversion of uranium-rich granite into a readily leachable sediment (protore) in which the uranium is contained interstitially as uraninite and coffinite or possibly as urano-organic compounds and absorbed on woody or humic substances is the preferred source. Uranium within refractory numerals, such as monazite or detrital grains of arkosic sands, is not considered a potential source. It has not been adequately established that the sediment contains enough uranium to provide the necessary supply. The uranium available within the protore leached by the geochemical cell is the maximum available, if this is considered the only source. The calculations of Gruner (1956b) and Helgeson (1967) for the metals available do not apply to the geochemical-cell situation, because there is a finite, although large, volume of leached protore within the cell at any time.

Davis (1969) and Harshman (1972) present information that the uranium content of the unaltered sediment ahead of the front of a geochemical cell is less than in the altered interior of the cell, a condition which would dissipate rather than accumulate an ore body. There is a relationship between the source of uranium and the time of mineralization for all sources except the protore source. If the host rock is deeply buried and mineralizing solution has limited access, the period of mineralization would be limited to those times when uplift and erosion increases the accessibility from the granitic or volcanic sources. Mineralization from the volcanic sources would be further limited to those periods subsequent to the deposition of the volcanic debris.

The contribution of elements from volcanic sources which were transported in solution into the geochemical cell cannot be denied: however, the mechanics of transportation are more complex. They will be concentrated by a cell if they are introduced with oxygen in a form available for biologic processes. This statement can also be made of elements from any source. Once the epigenetic minerals had been accumulated by the cell, they would continue to migrate with it. Minerals or elements in the host sediment which can be concentrated by the cell would continue to be accumulated as it migrates and expands. With these possibilities there is no way to exclude any of the possible sources. Davis (1969) and Harshman (1972) accept multiple sources: Davis from the volcanics and the arkosic host rock but does not comment on the granite of the mountain range; Harshman's source is the granite of the mountain range supplemented by possible additions from the volcanics overlying the basin, but denies the possibility of the sediment contributing to the ore.

Notwithstanding the problems of producing ore bodies by the leaching of the uranium from the host rock, there is a substantial number of supporters for this source. Melin

(1964), Rackley et al. (1968), Shockey et al. (1968) and Anderson (1969) advocate the leaching of the uranium from the host sediment for the source of Wyoming deposits. Gruner (1956b), Shawe (1956), and Shawe et al. (1959) advocate the uranium contained within the host rock as a source for the uranium deposits of the Uravan mineral belt and possibly other areas of the Colorado Plateau. Rapaport (1963) indicated the uranium deposits in the Ambrosia Lake area, New Mexico, were derived from the host sediment, and a similar view is held by Moench and Schlee (1967) for the deposits at Laguna, New Mexico. Rackley et al. (1968) calculated that the volume of the geochemical cell of the Gas Hills could have accumulated 400 million pounds of U_3O_8, if 2 ppm were leached and concentrated by the cell, an amount of only half the average crustal abundance and possibly only 10% of the uranium in the granite from which the arkose is derived. They also calculated on the same basis that the Grants mineral belt could contain over two billion pounds of U_3O_8 on the margins of the geochemical cell.

The source of uranium is one of the facets of the formation of uranium deposits that obviously needs much more research. If the tuffaceous sediment is considered the source, then the search for new deposits must be limited to areas of volcanic activity. If the granites are considered to be the source, then the search can be broadened to include any arkose or feldspathic sandstone. The condition of weathering and erosion may play an important role in making the uranium available for the development of ore bodies and some comments on this subject are given below.

There is one essential ingredient of all the significant uranium occurrences, and that is "ground preparation" of the host rock. This "ground preparation" is the development of a reducing environment, with carbonaceous material and pyrite, strong enough to resist the invasion of oxidizing solutions in a manner which permits the maintenance of reasonably sharp boundaries between the two environments. Poorly developed reducing conditions permit massive invasion by oxidizing conditions in which local reduction centers may accumulate minerals for a short period before they are destroyed by the same solutions that mineralized them.

The study of the tectonic and sedimentary history, as outlined earlier, of all the districts leads to the conclusion that mineralization occurred as a result of the development of geochemical cells during the erosion of portions of the depositional basins relatively soon after the deposition of the host rock. This erosion takes place during the fourth phase of development, as described earlier in "Tectonic condition". During this period of erosion, the physical relation between the granite source area and the recharge area of the uranium host sequence was well suited for the direct transportation of uranium-bearing solutions from the source area into the geochemical cell. The erosion within the basin provided the hydrodynamic gradient which permitted the geochemical cell host sequence to accept water from the streams in the recharge area. Weathering and chemical conditions were probably near optimum for the oxidation and dissolution of uranium from the granitic rock, or from any other source of leachable uranium, in the drainage area. This direct transportation of uranium-bearing solutions from the sediment-source area into the groundwater recharge area of the host sequence would occur under well oxygenated conditions — conditions under which hexavalent uranium is readily mobile.

This unfortunately does not clearly establish a source because there are three potential sources available in all areas: the granitic rock of the source area; the host sediment; and, some intrabasinal volcanic material.

The behavior of uranium in the weathering and erosion processes of a weathering mantle or crust may play a significant role in the formation of uranium deposits. Samama (1973) states that continental weathering and erosion processes influence the nature of sedimentary supply and the nature and geochemistry of the sediment. Numerous economic concentrations of lead, zinc, copper, vanadium, or uranium are found in formations of continental facies of the "sandstone type". These are characterized by the association of a terrigenous residual phase cemented by a chemical phase, unstable in surface conditions, which contains heavy metals as sulfides or oxides (Samama, 1973). Perel'man (1967) indicates the processes of weathering are: (1) comminution of rocks and minerals; leading to (2) a decrease in density; (3) an increase in porosity; (4) an increased dispersion of the chemical elements; and (5) aquatic migrants are removed. Weathering is relatively slight in water-bearing strata and disappears entirely with depth. However, the processes of leaching, cementation, and recrystallization are common in all water-bearing strata and intensify with depth (Perel'man, 1967).

Because of the difference between the behavior of an element at the crystal level (mobile or immobile) and its behavior on a regional or continental level, Samama (1973) introduces the concept of migrating elements and residual elements. Under some weathering processes an element may be a residual element, but the weathering processes may change with time causing the elements previously accumulated to be eliminated, thus causing the weathering cover to act as a very efficient separating filter. A continental area, both rich in a chemical element and weathered under conditions concentrating that element, can give rise to a really important metalliferous supply to the basin, and induced in appropriate sedimentary conditions, lead to significant ore deposits (Samama, 1973). The possibility that processes of these types have influenced the accumulation of uranium deposits is great enough to warrant further investigations.

Samama's (1973) work on weathering profiles indicates uranium is accumulated by allitization weathering processes and is eliminated by the bisiallitization processes. Perel'man (1967) partially confirms this indirectly by the sorption of uranium by colloidal hydroxides of aluminum and iron which forms under hot humid climates or allitization weathering processes. He also indicates in the weathering of siliceous rocks in temperate climates, that uranium has a strong migrational intensity in an oxidizing environment.

GENETIC MODEL

The preceding review of the literature concerning the various aspects of the origin of the western-states type uranium mineralization may leave the reader with an unclear impression of the central thesis of this chapter. The concept of a series of simple related processes which produce uranium ore bodies is somewhat contrary to traditional ideas of ore formation. To present this concept as concisely as possible, a genetic model is used to summarize and tie together these processes.

The model, of necessity, began with an uplift which uncovered a granitic source area and increased the capacity of the stream, draining the uplift, to transport the granitic debris into an adjacent depositional area. Sediment was transported by braided streams on alluvial fans which merged into flood plains, on which the stream patterns changed to meandering. Climatic conditions were warm to hot and seasonally humid with natural irrigation supplementing the dry-season rainfall. Abundant vegetation grew in the depositional area and the plants and animals burrowed and mixed the sediment. Frequent reworking by the streams incorporated sufficient organic material in the sediment to produce reducing conditions by its decay. The sands deposited under these conditions were organic-rich, pyritic, light- to dark-gray and the clay deposits were light- to medium-gray or green, pyritic and commonly carbonaceous (the pyrite being of diagenetic origin). These conditions provided the "ground preparation" prerequisite for the subsequent mineralization.

In the weathering of the granite, the minute uranium-mineral grains interstitial to the common rock-forming minerals were oxidized and leached well in advance of the development of a soil profile. This supplied uranium to ground- and surface-water well before that specific portion of the granite was physically eroded. Because the supply of granite is typically very large, the granitic mass may continue to supply uranium to the depositional basin when physical erosion is very slow. The uranium released by weathering migrated through the basin and was lost to the sea unless it came into contact with reducing conditions present in the organic-rich sediment a short distance beneath the sediment—water interface, in which case it enriched the sediment.

In the late stage of erosion of the source area, the relative increase in silt and clay caused the host sands to be overlapped by a confining cover of less permeable sediment. When sediment supply to the depositional area was less than stream capacity, erosion began in the depositional area. Exposure of the host sediment to oxidizing conditions at the surface permitted an invasion of the reduced sediment by oxygenated water. This water was derived, in part, from the granitic mountain core and carried trace amounts of uranium and other elements mobile in an oxidizing environment. In some cases this period of erosion almost destroyed the entire favorable host, the remnants of which accumulated uranium from the oxidation and erosion of the overlying sediment.

In other cases, the oxidizing environment invaded the reduced sediment for considerable distances from the eroded basin margins and far below the static water table. This caused destruction of carbonaceous material, oxidation of the diagenetic pyrite and accumulation of uranium and other susceptible metals from both the water and from the sediment being invaded. The metals were concentrated in a wave or front just ahead of the invading oxidizing environment. The invading oxidation was a dynamic, expanding process which moved through the permeable zones until its dimensions measured miles in areal extent and hundreds of feet in thickness. This oxidizing invasion is a geochemical cell which had a sharply defined boundary produced by biochemically controlled changes in physical and chemical conditions. Oxygenated water, aided by the bacteria *Thiobacillus ferrooxidans* oxidized pyrite to produce sulfuric acid and ferric sulfate, a strong oxidizer, which leached uranium and other susceptible elements. In the reducing part of the cell, anaerobic bacteria, including the sulfate reducer *Desulfovibrio,* consumed the organic material in the sediment and the sulfates from the oxidizing area, to produce hydrogen, hydrogen sulfide, and a mildly alkaline, strongly reducing environment which precipitated pyrite, uranium and other metals on the front.

The physical development of a geochemical cell began in the upstream area of the fluvial system near the margin of the basin. The area in which the oxygenated water invaded the reduced, organic pyritic sediment and established an oxidizing environment can be considered a point source in the overall scale of the geochemical cell which resulted. From this small beginning, the cell grew by the energy derived from the oxidation of the oxidizable constituents of the reduced sediment. Gradually expanding from the original point of beginning, the cell developed preferentially down the hydrostatic gradient and in general followed the thicker more permeable portions of the fluvial system. The continued growth of the cell caused it to expand further down the hydrostatic gradient and also laterally from the central permeable portion of the host sequence into the thinner fine-grained units along its margins. Carbonaceous material and pyrite tend to be more abundant along these margins, so the cell was retarded by both the decrease in permeability and the increase in reactive material in the sediment.

The development of the mineralization on the margin of the cell began as soon as the cell developed an Eh gradient across the front which would act as a reduction barrier for the elements mobile in an oxidizing environment. The size of the cell may have been as little as a few meters long and probably not more than a few hundred meters long. Once the reduction barrier or Eh gradient was established, the mineralization began to accumulate. A unit of uranium carried by the oxygenated water from the weathering granitic core of the mountain (or any other external source) was added to a unit of uranium intrinsic to the sediment. As the cell continued to grow, other units of external uranium were added to adjacent intrinsic units. However, as the oxidizing environment expands at the expense of the reduced environment, the previous site of uranium deposition was overrun by the oxidizing zone and the uranium was oxidized and remobilized. The remobilized elements were moved across the reduction barrier again and were reprecipitated at a new site where other units from external and intrinsic sources had been previously deposited. Through many repetitions of this process the size of the mineralized body slowly grew from the small beginning to the ore bodies now being produced.

Erosion of the strata covering the host formation tended to accelerate growth of the cell by enlarging the surface area exposed to recharge. It is important to understand that the cell originates essentially at a point and expands to form a continuous, three-dimensional, finite body. As the geochemical cell moved farther through the host, the ore bodies along its margin increased in size and grade. The cell migrated under and around shale parting, but always maintained its continuous finite body. Islands of unaltered sand may be surrounded by the cell just as shales are enveloped by it. The reverse is never true; the cell does not form islands of alteration in the unaltered rock.

The mineralization on the margin of the cell is far from uniform. There is a tendency for the thicker, higher-grade margins of the cell to have preferred orientations. This suggests that there is a direction of groundwater flow or cell movement and those segments of the cell perpendicular to that direction accumulate more mineralization than those segments parallel to it. This is most noticeable in plan view, but the same kind of non-uniformity is also true in cross-section views.

Migration of the cell was controlled by the permeability of the sandstone and by availability of carbon and pyrite. The cell advanced faster in the more permeable zones and was retarded in zones of reduced permeability and areas of greater pyrite and carbon content. The position of the geochemical cell and the mineral fronts on its margins was controlled by the initial sedimentary pattern and conditions. When the hydrodynamic system was disrupted and the oxygen supply was cut off, the invasion stopped. If the conditions permitted a renewal of the supply of oxygen to the front, they resumed expansion.

DISCUSSION

In recent years there has been a growing awareness that the uranium deposits described herein as the western-states type have much more in common than originally thought. Although old ideas and terms "die hard", new work and new ideas filter into the professional working knowledge to replace older concepts which cannot meet the test of scientific verification. The mineralization of the roll or geochemical-cell deposits, regardless of their physical shape, has been singled out as the most important process in the series of events leading to the formation of a uranium deposit and some work has been done on the subject. Harshman (1972) made an extensive study of the mineralogy and trace-element distribution of the Shirley basin ore bodies. Harshman (1974) has extended these studies to other uranium-producing areas, including Texas, from which he has established limits on the ore-forming fluids. The transporting solution was alkaline and oxidizing although he advocates a drop in pH, to acidic levels, from the oxidation of pyrite in the ore body in the vicinity of the front. The deposition of the ore is a result of a reduction in the Eh of the transporting fluid. The reductant is probably hydrogen sulfide of biogenic origin (Harshman, 1972).

Harshman (1974) provides a Eh—pH diagram showing the separation between oxidized and reduced species of the ore and related trace elements of a geochemical cell. This diagram clearly indicates the increasingly lower Eh values required by the various elements from the roll front into the reducing side of the cell. Another equally important aspect of the diagram is the fact that the reverse is also true; that is, the elements are arranged according to their increasing stability in an oxidizing environment. This serves to re-emphasize Harshman's (1972) earlier statement that there are a series of nested and commonly overlapping frontal zones in which each of the elements are concentrated. The front normally indicated in discussions of roll-front geology is the contact between the zone of oxidized iron minerals and the carbonaceous pyrite zone at or near the zone of uranium concentration.

Granger and Warren (1969) have proposed a process whereby the partial oxidation of sulfide minerals produces unstable soluble sulfur species at the front. These are moved promptly into the reducing environment, where they spontaneously undergo decomposition by disproportionation, a reaction in which part is oxidized and part is reduced. The end-products are a mixture of an inert oxidizing agent and active reducing agents. The laboratory experiments by Granger and Warren (1969) have produced some very interesting results, and it is hoped that they ultimately will produce some definitive answers. The principal purpose of this work was to establish an inorganic process that could produce a well-defined reduction barrier without assistance from bacteria. Although the results may prove useful, the basic assumptions are not necessarily valid, particularly the assumption that the scattered organic fragments could not provide nutrients uniformly along the roll front.

Cheney and Tramell (1973) consider the diagenetic formation of bacterial pyrite as ground preparation for the later and unrelated formation of roll ore bodies. Their "possible" evidence for their support of a non-biogenic origin of the roll ore bodies is the "inference" that the unaltered rock through which the roll is passing has nonpyritic areas. The nonpyritic areas cause the dissipation of the ore as the altered zone moved through it and became juxtaposed on the unaltered nonpyritic area (Cheney and Trammell, 1973). Unfortunately there are no known observations which support the inference that the host rock has major (more than a few meters wide) nonpyritic areas. On the contrary, the uranium host beds are characterized by a consistent minimum amount of pyrite with some locally enriched zones in areas of abundant carbonaceous material.

It cannot be determined just what is meant by the juxtaposition of the altered (IBG)* and unaltered (EBG)* areas, but it is an inherent part of the geochemical-cell concept that it moves at a rate determined by the reactive constituents of the rock so that pyrite and/ or carbon-poor areas would be traversed relatively quickly. The geochemical cell does not develop holes in its exterior reaction zone just as inflating balloons do not have holes. Without the nonpyrite areas neither of Cheney and Trammell's (1973) "geologic evidence" are valid. As mentioned heretofore, the weakly or nonmineralized portions of a geochemical cell appear to be related to the direction of cell movement.

---

* IBG = interior barren ground, EBG = exterior barren ground.

Granger and Warren (1974) have modified their earlier ideas somewhat to explain the generation of the unstable soluble sulfur species and the zonation of the alteration near the ore. They cite Kashirtseva (1964) for evidence of siderite and elemental sulfur in a Russian uranium occurrence as evidence on which to develop their process. Berner (1973) indicates siderite and/or glauconite will be stable if the concentration of sulfide ions is low, which makes the development of a western-states type uranium deposit dissimilar to the deposit Kashirtseva describes. Kashirtseva (1964) shows in his fig. 6 that the distribution of pyrite is restricted to the immediate vicinity of the roll which is overlapped by a much more extensive siderite zone. Furthermore he concludes: "Most likely it is rocks with predominantly sulfide iron that shows the steepest redox-potential gradient, which promotes a considerable uranium accumulation. Conversely, rock with predominantly carbonate iron probably are unfavorable for uranium accumulation" (Kashirtseva, 1964, pp. 44–45).

In the Shirley Basin and in the Powder River basin ore bodies, hematite and calcite are found together, but siderite is not known to be associated with the ore. Granger and Warren (1974) offer no evidence that either siderite or elemental sulfur are present in the districts they describe, and the acceptance of their proposed processes should be withheld until more evidence is offered.

Warren (1971) offers another line of evidence to support the chemical origin of the ore-stage pyrite and uranium accumulation in a roll-type uranium deposit. He proposes that a biogenic origin of the pyrite would cause a much larger volume of pyrite in the ore bodies than is now found, whereas the chemical origin would produce the volume found in the deposits. There is, however, one facet of this reaction which was not considered. The formation of pyrite is dependent upon the availability of reactive iron (Berner, 1973), as well as sulfide in the solution. The geochemical cell throws off iron by the hydrolysis of ferric sulfate to sulfuric acid and the insoluble ferric hydroxide as shown in Fig. 16. Even if the validity of that reaction is questioned, the iron content of the altered area is sufficient to indicate much of the iron is retained there. Warren (1972) repeats the same argument based on sulfur-isotope considerations for chemical disproportionation as the means of ore-body formation and the same limit of available reactive iron also applies to this argument.

Gruner's (1956b) multiple migration—accretion hypothesis has been accepted by many uranium geologists and the evidence he presented has guided much of the thinking leading up to recent, more comprehensive concepts of uranium ore deposition. Gruner summarized his ideas from knowledge of most of the presently known uranium districts which had been discovered and were partly explored or in production at the time. Mineralogic, geologic, and geochemical observations and experiments were considered to establish a conceptual model of sandstone-type uranium deposits. Gruner's hypothesis called for the accumulation of uranium and other metals in a swamp or peat bog by drainage from higher ground. Each swamp accumulated most metals present in its drainage basin. After burial and renewed erosion of the swamp the metals were oxidized and remobilized as the swamp was destroyed by erosion, and surface waters transported the metals to enrich the next swamp. The metals were accumulated in another swamp from the destruction of this and perhaps other swamps, and from igneous and tuffaceous rocks within its drainage basin. "Each oxidation–solution–migration–precipitation cycle adds to the enrichment of the last stage of accretion" (Gruner, 1956b).

If one substitutes the physical erosion of a swamp or bog for the oxidation and alteration in place of sandstones originally deposited in a reducing – and certainly swamp like – environment, Gruner's hypothesis would adequately explain the concentration of disseminated minerals into ore bodies. This has been the interpretation many workers have placed on this hypothesis and perhaps Gruner intended this.

TOPICS FOR FUTURE RESEARCH

Creative research is required to transform the empirical art of uranium geology into the science needed to provide the resources for the future. Since economic geologists and students of ore deposits have lost hydrothermal solutions as a "magic wand" or crutch to explain the origin of many strata-bound ore deposits, it becomes necessary to put genesis in context with the overall sedimentary rock-forming process. Fortunately "giant steps" are being made in the knowledge of the physical processes of sedimentation, but equally large steps are required in the knowledge of the biological and chemical processes which are an inseparable part of the sedimentary rock and strata-bound ore-forming processes.

In this chapter five topics for future research have been suggested. These are:

(1) The role of bacteria in the formation of ore bodies as distinguished from ground preparation.*

(2) The means of recognition of geochemical alteration in outcrop and in subsurface samples.

(3) Further definition of the time of mineralization in relation to other geologic events as well as absolute age.

(4) What is the source or sources of the mineralization?**

(5) What is the behavior of uranium in weathering and erosion in various climates?

NOTES ADDED IN PROOF

(1) Childers (1974) has interpreted the term "geochemical cell" to refer to a geometric shape. It was never been intended to denote a shape but rather a process of alteration and mineralization which can conform to any shape determined by the sediment.

---

* Editor's note: see the chapter by Trudinger on bacterial processes, Vol. 2, Chapter 6.
** Editor's note: see the contribution by the editor on conceptual models, Vol. 1, Chapter 2.

(2) Childers (1974) proposes that the alteration and mineralization developed while the host sediment was either exposed at the surface or only slightly buried. He does not consider the question of erosion but the change from a wet to a dry climate almost implies that erosion of the host sediment may take place with the oxidation and mineralization.

(3) Childers (1974) offers the evidence that mineralization of Eocene sediment in the Cyclone Rim area of the Great Divide Basin of Wyoming is probably older than the Middle Oligocene. This evidence is the faulting of mineralization by faults which were active during the deposition of the Oligocene White River formation as determined by differences in thickness of that formation in various faulted segments.

REFERENCES

Adams, S.S., Curtis, H.S. and Hafen, P.L., 1974. Alteration of detrital magnetite and ilmenite in uranium-bearing continental sandstones of the Morrison Formation, northwest New Mexico. *I.A.E.A. Symp. Form. Uranium Ore Deposits, May 6–10, 1974, Athens, Greece.*

Adler, H.H., 1964. The conceptual uranium ore roll and its significance in uranium exploration. *Econ. Geol.,* 59: 46–53.

Adler, H.H., 1970. Interpretation of color relations in sandstone as a guide to uranium exploration and ore genesis. In: *Uranium Exploration Geology.* International Atomic Energy Agency, Vienna, pp. 331–344.

Adler, H.H., 1974. Concepts of uranium-ore formation in reducing environments in sandstones and other sediments. *I.A.E.A. Symp. Form. Urianium Ore Deposits, May 6–10, 1974, Athens, Greece.*

Allen, J.R.L., 1970. *Physical Process of Sedimentation.* American Elsevier, New York, N.Y., 248 pp.

Anderson, D.C., 1969. Uranium deposits of the Gas Hills. *Univ. Wyo. Contrib. Geol.,* 8 (2, part 1): 93–103.

Austin, S.R., 1970. Some patterns of sulfur isotope distribution in uranium deposits. *Wyo. Geol. Assoc. Earth Sci. Bull.,* 3 (2): 5–22.

Baas Becking, L.G.M. and Moore, D., 1961. Biogenic sulfides. *Econ. Geol.,* 56: 259–272.

Bailey, R.V., 1969. Uranium deposits in the Great Divide basin–Crooks Gap area, Fremont and Sweetwater counties, Wyoming. *Univ. Wyo. Contrib. Geol.,* 8 (2, part 1): 105–120.

Barthel, F.H., 1974. Review of uranium occurrences in Permian sediments in Europe with special reference to uranium mineralization in Permian sandstone. *I.A.E.A. Symp. Form. Uranium Ore Deposits, May 6–10, 1974, Athens, Greece.*

Bernard, H.A. and Major Jr., C.F., 1963. Recent meanderbelt deposits of the Brazos River: an alluvial "sand" model. *Am. Assoc. Pet. Geol. Bull.,* 47: 350 pp.

Bernard, H.A., Major Jr., C.F., Parrott, B.S. and LeBlanc Sr., R.J., 1970. Recent sediments of southeast Texas. A field guide to the Brazos alluvial and deltaic plains and the Galveston barrier island complex. *Univ. Tex. Bur. Econ. Geol. Guideb.,* 11: 131 pp.

Berner, R.A., 1973. Pyrite formation in the oceans. In: *Proc. Symp. Hydrogeochemistry and Biogeochemistry, Tokyo, 1970.* The Clarke Company, Washington, D.C., 1: 402–417.

Botinelly, Th. and Fischer, R.P., 1959. Mineralogy and geology of the Rifle and Garfield mines, Garfield County, Colorado. *U.S. Geol. Surv. Prof. Pap.,* 320: 213–218.

Brown Jr., L.F., 1973. Cratonic basins, terrigenous clastic models. *Univ. Tex. Bur. Econ. Geol. Guideb.,* 14: 10–30 pp.

Cheney, E.S. and Jensen, M.L., 1966. Stable isotopic geology of the Gas Hills, Wyoming, uranium district. *Econ. Geol.,* 61: 44–71.

Cheney, E.S. and Trammell, J.W., 1973. Isotopic evidence for inorganic precipitation of uranium roll ore bodies. *Am. Assoc. Pet. Geol. Bull.,* 57 (7): 1297–1304.

Childers, M.O., 1974. Uranium occurrences in Upper Cretaceous and Tertiary Strata of Wyoming and northern Colorado. *Mt. Geol.*, 11 (4): 131–147.

Coffin, R.C., 1921. Radium, uranium, and vanadium deposits of southwestern Colorado. *Colo. Geol. Surv. Bull.*, 16.

Coleman, J.M., 1969. Bramaputra River: channel processes and sedimentation. *Sediment. Geol.*, 3 (2/3): 129–239.

Coleman, J.M., 1971. Processes in river systems and their relation to the variability observed in modern deltas: Casper, Wyoming. *Wyo. Geol. Assoc. Contin. Educ. Lect.*, Feb. 9–11, unpublished.

Dahl, A.R., and Hagmaier, J.R., 1974. Genesis and characteristics of the southern Powder River basin uranium deposits, Wyoming, U.S.A. *I.A.E.A. Symp. Form. Uranium Ore Deposits, May 6–10, 1974, Athens, Greece.*

D'Arcy, G., 1949. Mineralogy of Uranium and Thorium Bearing Minerals. *U.S. A.E.C. RMO*, 563: 198 pp.

Davis, J.F., 1969. Uranium deposits of the Powder River basin. *Univ. Wyo. Contrib. Geol.*, 8 (2, part 1): 131–141.

Denson, N.M. and Gill, J.R., 1956. Uranium-bearing lignite and its relation to volcanic tuff in eastern Montana and North Dakota. *U.S. Geol. Surv. Prof. Pap.*, 300: 413–418.

Dietz, R.S. and Holden, J.C., 1970. The breakup of Panagaea. *Sci. Am.*, Oct. 1970. Reprinted in: *Continents Adrift.* Freeman, San Fancisco, Calif., pp. 102–113.

Dodd, Philip H., 1956. Examples of uranium deposits in the Upper Jurassic Morrison Formation of the Colorado Plateau. *U.S. Geol. Surv. Prof. Pap.*, 300: 243–262.

Doeglas, D.J., 1962. The structure of sedimentary deposits of braided rivers. *Sedimentology*, 1: 167–190.

Dooley Jr., J.R., Granger, H.C. and Rosholt, J.N., 1966. Uranium-234 fractionation in the sandstone-type uranium deposits of the Ambrosia Lake district, New Mexico. *Econ. Geol.*, 61 (8): 1362–1382.

Dooley Jr., J.R., Harshman, E.N. and Rosholt, J.N., 1974. Uranium–lead ages of the uranium deposits of the Gas Hills and Shirley Basin, Wyoming. *Econ. Geol.*, 69 (4): 527–531.

Douros, J.D., 1967. The relationship of microorganisms to uranium and other mineral deposits. *U.S. A.E.C. Open-File Rep.*, 51 pp.

Eargle, D.H. and Weeks, A.M.D., 1973. Geologic relations among uranium deposits, south Texas, Coastal Plain region, U.S.A. In: G.C. Amstutz and A.J. Bernard (Editors), *Ores in Sediments.* Springer, New York, N.Y., Series A, number 3.

Everhart, D.L., 1951a. Geology of uranium deposits – a condensed version. *U.S. A.E.C. Rep. RMO*, 732: 33 pp.

Everhart, D.L., 1951b. *Uranium Deposits in Sedimentary Formations of Triassic and Jurassic Age.* Am. Assoc. Pet. Geol. Ann. Meet., St. Louis, Mo., April 26, 1951, 7 pp., unpublished.

Fischer, R.P., 1937. Sedimentary deposits of copper, vanadium–uranium, and silver in southwestern United States. *Econ. Geol.*, 32: 906–951.

Fischer, R.P., 1942. Vanadium deposits of Colorado and Utah. *U.S. Geol. Surv. Bull.*, 936-P.

Fischer, R.P., 1970. Similarities, differences, and some genetic problems of the Wyoming and Colorado Plateau types of uranium deposits in sandstone. *Econ. Geol.*, 65: 778–784.

Fischer, R.P., 1974. Exploration guides to new uranium districts and belts. *Econ. Geol.* 69 (3): 362–376.

Fischer, R.P. and Hilpert, L.S., 1952. Geology of the Uravan mineral belt: *U.S. Geol. Surv. Bull.*, 988-A.

Fisher, W.L. and Brown Jr., L.F., 1972. Clastic depositional systems – A genetic approach to facies analyses (annotated outline and bibliography). *Univ. Tex. Bur. Econ. Geol.*, 211 pp.

Gabelman, J.W., 1970. Metallotectonic Control of Uranium Distribution. In: *Uranium Exploration Geology.* International Atomic Energy Agency, Vienna, pp. 187–204.

Gabelman, J.W., 1971. Sedimentology and uranium prospecting. *Sediment. Geol.*, 6 (3): 145–186.

Garrels, R.M., Larsen 3rd, E.S., Pommer, A.M. and Coleman, R.G., 1959. Detailed chemical and mineralogical relations in two vanadium–uranium ores. *U.S. Geol. Surv. Prof. Pap.*, 320: 165–184.

Germanov, A.N., 1958. Some regularities of uranium distribution in underground waters. In: *Proc. United Nations International Conference on the Peaceful Uses of Atomic Energy, 2nd, Survey of Raw Material Resources.* Volume 2.

Germanov, A.N., 1960. Main genetic features of some infiltration-type hydrothermal uranium deposits. *Akad. Nauk S.S.S.R. Izv. Ser. Geol.*, 8: 75–89.

Glennie, K.W., 1970. *Desert Sedimentary Environments. Develop. Sedimentol.*, 14, Elsevier Amsterdam, 222 pp.

Gould, W., Smith, R.B., Metzger, S.P. and Melancon, P.E., 1963. Geology of the Homestake–Sapin uranium deposits, Ambrosia Lake area. *N. M. Bur. Min. Miner. Resour. Mem.*, 15: 66–71.

Granger, H.C. and Warren, C.G., 1969. Unstable sulfur compounds and the origin of roll-type uranium deposits. *Econ. Geol.*, 64: 160–171.

Granger, H.C. and Warren, C.G., 1974. Zoning in the altered tongue associated with roll-type uranium deposits. *I.A.E.A. Symp. Uranium Ore Deposits, May 6–10, 1974, Athens, Greece.*

Granger, H.C., Santos, E.S., Dean, B.G. and Moore, F.B., 1961. Sandstone-type uranium deposits at Ambrosia Lake, New Mexico – an interim report. *Econ. Geol.*, 56 (7): 1179–1210.

Gruner, J.W., 1956a. A comparison of black uranium ore deposits in Utah, New Mexico, and Wyoming. *U.S. Geol. Surv. Prof. Pap.*, 300: 203–205.

Gruner, J.W., 1956b. Concentration of uranium in sediments by multiple migration–accretion. *Econ. Geol.*, 51 (6): 495–520.

Grutt, E.W., 1957. Environment of some Wyoming uranium deposits. In: *Nuclear Engineering and Science Conference, 2nd, March 11–14, 1957.* The American Society of Mechanical Engineers, New York, N.Y., 12 pp.

Grutt Jr., E.W., 1972. Prospecting criteria for sandstone-type uranium deposits. In: *Uranium Prospecting Handbook.* Inst. Min. Metall. Trans., London, pp. 47–76.

Haji-Vassilious, A. and Kerr, P.F., 1973. Analytic data on nature of urano-organic deposits. *Am. Assoc. Pet. Geol. Bull.*, 57 (7): 1291–1296.

Ham, W.E. and Johnson, K.S., 1964. Copper deposits in permian shale, Creta Area. *Okla. Geol. Surv. Circ.*, 64: 32 pp.

Harshman, E.N., 1966. Genetic implications of some elements associated with uranium deposits, Shirley basin, Wyoming. *U.S. Geol. Surv. Prof. Pap.*, 550C: C167–C173.

Harshman, E.N., 1970. Uranium ore rolls in the United States. In: *Uranium Exploration Geology.* International Atomic Energy Agency, Vienna, pp. 219–232.

Harshman, E.N., 1972. Geology and uranium deposits, Shirley basin area, Wyoming. *U.S. Geol. Surv. Prof. Pap.*, 745: 82 pp.

Harshman, E.N., 1974. Distribution of elements in some roll-type uranium deposits. *I.A.E.A. Symp. Form. Uranium Ore Deposits, May 6–10, 1974, Athens, Greece.*

Helgeson, H.C., 1967. Silicate metamorphism in sediments and the genesis of hydrothermal ore solutions. *Econ. Geol. Monogr.*, 3: 333–342.

Hem, J.D., 1970. Study and interpretation of the chemical characteristics of natural water. *U.S. Geol. Surv. Water Supply Pap.*, 1473: 363 pp., 2nd ed.

Hess, F.L., 1933. Uranium, vanadium, radium, gold, silver, and molybdenum sedimentary deposits. In: *Ore Deposits of the Western States.* AIME, New York, N.Y., pp. 450–481.

Hilpert, L.S., 1969. Uranium resources of northwestern New Mexico. *U.S. Geol. Surv. Prof. Pap.*, 603: 166 pp.

Houston, R.S., 1969. Aspects of the geologic history of Wyoming related to the formation of uranium deposits. *Univ. Wyo. Contrib. Geol.*, 8: (2, part 1): 67–79.

Jensen, M.L., 1958. Sulfur isotopes and the origin of sandstone-type uranium deposits. *Econ. Geol.*, 53: 598–616.

Jensen, M.L., 1963. Sulfur isotopes and biogenic origin of uraniferous deposits of the Grants and Laguna districts. *N.M. Bur. Min. Miner. Resour. Mem.*, 15: 182–190.

Jobin, D.A., 1962. Relation of the transmissive character of the sedimentary rocks of the Colorado Plateau to the distribution of uranium deposits. *U.S. Geol. Surv. Bull.*, 1124: 151 pp.

Jones, G.E. and Starkey, R.L., 1962. Some necessary conditions for fractionation of stable isotopes of sulfur by *Desulfovibrio desulfuricans*. In: *Biogeochemistry of Sulfur Isotopes – Symposium.* Yale University, Department of Geology, New Haven, Conn., pp. 61–79.

Kashirtseva, M.F., 1964. Mineral and geochemical zonation of infiltration uranium ores. *Sov. Geol.,* 10: 51–65.

Kerr, P.F., 1958. Uranium emplacement in the Colorado Plateau. *Geol. Soc. Am. Bull.,* 69 (9): 1075–1112.

King, J.W. and Austin, S.R., 1965. *Some Characteristics of Roll-type Uranium Deposits at Gas Hills, Wyoming.* U.S. A.E.C. Resour. Appraisal Branch, Prod. Eval. Div., Grand Junction, Colo., 40 pp.

Kuznetsov, S.I., Ivanov, M.V. and Lyalikova, N.N., 1963. *Introduction to Geological Microbiology.* McGraw-Hill, New York, N.Y. 252 pp., translated from the Russian.

Laverty, R.A., Ashwill, W.R., Chenoweth, W.L. and Norton, D.L., 1963. Ore processes. *N.M. Bur. Min. Miner. Resour. Mem.,* 15: 191–204.

Leopold, L.B., Wolman, M.G. and Miller J.P., 1964. *Fluvial Processes in Geomorphology.* Freeman, San Francisco, Calif., 522 pp.

Lisitsyn, A.K. and Kuznetsova, E.C., 1967. Role of microorganisms in development of geochemical reduction barriers where limonitization bedded zones wedge-out. *Intern. Geol. Rev.,* 9: 1180–1191.

Love, J.D., 1952. Preliminary report on uranium deposits in the Pumpkin Buttes area, Powder River basin, Wyoming. *U.S. Geol. Surv. Circ.,* 176: 37 pp.

Love, L.G., 1964. Early diagenetic pyrite in fine-grained sediments and the genesis of sulfide ores. In: G.C. Amstutz (Editor), *Sedimentology and Ore Genesis. Develop. Sedimentol.,* 2. Elsevier, Amsterdam, pp. 11–17.

Love, L.G., 1967. Diagenesis and the origin of the ores. *Econ. Geol. Monogr.,* 3: 343–348.

Masursky, H., 1962. Uranium-bearing coal in the eastern part of the Red Desert area, Wyoming. *U.S. Geol. Surv. Bull.,* 1099-B: 152 pp.

McGowen, J.H. and Garner, L.E., 1970. Physiographic features and stratification types of coarse-grained point bars: modern and ancient examples. *Sedimentology,* 14: 77–111.

McKelvey, V.E., Everhart, D.L. and Garrels, R.M., 1955. Origin of uranium deposits. *Econ. Geol.,* 50: 464–533, anniv. vol.

Melin, R.E., 1964. Description and origin of uranium deposits in Shirley basin, Wyoming. *Econ. Geol.,* 59: 835–849.

Melin, R.E., 1969. Uranium Deposits in Shirley Basin, Wyoming. *Univ. Wyo. Contrib. Geol.,* 8 (2, part 1): 143–149.

Miller, D.S. and Kulp, J.L., 1963. Isotopic evidence on the origin of the Colorado Plateau uranium ores. *Geol. Soc. Am. Bull.,* 74: 609–630.

Mitchell, A.H. and Reading, H.G., 1969. Continental margins, geosynclines, and ocean-floor spreading. *J. Geol.,* 77: 629 pp.

Mittempergher, M., 1974. Genetic characteristics of the uranium deposits associated with the Permian sandstones in the Italian Alps. *I.A.E.A. Symp. Form. Uranium Ore Deposits, May 6–10, 1974, Athens, Greece.*

Moench, R.H. and Schlee, J.S., 1967. Geology and uranium deposits of the Laguna district, New Mexico. *U.S. Geol. Surv. Prof. Pap.,* 519: 117 pp.

Nininger, R.D., 1973. Uranium reserves and requirements. *U.S. A.E.C. (Washington)* pp. 9–28.

Ore, H.T., 1963. Some criteria for recognition of braided stream deposits. *Univ. Wyo. Contrib. Geol.,* 3: 1–14.

Ore, H.T., 1965. Characteristic deposits of rapidly aggrading streams. *Wyo. Geol. Assoc. 19th Field Conf. Guideb.,* pp. 195–201.

Perel'man, A.I., 1967. *Geochemistry of Epigenesis: Monographs in Geoscience.* Plenum, New York, N.Y., 266 pp.

Rackley, R.I., 1972. Environment of Wyoming Tertiary uranium deposits. *Am. Assoc. Pet. Geol. Bull.,* 56 (4): 755–774.

Rackley, R.I. and Johnson, R.L., 1971. The geochemistry of uranium roll-front deposits with a case history from the Powder River basin. *Econ. Geol.,* 66 (1): 202–203, abstract.

Rackley, R.I., Shockey, P.N. and Dahill, M.P., 1968. Concepts and methods of uranium exploration. *Wyo. Geol. Assoc. 20th Field Conf. Guideb.,* pp. 115–124.

Rapaport, I., 1963. Uranium deposits of the Poison Canyon ore trend, Grants district. *N.M. Bur. Min. Miner. Res. Mem.,* 15: 122–135.

Renfro, A.R., 1969. Uranium deposits in the Lower Cretaceous of the Black Hills. *Univ. Wyo. Contrib. Geol.,* 8 (2, part 1): 87–92.

Rosholt, J.N. and Bartel, A.J., 1969. Uranium, thorium, and lead systematics in Granite Mountains, Wyoming. *Earth Planet. Sci. Lett.,* 7: 141–147.

Rosholt, J.N., Harshman, E.N., Shields, W.R. and Garner, E.L., 1964. Isotopic fractionation of uranium related to roll features in sandstone, Shirley Basin, Wyoming. *Econ. Geol.,* 59: 570–585.

Rubin, B., 1970. Uranium roll front zonation in the southern Powder River basin, Wyoming. *Wyo. Geol. Assoc. Earth Sci. Bull.,* 3 (4): 5–8.

Samama, J.C., 1973. Ore deposits and continental weathering: a contribution to the problem of geochemical inheritance of heavy metal contents of basement areas and of sedimentary basins. In: G.C. Amstutz and A.J. Bernard (Editors), *Ores in Sediments.* Springer, New York, N.Y., Series A, No. 3, pp. 247–265.

Seyfert, C.K. and Sirkin, L.A., 1973. *Earth History and Plate Tectonics, an Introduction to Historical Geology.* Harper and Row, New York, N.Y., 504 pp.

Shawe, D.R., 1956. Significance of roll ore bodies in genesis of uranium–vanadium deposits on the Colorado Pateau. *U.S. Geol. Surv. Prof. Pap.,* 300: 239–241.

Shawe, D.R., Archbold, N.L. and Simmons, G.C., 1959. Geology and uranium–vanadium deposits of the Slick Rock district, San Miguel and Dolores counties. Colorado. *Econ. Geol.,* 54: 395–415.

Shockey, P.N., Rackley, R.I. and Dahill, M.P., 1968. Source beds and solution fronts. *Remarks Wyo. Met. Sect. AIME, Feb. 27, 1968:* 7 pp.

Silverman, M.P., 1967. Mechanism of bacterial pyrite oxidation. *J. Bacteriol.,* 94: 1046–1051.

Smith, N.D., 1970. The braided stream depositional environment: comparison of the Platte River with some Silurian clastic rocks, north central Appalachians. *Geol. Soc. Am. Bull.,* 81: 2993–3014.

Soule, J.H., 1956. Reconnaissance of the "red-bed" copper deposits in southeastern Colorado and New Mexico. *U.S. Bur. Min. Inf. Circ.,* 7740: 74 pp.

Squyres, J.B., 1972. Uranium deposits of the Grants region, New Mexico. *Wyo. Geol. Assoc. Earth Sci. Bull.,* 5 (3): 3–12.

Stanier, R.V., Doudorff, M. and Adelberg, E.A., 1963. *The Microbial World.* Prentice-Hall, Englewood Cliffs, N.J., 2nd ed., 750 pp.

Szalay, A. and Samsoni, Z., 1973. Investigation of the leaching of uranium from crushed magmatic rocks. In: *Proc. Symp. Hydrogeochemistry and Biogeochemistry, Tokyo.* The Clarke Company, Washington, D.C., 1: 261–272.

U.S. Atomic Energy Commission, 1974. Statistical data of the uranium industry, Jan. 1, 1974. *U.S. A.E.C.,* GJO-100 (74): 67 pp.

Vickers, R.C., 1957. Alteration of sandstone as a guide to uranium deposits and their origin, northern Black Hills, South Dakota. *Econ. Geol.,* 52 (6): 599–611.

Warren, C.G., 1971. A method of discriminating between biogenic and chemical origins of the ore-stage pyrite in a roll-type uranium deposit. *Econ. Geol.,* 66: 919–928.

Warren, C.G., 1972. Sulfur isotopes as a clue to the genetic geochemistry of a roll-type uranium deposit. *Econ. Geol.,* 67: 759–767.

Waters, A.C. and Granger, H.C., 1953. Volcanic debris in uraniferous sandstones and its possible bearing on the origin and precipitation of uranium. *U.S. Geol. Surv. Circ.,* 224: 26 pp.

Williams, P.F. and Rust, B.R., 1969. The sedimentology of a braided river. *J. Sediment. Petrol.,* 39 (2): 649–679.

Wolman M.G. and Miller, J.P., 1960. Magnitude and frequency of forces in geomorphic processes. *J. Geol.,* 68 (1): 54–74.

Woodward, L.A., Kaufman, W.H., Schumacher, O.L. and Talbot, L.W., 1974. Strata-bound copper deposits in Triassic sandstone of Sierra Nacimiento, New Mexico. *Econ. Geol.,* 69 (1): 108–120.

Wright, R.J., 1955. Ore controls in sandstone uranium deposits of the Colorado Plateau. *Econ. Geol.,* 50 (2): 135–155.

Young, R.G., 1964. Distribution of uranium deposits in the White Canyon–Monument Valley district, Utah–Arizona. *Econ. Geol.,* 59: 850–873.

Zajic, J.E., 1969. *Microbial Biochemistry.* Academic Press, New York, N.Y., 330 pp.

Chapter 4

ORIGIN OF THE PRECAMBRIAN BANDED IRON-FORMATIONS

JUERGEN EICHLER

INTRODUCTION

Banded iron-formations represent one of the most distinctive, though peculiar, types of rock which occur widespread in space and in time throughout the Precambrian on practically all shield areas of the world. Major iron-formations may form enormous blanket deposits with stratigraphic thicknesses of hundreds of metres and a lateral extent of several hundred to more than a thousand kilometres. The quantity of iron contained is immense — probably somewhere between 10^{14} and 10^{15} tons. Single iron-formations may have originally contained as much as 10^{14} tons, such as in the Hamersley basin of Western Australia (Trendall and Blockley, 1970) or, for example, $10^{12} - 10^{13}$ tons of iron in the Minas itabirites of Minas Gerais, Brazil (Dorr II, 1973b).

There is no doubt that iron-formations are by far the economically most important source of iron ore mined in the world and, because of their wide distribution, also the most prominent type of iron deposit.

However, despite countless detailed studies of single iron-formation deposits, the knowledge of the origin of this rock is still fragmentary. The problems start with the lack of a clear and generally acceptable definition of what is exactly meant by the term "Precambrian banded iron-formation"; thus, it is deemed necessary to start this paper with a discussion of terminology and definition of iron-formation.

The term "Precambrian banded iron-formation" includes coincidentally the key-words for the problems concerning the origin of these rocks. Why are banded iron-formations confined to the Precambrian? What is the explanation for the peculiar characteristic banding of interlayered chert and iron-rich layers? From where have the enormous iron concentrations been derived? What was the method of transportation and deposition of the iron and silica and of the separation of iron from other elements?

Many hypotheses as to the origin of iron-formations have been suggested for particular occurrences, but none of these have been able to offer a generally acceptable model to explain the genesis of all iron-formations. As it will be shown, iron-formations are diversified rocks and despite many commonly shared features, any hypothesis based on studies of a single deposit is most likely equivocal if applied on a universal scale.

The reason for the lack of a generally valid genetic model is probably that principles of actualistic geology are difficult to apply to Precambrian iron-formations which, with a few questionable exceptions, are strictly confined to the Precambrian. Some distinctive features, however, such as their depositional and paleogeographical environments, sedimentary rock assemblages and facies distribution in shallow-marine basins can be fittingly compared with younger iron deposits. There is strong evidence that iron-formations are chemical and possibly biochemical sediments, but the problem of from whence the iron and silica was derived and how the typical banding originated, is still unclear. The answer is probably connected with the indispensable assumption of fundamentally different environmental conditions in the Precambrian, first of all an atmosphere and a hydrosphere lacking oxygen during the deposition of iron-formations. If at all true, this is of course difficult to prove.

However, in further studies on a worldwide scale, iron-formations may turn out to be a helpful tool in the understanding of the sedimentary and tectonic development of the Precambrian crust. For example, Archean iron-formations, being most readily distinguishable and very widespread rock units, have already proved to be key-criteria in the recognition of Archean basins, as Goodwin (1973) has explicitly demonstrated for the Canadian Shield. They have also provided further evidence for the former connection of the Gondwana landmass and their regional distribution suggests that the bulk of the Proterozoic iron-formations was laid down in depositional environments which follow major fractures in a segmented ancient crust.

The present chapter is an outgrowth of a review of the comprehensive literature on iron-formations which tries to give a general view of the geology, the distribution and origin of this fascinating rock. The writer is aware of the fact that many important contributions on the subject may not have been adequately acknowledged in this paper, due to the vast amount of information to be digested. For more details the interested reader is referred to the recently published volumes of the Kiev symposium on the genesis of Precambrian iron deposits (*UNESCO, Earth Sciences*, Vol. 9, 1973) and to the topical iron-formation symposium in *Economic Geology*, Vol 68, 1973. The references herein cited comprise most of the more pertinent literature on iron-formation, including a very valuable inventory of the Russian literature.

TERMINOLOGY AND DEFINITION OF IRON-FORMATION

An internationally accepted nomenclature to describe the banded cherty iron-formation sediments in accordance with the principles of stratigraphic classification of sedimentary rocks has not yet been established. The usage of different terms in different countries for the same iron-rich sediments still complicates a common understanding as to what exactly is defined as "banded iron-formation", so much the more since identical terms are occasionally also used for different rocks.

A most valuable discussion of the problems of nomenclature for banded ferruginous-cherty sedimentary rocks has been given by Brandt et al. (1972), recommending the usage of the term "iron-formation" as a generic lithologic name, strictly on a parallel, for example, with "limestone". The words are in this case hyphenated but capitalized when using them in a stratigraphic sense as, for example, "Brockman Iron Formation" as suggested by Trendall and Blockley (1970).

Contracting the old term "iron-bearing formation" of Van Hise and Leith (1911) to "iron-formation", James (1954) supplied the first strict definition, now widely accepted by most geologists as "... a chemical sediment, typically thin-bedded or laminated, containing 15% or more iron of sedimentary origin, commonly but not necessarily containing layers of chert".

A similar definition is given by Gross (1965), but, extended also to layered iron-rich rock units of clastic sedimentary origin.

The typical features of iron-formation as defined above are physically a thin layering in the range of less than a millimetre to some centimetres, with lamination on a scale of sometimes less than 1 mm and chemically the composition of one or more iron-rich minerals interbanded with chert. Chert or jasper is a term loosely used for silica-rich material, regardless of degree of crystallinity. Thus, in metamorphosed iron-formations the original chert normally has been recrystallized into granular quartz.

The primary iron-rich minerals alternating with the silica-bands may consist of iron oxides, carbonates, silicates or sulfides, indicating the physico-chemical conditions of the environment of deposition of the iron-formation as shown by Krumbein and Garrels (1952) and Krauskopf (1967). James (1954) very usefully adapted these existing differences in the content of distinct iron minerals to divide the iron-formations into facies-types, such as oxide-facies iron-formation (hematite and/or magnetite), silicate-facies iron-formation, etc.

This concept of facies of iron-formations seems to be acceptable worldwide, as it offers by itself a simple, descriptive characterization of a certain kind of iron-formation, regardless of the degree of metamorphism. The latter factor should be excluded from the basic definition of this rock.

Gross (1965) suggests a classification of the Precambrian iron-formations of Canada into two major groups, according to general features and characteristics of their depositional environments and typical rock associations. The Algoma-type is characterized by relatively small lenticular bodies, closely associated with and genetically related to volcanic rocks and graywacke sediments in eugeosynclinal belts. The Superior-type iron-formation is associated with clastic sedimentary rocks of shelf or miogeosynclinal environments, such as quartzites, dolomites and pelitic rocks, without showing any direct relationships to volcanic associations. This type is extensively developed in Middle to Late Precambrian shield areas throughout the world and forms prominent iron ranges that can be followed over several hundred to more than a thousand kilometres, attaining thicknesses of up to several hundred metres. (Cf. Chapter 3, Vol. 1, on classifications.)

To avoid further confusion, it seems appropriate at this point to give a short review of the terms used synonymously for iron-formation, most of them being applied to oxide-facies iron-formation, which is the most widespread, economically the most important and therefore, geologically the best-studied type.

Synonymous terms being used in the literature for layered ferruginous rocks and iron-formation are, for example: taconite, itabirite, banded iron-formation (BIF), banded iron ore, banded ironstone, banded hematite quartzite (BHQ), ferruginous quartzite, ferruginous chert, banded hematite jasper, jasper, jasper bars, calico rock, zebra rock, specularite schist, iron hornfels and even iron ore which is the occasionally used Russian equivalent for the English term iron-formation.

Taconite and jaspilite are terms for oxide-facies iron-formation that originated in the Lake Superior region and which are still widely used, but unfortunately jaspilite has been applied also to rocks that would not be called jaspilite in the Lake Superior area. Similarly, the term ironstone as used in South Africa for iron-formation is in conflict with the already established ironstone as applied in America and elsewhere for massive non-banded iron ores of the minette-type.

Terms like ferruginous quartzite (Eisenquartzite, quartzites ferrugineaux) are also widely used but should be reserved, despite their occasional banding, for iron-rich clastic rocks of varying iron content.

Itabirite, as defined by Dorr II et al. (1959), is the Brazilian term for iron-formation, but it is strictly confined to the metamorphosed oxide-facies. However, principally in South America, West Africa and also in Russia, the term itabirite is commonly used in a broader sense as a synonym for iron-formation and as the generic name for this rock, in order to avoid confusion with the term "formation" of the stratigraphical nomenclature. For example, an oxide-facies iron-formation, predominantly hematitic and with lesser amounts of magnetite, would thus be described as "hematite/magnetite-itabirite", as the present writer (Eichler, 1970) has suggested. As in nature more than one facies of iron minerals may compose the rock and the interbanding may consist of quartz (metachert) and/or other minerals like dolomite, hornblende, etc., in this broad definition, the nomenclature is controlled only by the dominant iron mineral, hyphenated with the term itabirite, using it as the generic lithologic name, parallel, for example, to biotite-granite.

For the banded ferruginous cherty rocks, as described and defined here, the term "iron-formation" is tentatively adopted, despite the fact that "formation" coincides with the identical term of the lithostratigraphical classification of sedimentary sequences and might be misleading when translated into other languages.

However, the usage of the term "iron-formation" is now so widely employed in the nomenclature of the Western World, and so generally accepted by most geologists for this specific type of iron-rich sedimentary rock, that it would be presumptuous of the writer to attempt to change the term.

REGIONAL GEOLOGIC DISTRIBUTION

The banded iron-formations are confined to Precambrian shield areas. They are comparable by their significant features on both the Northern Hemisphere and the Southern Hemisphere continents and, in fact, there is no major cratonic area which lacks iron-formations as prominent members of its stratigraphical column.

As most, but not all, iron-formations are metamorphosed and are parts of the regionally metamorphosed and often strongly folded sedimentary sequences that build up the consolidated masses of the Precambrian shields, they occur frequently as resistent erosional remnants of folded ancient sedimentary basins. In many cases, they can be traced as parts of synclinal or anticlinal structures over hundreds or even more than a thousand kilometres in lateral extent, forming prominent iron ranges.

Apparently, oxide-facies iron-formations represent the bulk of all economically significant iron-formations. Hence, most of the geological literature on the subject is based on this type which is the host rock of the largest and best-studied iron ore mines, at present being worked predominently on the Southern Hemisphere continents — South America, Africa, India and Australia. In these areas of subtropical climates, many of the originally low-grade iron-formations have been enriched under favourable conditions by supergene weathering processes to high-grade iron ores with 60—69% iron content (e.g., Dorr II, 1964; Campana, 1966).

In Fig. 1 is shown the distribution of the most important occurrences of iron-formations on the Precambrian shield areas of the world. It is obvious that many of them lie close to the borders of the continents or on the margins of the cratonic masses now surrounded by younger fold belts and platform sediments. As Gross (1973) has pointed out, this distribution may lead to the supposition that the margins of the old continental masses have been favourable areas for the development of depositional basins with sedimentation of iron-formations. Gross suggested that some of the iron-formations now on the borders of different continents may have formed parts of the same sedimentary basins and fold belts of consistent shield areas as they may have appeared prior to continental drift.

This regional distribution of iron-formations near and along the coastal parts of the continents is clearly seen in South America and Africa as well as in Australia and India.

Where the general geological setting has been studied in more detail, a comparison of iron-formations on opposite continents fits fairly well with the assumption of originally coherent iron-formation belts. This is the case for iron-formations on the Guayana and Liberian shields, as Gruss (1973) has shown, comparing the occurrences of the Imataca-Series of Venezuela with those of Liberia and Sierra Leone. The type and depositional environment of these iron-formations with their associated rocks are similar, if not identical, and so are their ages and their orogenic and metamorphic histories.

It is most interesting to note that the iron-formations of Venezuela and Western Africa, both deposited 2,500—3,000 m.y. ago, were affected by the same younger meta-

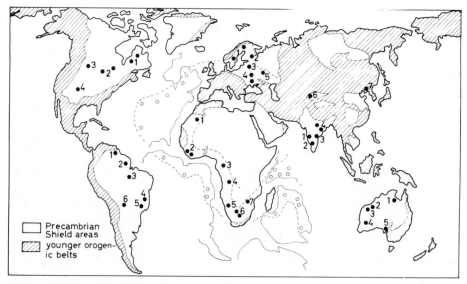

Fig. 1. Distribution of prominent Precambrian banded iron-formations and reconstruction of probable situation prior to continental drift (Proterozoic iron-formation belts).

North America: *1* = Labrador-Ungava; *2* = Lake Superior region; *3* = northern Rocky Mts.; *4* = southwest U.S.

South America: *1* = Imataca Series, Venezuela; *2* = Amapá, Brazil; *3* = Serra dos Carajás, Pará; *4* = Bahia; *5* = Minas Gerais, iron-ore quadrangle; *6* = Urucum, Mato Grosso.

Africa: *1* = Mauritania, Ford Gouraud; *2* = Sierra Leone, Liberia; *3* = Gabon, Mekambo; *4* = Angola, Cassinga and Cassala; *5* = Damara, S.W. Africa; *6* = South Africa, Witwatersrand and Transvaal Supergroups; *7* = Limpopo metamorphic belt.

India: *1* = Goa; *2* = Mysore; *3* = Andhra Pradesh; *4* = Bihar and Orissa.

Australia: *1* = McArthur Basin; *2* = Pilbara Block; *3* = Hamersley Group; *4* = Yilgarn Block; *5* = Middleback Range.

Europa and Asia: *1* = Scandinavian Shield; *2* = Karelia; *3* = Bielorussia; *4* = KMA, Krivoy Rog and Ukrainian Shield; *5* = Urals; *6* = Tuva, Sayan, Baykal, South Yakutia; *7* = Anshan.

morphic event at 1,800 m.y. and underwent deformation by folding, symmetrical to a central crest zone.

This would mean that the segmentation and continental drift of the Gondwana landmass, supposed to have started in many places during the Early Cretaceous, has followed a latent and much older Precambrian fault and tectonic pattern of worldwide dimensions, which may have controlled the suitable conditions for the depositional environments of iron-formations.

It is a most remarkable fact that the distribution of Precambrian iron-formations (see next section) in several great cycles coincides fairly well with the ages of profound magmatic and metamorphic events during the evolution of the earth's crust.

Runcorn (1962) advocated a repeated continental drift and delivered a theory of Precambrian continental drift, caused by changes in the convection mechanism of the earth's mantle by periodical growth of the core. Such changes, as Runcorn presumes, occurred in the intervals between 2,750 and 2,450 m.y.; 1,900–1,600 m.y.; and 1,150–900 m.y. ago, thus corresponding in time with the main epochs of deposition of iron-formations many of which lie inside the worldwide fold belts of the "Superior Regime" (2,750–1,950 m.y.) as plotted by Dearnley (1965) on the presumed pre-Gondwana landmass.

Thus, the fundamental reasons for the regional distribution of such huge accumulations of iron and silica seem to be basically connected with certain universal principles in the behaviour of the sialic crust. It is almost certain that any attempt to decipher the final reasons for the deposition of the Precambrian iron-formation has to consider not only detailed studies of single iron-formation environments but relies heavily on more knowledge of the superimposing basic factors of worldwide significance.

AGES OF PRECAMBRIAN BANDED IRON-FORMATIONS

Due to the lack of minerals within the iron-formations suitable for radiometric age determinations, a precise dating of these rocks has been possible only in rare cases. However, the progress in radiometric dating techniques and the great number of samples determined in recent years from associated metasedimentary and volcanic rocks makes it possible at least to mark the age limits of many prominent iron-formations of all parts of the world. Compilations of age determinations have been given by Lepp and Goldich (1964), Govett (1966), James (1966) and recently by Goldich (1973). The review in this chapter is essentially based on these papers.

Though banded iron-formations occur during a period of at least 3,000 m.y. throughout the Precambrian, their prevailing development is confined to a single epoch between 2,600 and 1,800 m.y. ago (Goldich, 1973). As Bayley and James (1973) have shown, this interval was clearly the principal time of deposition in North America, far outweighing by their extent and iron content the more limited older and younger iron-formations. The same is the case for many major iron-formations on other continents such as those of Russia (Krivoy Rog, Kursk), South Africa, Brazil and Western Australia, all of which seem to have been deposited approximately contemporaneously between 2,600–1,800 m.y. ago. In all these shield areas apparently, there is a progressive decrease in the abundance of iron-formations, in size as well as in quantity, in the post-1,800 m.y. period just as in the pre-2,600 m.y. epoch.

Following the framework classification given by Goldich (1973), the iron-formations should be grouped, according to their ages, in the categories: (1) older than 3,000 m.y.; (2) 3,000–2,600 m.y.; (3) 2,600–1,800 m.y.; and (4) younger than 1,800 m.y.

(1) With few but notable exceptions, the bulk of the Early Precambrian, Archean iron-formations, though not restricted to the pre-2,600 m.y. period, belong to the Algoma-type as defined by Gross (1965). They are closely related to greenstone belts and

form relatively small lenticular bodies. The oldest known iron-formations, close to or older than 3,000 m.y., are found in the Swaziland System of South Africa (3,000–3,400 m.y.), in the Pilbara and Yilgarn Blocks of Western Australia (2,670–3,000 m.y.), in the Imataca Complex of Venezuela (3,000–3,400 m.y.) and in the Ukrainian Shield in the Greater Krivoy Rog area (3,100–3,500 m.y.).

(2) In the range from 3,000–2,600 m.y. numerous occurrences are known on the Canadian Shield, most of them closely associated with greenstone belts. A great number of them was deposited in the remarkably brief interval from 2,750–2,700 m.y. ago (Sims and Morey, 1972). In South Africa iron-formations in the Sebakvian, Bulavayan and Shamvayan Systems, stratigraphically associated with volcanic rocks, were dated at more than 2,700 m.y. (see Beukes, 1973). The same ages of >2,700 m.y. are found in some small Algoma-type occurrences in the Rio das Velhas-Series of Brazil, in India in Mysore and in the "Iron Ore Series" of Bihar–Orissa and also in eastern Karelia on the Baltic Shield (for references see Goldich, 1973). Thus, it appears that the span of time between 3,000 and 2,600 m.y., especially around 2,700 m.y., marks a significant epoch, very favourable for the deposition of iron-formations.

(3) The most abundant development of iron-formations in the world is found in the interval between 2,600 and 1,800 m.y. On the Canadian shield the ages of the major iron-formations of Labrador and the Lake Superior region range between 2,200 and 1,900 m.y. The interval of the main deposition was probably much less, since for the iron-formations in Minnesota, thought to be largely contemporaneous with others in North America, a minimum age of 2,000 m.y. has been determined. In Australia the Brockman Iron Formation of the Hamersley Group is bracketed between 2,200 and 2,000 m.y. Similar ages are given for Krivoy Rog/Ukrainia (2,200–1,900 m.y.), for the Brazilian itabirites in Minas Gerais and in the Serra dos Carajás/Pará (about 2,000 m.y.) and also for iron-formations of the Svecofennian of the Baltic Shield (minimum age of 1,900 m.y.) and of the Aldan Shield on the southeastern margin of the Siberian platform (2,000–2,750 m.y.). In South Africa iron-formations in association with clastic rocks are predominantly developed during the interval from 2,300–3,000 m.y., whereas the shelf-carbonate and carbonate–manganese associations belong to the period prior to 2,300 m.y.

(4) The post-1,800 m.y. banded iron-formations known in the world are quantitatively much less important; compared with the overwhelming concentration in the Lower Proterozoic and Archean they should rather be considered as exceptions. If a clear definition of "iron-formation" should exist, it most probably would not fit the characteristics of "iron-formation", principally of the problematic younger iron-formations, described by O'Rourke (1961). Examples for these are occurrences on Nepal and in Mato Grosso/Brazil (Dorr II, 1973a). These Late Proterozoic or Early Cambrian cherty iron-formations are also typically banded but, averaging about 56% Fe, they are much richer in iron than the older types. Their origin is still enigmatic.

In North America only a few minor occurrences of Late Precambrian age are known.

In the Rapitan Group of the Yukon and Northwest Territories the age of an iron-formation is correlated with that of the Windermere Group (800–600 m.y.). The iron-formation in the Yavapai Series of central Arizona was metamorphosed between 1,820 and 1,760 m.y. ago and may be coeval with those of the Lake Superior region. The iron-formation in the lower part of the Damara Supergroup of South West Africa has been deposited between 1,000 and 620 m.y. ago (see Beukes, 1973).

It is a most remarkable fact that major iron-formations all over the world can be fairly well grouped in several time intervals of the Precambrian, between 3,400 and 3,000 m.y., about 2,700 m.y. and outstandingly in one period between 2,600 and 1,800 m.y. ago with an accumulation at about 2,000 m.y. This last statement has been also made for the major iron-formations of the Soviet Union (Alexandrov, 1973). Many of them have metamorphic ages of about 2,000 m.y. Younger ages are thought to correspond to the age of the final orogeny in the evolution of the geosyncline, which went across the Russian platform so that they do not reflect the time of deposition. The iron-formations of the Algoma-type generally are limited in size, but occur over a greater span of time, from the earliest Precambrian through the Phanerozoic, whereas the Superior-type is strictly confined to the Precambrian, the bulk of it most probably to the period prior to about 2,000 m.y. ago.

It must be pointed out that the data for single iron-formations should be used with caution as many of them might represent not the true age of deposition but mixed ages from subsequent metamorphic or orogenic events which have overprinted the old craton areas, for instance, the 500 m.y. "Panafrican Thermal Event" advocated by Kennedy (1964). Nevertheless, these factors as well as uncertainties in the use of decay constants in the different laboratories should not affect the general statement that the deposition of many major iron-formations of the world was synchronous in certain epochs of the Precambrian.

Fig. 2 suggests that the development of iron-formations fell into relatively stable

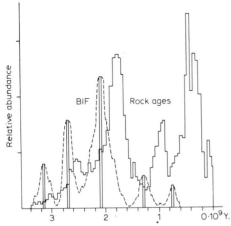

Fig. 2. Ages of major magmatic and metamorphic events in earth's history (mineral and rock ages compiled from Dearnley (1965); 3,400 age determinations) and relative abundance of iron-formations on the time scale.

epochs precursory to and partly overlapping with the initial stages of major magmatic and metamorphic cycles during the Precambrian.

Unequivocally, as it is also pointed out by Cloud (1973), the epoch between about 2,600 and 2,000 m.y. ago marks a profound change of conditions in the earth's evolution, terminating the vigorous growth of procaryotic organisms and giving rise to a development under increasingly oxidizing conditions.

GEOLOGICAL SETTING

Depositional environments

Despite many common features such as banding, mineral assemblages, sedimentary facies and chemical composition, iron-formations occur in quite different sedimentary environments.

Most of the Algoma-type iron-formations are found in Archean eugeosynclinal basins, whereas most of the Middle Precambrian Superior-type iron-formations are found most commonly on the margins of stable continental shelves in miogeosynclinal environments of intercratonic and cratonic basins.

Archean basins. The most complete description of Archean tectonic basins of the Canadian Shield is given by Goodwin and Shklanka (1967) and Goodwin (1973). Ten major Archean basins have been recognized in the Superior and Churchill provinces and, to a more limited extent, also in the Slave Province of the Canadian Shield, mainly identified on the basis of iron-formations, which are typically associated with greenstone belts within the Archean basins. The elliptical basins are, in their present structurally deformed state, about 350–700 km long and are thought to represent remnants of originally quasi-circular structures in the tectonically mobile Archean crust, with diameters of between 800 and 1100 km (Goodwin, 1973).

Similar large basins have been recognized on shield areas elsewhere in the world, in Australia and in the Rhodesian and Kaapvaal Cratons of South Africa (Beukes, 1973).

Recently Kloosterman (1973) has described several giant "ring volcanoes", with diameters of between 300 and 900 km, from the Amazon part of the Guiana Shield, which, however, have a younger age and were emplaced between 1,900 and 1,800 m.y. ago. The relationship of some known iron-formation deposits with these structures is not yet clear.

It is proposed by Goodwin (1973) that Archean basins of the Canadian Shield represent centres of crustal speading in areas where vertical thermal streams ("thermal plumes" or "hot spots") have been particularly active in the thin Archean crust. A meteorite impact scar theory is considered unlikely. The wide distribution of basins of this type in outcropping and uneroded Archean shield areas suggests that Archean basins have to be considered as first-order features of the crustal evolution in Early Precambrian time and perhaps as the ancient counterparts of modern oceans. The development of the present oceans could well have originated from zones of fragility in the Precambrian crust, indicated by the distribution of many of the major iron-formation bearing old geosynclines, now broken apart by "continental drift" in the course of younger plate-tectonic movements.

The Michipicoten area of north-central Ontario is quoted by Goodwin (1973) as a typical example of such volcano-tectonic Archean basins. It encompasses several greenstone belts and intervening batholithic complexes. Arc-type volcanics with mafic effusions and felsic pyroclastics, coarse-grained clastics, including graywackes and thick conglomerates, and iron-formations from oxide to sulfide facies are the most important lithologic associations of the marginal parts of such basins.

The distribution of iron-formations within the ambient volcanic sequences in the greenstone belts follows the normal depositional pattern, with oxide-, carbonate- and sulfide-facies in that order from the marginal to the inner parts of a basin. Oxide-facies is by far the most common facies. Carbonate- and sulfide-facies iron-formations are equally widely developed but, in general, form only thin and discontinuous lenticular bodies of lesser significance. Commonly, iron-formations of this type are closely related to pyroclastic members of mafic to felsic volcanic sequences and shale—graywacke successions. Thus, there is common agreement to attribute the derivation of these iron-formations to volcanic activities.

Figs. 3 and 4 taken from Goodwin (1973), demonstrate with a stratigraphic section of the Michipicoten basin, Ontario, the facies transitions from the shelf to the inner parts in a typical Archean basin.

Miogeosynclinal environments. Contrary to the Archean iron-formations, which are closely associated with volcanic successions in giant interarc basins of the Archean basement, the bulk of the major Middle to Early Proterozoic iron-formations was deposited in miogeosynclinal or epicontinental environments, together with clastic sequences, transgressive on the older basement. Oxide facies is the most abundant type and it is commonly not associated with volcanic rocks. These iron-formations of the Superior-type are enormous sheet deposits with thicknesses of up to several hundred metres. They are persistent over many hundreds of kilometres to more than a thousand kilometres in extent and several hundreds of kilometres in width. The major iron-formations with an age bracketed between 2,600 and 1,800 m.y., many of them probably coeval at about 2,000 m.y., are prominent rock units of the shelf parts of elongated, large miogeosynclinal or intercratonic basins along the Archean shield areas, which they commonly overlie with profound angular and erosional unconformity. The dimensions of these Proterozoic troughs, with extents of not much less than 1,000 km to more than 1,000 km, widths in the order of 100 km to several hundreds of kilometres and sedimentary thicknesses of several thousand metres, are comparable worldwide as Pflug (1967) has pointed out in his comparison of Precambrian miogeosynclines. Thus, it appears that this kind of deposi-

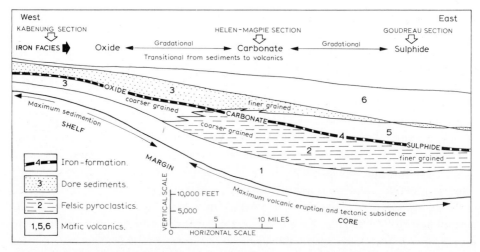

Fig. 3. Reconstructed stratigraphic section of the Michipicotan basin (from Goodwin, 1973, p. 29, with permission of *Economic Geology*).

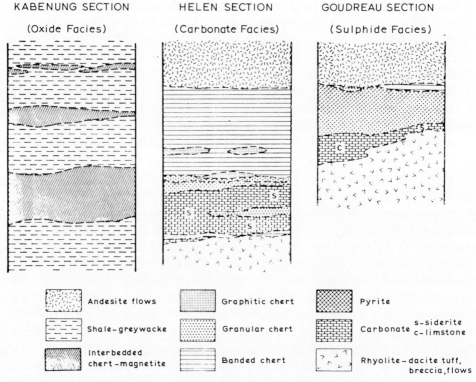

Fig. 4. Typical stratigraphic sections of oxide, carbonate and sulphide facies of iron-formation in the Michipicoten basin (from Goodwin, 1973, p. 30, with permission of *Economic Geology*).

tional environment for iron-formations represents a characteristic feature of the Precambrian evolution about 2,100–2,000 m.y. ago.

Prominent examples of the wide lateral distribution of continuous iron-formations are the Labrador Trough and the occurrences of the Lake Superior region, which correspond in age and other features and which can be followed over a distance of about 3,200 km along an old shoreline bordering the Canadian Shield (Gross, 1965).

The sedimentary basin of the itabirites in Minas Gerais, Brazil, had a minimum extent of 500 km and a minimum width of 160 km (Barbosa and Grossi Sad, 1973).

Iron-formations of the Superior-type are, however, not restricted to miogeosynclinal or platform environments in sedimentary troughs between older cratons. They are also frequently found in younger depressions on Archean cratons (intracratonic basins) such as the Witwatersrand, Transvaal and other iron-formations as described by Beukes (1973) from South Africa.[1] Many of these basins, generally, but not always, are lacking contemporaneous volcanism. They reflect conditions of restricted basins with deposition of iron-formation in shallow and quiet water, sometimes under highly saline conditions. This is indicated, for example, in the Kuruman and Penge Iron-Formations by locally high sodium concentrations. The deposition of the iron-formation in the Hamersley basin, Western Australia, an originally ovoid basin of 500 by 250 km, is believed by Trendall (1973a) to have taken place under essentially quiescent sedimentary conditions in water depths of 50–200 m. The remarkable continuity of microbanding over almost 300 km for single bands resembles strongly younger evaporite deposits and suggests deposition in a restricted basin free from currents and wave activity, similar to evaporitic formations.

In detailed studies of iron-formations of the Labrador trough, Quebec, Dimroth (1972) recognizes two main depositional facies: a lagoonal platform facies of thin-bedded oolitic, granular and conglomerate alternations with chert, deposited in water probably less than 10–15 m deep and a basin facies deposited at less than 100 m (perhaps less than 50 m) depth. Presumable pseudomorphs of chalcedony after gypsum suggest local evaporitic conditions and deposition in a probably warm and dry climate (see separate chapter by Dimroth, this volume).

In opposition to this, some other Late Proterozoic iron-formations appear to have been deposited under cold-climate conditions. In the Northern Hemisphere the iron-formation of the Rapitan Group in the Mackenzie District of northwest Canada, deposited between 800–600 m.y. ago (Gabrielse, 1972), alternates with clastics of probably glacial origin. In the Southern Hemisphere, similarly, Martin (1965) describes glacio-marine associations with iron-formations in both miogeosynclinal and eugeosynclinal environments of the Damara Supergroup of South West Africa, the age of which is bracketed between 620–1,000 m.y. ago (cf. Beukes, 1973). It is of interest that these two roughly contemporaneous iron-formations on opposite sides of the globe reflect similar glacial depositional conditions. The conclusion arises that they have been located in the peri-glacial outskirts of extensive continental glaciers or perhaps of the then polar ice caps of the ancient globe.

---

[1] See Chapter 7 by Anheusser and Button, Vol. 5.

However, cold-climate sedimentary conditions for deposition of iron-formations in general cannot be considered as a crucial factor, since most of the major Superior-type iron-formations, grouped in the interval between 2,600–1,800 m.y. ago, have been deposited contemporaneously around the world, including the equatorial zones. Hence, different climatic factors appear to be of basically little significance for the deposition of iron-formation.

Iron-formations in Proterozoic miogeosynclines and post-orogenic intracratonic basins are major and extensive rock units. They represent a characteristic facies laid down during a certain phase in the evolution of Proterozoic geosynclines under relatively shallow-water epicontinental or shelf conditions. The typical lithofacies associations of these miogeosynclinal rock sequences are essentially thick coarse- to fine-grained quartzites with conglomerates and pelitic interruptions in the marginal and bottom parts of the transgressive sequence and predominantly pelitic rocks, sometimes graphitic shales, with local intercalations of quartzites, limestones or dolomitic rocks in the higher parts. Iron-formation, frequently in several horizons interrupted by shales and/or quartzites, was normally laid down in the lower and middle parts of the section. With thicknesses of several hundreds of metres, it may make up as much as 10% of the total basin filling. In general, these clastic-chemical sequences are devoid of any volcanic associations, in opposition to Archean banded iron-formations. However, volcanic activity contemporaneous with deposition of iron-formation may also be observed, presumably merely parallelling the clastic-chemical deposition in the course of the structural development of the basin and without any direct connection with the origin of the iron-formation.

In many major iron districs, such as, for example, the Lake Superior region (Bayley and James, 1973, p. 936, fig. 2) or in the "Quadrilatero Ferrifero" of Brazil (Dorr II, 1973b, p. 1009, fig. 2), it can be observed that the main iron-formation of the miogeosynclinal sequence was laid down in the lower part, underlain and overlain by non-volcanic clastic rocks.

Fig. 5 gives an example of the progressive evolution of the Minas geosyncline from Minas Gerais, Brazil. The section is compiled from the data of several authors: Pflug (1965) who studied the marginal parts in the Diamantina area, Dorr II et al. (1959) in the central area of the basin and the author's own investigations in the southeastern part of the "Iron Ore Quadrangle", where several features indicate an offshore uplift zone, which can be traced further to the north, parallel to the old "São Francisco Craton", as an island-arc zone restricting the miogeosynclinal basin (Kehrer, 1972).

The thickness of the Cauê Itabirite varies from about 50 m to more than 600 m with an average of about 250 m. The principal iron-formation covers an area of about 160 km lateral width and can be traced over an extent of at least 500 km in a NNE–SSW direction (Barbosa and Grossi Sad, 1973).

The diagrammatic section shows a transgressive overlap of lower Minas Series quartzites and phyllites on the pre-Minas basement (Rio das Velhas Series; plus 2,700 m.y.) and the successive deposition of the Cauê-Itabirite in an at least partly barred and continuous-

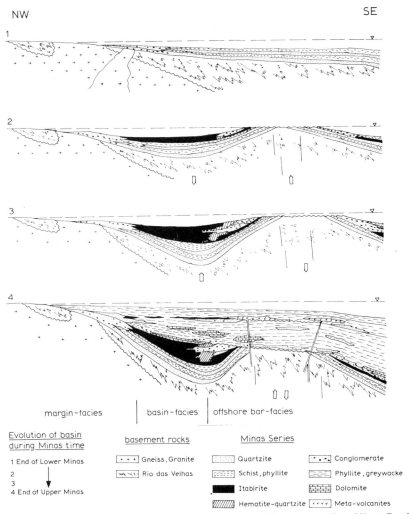

NW   SE

margin-facies | basin-facies | offshore bar-facies

Evolution of basin
during Minas time   basement rocks   Minas Series

1 End of Lower Minas   [· + +] Gneiss, Granite   [░░░] Quartzite   [· ·.·] Conglomerate
2   [~~ ~~] Rio das Velhas   [≡≡≡] Schist, phyllite   [≡≡≡] Phyllite, greywacke
3
4 End of Upper Minas   [■■] Itabirite   [⊞⊞] Dolomite
                                                       [▨▨] Hematite-quartzite [٧٧٧] Meta-volcanites

Fig 5. Structural and stratigraphic development of the Minas geosyncline, Minas Gerais, Brazil (from
Eichler, 1968; slightly modified from Gruss, 1967).

ly subsiding basin. Increasing subsidence stopped deposition of itabirite and led subsequently to eugeosynclinal sedimentary conditions with thick sequences of shales (phyllites) and graywackes with local quartzite wedges and dolomite lenses. Conglomerates and
clastic hematite quartzites, probably reworked itabirites, are locally interfingering with
the itabirites.

Thin and insignificant iron-formations of commonly lenticular shape may locally follow in the higher parts of the sections, embedded in eugeosynclinal sediments with or
without adjacent rocks of volcanic origin. It is here suggested that these minor successive
horizons represent stragglers of the vanishing stages of iron-formation deposition inciden-

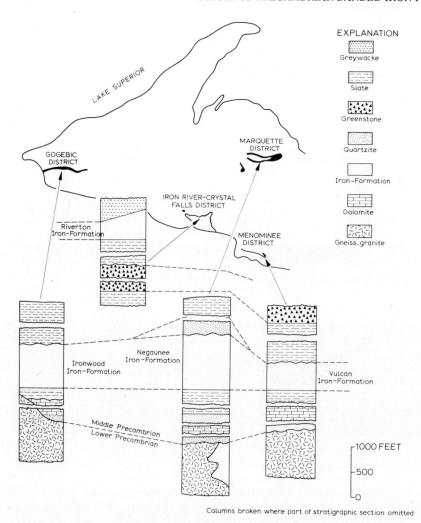

Fig. 6. Correlation of major lithologies in iron-formations of the Lake Superior District (from Gair, 1973, p. 367).

tally conflicting with volcanic material when volcanic activity started in the progressively subsiding basin. It is likely that major depositional troughs have been divided into several separate shallow basins. This may be supposed when lithologic associations of single correlative iron-formations differ considerably from one to another in the same district as it is the case in the Menominee, Marquette, Gogebic, Mesabi and Gunflint ranges of the Lake Superior District (Fig. 6 from Gair, 1973, p. 367).

Summary of depositional types of iron-formations. Relative to the principal environments of deposition, a grouping into two main types of banded iron-formation has been explicit-

TABLE I

Characteristic features of Algoma- and Superior-type banded iron-formations

	Algoma-type (Archean-type)	Superior-type (Animikie-type)
Age	pre-2,600 m.y. (also Proterozoic and Phanerozoic)	pre-1,800 m.y.
Sedimentary environment	eugeosynclinal tectonic basins of several 100 km diameter; iron-formation in marginal parts in connection with greenstone belts	miogeosynclinal; iron-formation along margins of stable continental shelves; shallow water; restricted intra-cratonic basins
Extent	commonly lenticular bodies of a few km	extensive formations persistent over some 100 km to more than 1,000 km
Thickness	0.1 m to some 10 m	several m to more than 100 m (1,000 m)
Location in sedimentary sequence	irregular, lenticular bodies within Archean "basement" rocks	in bottom and middle parts of sedimentary sequences as sheet-deposits, transgressive on older "basement" rocks
Associated rocks	graywackes and shales; carbonaceous slates; mafic volcanis; felsic pyroclastics; ryolithic flows; pillowed andesites.	coarse clastics; quartzites, conglomerates dolomites, black shales (graphitic)
Volcanics	close association to volcanism in time and space	no direct association with contemporaneous volcanism; volcanics normally absent
Sedimentary facies	oxide-facies predominant; carbonate- and sulfide-facies thin and discontinuous; silicate-facies; all facies frequently closely associated	oxide-facies most abundant; silicate- and carbonate-facies frequently intergradational.
	sulfide- and carbonate-facies near the center of volcanism; oxide-facies on the margins	sulfide-facies insignificant or absent
	heterogeneous lithological assemblages with fine grained clastic beds.	more homogeneous (especially oxide-facies); little or no detritus.
	granular and oolitic textures	granular and oolitic textures
Examples	Canada: Archean basins (e.g. Michipicoten)	Labrador Trough
	U.S.A.: Vermilion District, Minnesota	Lake Superior Region
	S. Africa: greenstone belts, Kaapvaal and Rhodesia Cratons	Transvaal and Witwatersrand Supergroups
	Brazil: Rio das Velhas Series	Minas Series (itabirites); Carajás/Pará
	India: southern Mysore	Bihar, Orissa, Goa, Mysore
	Australia: Yilgarn and Pilbara Blocks	Hamersley Group
	U.S.S.R.: Taratash/Urals	Krivoy Rog, Kursk; Ukrainian Shield

ly established by Gross (1965): the Algoma-type and the Lake Superior type. A comparison of the characteristic features of these two types is shown in Table I.

The late Proterozoic iron-formations with an age of less than 1,600 m.y. show many features common with the bulk of the older iron-formations. However, there are some notable differences in their general geological setting. First of all, their regional distribution is much less abundant in time and in space and they are also less prominent units in the associated rock sequences. The mineralogical and chemical composition seems to·be more variable. Chert is normally observed but may also be lacking. In the silicate-facies, high-aluminous chamosite is more common than low-aluminous greenalite. In some deposits essentially higher contents of iron, far exceeding the normal range in banded iron-formations, can be observed. Thus, Gabrielse (1972) mentioned from the Snake River iron-formation, at the base of the coarse clastic Rapitan Group in northwest Canada, an average content of 46% iron in the hematite-jasper. Dorr II (1945; 1973a) describes from the Mato Grosso, Brazil the jaspilitic banded hematite deposit of Urucum, which has an average iron content of 56.9% (range 48.7–62.1% Fe) and is probably the highest grade sedimentary iron-formation in the world. The deposit is interbedded with detrital clastic material and, abnormally, with horizons of high-grade sedimentary manganese oxides.

Occurrences of Palaeozoic (?) banded hematite jaspers with an average iron content of 56.5% are known in the Himalayas of Nepal (O'Rourke, 1961). The origin of these deposits, as well as those of most of the younger Phanerozoic banded iron-formations summarized by O'Rourke (1961), is in many respects not comparable with the older iron-formations and remains enigmatic.

Sedimentary facies of iron-formations

The development of different facies of iron-formation dependent on sedimentary environments is similar to that of Phanerozoic marine-sedimentary iron deposits of the Minette-type explicitly defined by Borchert (1952, 1964). As is commonly known, iron occurs in nature in different oxidation states, depending mainly on the environment of deposition. The kind of chemically precipitated iron minerals is dependent principally on the pH and Eh conditions as the chief controlling factors of kind and amount of the precipitate, as has been demonstrated by Krumbein and Garrels (1952). Concentrations as well as changes of p/T conditions have no significant influence on the kind of the precipitates. As stressed by Krumbein and Garrels (1952, p. 3), the pH and Eh values in normal marine environments show only slight variations between pH 8.4/Eh + 0.4 near the surface and pH 7.5/Eh + 0.1 near the bottom. For iron-formation facies reflecting reducing depositional conditions, James (1954) consequently suggested that iron-formations containing sulfide-facies have been deposited in basins which were partly cut off from the open sea by bars, thus allowing the formation of restricted conditions with strongly negative Eh for the deposition of iron-sulfides. James (1954) and later Gross

(1965) stressed the close relationship between composition, mineralogy and the oxidation state of chemically precipitated sediments and depositional environment, which allows a classification of distinctive facies types related to controlling physico-chemical factors. Thus, James (1954) separated four distinctive facies of iron-formation, namely oxide, silicate, carbonate and sulfide facies, which were deposited in that order from shallow to deep water within the basin, in chemical environments with relatively high Eh (oxide facies) to strongly negative Eh (sulfide-facies) and intermediate Eh values in the carbonate and silicate facies. This concept can be applied worldwide to all types of banded iron-formation, to the Algoma-type as well as to the Superior-type. Fig. 7 illustrates the relative position of iron-formation facies in a restricted sedimentary basin. It has to be noted that the facies are commonly intergradational and a complete successive pattern is, to the writer's knowledge, not developed in nature. Associations of carbonate—sulfide facies have already been described in an earlier chapter from the Michipicoten basin (Goodwin, 1973). Sulfide facies is practically absent in all major iron-formations and apparently confined to the Archean type. Dorr II (1973b, p. 1021) mentions only a thin one in Gabon, Africa. There is a remarkable difference between the great iron-formations of the Northern and the Southern Hemispheres as to their homogeneity and facies association as Dorr II (1973a) has pointed out. Contrary to many major deposits in North America and Russia, in the iron-formations of the Southern Hemisphere, the carbonate and silicate facies are rare exceptions and oxide facies is by far the dominant type.

Transitions between hematite—magnetite and silicate—carbonate facies have been described by Gastil and Knowles (1960) from the Labrador trough. From the Gunflint Iron Formation, Minnesota, Goodwin (1956) describes lateral transitions between magnetite—silicate and carbonate facies.

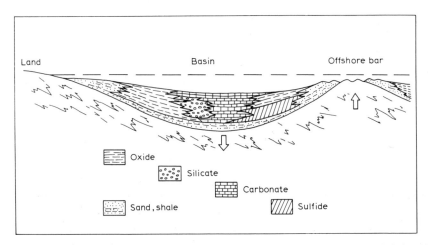

Fig. 7. Schematic section showing the lateral and vertical distribution of different facies of iron-formation in a barred depositional basin (slightly modified from James, 1954).

TABLE II

Special features of sedimentary facies of iron-formations (slightly modified from James, 1954)

	Oxide-facies		Silicate-facies	Carbonate-facies	Sulfide facies
	hematitic	magnetitic			
Lithology	evenly to maculate banded; alternating layers of hematite and quartz (chert)	evenly to maculate banded; layers of magnetite and silicate–carbonate- chert	± well banded granular green silicates, interlayered with quartz (chert) and magnetite	± well banded layers of carbonates and quartz (chert)	finely banded pyritic and carbonaceous slate with chert
Iron minerals	hematite (martite)	magnetite	hydrous iron silicates; greenalite; stilpnomelane; minnesotaite: (carbonates, iron oxides)	iron carbonates siderite, ankerite (magnetite, pyrite, iron silicates)	pyrite (iron silicates, carbonates)
Iron content (average % Fe)	30–42 (φ38)	25–35	20–30	20–35 (φ21)	15–25
Special features	no detrital dilution; (oolites)	granules, oolites	transitional to magnetite-oxide and carbonate-facies	stylolites, graphitic	commonly graphitic
Chemical environment	strongly oxidizing	weakly oxidizing to weakly reducing	weakly reducing	reducing	strongly reducing

The characteristic features of different chemical facies of iron-formation are summarized in Table II.

Sedimentary structures

One of the most distinctive features of iron-formations is their typical layering of alternating iron-rich and silica-rich bands. Despite some conflicting hypotheses, there is strong evidence that the banding represents a pre-metamorphic fabric. In metamorphosed iron-formations, such as the itabirites of the Minas Series of Brazil, this can be firmly concluded where locally penecontemporaneously reworked, already banded but not folded itabirite boulders are found in the iron-formation, apparently reworked pre-orogenically by intra-environmental sedimentary processes.

The lamination of different iron-formations ranges from less than one millimetre to several centimetres. It is caused above all by the mineralogical change in iron-rich and silica-rich layers and, if metamorphosed, can be accentuated by recrystallization of the primary mineral constituents, which leads to a certain purification of the individual layers. Thus, metamorphism generally preserves the original banding. As Dorr II (1964, 1973b) and Eichler (1968) have already pointed out, an increasing degree of metamorphism increases the grain size of quartz and iron-oxide minerals, which ranges from 0.01 mm for quartz and 0.001 mm for hematite in the lower greenschist-facies to 0.5 mm for quartz and 0.4 mm for hematite in the lower almandine-amphibolite-facies of the "Iron Quadrangle" in Minas Gerais/Brazil. In cases of extreme recrystallization, a metamorphic banding may obscure or be superimposed on the original fine lamination if the individual minerals grow to grain sizes which exceed the thickness of the primary banding. Normally, this recrystallization is parallel to the primary bedding planes, but it may also follow the schistosity of the rock, thus obliterating the original bedding.

The typical features and scales of banding have been described in detail from the iron-formation of the Dales Gorge Member of the Hamersley Group in Western Australia by Trendall and Blockley (1970) and Trendall (1965, 1973a, 1973b). As the Hamersley Group has nowhere undergone metamorphism, the primary banding is here in its original state and can be studied better, of course, than in metamorphosed iron-formations. According to their size and thicknesses, Trendall distinguishes three scales of banding:

(1) Large-scale macrobands are defined by alternations between thin layers of shale and thicker layers of banded cherty iron-formation. The alternating change of these two distinct lithologies, ranging between 0.6–15 m in thickness, results in a cycle of 33 macrobands in the Dales Gorge iron-formation. A similar cyclicity in the deposition of iron-formations could be observed also in Minas Gerais/Brazil (Eichler, 1968), where the Cauê-Itabirite shows a five-fold interruption by intercalated pelitic-dolomitic layers, which can be followed in one area over a distance of about 30 km. This has been attributed by the writer to repeated changes of transgressive and regressive phases which interrupted a constant deposition of the iron-formation (see Fig. 8).

(2) The medium-scale mesobands are defined by Trendall as the banding of the scale which is usually referred to when one uses the term "banded iron-formation". Mesobands are the alternating layers, some millimetres to centimetres thick, of iron-poor chert (quartz) and iron-rich "chert-matrix" bands.

(3) Microbands mark the internal repetitive lamination of most chert mesobands by evenly distributed iron minerals within the chert in thin (0.2–2 mm) layers. According to Trendall, microbanding is the only primary structure now preserved which reflects seasonal alternations of the original colloidal precipitate, and he therefore called them "varves". The medium-scale banding is thought to result from post-depositional compaction of the laminated precipitate and understood to be a secondary diagenetic structure. The question as to where to draw the limit between the primary and secondary origin of the banding, i.e., laminations caused by direct precipitation versus those formed by early

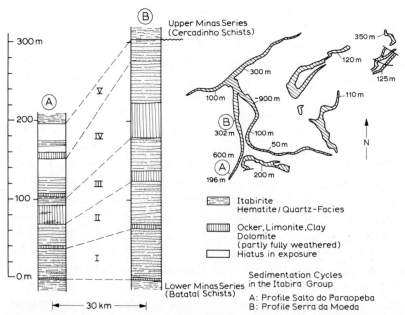

Fig. 8. Stratigraphic sections of the Cauê-Itabirite in the "Iron-Ore Quadrangle" of Minas Gerais Brazil, showing a cyclicity of deposition of iron-formation. The map shows the distribution of iron-formation in the iron-ore quadrangle with local thicknesses (from Eichler, 1968, p. 45).

diagenesis in the colloidal precipitate, perhaps in some form of a Liesegang phenomenon, is not yet clear.

As Trendall (1973a) has shown, microbanding and mesobanding are continuous over the whole Hamersley Group outcrop and could be correlated so far over a lateral distance of 296 km. Based on analogies with numerous iron-formations elsewhere in the world, such as of the Transvaal System of South Africa, the Marquette Range, Indian and other Australian occurrences, Trendall believed that the wide lateral extent of all kinds of banding is a typical original feature of iron-formations in general. In metamorphosed and, due to subsequent orogenies usually folded, iron-formations this is of course, difficult to prove. However, observations elsewhere confirm that macrobanding is continuous at least over some tens of kilometres and the fine lamination is traceable over tens to hundreds of metres.

Another remarkable feature of the Hamersley iron-formation is the occurrence of lenticular biconvex chert lenses along the bedding planes of the evenly banded iron-formation. These blobs or chert pods, as Trendall and Blockley (1970) have described them, are completely enclosed by the layered chert-matrix, the microbands of which are not abruptly truncated but continue with larger intervals across the chert-pod. The present author fully agrees with Trendall, that this feature demonstrates clear evidence for an early diagenetic compaction of the original sediment. Assuming that the chert-pod represents the original thickness of the adjacent micro-banded layer, this has then been com-pacted at a ratio of about 7 : 1, average from a large number of examples measured by Trendall. In analogy to this, many of the quartz pebbles and elongated nodular structures, commonly found in metamorphosed iron-formations elsewhere in exactly the same rela-tionship to the surrounding banding, may be considered as recrystallized relicts of meta-morphosed chert pods and pinch-and-swell structures.

Primary depositional sedimentary features, other than the banding, are rarely de-scribed in the literature. Clastic components, such as allochthonous heavy minerals and clastic quartz or feldspar as well as sedimentary features like cross-bedding and graded bedding, are normally absent in iron-formations.

There are, however, certain sedimentary structures noted in various iron-formations, which indicate occasional changes of the surmised quiet-water conditions during deposi-tion. In the Gunflint and Vulcan Iron Formations of the Lake Superior region, Cumber-lidge and Stone (1964) and Bayley and James (1973) described iron-silicate granules, interlayered with chert and grading laterally into iron oxide and/or iron-silicate oolites.

Oolitic textures in connection with cross-bedded cherts are also observed in iron-for-mations of various greenstone belts of South Africa (cf. Beukes, 1973) and in Superior-type iron-formations of a shallow-water, lagoonal platform facies in the Circum-Ungava geosyncline of Canada (Dimroth, 1972).

Algal structures, which occur commonly within conglomeratic and oolitic zones of the Biwabik Iron Formation in the Gunflint District of Ontario are reported by Goodwin (1956), Barghoorn and Tyler (1965) and Bayley and James (1973) and likewise in the Kuruman Iron Formation of the Transvaal Group by Beukes (1973).

Other sedimentary features mentioned in the literature include stylolites, common in the carbonate-facies; scour-and-fill structures; prelithification slump structures; shrinkage cracks and pygmatically folded chert bands (Gross, 1972). These diagenetic deforma-tional features clearly indicate that both the chert and the iron were deposited originally as a colloidal mass. Thus, most of the textural elements are results of the compaction, desiccation and diagenetic alteration of the original amorphous precipitate. Most prob-ably the micro-banding also represents a diagenetic, rather than a primary sedimentary structure.

A survey of the literature reveals that iron-formations of the Middle Precambrian Superior-type can be grouped, according to their sedimentary features, basically into two types: an evenly banded, non-granular type and a granular type, composed of granules and oolites in a chert matrix, the latter probably resulting from reworking in the still pre-lithification stage of the proto-sediment.

Diagenetic and metamorphic alterations of the mineral phases

It is now widely accepted that iron-formations were deposited as a chemical precipi-tate of silica- and iron-rich gels and possibly some less important colloidal substances and

TABLE III

Comparative mineral assemblages in diagenetic and metamorphic iron-formation

Facies	Oxide	Silicate	Carbonate	Sulfide
Diagenetic pre-metamorphic	Fe-hydroxides hydrohematite magnetite	Fe-SiO$_2$-gels (cryptocrystalline) greenalite, chamosite (magnetite, carbonates)	Fe-carbonates (Fe-silicates, magnetite)	Fe-sulfides in bituminous slate
	chert, cryptocrystalline quartz	chert (quartz)	chert (quartz)	chert
Low-grade metamorphic	hematite magnetite	chlorite minnesotaite stilpnomelane chamosite (?) (clay minerals)	siderite ankerite magnetite Fe-silicates (clay minerals)	pyrite graphite magnetite carbonates (clay minerals)
	quartz	quartz	quartz	quartz
Metamorphic	hematite magnetite (martite)	minnesotaite stilpnomelane cummingtonite grunerite riebeckite micas (olivine)	siderite ankerite magnetite clino-pyroxene ortho-pyroxene riebeckite	pyrrhotite pyrite magnetite graphite sericite
	quartz	quartz	quartz	quartz
Fe-content (%)	30–42 (ϕ38)	20–30 (ϕ26)	20–35 (ϕ21)	15–25 (ϕ20)

small amounts of synsedimentary clay minerals (see paper in *Econ. Geol.*, 1973, pp. 913–1179). The result of the diagenetic alteration of these precipitates is an alternation of silica-rich and iron-rich layers with the sedimentary and compaction features already described above.

The original mineral composition of diagenetic and low-grade metamorphic iron-formation comprises fine-grained chert, jasper or quartz and the characteristic iron minerals of the different sedimentary facies, such as oxides (hematite, magnetite, hydro-hematite), iron phyllosilicates (chamosite, chlorite, greenalite, minnesotaite, stilpnomelane), carbonates (ferro-dolomite ankerite, siderite) and iron sulfides (pyrite). The appearance of iron-rich cummingtonite–grunerite amphiboles marks the boundary to metamorphic iron-formation. The boundary between diagenetic and low-grade metamorphic minerals cannot clearly be drawn, since secondary quartz, ankerite and siderite are observed in unmetamorphosed iron-formations (Edwards, 1958; Trendall and Blockley, 1970) and secondary magnetite and iron-silicates formed during diagenetic conditions (Dimroth and Chauvel, 1972) as well as during low-grade metamorphism (La Berge, 1964).

Distinct mineralogical facies depend chiefly on physico-chemical variations during deposition of iron-formations but reflect also, as French (1973) pointed out, mechanical differences in the depositional environment: silicates, such as greenalite and chamosite, are common in granule-bearing cherts, whereas in evenly layered iron-formations, which reflect more quiet-water conditions, oxides, silicates and carbonates together with non-granular chert occur in more homogeneous layers of frequently mono-mineralic composition. A comprehensive review of the changes in mineral assemblages with increasing metamorphism is given by French (1973), Klein (1973) and Melnik and Siroshtan (1973). See also Table III, compiled by the present author, and Chapter 5 by Mookherjee, Vol. 4.

The oxide-facies of unmetamorphosed iron-formation normally consists of alternating bands of finely grained chert (quartz) and hematite and/or magnetite. Increasing metamorphism is accompanied by a gradual increase in grain size of the quartz and iron oxides so that the grain size, especially that of quartz, can be used as an indicator of metamorphic grade, as James (1954) and Gross (1961) have shown. Similarly, Dorr (1964) notes a common increase of the grain sizes quartz form 0.01 mm in the greenschist facies to 0.5 mm in the garnet-amphibolite facies of metamorphosed iron-formations in Brazil.

The main influence of metamorphism is restricted to recrystallization textures superimposed on the original banding, which is normally preserved in the metamorphosed iron-formation. The result is a neat banding, to a certain degree purified by the recrystallization, of quartz–hematite (specularite), quartz–magnetite or quartz–magnetite–hematite. Reactions among the original mineral phases do not take place and also the chemical composition is persistent through progressive metamorphism of oxide-facies iron-formation.

In predominantly hematitic oxide-facies iron-formation it is frequently noted that the magnetite content increases with depth, i.e. towards the bottom of synclinal structures. This is the case in the itabirite deposits of Brazil as mentioned by Dorr II (1973b, p. 1011) and also in some occurrences in Liberia, known to the author. It is not clear whether this systematic increase of magnetite towards the lower parts of folded rock units is related to metamorphism or reflects a primary, diagenetic feature of the sequences.

The carbonate-facies, in its original state, generally is composed of chert (quartz) and one or more iron-bearing carbonates as well as smaller amounts of magnetite and iron silicates. If iron silicates are absent, metamorphism does not provoke any chemical reactions among the constituent phases and the only result is a recrystallization and increase in grain size. However, according to Klein (1973), several reactions among chert and the carbonates, forming new silicates (e.g., clinopyroxene or orthopyroxene), can take place if the potential of CO_2 is reduced during metamorphism. Actinolite may form from ferroan dolomite if the chemical potential of H_2O is high enough, while that of CO_2 is low during metamorphism. The association of the normal quartz–carbonate–magnetite assemblage of carbonate-facies iron-formations with metamorphic silicates indicates local changes in the chemical potential of CO_2 of the system, which normally has been essentially closed to CO_2 even under high-grade metamorphic conditions. Thus, depending both on physico-chemical changes during metamorphism and on detrital sedimentary dilutions, carbonate-facies iron-formations may contain locally crystallized iron silicates such as riebeckite, stilpnomelane or minnesotaite. This assemblage is thought to have formed under low-grade metamorphic conditions (2–5 kbar; 200–350°C) whereas siderite, ferrodolomite–ankerite and chlorite comprise the late diagenetic assemblage (1–2 kbar; 150–200°C). Riebeckite and crocidolite may be formed both in the diagenetic and low-grade metamorphic stages when sufficient soda is available (French, 1973).

Hydrous iron silicates such as greenalite, stilpnomelane and minnesotaite together with carbonates, hydrous iron oxides and chert are the main constituents of the unmetamorphosed silicate-facies. Progressive metamorphism results essentially in a decarbonization and dehydratation of the original phases accompanied by numerous reactions between the carbonates, cherts and progressively formed silicates, mostly of the cummingtonite–grunerite family. With increasing metamorphism both clino- and ortho-amphiboles, garnet and ortho- and clino-pyroxenes can be formed. Sodium-rich members of amphibole and pyroxene may be formed locally in chemically suitable environments. The appearance of olivine (fayalite) has only been reported from contact metamorphic iron-formations, for example along the contact of the Duluth Gabbro and the Biwabik Iron Formation, but was never yet found in regional metamorphic iron-formations (Klein, 1973).

The typically banded amphibole- and pyroxene-rich iron-bearing schists and gneisses, which are frequently alternating with quartz–carbonate–magnetite layers are considered to be high-metamorphic silicate-facies. In certain cases, if the original aluminum content was low, the metamorphosed silicate-facies may be indistinguishable from a metamorphosed chert–carbonate facies.

Sulfide-facies is the least important rock type of iron-formation. It has been described by James (1954) from the Lake Superior region as a finely banded pyritic and carbonaceous cherty slate. Common accessory minerals are chlorite, stilpnomelane along with magnetite and amorphous carbon, as also described by Trendall and Blockley (1970) from the Hamersley Group in Western Australia. With increasing grade of metamorphism, an increase of the grain size of pyrite is generally noted (James, 1955). Under high-grade metamorphic conditions pyrrhotite forms at the expense of pyrite (Thompson, 1972) and the amorphous carbon, probably organic matter, gives way to well-crystallized graphite, as French (1968) concluded from studies of the Biwabik Iron Formation.

In conclusion, it can be stated that metamorphism of all facies-types of iron-formation does not significantly change the original chemical bulk composition of the precursor material, the original sedimentary features of which are generally preserved in the metamorphosed rock. However, there can be noted a broad variety of reactions among the

constituent original phases in consequence of different grades of metamorphism, specific
to a given facies-type of iron-formation.

Organic remains

A close association between organic remains and iron-formations is frequently observed and has already been mentioned by Leith (1903), Harder and Chamberlin (1915)
and Gruner (1922) who suggested a connection between organic matter and precipitation
of cherty iron-formation. The most conspicuous features are the algal stromatolites,
already mentioned in the section above, and presumably formed by colonies of blue-green
algae and bacteria, which are similar to Phanerozoic and younger forms (Cloud, 1973).

Microfossils have been identified in the cherty matrix of such algal horizons in the
Gunflint District of Ontario, by Barghoorn and Tyler (1965). In South Africa, microfossils are found in carbonaceous chert bands of greenstone belts as well as in cherts of the
Kuruman Iron Formation (cf. Beukes, 1973), where primitive oils and amino-acids have
also been isolated from crocidolite by Harington (1962 – cf. Beukes, 1973). These organic
substances are believed to have been derived from primitive organisms.

In more highly metamorphosed iron-formations the existence of organic matter is
difficult to prove. However, occurrences such as the itabirites of the "Iron Quadrangle"
of Brazil, which are frequently closely associated with graphitic schists, probably original
bituminous pelites, and high contents of carbon particularly in the carbonate-facies,
suggest the presence of organic life in the depositional environments of those iron-formations.

La Berge (1967, 1973) described in a comprehensive study microfossils in Precambrian
iron-formations and their possible influence during deposition. His petrographic studies of
many weakly or non-metamorphic iron-formations from North America, Australia and
South Africa reveal the common presence of spheroidal structures, ranging from 5 to 35
μm and averaging about 30 μm in diameter, in both Early Precambrian Algoma-type and
Middle Precambrian Superior-type iron-formations. The structures occur within granules,
which build up the sedimentary fabric of the iron-formation. They are preserved by a
pigmentation of extremely fine hematite, iron-silicates or organic matter as well as by
siderite and pyrite but preservation by magnetite was never observed. As La Berge (1967)
pointed out, the ubiquitous occurrence in cherts of Precambrian iron-formations in time
and space, the presence in all sedimentary facies of iron-formation, the uniform size of
these structures also in different depositional environments, and the similarity to distinctive
organic forms, can best be explained by the interpretation that the spherical structures
are relict microfossils rather than local diagenetic or metamorphic structures.

Similar structures have already been earlier described in iron-formations form Singhbhum, India, by Spencer and Percival (1952), from Krivoy Rog, Soviet Union, by Piatnitsky (1924) and from South Africa by Wagner (1928).

It should be noted that several authors (cf. La Berge, 1973) favour an origin other than biological for the spheroidal structures, such as abrasion of granules or post-depositional contraction phenomena in an original colloidal silica layer, as suggested by Spencer and Percival (1952). However, as La Berge (1967, 1973) has demonstrated, many features strongly support the conclusion that the spheroidal structures are of biogenic origin, so that the supposition cannot be excluded that these micro-organisms may have been directly involved in the deposition of the colloidal materials. In addition to these conclusions, special studies on carbon-isotope variations in Early Precambrian cherts by Perry Jr. and Tan (1973) and Perry Jr. et al. (1973) suggest an organic activity within the depositional basins. The fact that the $^{13}C/^{12}C$ ratio of carbonates from Precambrian iron-formations is considerably lower than that of Phanerozoic marine carbonates is explained by a major contribution of volcanic carbon, by contemporaneous organic activity during sedimentation or by diagenetic and postdiagenetic reactions with ^{13}C exchange between carbonates and carbon-bearing organic matter. Sinc many of the depositional environments are lacking evidence of volcanic activity during deposition of iron-formations, the investigations of Perry Jr. et al. supply further evidence that a biologic mechanism was involved not only in the precipitation of silica but also of iron-oxides in Precambrian iron-formations. These results also support Cloud's (1968; 1973) suggestion that ferrous iron may have acted as an oxygen-receptor for primitive photo-synthetic organisms in the presumably oxygen-free contemporaneous atmosphere and hydrosphere. If Cloud's theory is factual then the iron-rich laminae might be considered as the result of a seasonal growth of procaryotic micro-organisms, which acted as the source of oxygen needed for the precipitation of dissolved ferrous oxides as unsoluble hydroxides or ferric oxides.

Chemical composition

The chemical composition of iron-formations varies in a wide range according to the original sedimentary facies. Since in nature the changes from one facies type to another generally are gradational, it is almost impossible to establish a representative average chemical analysis for a distinct facies of iron-formation, with the exception of the oxide-facies. In all iron-formations, of course, silica and iron are the chief constituents, the balance being made up by subordinate elements — mainly alumina and alkalies — and trace elements. Base metals (Cu, Pb, Zn, Co, Ni) are very low or completely absent and phosphorus also is very low, but manganese may reach considerable percentages in some iron-formations. (Cf. Chapter 9 by Roy, this volume.)

The writer has attempted to select some typical chemical analyses from the extensive literature — almost every article on iron-formations quotes the respective analyses — for comparison of distinct facies types from different shield areas (see Tables IV and V). A more complete review of the chemistry of iron-formations is given by James (1966) to which publication the interested reader is referred for more details.

The iron contents of a distinct facies of iron-formations other than oxide-facies show

TABLE IV

Chemical composition of carbonate-facies iron-formations

	Minas Gerais		Lake Superior Region		Krivoy Rog/Ukraine	
	Average	Range	Gunflint District	Range		
	1	2	3	4	5	6
Fe	21.23	14 −28.2	20.87	20.8 −32.4	25.32	17.98
FeO	22.22	15 −30	26.28	26.3 −35.2	28.07	20.90
Fe_2O_3	5.74	1 −11	0.64	0.3 − 5.3	4.90	2.40
SiO_2	48.72	38 −60	46.46	24 −46.5	38.58	58.22
Al_2O_3	0.15	0 − 0.5	0.24	0.24− 2.9	3.27	0.48
Mn	0.50	0 − 0.5	0.13	0.1 − 1.4	0.03	0.01
P	0.07	0.05− 0.1	0.057	0.01− 0.4	n.d.	n.d.
CaO	4.60	3 − 7	3.10	0.5 − 1.9	1.79	1.33
MgO	0.84	0.5 − 2	1.87	1.8 − 4.8	0.47	0.44
K_2O	+	0 − 0.05	n.d.	0 − 0.2	0.12	0.04
Na_2O	0.01	0 − 0.2	n.d.	0.04− 0.09	0.39	0.27
TiO_2	+	0 − 0.01	+	0 − 1.15	0.03	0.02
CO_2	3.58	3 −21	19.96	19.4 −27.6	19.02	13.00
S	2.76	0 −10	0.05	0 − 0.05	n.d.	n.d.
H_2O+	2.67	0.1 −16	1.15	0.2 − 1.8	0.81	0.50
L.O.I.	10.62	10 −16				

1 = "Iron-Ore Quadrangle", Minas Gerais, Brazil (Gair, 1962).
2 = Range of determinations.
3 = Gunflint District, Minnesota (Irving and Van Hise, cf. James, 1954, table 3F).
4 = Lake Superior region (range, cf. James 1954, tabel 3A–H).
5,6 = Krivoy Rog, Ukraine (Semenenko et al., 1956, cf. James 1966, table 17O–P).
L.O.I. = loss on ignition.
n.d. = not determined.

considerable variations, due to other accompanying elements, which are virtually absent in the oxide-facies. Thus, the content of carbon (graphite) in the sulphide-facies may occasionally reach amounts of as much as 8%, and silicate-facies iron-formation may have considerable amounts of sodium, up to several percent.

Contrary to the wide range in chemical composition of the silicate- and carbonate-facies the oxide-facies, especially the hematite–quartz assemblages, is characterized by a striking chemical homogeneity in occurrences all over the world. Most remarkable is the constant iron content, averaging about 38% Fe. The tabulation given in Table V could easily be extended with analogous analyses of oxide-facies iron-formations from India, Russia, South Africa or elsewhere. Thus, for instance, Krishnan (1973) mentioned for

TABLE V

Chemical composition of oxide-facies iron-formations

	Minas Gerais	Liberia		Lake Superior	U.S.S.R.	Western Australia
	1	2	3	4	5	6
Fe	37.80	38.36	39.55	36.26	37.65	36.80
FeO	2.10	12.95	4.36	1.6	0.71	1.41
Fe_2O_3	51.69	40.45	51.70	50.1	53.08	51.00
SiO_2	42.89	41.24	40.90	40.15	44.80	46.94
Al_2O_3	0.42	0.87	0.24	0.8	0.37	0.00
Mn	0.3	0.12	0.26	0.13	+	0.02
P	0.03	0.058	0.112	0.03	+	0.17
CaO	0.1	0.84	0.17	2.0	0.28	+
MgO	+	1.35	0.10	1.4	0.07	0.00
K_2O		⎰0.20	n.d.	n.d.	⎰0.12	0.00
Na_2O		⎱	n.d	n.d	⎱	0.00
TiO_2	+	0.17	n.d	n.d	0.07	+
CO_2	–	0.19	n.d.	2.6	n.d.	–
S	–	0.03	n.d.	0.009	n.d.	–
H_2O+	0.43	0.27	0.60	n.d.	0.04	0.68
L.O.I.				2.6		

1 = "Iron Ore Quadrangle", Minas Gerais, Brazil (Eichler, 1970).
2 = Bong Range, Liberia, Drillhole 1 (Thienhaus, 1964).
3 = Nimba Mts., Liberia, Channel Sample, taken by the author 1961.
4 = Menominee District, Michigan (James, 1966, table 10).
5 = Krivoy Rog, Ukraine (Semenenko et al., 1956, cf. James, 1966, table 10A).
6 = Middle Back Range, Western Australia (Edwards, 1956, cf. James, 1966, table 10G).
L.O.I. = loss on inginition.
n.d. = not determined.

"magnetite-quartzites" from Madras/India an average iron content of 38% and Plaksenko et al. (1973) give various analyses of "specular iron hematite–magnetite quartzites", ranging between 36.89–39.61% Fe and aound 40% SiO_2. The regional average of unweathered itabirites (oxide-facies) from Minas Gerais/Brazil is given by Dorr II (1964) as 37.9% Fe and the balance of 44.7% SiO_2 consists almost exclusively of quartz. Therefore, understandably, the ratio of iron to silica varies only in a small range in this facies type. In several iron-formations of the hematite–quartz assemblage the writer (Eichler, 1970) calculated a ratio of Fe_2O_3/SiO_2 of 0.98–1.26 with an average of 1.16. It is of interest that these values correspond to the ratio of iron to silica as determined by Reifenberg (1927) in artificial precipitates of colloidal iron-hydroxides and silica (Fe_2O_3/SiO_2 = 0.84–1.4). Incidentally, the same value (average ratio 1.21) can be found in some Jurassic chamositic ores (Harder, 1951).

The ubiquitous chemical analogies of oxide-facies iron-formations, apparently indepen-

TABLE VI

Comparative chemical analyses (average) of sedimentary facies of iron-formation (compiled from James, 1966 and Eichler, 1968, 1970)

	Oxide-facies	Silicate-facies	Carbonate-facies	Sulfide-facies
Fe	37.80	26.5	21.23	20.0
FeO	2.10	28.9	22.22	2.35
Fe_2O_3	51.69	5.6	5.74	–
FeS_2	–	–	–	38.70
SiO_2	42.89	50.7	48.72	36.67
Al_2O_3	0.42	0.4	0.15	6.90
Mn	0.3	0.4	0.50	0.001
P	0.03	–	0.07	0.09
CaO	0.1	0.1	4.60	0.13
MgO	+	4.2	0.84	0.65
K_2O	+	–	+	1.81
Na_2O	+	–	0.01	0.26
TiO_2	+	+	+	0.39
CO_2	–	5.1	14.10	–
S	–	+	2.76	
SO_3	–	–	–	2.60
C	–	+	++	7.60
H_2O+	0.43	5.2	2.67	1.25

dent from the thickness of banding, and the close association of iron and silica may only be attributed to a generally valid chemical (or biochemical) precipitation process and cannot be explained only by local environmental conditions.

Table VI is compiled by the author from numerous assays found in the literature. It does not claim to be strictly representative but attempts to give a general impression of the typical chemical composition of different facies.

Contrary to the vast number of chemical analyses available for the major elements in iron-formations, trace element studies are relatively scarce.

Information on trace elements in some iron-formations are provided by Plaksenko et al. (1973) for the silicate- and oxide-facies in the Kursk Magnetic Anomaly. In the order of decreasing amounts Ba, Ti, Cu, Ni and V lie in the range between 110–28 p.p.m. These elements do not show any significant differences between distinct facies types. Barbosa and Grossi Sad (1973) studied the distribution of trace elements in hematite/quartz and dolomitic itabirite from Minas Gerais/Brazil (Table VII).

It is difficult to draw any conclusion as to the significance of these trace elements for the different iron-formation rocks. Barbosa and Grossi Sad concluded that the average values for some elements are concordant with the world average for ultramafic rocks, while other elements correspond with the average in limestone rocks.

TABLE VII

Spectrographic analyses (average, in p.p.m.) for trace elements in itabirite from Casa de Pedra Deposit, Minas Gerais, Brazil (from Barbosa and Grossi Sad, 1973, p. 129)

	Hematite	Itabirite	Dolomite-itabirite
V	44.5	35.0	41.6
Cu	19.0	22.0	7.0
Ni	22.0	20.5	15.0
Cr	35.0	28.5	21.0
Ba	91.0	179.0	27.3
Co	18.0	69.0	–
Zr	31.0	17.3	–
Ti	657.0	216.6	150.0
Mn	1,180.0	1,785.0	1,600.0

SIMILARITIES AND DIFFERENCES BETWEEN BANDED AND OOLITIC IRON-FORMATIONS

In spite of many lithologic and sedimentologic similarities as to their sedimentary environments and chemical facies there exist, in many respects, profound differences between Precambrian banded iron-formations and Phanerozoic marine-sedimentary chemically precipitated iron rocks. It should be mentioned, however, that banded iron-formations which resemble each other mainly in age, size and evolution of their depositional basins, chemistry and mineralogy and presence of chert, may differ considerably in their stratigraphic sequence and continuity, thickness, thickness variation, scale of banding and in their lithologic association with clastic or volcano-clastic rocks. These contrasts between different basins of deposition may be of local or regional importance as has been demonstrated in a comparison of the Hamersley, Animikie and Transvaal basins by Trendall (1968). The basic and significant similarities of the Precambrian banded iron-formations, however, justify their classification as one major group of iron-rich sediments in contrast to the younger non-banded iron-formations.

Both the Archean and the Proterozoic iron-formations are characterized by their typical banding of iron-rich and iron-poor chert layers containing little or no clastic debris, comparatively low phosphorus, alkali and alumina and high iron contents and dwarfing by their enormous size all younger iron-ore deposits. A comparison between iron-formations and Minette-type ironstones, their most abundant counterpart in the Phanerozoic era, is briefly summarized in Table VIII showing the principal characteristics of both.

Considering the extensive distribution in space and time, banded iron-formations are certainly not mineralogical rarities; this description could be rather attributed to the non-banded great oolitic deposits of whatever size. Factors of only local significance, however, are not suitable to explain the accumulation of such immense concentrations of chemically precipitated iron and silica and the distinctive features of iron-formations.

TABLE VIII

Comparison of banded iron-formations and marine-sedimentary iron ores (Minette-type)

	Banded iron-formations	Minette-type iron-formations
Age	Precambrian most abundant in the pre-1,800 m.y. era	Phanerozoic most abundant in Mesozoic and Tertiary rocks
Dimension of sedimentary basins	extension: 600–1000 km width: 40–150 km	a few km
Thickness of single units	some 10 m to several 100 m	1 m to some 10 m
Volume of single deposits	some $100 \cdot 10^6$ tons to more than $1,000 \cdot 10^6$ tons	some $0.1 \cdot 10^6$ tons; rarely some $100 \cdot 10^6$ tons
Sedimentary environments	shallow-marine; miogeosynclinal; also eugeosynclinal; restricted basins (?); usually not reworked.	shallow-marine; epicontinental; near offshore; rarely brackish or limnic; frequently reworked.
Sedimentary structures	typically banded by interlayering with chert (quartz); clastic detritus insignificant or absent; sometimes oolitic	massive rocks with oolitic textures; commonly clastic impurities; no chert.
Sedimentary facies	oxide, carbonate, silicate, sulfide	oxide, carbonate, silicate, (sulfide)
Chemistry	P: usually less than 0.1% Al_2O_3: 0.1 – 1.5% alkalies: usually less than 2%	up to plus 1% frequently plus 4% up to plus 10%

HYPOTHESES OF ORIGIN

As a review of the vast literature on the genesis of iron-formations indicates, there is absolutely no shortage of theories as to their origin. Almost every study of an iron-formation deposit proposes a different model of genesis based on a careful analysis of the local features. However, a generally acceptable fundamental model for all iron-formations has, so far, not yet been established despite the fact that probably all the major iron-formations of the world are known and have been studied since mining of this important type of iron-ore deposits started at the beginning of the last century. The reasons for the lack of a uniform genetic model may be the impossibility of applying actualistic comparisons for many of the characteristic features of banded iron-formations, the deposition of which was definitely terminated in the Precambrian and, on the other hand, the obvious fact that comparable iron-formations were actually formed under rather different conditions. In fact, it is not really possible to explain all banded iron-formations by a uniform theory.

As pointed out by Eugster and Chou (1973) banded iron-formations are diversified rocks, in spite of their obvious common peculiarities, and are not likely to fit a single depositional model.

It is the author's opinion that there is nothing peculiar in explaining one type of sediment by basically similar, but in detail different processes. Take, for example, the enormous coal deposits of the Carboniferous, which are also episodic sedimentary accumulations that have formed under quite different depositional and climatic conditions almost contemporaneously: in paralic environments in a tropical zone (Northern Hemisphere) and in a cold peri-glacial environment in the southern Gondwana hemisphere. The discussion on the genesis of banded iron-formations goes back to the last century and already Winchell and Winchell (1891), who reviewed eighteen different theories for the Lake Superior iron-formations, came to the conclusion that it is evident "that no thoughtful person can ever again attempt to explain all deposits of iron by any one theory". Special emphasis on genetical aspects is given by Van Hise and Leith (1911), Gruner (1922), Moore and Maynard (1929), Woolnough (1941), Sakamoto (1950), James (1954), Hough (1958), Huber (1959), Lepp and Goldich (1964) and James and Sims (1973).

Any attempt to explain the origin of banded iron-formations has to take into account that this is a major rock type which was deposited during more than 85% of the earth's history and hence has to be considered as the principal and most typical type of iron-rich sediments on the whole. The lack of actualistic examples can only be explained by fundamentally important environmental conditions which had changed by the end of the Precambrian. One key factor in enabling the development of banded iron-formation was probably a generally anoxygenous atmosphere and hydrosphere in the Precambrian, thus facilitating the solution of iron in the ferrous state. The question arises as to how the iron could precipitate in an environment free of oxygen. This is commonly answered by the assumption that oxygen-generating microorganisms that were dependent on some oxygen-depressing matter, such as ferrous iron, have been involved in the precipitation processes. In fact, there is some firm evidence for the existence of microorgansisms contemporaneous with the deposition of iron-formation. Also, an extraordinary growth of oxygen-generating microorganisms in the depositional environments of Precambrian iron-formations is suggested to be an essential factor for iron precipitation, which is different from recent iron sediments. One of the most difficult problems still remaining is to find an explanation as to how iron and silica, devoid of other clastic constituents, could be separated in alternating layers of iron-rich and silica-rich layers. On the other hand, iron-formations show many familiar features similar to younger iron deposits, such as stratigraphic associations, deposition during transgressive phases in marine epicontinental environments and distinctive facies assemblages of the iron minerals. There is sufficient evidence to state that iron-formations are chemical sediments: the lack of clastic constituents in all major blanket deposits (no clastic quartz and heavy minerals), diagenetic features typical for colloidal precipitates, and the remarkably small range in chemical composition of a given facies of iron-formation.

The principal points for discussion as to the genesis of banded iron-formations are still the following:

(1) Sedimentary environment (marine epicontinental vs. intracratonic basins).

(2) Source of iron and silica (volcanogenic; terrigenic; biogenic).

(3) Mode of transport to the depositional site (as constituent of clastic material; colloidal solution; true solution).

(4) Deposition (anorganic or organic precipitation; clastic sedimentation).

(5) Cause of banding (chemical or biochemical; syngenetic-sedimentary; epigenetic during diagenesis or metamorphism).

Environments of deposition

Because of the most obvious sedimentological characteristics of banded iron-formations, that is the rhythmic banding and the scarcity of clastic components, many students have advocated a depositional environment in quiet intracratonic basins (Woolnough, 1941; Alexandrov, 1955 and others) and also in fresh-water lakes (Hough, 1958). More recently a continental playa-lake evaporite basin has been suggested by Eugster and Chou (1973) as a possible model for deposition of part of the iron-formations.

As it has been explicitly demonstrated by Goodwin (1973) almost all of the Archean banded iron-formations are confined to large cratonic basins of volcanic origin which cannot be compared with typical Proterozoic geosynclines or modern oceans. In opposition to this, the bulk of Proterozoic iron-formations represents enormous blanket deposits that were laid down in a marine shelf or epicontinental environment during certain stages of the geosynclinal evolution. This seems to be proved by the association with typical shelf sediments in many major iron-formation districts, for example in the Labrador trough (Gross, 1965; Dimroth, 1972) or in the Minas geosyncline of Brazil (Dorr II et al., 1959; Dorr II, 1973b; Eichler, 1968). As discussed earlier, many depositional basins have been arranged in barred or partially barred lagoons which held off terrestrial debris and permitted an undisturbed sedimentation in quiet shallow-water environments. From the writer's own observations, these conditions are obvious in the case of the itabirites of Minas Gerais, Brazil. Similarly, Dimroth (1972) described from the Labrador trough a lagoonal platform facies and a slightly deeper basin facies. (See his Chapter 5, this Vol.)

A barred basin of enormous dimensions has been suggested by Becker and Clayton (1972) and more recently by Trendall (1973) for the Hamersley iron-formation and also by Beukes (1973) for the Kuruman and Penge Iron Formations of South Africa which contain appreciable amounts of sodium and suggest that deposition took place in local, restricted basins under saline, shallow-water conditions, probably in a warm climate. Comparing the microbanding of iron-formation with saline, varved evaporites Trendall (1973) suggested that many iron-formations may have an evaporitic origin. But this model can not be generally valid since, on the other hand, iron-formations possibly have also been deposited together with glacio-marine associations in a cold climate, for example, those of the Rapitan Group and of the Damara Supergroup (Martin, 1965). As Beukes (1973, p. 981) pointed out, the same relationship probably holds for the iron-formations in the Witwatersrand and Transvaal Supergroups, as indicated by tillites and poorly sorted conglomerates which may represent glacial deposits. However, in accordance with Beukes and many other respected colleagues, the writer is of the opinion that more conclusive evidence for a glacial origin is needed. If this could be demonstrated, a single sedimentary environment model for deposition would not be applicable for all iron-formations, however, a marine environment has very likely been the most favourable.

Source of iron and silica

Sufficient information is available that both volcanic and weathering processes contributed to the deposition of iron-formations as a source of the constituent elements and hence a generally valid model for the source of iron and silica cannot be given. A direct relationship between iron-formations and contemporaneous volcanism is beyond doubt where these are stratigraphically closely associated with volcano-clastic material, as is the case in Archean basin deposits in Canada and in greenstone belts in South Africa and elsewhere. The silica was directly derived from acid volcanism (Beukes, 1973), whereas the iron possibly originated from weathering of preexisting iron-containing rocks. Subaquatic volcanic exhalations (Geijer and Magnusson, 1952; Goodwin, 1956) and subaquatic decomposition of lavas (Van Hise and Leith, 1911; Huber, 1959) are also supposed to be sources of the iron. On the other hand, many of the major Proterozoic iron-formations are evidently lacking contemporaneous volcanic activity, so that many authors suggest intensive weathering processes on the adjacent land masses as the chief source of iron and silica for these iron-formations. As discussed earlier in this chapter, epicontinental blanket deposits of iron-formation may be locally associated with contemporaneous volcanic rocks. But, as a general rule, these cannot be directly connected with the deposition of iron-formation since many other iron-formations are absolutely devoid of volcanic rocks.

The derivation of iron and silica from chemical weathering on land implies some serious problems concerning the transportation of such vast amounts, separated from detritus, to the quiescent depositional sites. Nevertheless, this hypothesis is favoured by many students as the most likely alternative, as for example by Gruner (1922), Woolnough (1941), Sakamoto (1950), Guild (1957). Dorr II (1963), Lepp and Goldich (1964) and many Russian authors (cf. Alexandrov, 1973). In fact, the volume of the iron contained in iron-formation deposits can easily be attributed to the iron leached from not too large masses of adjacent country rocks, as has been calculated, for example, for the Krivoy Rog area (see Alexandrov, 1973, p. 1055). In this case, of course, the environment must have been anoxygeneous, thus preventing the fixation of the iron and enabling a solution in the ferrous state during transport.

An interesting approach to the problem has been made by Holland (1973) who argues that a derivation of iron from both weathering and volcanic sources is unlikely and demonstrates quantitatively that upwelled sea-bottom water with only a few mg/l Fe may have been a possible source of iron*. This attractive hypothesis resembles that of Borchert (1952) who suggests that iron was concentrated within the basin by re-solution and mobilization from iron-bearing detritus in a "CO_2-zone". It may be suggested that such subaquatic (halmyrolytic) reactions, which are active in recent shelf environments (iron, manganese and phosphate nodules), could have been of much more importance in Precambrian shallow-marine basins.

To complete the review on source of iron and silica in iron-formations, some rather strange hypotheses should be mentioned invoking metasomatic, magmatic and even cosmic processes as cited by Alexandrov (1973). For some banded iron-formations in New Mexico, McLeRoy (1970) suggests an origin by hydrothermal replacement reactions in a pre-existing rock. These examples are certainly exceptions which do not fit into the well-established sedimentary pattern of all major iron-formations.

Transport, deposition and banding

There is common agreement that iron-formations are chemical rather than clastic sediments which is clearly proved by the sedimentological aspects, by the extraordinarily homogeneous chemical composition, especially of the oxide-facies, and by the scarcity or lack of clastic material. The quartz in metamorphosed iron-formations is certainly not of clastic origin as believed by Harder and Chamberlin (1915) and some other authors, but the product of recrystallization of primary amorphous silica during metamorphism. Also the hypothesis favoring a metasomatic silicification of sideritic carbonates (for instance Aldrich, 1929; Goodschild, 1953) cannot be upheld any longer since the deposition of chert clearly shows pre-lithification features of an autochthonous sediment, i.e. a chemical precipitate.

In the previous section three main probable sources of iron and silica have been discussed: weathering products from land areas adjacent to the basins, volcanic emanations within the basins, and derivation of these elements from the sea water itself. Any hypothesis has to come to terms with the question of how the chemical matter was transported to the site of deposition and how it was finally concentrated.

---

* Oceanic upwelling has been proposed for some time now as being responsible for the origin of phosphorite (see Cook, 1974, Chapter 11, this volume), but more recently has also been suggested as having supplied metals for such ore deposits as the Kupferschiefer (Brongersma-Sanders, 1965, and Chapter 7, Vol. 6).

Neglecting some unlikely hypotheses which ascribe the origin of iron-formation to metamorphic or metasomatic processes (for instance Tanatar, 1924; Marmo, 1956 and others) and accepting the obvious sedimentary character of this rock, the following hypotheses as to the deposition and banding can be specified:

(1) Due to their opposite electric charge, mutual precipitation of Fe-hydrosols and colloidal silica from the seawater (Moore and Maynard, 1929).

(2) Rhythmic banding by precipitation from alternately SiO_2- and Fe-containing volcanic emanations (for instance, Goodwin, 1956).

(3) Seasonal delivery predominantly of silica in dry seasons and of iron in rainy periods with solutions derived from the bordering land (Sakamoto, 1950; Alexandrov, 1955; Hough, 1958).

(4) Transport in rivers with periodically changing intensity and fractional deposition of coarse clastic, pelitic and chemically dissolved material, according to the force of the currents.

It appears highly improbable that large perennial rivers should have carried only such enormous amounts of dissolved matter without leaving any significant coarse clastic residue at the site of deposition. The environmental quiescence, undisturbed by torrential floods, must have been prevalent for long periods since uniformly banded iron-formations reach thicknesses of several hundred metres. Hence, a climate arid enough to impede large rivers has to be assumed (Holland, 1973). Cloud (1973) presumes that long periods of glaciation in which the surrounding land was worn down to low levels preceeded the deposition of the Late Proterozoic iron-formations free of land-derived debris. On the other hand, it is frequently noted that thick units of clastic sediments were laid down penecontemporaneously with the iron-formations, which does not favour a generally valid glaciation theory. Therefore, it is highly likely that the iron and the silica of whatever source, was transported by clastic-free solutions to the site of deposition.

A transport of dissolved iron over large distances implies the assumption of an atmosphere and hydrosphere which was free or nearly free of oxygen, thus allowing the iron to remain in solution in the ferrous state. As discussed by Cloud (1973), Garrels et al. (1973) and others, there is strong evidence for the absence of free atmospheric oxygen prior to about 1.8 billion years ago. This is indicated by the presence of easily oxidizable clastic grains or uraninite and pyrite in sedimentary rocks of about the same age as iron-formations in Canada, Brazil, the Baltic Shield and South Africa (see Cloud, 1973, p. 1137) and by the fact that continental red-bed deposits are absent in Archean and Late Proterozoic rock sequences.

The pronounced banding of iron-formation as a consequence of regularly repeated precipitation of iron and silica, originally deposited as amorphous colloidal phases, might be explained by both inorganic and organic processes. The probable mechanisms of deposition have been discussed in detail already by Borchert (1952) and James (1954; 1966) and more recently by Cloud (1973), Eugster and Chou (1973), Holland (1973) and Garrels et al. (1973). Precambrian ocean water is assumed to have been near saturation or saturated with respect to amorphous silica and to calcium carbonate. The concentration of dissolved iron should have been considerably higher in anoxygenic water, in the order of several mg/l Fe^{2+}, as pointed out by Holland. The chemical load of upwelling, deep, ocean water would be precipitated whenever suitable conditions were reached: ferric hydroxides precipitate if free oxygen becomes available, while ferrous hydroxides, iron-silicates and silica precipitate in response to pH and temperature changes in the shallower parts of the basins. The occurrence of stromatolites and algal-like procaryotic microorganisms in Precambrian iron-formations makes it very likely that these primitive photosynthesizing organisms were directly involved as oxygen donors for the precipitation of ferric iron oxides from ferrous solutions.

Any reconstruction of the banding mechanism remains highy speculative, but the most likely explanation would be to assume a more or less continuous inorganic precipitation of silica as a consequence of proper physico-chemical conditions, superconcentration or evaporation and, on the other hand, a periodical precipitation of Fe^{3+} with catalytic oxidation of Fe^{2+} by oxygen-generating microorganisms. The microbanding reflects a cyclicity which may represent seasonal, annual or also longer periodical changes in the chemical properties of the water and probably seasonal changes in the procaryotic metabolism, as suggested by Cloud (1973). For the origin of the mesobanding, Trendall 1973b suggests a long-term astronomical control with 23 year cyclicity in the Weeli Wolli Formation of the Hamersley Group. A valid explanation for the macrobanding is a secondary diagenetic segregation within on originally homogeneous gelatinous precipitate of iron and silica caused by compaction and dehydration. As suggested by the writer (Eichler, 1970) the iron would be mobilized in upward-streaming water in the highly porous sediment, to be precipitated near the water—sediment interface in response to the release of compaction pressure and change of pH/Eh conditions. Thus, the macrobanding, which is the typical scale of banding in iron-formations, might represent a secondary diagenetic feature of rhythmic precipitation, rather than a primary sedimentary alternation. Therefore, as can be frequently noted, the mesobands show only faint remains or may be devoid of the original microbanding.

To explain the remarkable scarcity of carbonate rocks in direct association with iron-formation and the exceptional separation of Fe, Ca and Mg it is suggested that, in a generally CO_2-rich environment, either the saturation with calcium and magnesium ions was not reached (Garrels et al., 1973) or that the relation between P_{CO_2} and the alkalinity and silicate buffering systems kept the pH too low for carbonate precipitation at the time of iron and silica precipitation (Cloud, 1973).

Following the interpretations given by Garrels et al. (1973) and Holland (1973) the paucity of banded iron-formation in Late Proterozoic and Phanerozoic sediments could be explained by an excess of free oxygen in the atmosphere and hydrosphere. In the evolution of primitive life eventually, about 700—1,000 m.y. ago (Garrels et al., 1973), a level was reached when photosynthetic oxygen production by procaryota surpassed the storage in O_2-consuming reservoirs and atmospheric oxygen began to rise. From then on the transport of dissolved ferrous iron was largely restricted to still remaining small portions of anoxic ocean basins as potential source areas of mobilized iron in the younger banded iron deposits. The banding of these deposits akin to banded iron-formations might be explained by a mechanism of reciprocal precipitation of iron-hydroxides and amorphous silica with diagenetic differentiation during compaction of the sludge.

CONCLUSIONS

It is commonly said that iron-formations are spread over at least 3,000 m.y. of the earth's early history, confined to the Precambrian with few unimportant enigmatic off-shoots in the Early Paleozoic. However, one of the most remarkable facts to result from the recent literature is that major iron-formations throughout the world can be grouped, according to their ages, into various epochs of deposition, most abundantly between 1,800 and 2,600 m.y. ago and probably with a climax at about 2,000 m.y. ago. These main epochs of repeated and presumably contemporaneous deposition on a world-wide scale and the obviously controlled distribution within mobile zones of the ancient con-tinents are thought to coincide with and to mark significant events in early crustal evolution.

One group of iron-formation – the Algoma-type – is predominantly connected with large Archean basins of volcano-tectonic origin and the derivation of iron and silica from volcanic sources seems beyond doubt. The second great group is represented by the Superior-type of iron-formation which forms enormous blanket deposits in miogeosyn-clinal and epicontinental marine environments along the margins of the old craton areas and is in general devoid of volcanic rock associations contemporaneous with deposition. Because of the obvious lack of detrital clastic constituents and the remarkably small range in chemical composition, there is common agreement that banded iron-formations are chemical sediments. Similarly to Phanerozoic iron deposits, all chemical facies of iron-formation can be distinguished. The hematite–magnetite–quartz association, by far the most abundant facies type of iron-formation, is one of the chemically most uniform kinds of rock.

Based on detailed studies of particular deposits, many theories have been suggested to explain the source of the chemical constituents, the mode of transport and the mecha-nism of banding, but no one explanation is appropriate as a general model for the origin of all iron-formations. As to the derivation of iron and silica, there is no question but that both volcanic sources and terrestrial weathering are conceivable alternatives, and even the ocean-water itself could have been a potential reservoir which brought the chemicals to the site of deposition by upwelling. The mode of transport of such enormous amounts of clastic-free matter to the site of deposition can only be understood by assuming solutions with the iron dissolved and transported in the ferrous state in an essentially anoxygenic environment. Catalytic processes related to seasonal growth of oxygen-generating microorganisms are thought to have been responsible for the precipitation of the dissolved ferrous iron in suitable shallow-water environments, whereas the layers of silica resulted from a continuous inorganic precipitation in response to pH and temperature changes, thus giving rise to the typical microbanding of the rock.

Frequently recognizable remains of stromatolites and algal-like microorganisms in many iron-formations are strong indications that primitive photosynthesizing organisms have played a key role during deposition of iron-formation, and a valid explanation is that they have acted as O_2-donors for the precipitation of ferric iron from the ferrous solutions.

Indications are that deposition of iron-formations took place in warm marine environments and, provided that intercalated so-called tillites and glacio-marine sediments could be proven as such, also under cold climate conditions. If so, then climate would not be a significant controlling factor for the deposition of banded iron-formations.

The final conclusion is that banded iron-formations are diversified rocks and this means that a single and generally applicable model of origin is not possible, despite many common features of this extremely widespread rock type which lacks actualistic comparisons.

ACKNOWLEDGEMENTS

This paper is based on the work of many colleagues cited herein, with many of whom the writer had personal contacts and valuable discussions over the years. Although it is unfair to select individuals, special thanks are due to J.V.N. Dorr II for many stimulating discussions and helpful suggestions. The writer is also indebted to the editor of this volume, Dr. K.H. Wolf, for his assistance and for making constructive comments on the paper.

REFERENCES

Aldrich, H.R., 1929. The Geology of the Gogebic iron range of Wisconsin. *Wis. Geol. Nat. Hist. Surv. Econ. Ser. Bull.*, 71.

Alexandrov, E.A., 1955. Contributions to studies of origin of Precambrian banded iron ores. *Econ. Geol.*, 50: 459–468.

Alexandrov, E.A., 1973. The Precambrian banded iron ores of the Soviet Union. *Econ. Geol.*, 68: 1035–1062.

Barbosa, A.L.M. and Grossi Sad, J.H., 1973. Tectonic control of sedimentation and trace-element distribution in iron ores of central Minas Gerais (Brazil). In: *Proc. Kiev Symp., UNESCO Earth Sci.*, 9: 125–131.

Barghoorn, E.S. and Tyler, S.A., 1965. Microorganisms from the Gunflint chert. *Science*, 147: 563–577.

Bayley, R.W. and James, H.L., 1973. Precambrian iron-formations of the United States. *Econ. Geol.*, 68: 934–959.

Becker, R.H. and Clayton, R.N., 1972. Carbon isotopic evidence for the origin of a banded iron-formation in Western Australia. *Geochim. Cosmochim. Acta*, 36: 577–595.

Beukes, N.J., 1973. Precambrian iron-formations of Southern Africa. *Econ. Geol.*, 68: 960–1004.

Borchert, H., 1952. Die Bildungsbedingungen mariner Eisenerzlagerstaetten. *Chem. Erde*, 16: 49–74.

Borchert, H., 1964. Ueber Faziestypen von marinen Eisenerzlagerstaette. *Ber. Geol. Ges. DDR Gesamtgeb. Geol. Wiss.*, 9: 163–193.

Brandt, R.T., Gross, G.A., Gruss, H., Semeneko, N.P. and Dorr II, J.V.N., 1972. Problems of nomenclature for banded ferruginous-cherty sedimentary rocks and their metamorphic equivalents. *Econ. Geol.*, 67: 682–684.

Brongersma-Sanders, M., 1965. Metals of Kupferschiefer supplied by normal sea water. *Geol. Rundsch.*, 55: 365–375.

Campana, B., 1966. Stratigraphic-structural-paleoclimatic controls of the newly discovered iron ore deposits of Western Australia. *Miner. Deposita*, 1: 53–59.

Cloud, P., 1972. A working model of the primitive earth. *Am. J. Sci.*, 272: 537–548.

Cloud, P., 1973. Paleoecological significance of banded iron-formation. *Econ. Geol.*, 68: 1135–1143.

Cumberlidge, J.T. and Stone, J.G., 1964. The vulcan iron-formation at the Groveland mine, Iron Mountain, Michigan. *Econ. Geol.* 59: 1094–1106.

Dearnley, R., 1965. Orogenic fold-belts and continental drift. *Nature*, 206: 1083–1087; 1284–1290.

Derby, O.A., 1910. The iron ores in Brazil - The iron ore resources of the world. In: *11th Sess. Int. Geol. Congr. Stockholm*, pp. 813–822.

Dimroth, E., 1972. Superior-type iron-formations in Canada, with special references to localities in Quebec. In: *Soc. Econ. Geol. Symp. on Precambrian Iron-Formations, Duluth, Minnesota*, abstract.

Dimroth, E. and Chauvel, J.J., 1972. Petrographie des minéraux de fer la Fosse du Labrador. *Geol. Rundsch.*, 61: 97–115.

Dorr II, J.V.N., 1945. Manganese and iron deposits of Morro de Urucum, Mato Grosso, Brazil. *U.S. Geol. Surv. Bull.*, 946-A: 1–47.

Dorr II, J.V.N., 1963. Origin of high grade hematite ores of Minas Gerais, Brazil. *Econ. Geol.*, 58: p. 1185.

Dorr II, J.V.N., 1964. Supergene iron ores of Minas Gerais, Brazil. *Econ. Geol.*, 59: 1204–1240.

Dorr II, J.V.N., 1973a. Iron-formation and associated manganese in Brazil. In: *Proc. Kiev. Symp., UNESCO, Earth Sci.*, 9: 105–113.

Dorr II, J.V.N., 1973b. Iron-formation in South America. *Econ. Geol.*, 68: 1005–1022.

Dorr II, J.V.N., et al., 1958. Symposium on the stratigraphy of the Minas Series in the Quadrilátero Ferrífero, Minas Gerais, Brazil. *Bol. Soc. Bras. Geol.*, 7 (2): 14 pp.

Dorr II, J.V.N. et al., 1959. Esboço Geológico do Quadrilátero Ferrífero de Minas Gerais/Brasil. *Dep. Nac. Prod. Min. Publ. Espec.*, 1: 115 pp.

Edwards, A.B., 1958. Oolitic iron-formations in Northern Australia. *Geol. Rundsch.*, 49: 668–682.

Eichler, J., 1967. Das physikalisch-chemische Millieu bei der Verwitterung von Itabiriten in Minas Gerais/Brasilien. *Chem. Erde*, 26: 119–132.

Eichler, J., 1968. Geologie und Entstehung der itabiritischen Reicherze im "Eisernen Viereck" von Minas Gerais/Brasilien. Habilitationsschrift, Clausthal, manuscr., 192 pp.

Eichler, J., 1970. Die geologische Position der praekambrischen Quarzbaendererze (Itabirite) und die Problematik ihrer Genese. *Clausthaler Hefte, Lagerstaettenkol. Geochem. Miner. Rolst.*, 9: 6–26.

Economic Geology, 1973. Precambrian iron-formations of the world. *Econ. Geol.*, 68 (7): 913–1179.

Eugster, H.P. and Chou, J.M., 1973. The depositional environments of Precambrian banded iron-formations. *Econ. Geol.*, 68: 1144–1168.

French, B.M., 1968. Progressive contact metamorphism of the Biwabik iron-formation, Mesabi Range, Minnesota. *Minn. Geol. Surv. Bull.*, 45: 103 pp.

French, B.M., 1973. Mineral assemblages in diagenetic and low-grade metamorphic iron-formation. *Econ. Geol.*, 68: 1063–1074.

Gabrielse, H., 1972. Younger Precambrian of the Canadian Cordillera. *Am. J. Sci.*, 272: 521–536.

Gair, J.E., 1973. Iron deposits of Michigan, USA. In: *Proc. Kiev. Symp., UNESCO, Earth Sci.,* 9: 365–375.

Garrels, R.M., Perry, E.A. and Mackenzie, F.T., 1973. Genesis of Precambrian iron-formations and the development of atmospheric oxygen. *Econ. Geol.,* 68: 1173–1179.

Gastil, G. and Knowles, D.M., 1960. Geology of the Wabush Lake Area, southwestern Labrador and eastern Quebec, Canada. *Bull. Geol. Soc. Am.,* 71: 1243–1254.

Geijer, P., 1957. Die Herkunft der quarzgebaenderten Eisenerze. Eine Uebersicht der Problemlage. *Neues Jahrb. Mineral. Abh.,* 91: 223–238 (Festband Schneiderhoehn).

Geijer, P. and Magnusson, N.H., 1952. The iron ores of Sweden. In: *Symp. sur les gisements de fer du monde. In: Int. Geol. Congr. 19th, Algiers,* 2: 477–499.

Goldich, S.S., 1973. Ages of Precambrian banded iron-formations. *Econ. Geol.,* 68: 1126–1134.

Goodschild, J.H., 1953. Banded iron-formations. Dynamical significance in tropical surroundings. In: *Int. Geol. Congr., 19th, Algiers, Sect. 10,* 10: 35–37.

Goodwin, A.M., 1956. Facies relations in the Gunflint iron-formation. *Econ. Geol.,* 51: 565–595.

Goodwin, A.M., 1973. Archean iron-formations and basins. *Econ. Geol.,* 68: 915–930.

Goodwin, A.M. and Shklanka, R., 1967. Archean volcano-tectonic basins form and pattern. *Can. J. Earth Sci.,* 4: 777–795.

Govett, G.S., 1966. Origin of banded iron-formations. *Geol. Soc. Am. Bull.,* 77: 1191–1212.

Gross, G.A., 1961. Metamorphism of iron-formations and its bearing on their beneficiation. *Can. Min. Metall. Bull.,* 54 (545): 30–37.

Gross, G.A., 1965. Geology of iron deposits in Canada: general geology and evaluation of iron deposits. *Geol. Surv. Can. Econ. Geol. Rep.,* 22 (1): 181 pp.

Gross, G.A., 1972. Primary features in cherty iron-formations. *Sediment. Geol.,* 7: 241–262.

Gross, G.A., 1973. The depositional environment of principal types of Precambrian iron-formations. In: *Proc. Kiev Symp., UNESCO, Earth Sci.,* 9: 15–21.

Gruner, J.W., 1922. The origin of sedimentary iron formations: the Biwabik formation of the Mesabi Range. *Econ. Geol.,* 17: 407–460.

Gruss, H., 1967. Itabiritische Eisenerze in Minas Gerais, Brasilien. *Stahl Eisen,* 87: 1202–1209.

Gruss, H., 1973. Itabirite iron ores of the Liberia and Guyana shields. In: *Proc. Kiev Symp., UNESCO, Earth Sci.,* 9: 335–359.

Guild, P.W., 1957. Geology and mineral resources of the Congonhas District, Minas Gerais, Brazil. *U.S. Geol. Surv. Prof. Pap.,* 290.

Harder, E.C. and Chamberlin, R.T., 1915. The Geology of central Minas Gerais, Brazil. *J. Geol.,* 23: 341–478; 385–424.

Harder, H., 1951. Ueber den Mineralbestand und die Entstehung einiger sedimentaerer Eisenerze des Lias. *Heidelb. Beitr. Mineral. Petrogr.,* 2: 455–476.

Holland, H.D., 1973. The oceans: a possible source of iron in iron-formations. *Econ. Geol.,* 68: 1169–1172.

Hough, J.L., 1958. Fresh-water environment of deposition of Precambrian banded iron-formations. *J. Sediment. Petrol.,* 28: 414–430.

Huber, N.K., 1959. Some aspects of the origin of the Ironwood iron-formations of Michigan and Wisconsin. *Econ. Geol.,* 54: 82–118.

James, H.L., 1954. Sedimentary facies of iron-formations. *Econ. Geol.,* 49: 235–293.

James, H.L., 1955. Zones of regional metamorphism in the Precambrian of Northern Michigan. *Geol. Soc. Am. Bull.,* 66: 1455–1488.

James, H.L., 1966. Chemistry of iron-rich sedimentary rocks. In: *Date of Geochemistry, 6. U.S. Geol. Surv. Prof. Pap.,* 440 (W): 61 pp.

James, H.L. and Sims, P.K., 1973. Precambrian iron-formations of the world. *Econ. Geol.,* 68: 913–914.

Kehrer, P., 1972. Zur Geologie der Itabirite in der suedlichen Serra do Espinhaço (Minas Gerais, Brasilien). *Geol. Rundsch.,* 61: 216–249.

Kennedy, W.Q., 1964. The structural differentiation of Africa in the Pan-African (±500 m.y.) tectonic episode. *8th Annu. Rep. Sci. Results,* Leeds 1964.

Klein, C., 1973. Changes in mineral assemblages with metamorphism of some banded precambrian iron-formations. *Econ. Geol.,* 68: 1075–1088.

Kloosterman, J.B., 1973. Vulcoes gigantes do tipo anelar no escudo das Guianas. *Min. Metal.,* 341: 52–58.

Krauskopf, K.B., 1967. *Introduction to Geochemistry.* McGraw-Hill, New York, N.Y., 721 pp.

Krishnan, M.S., 1973. Occurrence and origin of iron ores of India. In: *Proc. Kiev. Symp., UNESCO, Earth Sci.,* 9: 69–76.

Krumbein, W.C. and Garrels, R.H., 1952. Origin and classification of chemical sediments in terms of pH and oxidation–reduction potentials. *J. Geol.,* 60: 1–33.

La Berge, G.L., 1964. Development of magnetite in iron-formations of the Lake Superior region. *Econ. Geol.,* 59: 1313–1342.

La Berge, G.L., 1966. Altered pyroclastic rocks in South African iron-formations. *Econ. Geol.,* 61: 572–581.

La Berge, G.L., 1967. Microfossils and precambrian iron-formations. *Geol. Soc. Am. Bull.,* 78: 331–342.

La Berge, G.L., 1973. Possible biological origin of Precambrian iron-formations. *Econ. Geol.,* 68: 1098–1109.

Leith, C.K., 1903. The Mesabi iron-bearing district. *U.S. Geol. Surv. Monogr.,* 43: 316 pp.

Lepp, H. and Goldich, S., 1964. Origin of Precambrian iron-formations. *Econ. Geol.,* 59: 1025–1060.

Marmo, V., 1956. Banded ironstones of the Kangari Hills, Sierra Leone. *Econ. Geol.,* 51: 798–810.

Martin, H., 1965. *The Precambrian Geology of South West Africa and Namaqualand.* University of Cape Town, 159 pp.

McLeroy, D.F., 1970. Genesis of Precambrian banded iron deposits Rio Arriba County, New Mexico. *Econ. Geol.,* 65: 195–205.

Melnik, Y.P. and Siroshtan, R.J., 1973. Physico-chemical conditions of the metamorphism of cherty iron rocks. In: *Proc. Kiev Symp., UNESCO, Earth Sci.,* 9: 209–216.

Moore, E.S. and Maynard, J.E., 1929. Solution, transportation and precipitation of iron and silica. *Econ. Geol.,* 24: 272–303; 365–402; 506–527.

Morey, G.B., 1973. Mesabi, Gunflint and Cuyyna Ranges, Minnesota. In: *Proc. Kiev Symp., UNESCO, Earth Sci.,* 9: 193–208.

Okamoto, G., Okura, T. and Goto, K., 1957. Properties of silica in water. *Geochim. Cosmochim. Acta,* 12: 123–132.

O'Rourke, J.E., 1961. Paleozoic banded iron-formation. *Econ. Geol.,* 56: 331–361.

Perry Jr., E.C. and Tan, F.C., 1973. Significance of carbon isotope variations in carbonates from the Biwabik Iron Formations, Minnesota. In: *Proc. Kiev Symp., UNESCO, Earth Sci.,* 9: 299–305.

Perry Jr., E.C., Tan, F.C. and Morey, G.B., 1973. Geology and stable isotope geochemistry of the Biwabik Iron Formation, northern Minnesota. *Econ. Geol.,* 68: 1110–1125.

Piatnitsky, P., 1924. The genetic relations of the deposits of ore in the Krivoy Rog. *Trans. Inst. Econ. Miner. Petrogr. (Lithogaca),* 9: 56 pp.

Plaksenko, N.A., Koval, J.K. and Shchogolev, J.N., 1973. Precambrian ferruginous–siliceous formations associated with the Kursk Magnetic Anomaly. In: *Proc. Kiev Symp., UNESCO, Earth Sci.,* 9: 89–94.

Pflug, R., 1965. Zur Geologie der suedlichen Espinhaço – Zone und ihrer praekambrischen Diamantvorkommen, Minas Gerais, Brasilien. *Z. Dtsch. Geol. Ges.,* 115: 177–215.

Pflug, R., 1967. Die praekambrische Miogeosynklinale der Espinhaço-Kordillere, Minas Gerais, Brasilien. *Geol. Rundsch.,* 56: 825–844.

Reifenberg, A., 1927. Ueber die Rolle der Kieselsaeure als Schutzkolloid bei der Entstehung mediterraner Roterden. *Z. Pflanzenernaehrung Dueng. Bodenkd. Teil A,* 10: 159–186.

Reifenberg, A., 1929. Die Entstehung der Mediterran-Roterde (Terra Rossa.). (Ein Beitrag zur angewandten Kolloidchemie). *Kolloidchem. Beih.,* 28: 55–147.

Runcorn, S.K., 1962. Paleomagnetic evidence for continental drift and its geological cause. Continental Drift, 1. Academic Press, New York, N.Y. (Also published in: *Nature*, 193: 311–314).

Sakamoto, T., 1950. The origin of precambrian banded iron ores. *Am. J. Sci.*, 248: 449–474.

Schweigart, H., 1965. Genesis of Iron Ores of the Pretoria Series, South Africa. *Econ. Geol.*, 60: 269–298.

Sims, P.K., 1972. Banded iron-formations in the Vermilion district. In: Sims, P.K. and Morey, G.B. (Editors), *Geology of Minnesota — A Centennial Volume. Minn. Geol. Surv.*, pp. 79–81 (Schwartz volume).

Sims, P.K. and Morey, G.B., 1972. Resumé of geology of Minnesota. In: Sims, P.K. and Morey, G.B. (Editors), *Geology of Minnesota — A Centennial Volume. Minn. Geol. Surv.*, pp. 3–17 (Schwartz volume)

Spencer, E. and Percival, F.G., 1952. The structure and origin of the banded hematite jaspers of Singhbhum, India. *Econ. Geol.*, 47 (4).

Tanatar, J., 1924. Genesis der Eisenerze von Krivoy Rog und der sie einschliessenden Quarzite. *Z. Prakt. Geol.*, 32: 129–132.

Thompson, J.B., 1972. Oxides and sulfides in regional metamorphism of pelitic schists. In: *24th Geol. Congr. Sect. 10*, pp. 27–35.

Trendall, A.F., 1965. Origin of Precambrian iron-formations. *Econ. Geol.*, 60: 1065–1070.

Trendall, A.F., 1968. The great basins of Precambrian banded iron formation deposition: a systematic comparison. *Geol. Soc. Am. Bull.*, 79: 1527–1544.

Trendall, A.F., 1973a. Precambrian iron-formations of Australia. *Econ. Geol.*, 68: 1023–1034.

Trendall, A.F., 1973b. Varve cycles on the Weeli Wolli Formation of the Hamersley Group, Western Australia. *Econ. Geol.*, 68: 1089–1097.

Trendall, A.F. and Blockley, J.G., 1970. The iron-formations of the Precambrian Hamersley Group, Western Australia. *West. Aust. Geol. Surv. Bull.*, 119: 366 pp.

Van Hise, C.R. and Leith, C.K., 1911. The geology of the Lake Superior region. *U.S. Geol. Surv. Monogr.*, 52: 641 p.

Wagner, P.A., 1928. The iron deposits of the Union of South Africa. *S. Afr. Geol. Surv. Mem.*, 26: 264 pp.

Wallace, R.M., 1965. Geology and Mineral Resources of the Pico de Itabirito District Minas Gerais, Brazil. *U.S. Geol. Surv. Prof. Pap.*, 341 (F).

Winchell, N.H. and Winchell, H.V., 1891. The iron ores of Minnesota. *Geol. Nat. Hist. Surv. Minn. Bull.*, 6: 430 pp.

Woolnough, W.G., 1941. Origin of banded iron deposits — a suggestion. *Econ. Geol.*, 36: 465–489.

Chapter 5

ASPECTS OF THE SEDIMENTARY PETROLOGY OF CHERTY IRON-FORMATION

ERICH DIMROTH[1]

INTRODUCTION

Definition and general description

Several distinct lithologies are called "iron-formation" in North America: massive and shale-laminated pyrite bodies, pyritiferous graphitic shale, massive ankerite and siderite rocks, magnetite greywacke, and iron-bearing chert. Thus, the term "iron-formation" (I.F.) is not clearly defined. This paper is concerned only with the iron-bearing cherts called "cherty iron-formation" in North America and "banded ironstone" or "cherty ironstone" in Europe and South Africa.

Cherty I.Fs. are composed of quartz, iron oxides (hematite, magnetite), carbonates (siderite, ankerite, dolomite, calcite), and iron silicates (greenalite, minnesotaite, stilpnomelane, riebeckite, iron-chlorite), as major minerals. Terrigenous components (sand and silt) are locally present and transitions from ferriferous cherts into slightly cherty ferriferous sandstones, siltstones and shales occur. Most cherty I.Fs. show a centimetric layering ("mesobanding"), defined by alternating layers rich in iron oxides with layers rich in quartz. The layers may be lenticular, anastomosing or nodular. This interbedding is spectacularly displayed in outcrop, and gave rise to the terms "banded iron-formation" and "banded ironstone". It is of diagenetic origin, as will be shown below. FeO, Fe_2O_3 and SiO_2 generally constitute >90% of cherty I.Fs. Contents of Ca, Mg, Al_2O_3 (<4%) and P_2O_5 (<0.1%) generally are low (Lepp and Goldich, 1964).

James (1954, 1966) distinguished five facies of I.F., on the basis of the predominating iron-mineral: hematite, magnetite, silicate, carbonate and sulfide facies. The sulfide I.Fs. generally are shales with high contents of organic matter, containing disseminations, laminae or nodules of pyrite or pyrrhotite; they grade into massive pyrite bodies by lateral and vertical coalescence of sulfide nodules and laminae. They are not considered in this paper. The writer uses a restricted mineralogical classification in hematite I.F. (hematite dust present) and silicate—carbonate I.F. (femicrite present). Gross (1965, 1972) defined two types of cherty I.Fs. by their sedimentary textures. Laminated (laminations defined by variations of the concentration of iron-minerals) cherts predominate in the Algoma-type to the virtual exclusion of intraclastic rocks, oolites are extremely rare. The

---

[1] Published with the permission of the Minister of Natural Resources of Quebec.

Lake Superior-type, on the other hand, comprises a high proportion of oolitic and intra-clastic rocks, as well as subordinate laminated cherts. The distinction is equivalent to the difference between "pelagic limestones" and "Bahama-type" shallow-water limestones.

The major units of both (Algoma, Lake Superior) types form extensive units, continu-ous for 100–1,000 miles and 100 m or more thick, deposited in Precambrian epiconti-nental and miogeosynclinal basins. Lake Superior-type I.Fs. are comparatively uncommon – their main development is in North America (see Gross 1965, 1968; Bayley and James, 1973) – whereas the most extensive I.Fs. of Australia (Trendall, 1973a, Trendall and Blockley, 1970), the USSR (Alexandrov, 1973), South America (Dorr, 1973), India (Spencer and Percival, 1952) and Mauritania (Besnus et al., 1969; Chauvel, oral communi-cation, 1973) belong to the laminated Algoma-type. Both types appear to occur in South Africa (Algoma-type: Penge and Kuruma Formations and others; Lake Superior-type: I.F. of Griqualand Group, Beukes, 1973).

The relations between cherty I.Fs. and Minette-type iron ores are a controversial sub-ject. Both rock types have significantly different composition. Chert is essentially absent from the Minette-type ores (although secondary quartz is common, Cayeux, 1909b). Compared to Minette-type ironstones, the cherty I.Fs. are depleted in Al_2O_3 and P_2O_5 (Lepp and Goldich, 1964; James, 1966) as well as in the rare-earth elements (Courtois, 1974). Cherty I.Fs. form considerably more extensive, and thicker, units than Minette-type ironstones (James, 1966). On the other hand, both rock types have identical sedi-mentary structures and textures and are amenable to identical textural classification. Their diagenetic textures also are similar; with few exceptions, every textural or structural feature of cherty I.Fs. described below, can also be documented from Minette-type ironstones. Furthermore, the Roper Bar and Constance Range I.Fs., North Australia, may be intermediate between both rock types (Edwards, 1958; Cochrane and Edwards, 1960).

It is not possible to present photographic documentation of the numerous features discussed in this paper within the framework set for a review article. The reader is referred to the original literature for documentation. Selected references to photographic documentation of observations are quoted in Table V, at the end of this paper.

Terminology

This paper follows the terminology of carbonate petrology. Number of the terms used in the earlier literature on I.Fs. (like "granule", etc.) have been abandoned. Terms for sedimentary textures are adapted from Folk (1959, 1962) and those for diagenetic and crystallization textures follow Friedman (1965), Folk (1965), Chilingar et al. (1967) and Bathurst (1958, 1971). The terms for porosity are adapted from Choquette and Pray (1970).

SEDIMENTARY FEATURES

Several generalizations stand out as basic to the understanding of I.F. deposition:

(1) The sedimentary textures and structures of I.Fs. are analogous to those of lime-stones and are amenable to analogous interpretation.

(2) Their depositional textures and structures are mainly determined by mechanical processes of sedimentation; cherty I.Fs. were mechanically deposited as particulate matter with a bi-modal (clay-size and sand-size particles) grain-size distribution.

(3) Limestone replacement cherts and Minette-type iron ores have sedimentary tex-tures and structures closely resembling those of cherty I.Fs.

Sedimentary textures

The textural elements of limestone and cherty I.Fs, are compared in Table I.

Matrix chert (composed mainly of fine-grained cherty quartz) and *femicrite* (composed of fine-grained iron silicate and/or carbonate) are equivalents of micrite in limestones. These materials were deposited as fine-grained (clay- or silt-size) particulate matter.

Three types of sand-sized particles (allochems) are considered to be analogous to the pellets, intraclasts and oolites of limestones. *Pellets* are eye-shaped or ovoidal bodies with somewhat fuzzy outlines, 0.1–0.2 mm long, embedded in matrix chert. Their origin is problematical: Dimroth (1968) interpreted them as agglomerated particles or flocculation units, but they might also be early diagenetic features.

Intraclasts are fragments of pene-contemporaneous sediment, produced by erosion within the sedimentary basin, transported and redeposited (Folk, 1959, 1962). Pebble-size intraclasts commonly show internal textures (lamination, pelletoidal, intraclastic or oolitic textures), that leave no doubt about their origin. Sand-size intraclasts ("peloids", Bathurst, 1971) commonly are devoid of internal textures. However, it is easy to prove that the peloids were detrital particles (see next page).

TABLE I

Textural elements of iron-formations compared with limestones

Iron-formation	Limestone
Matrix chert	micrite
Femicrite	
Cement chert	spar and other cements
Pellets	pellets
Intraclasts	intraclasts
Oolites	oolites
Pisolites	onkolites
Microfossils (skelettal debris absent)	fossils and skelettal debris

(1) Cementation of pore-space between peloids proves that peloids were deposited as discrete particles.

(2) Peloids are stored (Mengel, 1963, 1973; Dimroth and Chauvel, 1973).

(3) Peloid-bearing units are bedded, show cross-bedding and graded bedding, bedding is defined by grain-size variation of peloids.

(4) Sorting indices of peloid-bearing rock are a function of the mean grain-size, as in limestones.

Therefore, no doubt exists that peloids were deposited as discrete particles, and that they were transported and sorted before deposition.

The interpretation of peloids as small intraclasts is based on petrographic and paleo-geographic evidence: a complete grain-size spectrum exits from the smallest peloids (ca. 0.15 mm) to the largest intraclasts (ca. 5 cm), and no basis exists for an objective separation of both. Paleogeographic studies (Chauvel and Dimroth, 1974) suggest that intraclasts formed by several processes:

(1) By wave erosion of pene-contemporaneous sediment in the foreshore and on mud banks.

(2) By lateral erosion of migrating channels.

(3) By micro-mudcraking of sub-aerially exposed mud on mudflats, and by subsequent transport and rounding of fragments.

Intraclasts are not always well outlined. Some rocks are composed of densely welded, closely spaced, but comparatively undeformed intraclasts. Such rocks have little inter-particle porosity (e.g., Dimroth and Chauvel, 1973, Fig. 1F.). Few triangular pores with concave boundaries are present. In other cases, soft intraclasts have been deformed and closely welded during diagenesis (e.g., Dimroth and Chauvel, 1972, Fig. 9).

Intraclasts (fragments from within the basin) and extraclasts (fragments from outside the basin, Wolf, 1965a) should be distinguished, wherever possible. The differentiation of both is a matter of field geology and common sense rather than one of exact petrography (see Folk, 1962). For example, iron-formation fragments in a sandstone unconformably overlying I.F. are likely extraclasts. On the other hand, chert clasts in sandstone inter-fingering with iron-formation very likely are intraclasts.

Many authors (e.g., Spencer and Percival, 1952; Goodwin, 1956) suggested that intra-clasts ("granules") formed during diagenesis. However, in very few cases has the diagenetic origin of intraclast-like textures been documented; Gross (1972) described breccias pro-duced by syn-sedimentary deformation and Mukhopadhyay and Chanda (1972) the forma-tion of breccia lenses by brecciation in situ within the sediment. The latter two reseachers suggested that these breccias form by shrinkage; however, development of solution pores parallel to bedding and subsequent collapse is a plausible alternative. Fragments of both types of breccia are angular (but may be corroded), and lack sorting. The fragments of the syn-sedimentary deformation-breccias are embedded in a matrix, whereas the frag-ments in the shrinkage (or solution collapse?) breccias have been cemented by chert.

Oolites are coated grains composed of a nucleus and a concentrically laminated skin.

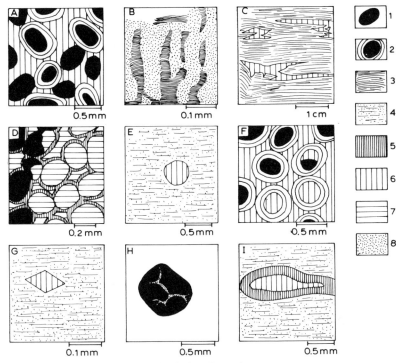

Fig. 1. Types of chert-filled porosity in iron-formations.
A. Intergranular porosity. B. Pillar-texture in stromatolites (Hofmann, 1969 = pallisade texture; Davies, 1970 = Molds of algal bundles?). C. Fenestral porosity (Dimroth and Dressler, in prep.). D. Intraclast-moldic porosity. E. Gas bubbles. F. Oolite-moldic porosity. G. Carbonate-moldic porosity (Mukhopadhyay and Chanda, 1972). H. Shrinkage porosity. I. Vugs.
1 = intraclasts; *2* = oolites; *3* = stromatolitic fabric; *4* = matrix chert; *5* = chalcedonic encrustation; *6* = encrustating quartz cement; *7* = calcite cement; *8* = microgranular quartz cement.

Any detrital particle (intraclasts, quartz grains, zircon grains) may serve as nucleus, but intraclasts are by far the most common. Laminations are due to variation of hematite or greenalite pigmentation. All carbonate or minnesotaite oolites observed so far have coarse grained recrystallization textures and are derived from hematite (and greenalite?) oolites. It is not yet clear whether the oolites of iron-formation formed by inorganic concentric accretion (Cayeux, 1922; Gross, 1972) analogous to limestone oolites, or by algal coating, as small pisolites (Hofmann, 1969), or perhaps by both processes.

Some intraclasts have complex (pelletoidal, intraclastic, oolitic) internal textures and are derived from partly lithified sediment. Multiple oolites, formed by agglutination of several oolites and their renewed oolitification, are common. Oolites with complex (intraclastic, oolitic) internal textures formed by pene-contemporaneous erosion of partly lithified oolite or intraclast sand followed by renewed precipitation of oolite skins. The particles give evidence of complex processes of reworking and of pene-contemporaneous cementation (Cayeux, 1922, 1935; Carozzi, 1964). Chauvel and Dimroth (1974) suggested that they form during the migration of bars of oolite and intraclast sand. Apparently some cementation took place in these bars. Multiple oolites would form where cementation is minor, so that fragmentation took place at grain boundaries. Complex intraclasts and oolites formed where cementation was strong enough to permit breakage across component grains. Thus, the aspect of composite grains (whether multiple or complex) may be a function of the average duration of their repose in the sand banks.

Terrigenous components are not uncommon at many localities; terrigenous quartz and feldspar grains are easily recognized because of their rounded or edge-rounded outlines (different from the ameboid or polygonal shapes of cherty quartz). Admixture of clay is betrayed only by the presence of aluminous minerals like chamosite (which is invariably associated with silt) and perhaps by stilpnomelane. Clastic zircon and tourmaline are also common. Goodwin (1956), LaBerge (1966a, b) and Trendall (1966) described silicified pyroclastic debris from some iron-formations. "Spastolites" (that is deformed oolites and intraclasts, p. 214) may superficially resemble volcanic shards. Care should be taken to distinguish both textures. Axiolitic textures (documented by LaBerge, 1966a) and bubble-wall shards are characteristic of volcanic material, relicts of concentric coatings are typical of spastolites.

Primary depositional porosity can be recognized where encrustating cements (p. 220) grew perpendicular to the pore walls. Fig. 1 gives an overview of the different types of porosity observed: interparticle porosity (Fig. 1A) remained between allochem grains (oolites, intraclasts) after deposition. Laminar fenestral pores have been observed in stromatolites (Fig. 1C, see fig. 4 in Dimroth and Dressler, in preparation). Finally some round pores in matrix cherts are perhaps derived from gas bubbles (Fig. 1E). All these pores have been filled with cementing materials. So far no case of internal sediment has been observed in iron-formation, but internal sediment is known from other cherts (Folk, 1973).

Sedimentary structures

Most of the sedimentary structures in I.Fs. are not easily recognized in outcrop, except in rare cases where they have been accentuated by differential weathering. Large polished or thin sections are generally required for their study. Furthermore, bedding features have been obscured in many cases by the development, during diagenesis, of an anastomosing system of layers rich in magnetite and hematite ("metallic" mesobands), and of siliceous pods and nodules. There are no systematic studies of sedimentary structures in I.Fs., except for the work of Trendall and Blockley (1970) and Trendall (1972, 1973b), on laminations. Gross (1972) briefly described the structures observed in Canadian I.Fs.

Matrix cherts and femicrites characteristically show tabular, millimetric or sub-millimetric, laminations defined by a variation of the content of iron-minerals, or by alternation of carbonate and silicate rich laminae. The aspect and thickness of laminations may change over brief distances, due to solution, reprecipitation of silica, and recrystallization processes (Trendall and Blockley, 1970; Trendall, 1973b).

Laminae of matrix cherts have the same character as the laminations of oolites, but are 10–100 times as thick. Many workers suspected that the regular laminations represent varves. Trendall and Blockley (1970) and Trendall (1972, 1973b) found that certain irregularities in the thickness of laminae occurred at predictable stratigraphic levels, basin-wide, in the Hammersley Iron Formation of West Australia. This is evidence for lateral continuity and correlation of laminae and, therefore, supports their interpretation as varves. However, not all laminations in matrix cherts and femicrites can be interpreted as varves. Centrimetric cross-laminae are present, here and there, in femicrites and also in matrix cherts (Gross, 1972, fig. 9).

Oolitic and intraclastic I.Fs. are thin to thick-bedded. Beds usually show some pinch and swell. Few observations of bedding surfaces are available. Gross (1968, 1972) makes passing reference to ripple marks. Gross (1972), Dimroth (1968) and Chauvel and Dimroth (1974) observed numerous wash-outs and erosion channels. Decimetric and meter-sized cross-bedding, probably produced by dune migration is fairly common (Bergeron, 1954; James, 1954; Goodwin, 1956; Mengel, 1963; Gross, 1968, 1972). Mengel (1963) and Dimroth and Chauvel (1973) describe two common types of graded bedding:

(1) The average grain size of cemented oolitic and intraclastic rocks decreases from base to top of beds (distribution grading, see Dimroth and Chauvel, 1973, for measurements).

(2) Matrix content of open-fabric intrafemicrites increases upwards, whereas the largest grain size decreases (content and coarse-tail grading).

Organo-sedimentary textures and structures

Stromatolites and pisolites are common in hematite, carbonate and carbon-bearing cherts of Lake Superior-type I.Fs. Hofmann (1969) presented the only detailed study of I.F. stromatolites. Detailed work on pisolites is lacking. Pisolites of the Labrador Trough resemble algal onkolites, but their organic origin has not been proved beyond doubt. Eugster and Chou (1973) re-interpreted them as caliche pisolites. Caliche might in fact occur in I.Fs. and should carefully be distinguished from onkolite beds. For this reason, the diagnosis of onkolites and caliche is briefly discussed in Table II, partly after Swineford et al. (1958) and Dunham (1969).

Shapes and growth-forms of I.F. stromatolites are comparable to those of calcareous stromatolites. Therefore, the morphological stromatolite classifications of Donaldson (1963), Logan et al. (1964) and Hofmann (1969) are integrally applicable. However, the internal textures of some I.F. stromatolites may be different, showing extremely fine laminations and, here and there, a peculiar pillar-texture. Well preserved single laminae in chert–hematite stromalites of the Gunflint Formation are about 2–4 μ thick (Hofmann,

TABLE II

Diagnostic features of onkolites in the Sokoman Formation and of caliche nodules

Onkolites (observed features)*	Caliche nodules **
1. Onkolite-bearing beds 5–30 cm thick, are unrelated to autochthonous caliche.	Autochthonous caliche units several meters thick. Seaward of caliche occur breccias with large transported caliche blocks, grading finally into bedded sediment with transported caliche nodules.
2. Admixture of pebble-size intraclasts, of oolite or intraclast sand, or of mud is common. No internal sediment.	Vadose silt forms geopetal internal sediment (Dunham, 1969, fig. 7, 9, 11). Perched silt inclusions in nodules form geopetal fabric in upper part of nodule.
3. Graded bedding occurs in pisolite-bearing storm conglomerates.	Reversed graded bedding common (Dunham, 1969, fig. 4).
4. Pisolites and other components form an intact clastic fabric. No polygonal patterns.	Pisolites may form closely fitting polygonal framework (Dunham, 1969, fig. 8, 9).
5. Pisolites buried in the plastic state are flattened parallel to bedding (Dimroth and Chauvel, 1972, fig. 11).	Pisolites grow downward, and commonly show vertical elongation (Dunham, 1969, fig. 9).
6. Complex sequence of accretion and fragmentation of onkolites in a dynamic medium is never interrupted by internal sedimentation.	Complex sequence of accretion and fragmentation in a static environment contemporaneous with internal sedimentation. Growth sequence of pisolites interrupted by internal sedimentation. (Dunham, 1969, fig. 5).
7. Imbrication occurs (Dimroth and Chauvel, 1972, fig. 12).	Imbrication absent.
8. Onkolite-bearing beds may show cross-bedding (Zajac, 1974, fig. 26).	Cross-bedding absent.

* Diagnostic features not observed in the pisolitic beds of the Sokoman Formation: cut-and-fill structure.
** After Swineford et al. (1958); Dunham (1969). These features have not been observed in the Sokoman Formation.

1969; Walter, 1972). This is the same order of magnitude as the laminations of siliceous stromatolitic encrustations of Yellowstone Park (Walter et al., 1972) and of bacterial iron stromatolites of the deap sea (Monty, 1973). On the other hand, calcareous stromatolites of Precambrian (Cloud and Semikhatow, 1969; Hofmann, 1969) and Recent age (Logan et al., 1964; Davies, 1970; Monty, 1972) have laminae 0.05—several mm thick. At first sight these measurements appear to document systematic differences between calcareous and I.F. stromatolites. However, thinly laminated (in part $<3\,\mu$) aragonite encrustations, similar to stromalites, have been described from the Trucial Coast, Persian Gulf (Purser and Loreau, 1973). Furthermore, not all I.F. stromatolites are as thinly laminated. Panella's (1972) values of the thickness of laminae are significantly different. Siderite—chert stromatolites from the Labrador Trough (Dimroth and Dressler, in preparation) have fairly thick laminae.

Some stromatolites show $10-50\,\mu$ wide pillars of pigmented, laminated material, oriented perpendicular to the laminae. Unpigmented, comparatively coarse-grained chert fills the spaces between the pillars. These interspaces commonly have a branching, anastomosing disposition. Hofmann (1969) interpreted pillars as a growth structure, but the interspaces between pillars might also represent chert-filled molds of algal bundles, analogous to Davies' (1970) pallisade structure. Similar voids occur in manganiferous deep-sea stromatolites (Monty, 1973).

Hofmann (1969) suggested that some oolites might be Osagia-type onkolites, and quoted the ellipsoidal to kidney-shaped form, and the overlapping nature and irregular thickness of laminae as evidence. However, not all I.F. oolites have these properties, and limestone oolites with these properties are known. Decisive evidence for an organo—sedimentary origin of I.F. oolites, in form of preserved organic filaments, has not been reported.

LaBerge (1967, 1973) drew attention to the presence of a fine ($10-50\,\mu$) mottling in many thin sections of cherty I.Fs., and interpreted the mottles as diagenetically altered fossils. This is one of the most complex problems of I.F. petrography. I.Fs. contain many petrographically distinct types of mottling: spherulites of chalcedony, spots of hematite dust in the cores of micro-polygonal quartz grains, small pellets of micro-granular siderite (some cored by quartz or by organic matter) and many others. Similar types of mottling occur in Phanerozoic cherts (e.g., Cayeux, 1929, fig. 77, 86, 87, 88; Folk and Pittman, 1971, fig. 9). Many are probably diagenetic. However, organic-induced diagenetic processes may also cause mottling on the $10-50\,\mu$ scale in cherts. For example, chert spherulites filling radiolarian molds are not rare in Alpine Jurassic cherts (Garrison and Fischer, 1969, p. 34) and in Permian jaspers from the Chichibu terrain, Japan (writer's observations). Diagnosis of microfossils and of fossil-derived diagenetic textures in I.Fs. is an extremely difficult art, which requires thorough knowledge of Recent microbiology, petrography of crystallites, and advanced micro-paleontological methodology (cf., Cloud, 1973b). The reader is directed to Schopf (1972), Cloud (1973a, b), Edhorn (1973) for the voluminous literature on micro-organisms in I.Fs.

Classification

Dimroth (1968) and Dimroth and Chauvel (1972, 1973) proposed a classification of cherty I.Fs. analog to the textural classification of limestone types of Folk (1959, 1962). The most important types and sub-types are briefly listed in Table III. Cherts which lack

TABLE III

Textured rock types of iron-formations

Type	Textural compo-nents	Ferric facies	Ferrous facies	Equivalent lime-stone type
Femicrite	femicrite	not present	laminated or thick bedded varieties	micrite
Matrix chert	matrix chert, pel-lets	ribboned, lami-nated	ribboned and lami-nated	micrite
Intrafemicrite oolitic matrix chert	intraclasts, femi-crite matrix	not present	subdivision accord-ing to mineralogy and size of intra-clasts	intramicrite intramicrudite
Intraclastic or oolitic matrix chert	intraclasts, oolites, pisolites, matrix chert	intraclastic and oolitic types; further subdivi-sion according to size of intra-clasts	oolites absent; further subdivision according to size of intraclasts	intramicrite intramicrudite oomicrite oomicrudite
Cemented intra-clastic or oolitic chert	intraclasts, oolites pisolites, cement chert	intraclastic and oolitic types; further subdivi-sion according to size of intraclasts	oolites absent; further subdivi-sion according to size of intraclasts	intrasparite oosparite intrasparrudite oosparrudite
Recrystallized chert	?			recrystallized lime-stones
Hematite and magnetite layers	spastolitic shards common, strongly compacted	in part derived from oolitic and intraclastic rocks	largely derived from carbonate femicrite	metasomatized limestones

well preserved relicts of the sedimentary textures due to advanced recrystallization have to be classified separately. Rocks transitional between cherty I.Fs. and clastic rocks should be classified according to Folk's (1968) diagram. Beukes (1973) proposed a classi-fication of rocks in the system I.F.—chert—limestone—clastic rocks.

DIAGENESIS

It is not easy to define petrographically meaningful stages of diagenesis. Compaction, filling of open pores-space, and the first crystallization of quartz provide a recognizable datum. Diagenetic textures and structures that formed before or during these processes are called early diagenetic, whereas textures and structures that formed after their com-pletion are called late diagenetic. There is a complete transition from late diagenesis to

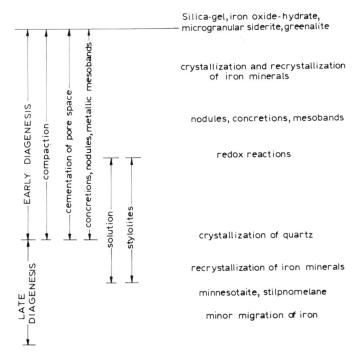

Fig. 2. Time-sequence of diagenetic processes in iron-formations.

low-temperature burial metamorphism. Late diagenesis, in the sense of this paper, includes what many petrologists would call a pre-kinematic load metamorphism. Only those processes related to, or following, a phase of deformation, or related to a mappable thermal aureole, are considered metamorphic in this paper. Fig. 2 presents a simplified flow-sheet of diagenetic processes in cherty iron-formations. High-temperature metamorphism is not considered here (see Klein, 1973).

Most previous papers use a different terminology, and distinguish "primary" and "secondary" minerals. French (1973) defined these terms as follows: "Primary" minerals do not show replacement textures and are not derived from known precursors, whereas "secondary" minerals show replacement textures. It is evident that "primary" minerals, in this sense, need not be syngenetic or even early diagenetic. For example, the minnesotaite of femicrites of the central Labrador Trough is not evidently derived from an earlier mineral, and is thought to be "primary" by Zajac (1972, 1974); nevertheless, it likely formed during late diagenesis (Dimroth and Chauvel, 1973).

Several general conclusions may be drawn from the study of the diagenetic features of cherty I.Fs.:

(1) I.Fs. are derived from hydrated sediments with the consistency of muds and sands.

(2) The sediments lost pore water during lithification. Consolidation is caused by two alternate processes: compaction and cementation.

(3) Migration of iron, silica, and of carbonate took place during the compaction and cementation.

(4) Solution and pressure solution occurred during the diagenesis.

Syn-sedimentary deformation

Gross (1972) presented an overview of the syn-sedimentary deformation features observed in I.Fs.: syn-sedimentary deformation breccias, pene-contemporaneous slump-folding, pene-contemporaneous faulting related to differential compaction or to slump-ing, load casting. These processes are controlled by the soil mechanical properties of the fresh sediment.

Shrinkage (syneresis) features

Information on syneresis features in cherty iron-formations is widely dispersed in the literature. Gross (1972) documented the pertinent observations: shrinkage cracks in intra-clasts, oolites and pisolites, shrinkage cracks in some beds of matrix chert, and septaria (nodules with internal shrinkage pattern, see Gross, 1972, fig. 10, 11). Syneresis cracks form due to shrinkage of hydrated substances by loss of water. Increase of the salinity of pore solutions (Jüngst, 1934; Burst, 1965) may cause shrinkage. The observed shrinkage features did not form sub-aerially during emergence; they formed within the sediment, before the cementation of allochemical rocks. The shrinkage features suggest that allo-chems were composed of a hydrated substance (probably silica-gel and mixed silica—iron-oxide hydrate gels), at an early diagenetic stage.

Compaction

Chilingarian and Wolf (1975–1976) discuss compaction in coarse-grained sediments. Spastolites — flattened and in some cases grotesquely distorted oolites — are the most evident indicator of compaction in iron-bearing rocks, but other processes are also in-volved in their formation. Similar distorted oolites are also known from limestones (Laugier, 1959; Carozzi, 1961; Sarkar, 1973) but they are more common in iron-bearing rocks (documented by Cayeux, 1922, 1923; Edwards, 1958; Cochrane and Edwards, 1960; Braun, 1964; Dimroth, 1968; Chauvel and Robardet, 1970; Dimroth and Chauvel, 1973, and others).

Apparently spastolites can be produced by three processes:

(1) By differential compaction, flattening, and distortion of oolites (Carozzi, 1961; Sarkar, 1973; Dimroth and Chauvel, 1973), during early diagenesis. Some spastolites are produced by compaction during temporary repose in oolite banks, and have been trans-ported and redeposited in their final shape (Carozzi, 1961; Sarkar, 1973).

(2) By shrinkage, opening of shrinkage cracks and distortion of parts of oolites during desiccation.

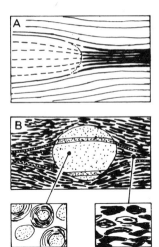

Fig. 3. Ideal relationships between hematite—magnetite ("metallic") mesobands and silica pods. A. Relationships in laminated iron-formation (after Trendall, 1972). B. Relationship in oolitic-intraclastic iron-formation (after Dimroth and Chauvel, 1973).

(3) By intrastratal solution and micro-stylolitization (Cayeux, 1923).

Flattening of oolites and intraclasts and folding of early diagenetic chert veins permit to estimate the degree of compaction (Gross, 1972; Dimroth and Chauvel, 1973). Bedding-planes are commonly distorted at the terminations of chert nodules ("pods") in iron-formations, as shown in Fig. 3. Similar distortion of bedding-planes around concretions and nodules is thought to be due to differential compaction (Dietrich et al., 1963; Amstutz and Bubenicek, 1967, fig. 23; Curtis et al., 1972; Oertel and Curtis, 1972). Differential flattening of oolites and intraclasts (Fig. 3) substantiates this interpretation.

Concretionary bodies

Concretionary bodies give evidence of intense diagenetic migration of material. Concretions of calcite, ankerite and siderite are common in cherty rocks. In many cases, they contain well preserved relict textures (for example, intraclasts and oolites with shrinkage cracks) proving their derivation from chert. Concretionary replacement of chert by carbonates is also common at the margin of veins and fissures. More important are the magnetite—hematite layers (or mesobands, in the terminology of Trendall and Blockley, 1970), and chert nodules ("pods") characteristic of most I.Fs. The mesobands form anastomosing, lenticular layers, generally parallel to bedding, composed predominantly of iron oxides. Chert pods also are more or less parallel to bedding. A primary, depositional, origin has been ascribed to all of these features by most early workers. Duff et al. (1967, pp. 187—188) apparently were the first to regard them as products of diagenesis.

Fig. 3 shows the idealized relations between chert nodules ("pods") and hematite—magnetite ("metallic") mesobands in laminated and in oolitic-intraclastic I.Fs. (after Trendall and Blockley, 1970; Trendall, 1972; Dimroth and Chauvel, 1973). Laminations are continuous from the "metallic" into the siliceous material. Lateral transitions between both materials are correlated with variations of bedding thickness that suggest differential compaction (compare Oertel and Curtis, 1972; Curtis et al., 1972; for analogous relations). In each case the iron-rich material has suffered much greater compaction than the chert nodule. Spastolitic shard textures derived from oolites and intraclasts in the "metallic" material, substantiate differential compaction (Fig. 3B). Therefore, it is evident that chert nodules and "metallic" mesobands are derived from the same material. Analogous observations by Beukes (1973) at South African I.Fs., and of the writer at iron-formations from the Archean in Quebec and from the Rapitan Group, Mackenzie Mountains, Canada, confirm that the relations described above are typical. Chert nodules in a siderite-fabric (e.g., at stop G9 of Franklin et al., 1972) are identical to nodules in limestones.

Diffuse discoloration haloes, and diffuse discoloured spots are present in virtually all I.Fs. composed of chert containing hematite, greenalite or graphite pigments. Discoloration in part follows sedimentary inhomogeneities, in part proceeded in completely irregular patches. However, it is always cross-cutting to the sedimentary structures and textures.

The concretions provide evidence for extensive diagenetic redistribution of iron and silica, but the controls and mechanisms of this process are not well understood. Trendall (1972) proposed that differential compaction and the enrichment of iron oxides in the compacted "metallic" mesobands is caused by expulsion of silica from the "metallic" layers and is controlled by subtle differences of the original composition. Dimroth and Chauvel (1973) noted that iron migration in Lake Superior-type I.F. appears to be controlled by rock texture and by differential permeability. Most metallic layers in Lake Superior-type hematite iron-formation apparently formed from oolitic and intraclastic material. The authors proposed complex redox reactions as the driving mechanism (see p. 225). Metallic layers in silicate—carbonate iron-formations appear to be derived from carbonate laminae.

Solution and solution-collapse features

The primary or secondary pore space (Fig. 1) of I.Fs. can be recognized only where it has been filled by encrusting quartz growing perpendicular to the surface of the pores. It is presently difficult to assess the role of secondary solution porosity in the evolution of cherty I.Fs. Dimroth and Chauvel (1973) noted in a few thin-sections that intraclasts had been dissolved after their partial or complete cementation. The resulting intraclast-moldic pores (Fig. 1D) had later been filled by calcite. Chert-cemented oolite-moldic (Fig. 1F) porosity has been observed in a few thin-sections of the Sokoman Iron Formation, Central Labrador Trough, Quebec, Canada. Further work is required before it can be critically compared with the "bi-partite" oolites of Choquette (1955), the "half-moon" oolites of Carozzi (1963) and the "shrunk" oolites of Folk and Pittman (1971), produced probably by dissolution of evaporite shells in oolites during diagenesis.

Mukhopadhyay and Chanda (1972) observed moldic pores due to the dissolution of carbonate porphyrotopes (Fig. 1G). Mukhopadhyay and Chanda (1972, pp. 118—119), furthermore, observed intraclastic rocks that had been produced by diagenetic autobrecciation during diagenesis of certain lenses and layers within the rock. The authors suggested that the autobrecciation was due to internal shrinkage. Development of bedding parallel solution pores, followed by collapse, is a plausible alternative that would account for these observations. The origin of number of chert-filled vugs in the Sokoman Iron Formation (Fig. 1I, Dimroth and Chauvel, 1973, fig. 2H) is undeterminable; they may be solution pores.

Stylolites

Stylolites are common in silicate—carbonate I.Fs.; in these rocks they are easily observed, because they are coated by residues of carbon (James, 1954) or iron ore (Dimroth and Chauvel, 1973). On the other hand, stylolites are also common in hematite-bearing cherts, where they are not coated by an insoluble residue and where they are consequently difficult to see.

All observations of Park and Schot (1968) on limestone stylolites integrally apply to stylolites in iron-formations. Most stylolites are parallel to stratification; oblique stylolites occur here and there and stylolite networks are not rare. Stylolitization has been observed at contacts between intraclasts, and at contacts between intraclasts and a matrix. In some cases, the development of stylolites is related to differential compaction.

CRYSTALLIZATION TEXTURES

Our knowledge on the crystallization textures of cherty I.Fs. is quite unsatisfactory. It is at present possible to give a comparatively clear, although probably imcomplete overview of the crystallization textures of quartz. Less is known about the extremely complex crystallization and replacement textures of the iron oxides, carbonates and silicates.

The following generalizations seem to follow from what is presently known of the crystallization textures of cherty I.Fs.:

(1) Factors controlling crystallization fabrics of quartz in cherty I.Fs. and of calcite in limestones appear to be basically the same (Mukhopadhyay and Chanda, 1972), except for the importance of surface tension effects in the former. For this reason it is possible to apply fabric criteria developed for limestones by Schmidegg (1928), Sander (1936), Bathurst (1958), Folk (1965) and many others, to the analysis of I.F. textures.

(2) Recrystallization textures of I.Fs. can be explained by aggrading neomorphism as defined by Folk (1965); grain diminution (Wolf, 1965b) does not appear to exist, except where due to tectonic deformation and ensuing blastomylonitization (strain recrystallization).

(3) Grain sizes and grain shapes of quartz are strongly influenced by dust inclusions, probably due to surface tension effects.

(4) There appears to be no distinct difference between the crystallization textures of quartz in I.Fs., radiolarites, and replacement cherts, regardless of their origin.

(5) Redox reactions between the iron oxides, silicates, carbonates, and sulfides, driven by the presence in the rock of organic matter and by infiltration of oxygenated ground-water, play an unsuspected role in the mineralogical evolution of cherty I.Fs. (see also Perry and Tan, 1973; Perry et al., 1973; French, 1973). These redox reactions appear to be amenable to actualistic interpretation.

Quartz in matrix cherts

Our present knowledge on the crystallization and recrystallization of quartz in matrix cherts is quite limited. Microscopic studies of chert in I.Fs. (Mukhopadhyay and Chanda, 1972; Dimroth and Chauvel, 1973) and few electron-microscopic studies of cherts and iron-formation (Folk and Weaver, 1952; Oldershaw, 1960; Zajac, 1972, 1974) are virtually the only data available. Folk and Weaver (1952) distinguish between micro-quartz (<30 μ) and macro-quartz (>30 μ) whereas Dimroth and Chauvel (1973) distinguished what appears to be an earlier generation of quartz ("primocrystalline" quartz) and quartz that is evidently a product of its recrystallization. Primocrystalline quartz takes two forms: (1) microgranular; (2) chalcedonic. Fig. 4 gives a synoptic overview of quartz textures.

Microgranular quartz forms an equigranular xenotopic fabric of micron-sized crystals that in thin section appear to have ameboid shapes. Electron-microscopic studies (Folk and Weaver, 1952; Zajac, 1972) revealed polygonal shapes. Chalcedony (normal length-fast and length-slow varieties) forms spherulites about 0.01–0.1 mm across; in many cases the spherulites nucleated at the surface of a small crystal of iron oxide (Mukhopadhayay and Chanda, 1972; Dimroth and Chauvel, 1973). Recrystallization of chalcedony to a micro-granular quartz fabric is common.

Recrystallization of the micro-granular quartz fabric generally produces an extremely inequigranular xenotopic fabric of irregularly polygonal grains, commonly with seriate grain-size distribution. Porphyrotopic textures are not common. Grain sizes of recrystallized quartz vary from a few microns to more than a millimeter, not uncommonly within an interval of a few millimeters. An equigranular-polygonal fabric of "micro-polygonal" grains 0.01–0.05 mm across is a relatively uncommon transitional stage.

The grain sizes and grain shapes of quartz depend to a large degree on the presence and density of dust particles (mainly hematite and graphite). Dust particles tend to inhibit grain growth, due to surface tension effects (compare Voll, 1960; Spry, 1969). Therefore, the grain size of quartz varies roughly inversely to the density of dust particles. Furthermore, grain boundaries of larger quartz grains tend to follow dust grains. In this way the outlines of quartz grains may perfectly mimick the onion-skin fabric of recrystallized

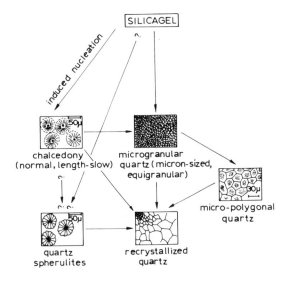

Fig. 4. Crystallization and recrystallization of quartz in iron-formations.

oolites. In certain cases quartz forms a columnar overgrowth perpendicular to the surface of magnetite or hematite crystals (Mukhopadhyay and Chanda, 1972, p. 123; Dimroth and Chauvel, 1973).

Mukhopadhyay and Chanda (1972) make an important distinction between guided and unguided recrystallization. Guided recrystallization may affect a complete laminae, whereas adjoining laminae remain unaffected, or it proceeded inward from boundaries of allochem grains, from shrinkage cracks, bedding planes and crosscutting veins. Unguided recrystallization affects diffuse spots and zones and cuts across sedimentary textures and structures. Both are probably in part controlled by the dust content.

Some I.Fs. contain spherulites, 0.01–0.1 mm across, of radiating prismatic quartz crystals, which in many cases nucleated at the surface of iron oxides (Spencer and Percival, 1952; Mukhopadhyay and Chanda, 1972; Dimroth, unpublished observations from the Gunflint Formation and Rapitan Group). Similar quartz spherulites occur in cherts (Cayeux, 1929). It is unclear whether the quartz spherulites may have formed by recrystallization of (length-slow?) chalcedony, or by radiating crystallization of prismatic quartz crystals from a central nucleus.

Quartz of cement chert

Folk and Weaver (1952), and Walker, T.R. (1962) were probably the first to realize that some quartz in cherts is a pore-space filling. Mukhopadhyay and Chanda (1972), and Dimroth and Chauvel (1973) defined the fabric criteria that permit to distinguish between open pore-space precipitate and matrix chert in I.Fs.; they are analog to the criteria that permit distinction between calcareous cements, micrite and microspar in limestones (compare Folk, 1965; Bathurst, 1971. p. 415 ff.). Cementing chert takes three forms:

(1) Encrustations by chalcedony or by columnar quartz ("flamboyant" quartz, cf., Bayley and James, 1973; Perry et al., 1973) growing perpendicular to the pore walls.

(2) Oriented overgrowth in optical continuity with quartz crystals of the pore wall.

(3) Filling of pores by microgranular quartz indistinguishable from matrix chert.

Only in the first two cases is it possible to recognize open pore-space filling without ambiguity; in the third case it must be known that a pore-space was present, for example, because the micro-granular quartz fills shrinkage cracks or veins. Cement textures observed so far are shown in Fig. 5.

Generally the grain size of encrusting quartz increases and the degree of its form orientation decreases away from the pore walls, just as is the case with sandstone cements (Pettijohn et al., 1972, p. 400). Typically chalcedony is precipitated at the pore walls, followed inward by columnar quartz and finally by a polygonal quartz fabric (Mukhopadhyay and Chanda, 1972; Perry et al., 1973). This sequence may be repeated or varied. Mukhopadhyay and Chanda (1972) noted that columnar pore-filling quartz had negative elongation in many cases. The writer, on the other hand, noted many thin sections where quartz columns grew parallel or subparallel to the crystallographic c-axis (positive elongation). Terminal faces are present in a few cases.

Alternating precipitation of bladed or tabular encrustations (oriented perpendicular to pore walls) of several minerals occur. The writer has observed crystallization of bladed siderite, tabular minnesotaite or chlorite, at the pore walls, followed by crystallization of columnar quartz. In other cases, chalcedony has been precipitated at the pore walls and calcite fills the remaining pore-spaces.

The conditions of formation of various cement textures are not yet completely clear. Folk and Weaver (1952), and Mukhopadhyay and Chanda (1972) inferred that cement fabrics depend on the ratio between nucleation and precipitation rates. Microgranular cement forms where this ratio is high, whereas encrusting cements form where it is low and where nucleation is induced at the pore walls. Dimroth and Chauvel (1973) suggested that induced nucleation requires a crystalline pore wall. In this case crystallization of chert in allochems preceded cementation. On the other hand, no effective pore wall exists where allochem grains consisting of silica-gel are cemented by amorphous silica; microgranular cements should form in this case. Finally, some micro-granular cements formed by recrystallization of chalcedony, as shown by transitions. Detailed measurements of the shapes of cement crystals might provide criteria to distinguish these cases (Bathurst, 1971, p. 415).

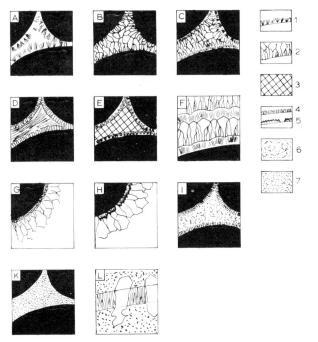

Fig. 5. Cement textures in iron-formations and other rocks.
A. Encrustating chalcedony. B. Encrustating quartz. C. Encrustating chalcedony followed by quartz.
D. Encrustating quartz followed by chalcedony (Cochrane and Edwards, 1960). E. Chalcedony followed by blocky calcite. F. Alternation of encrustating chalcedony (in part length-slow) and quartz (Fleming chert breccia). G. Minnesotaite followed by quartz. H. Siderite followed by quartz. I. Chlorite I (encrustating) followed by chlorite II (Braun, 1964). K. Microgranular quartz. L. Quartz overgrowth (vein in rhyolite).
1 = chalcedony; *2* = columnar quartz encrustation; *3* = blocky calcite; *4* = tabular minnesotaite or chlorite; *5* = encrustating calcite or siderite; *6* = unoriented chlorite; *7* = micro-granular quartz. Cementing quartz is affected by recrystallization as in Fig. 4.

Iron-minerals

Our knowledge on the extremely complex sequence of diagenetic processes involving iron-minerals in cherty I.Fs. is still very incomplete. Nevertheless, it is possible to construct a scheme of the most important reactions affecting the iron-minerals of the Sokoman, Gunflint and Biwabik Formations (Fig. 6), based on the petrographic data of Goodwin (1956), LaBerge (1964), French (1968, 1973) and Dimroth and Chauvel (1973). Data presented by Trendall and Blockley (1970), Grubb (1971) and Ayres (1972) suggest that iron-mineral diagenesis of the Hamersley Group I.Fs. followed a similar course. Blake (1965) and Han (1972) described some different reactions from I.Fs. south of Lake Superior. French (1973) summarized the paragenetic relations of iron-minerals in cherty I.Fs. However, French (1973) may have overestimated the temperatures of formations of

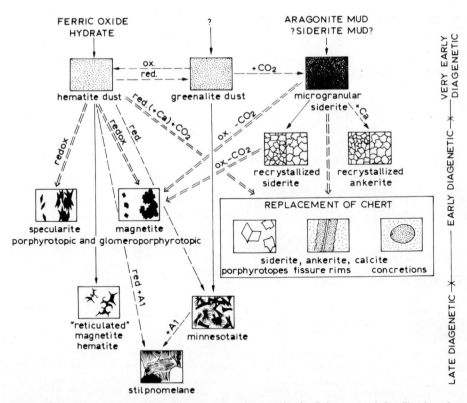

Fig. 6. Epigenesis of iron oxides, silicates and carbonates in the Sokoman and Gunflint iron-formations. Solid arrows: simple recrystallization; broken arrows: reactions not isochemical: *ox* = oxidation, *red* = reduction; *redox* = redox reactions implied; double arrows: transport and migration of material. Reaction greenalite dust → hematite dust: Goodwin (1968); other reactions, Dimroth and Chauvel (1973) and Dimroth (unpublished).

many minerals; for example, riebeckite (Milton and Eugster, 1959) and talc (Stewart, 1965) are known to occur in unmetamorphosed rocks, where they formed at very low temperatures.

Replacement relations (mineral pseudomorphism, replacement of femicrite and of allochem grains, growth of concretions) and the growth of porphyrotopes provide the best evidence for diagenetic reactions. Replacement of minerals containing ferrous iron by ferric minerals or vice versa is considered evidence for oxidation and reduction. In many cases, it is possible to determine whether replacement occurred before or after the complete cementation of allochemical rocks, that is at an early or late diagenetic stage. Furthermore, a generation of very early diagenetic minerals is distinguished for the purpose of this paper. Very early diagenetic iron-minerals (hematite and greenalite dust, micro-granular siderite and ankerite) are very fine grained, and rarely show replacement relations among themselves, whereas their replacement by the coarser grained early and late diagenetic iron-minerals is common; of course, they never were observed as replacement of early or late diagenetic minerals.

The relatively uncommon replacement relations between very early diagenetic iron-minerals have great genetic significance; therefore, they will be discussed in detail. Locally (for example, at stop G7 of Franklin et al., 1972), the Gunflint Formation consists of red, hematite-bearing, cemented intraclastic I.F. (called "taconite") in beds 5–30 cm thick, intercalated between black, graphitic shale. The taconite beds consistently have been discoloured at their contacts. Discoloration is due to replacement of hematite dust by greenalite, and very close to the contact by micro-granular siderite. Boundaries between the zones of replacement crosscut the sedimentary laminations. Similar relations are common in the Sokoman Formation, Labrador Trough, where hematite of laminated jasper beds has been replaced by iron silicate (minnesotaite) and siderite, at the contact to beds of silicate–carbonate I.F.; contacts of the replaced zone crosscut laminations. Thus, good evidence exists that hematite dust has been replaced by greenalite and by micro-granular siderite at the contact between hematite-bearing beds, and beds containing organic matter or reduced iron. Goodwin (1956), on the other hand, presented evidence that oxidation of greenalite to hematite locally occurred as well.

The observations described above leave little doubt about the mechanism of the replacement reactions between the very early diagenetic iron-minerals. The reducing reactions hematite → greenalite → siderite were driven by introduction of solutions containing reducing agents (probably dissolved organic substances) into the sediment, whereas the oxidation reactions described by Goodwin (1956) were driven by infiltration of oxidized solutions.

No change of iron-content or iron-distribution appears to have taken place; thus, reactions apparently took place by mineral replacement essentially without solution and reprecipitation. Analogous reactions accompanied by solution and removal of iron from the rock may explain the discoloration haloes that are common in I.Fs. stained by hematite, greenalite and graphite dust. Hematite dust may have been removed by reduction to Fe^{2+} and dissolution, graphite dust by oxidation; removal of greenalite requires that an environment of low Eh and high pS^{2-} and pFe^{2+} be established. Relations of discoloration haloes to shale layers and bedding planes suggests that diffusion of reducing or oxidizing solutions into the sediment is the cause.

Indirect evidence also proves the importance of diagenetic processes for the formation of very early diagenetic iron-minerals. Chauvel and Dimroth (1974) and Dimroth and Dressler (in prep.) pointed out that certain siderite-bearing rocks of the Sokoman Formation, Labrador Trough, have been deposited in the intertidal and upper sub-tidal zones. Red beds, containing andesite pebbles with oxidized weathering crusts, underlie the I.F. and prove that continental and shallow-marine deposition took place in a strongly oxidized environment. Precipitation of siderite is not possible at the presence of oxygen. Consequently, siderite I.Fs. deposited under these conditions are thought to have formed by replacement of calcareous mud during the earliest diagenesis.

The evolution of the coarser grained (specular hematite $>1 \mu$; siderite $>10 \mu$) iron-minerals during early and late diagenesis is so complex that only a few of the most important processes can be discussed here. All examples are from the Sokoman Formation (Dimroth and Chauvel, 1973), except where other sources are quoted. The processes will be discussed in terms of the following reaction mechanisms: isochemical recrystallization and allochemical neomorphism not involving oxidation or reduction, oxidation and reduction, complex redox reactions. Petrographic evidence, presented by Dimroth and Chauvel (1973) suggests that intense redox reactions took place in I.Fs. during early diagenesis (Dimroth and Chauvel, 1973, p. 132–133). The intensity of redox reactions decreased with increasing degree of lithification. They are quite unimportant during the metamorphism (Klein, 1973).

Siderite is sensitive to recrystallization; replacement of micro-granular siderite femicrite or of siderite intraclasts by a coarse-grained siderite fabric is common (LaBerge, 1964; French, 1973). A few porphyrotopes of specular hematite commonly are present in jaspers and may have formed by isochemical recrystallization. The bulk of the specular hematite of I.Fs., however, appears to have formed by the complex redox reactions discussed below. Large-scale recrystallization of hematite in I.Fs. does not occur, unless metamorphic conditions were attained (Klein, 1973).

The replacement of greenalite by minnesotaite and stilpnomelane, documented by French (1968, 1973) is the most important case of allochemical neomorphism not involving more than minor oxidation or reduction. Stilpnomelane also may replace minnesotaite (Dimroth and Chauvel, 1973). Growth of stilpnomelane may be due to reaction between iron-silicate minerals or iron-silicate gels and aluminous substances (clay minerals, volcanic glass). LaBerge (1966a, b) and Trendall (1966) reported replacement of volcanic debris by stilpnomelane. Replacement of siderite femicrite by coarse-grained ankerite is also common (LaBerge, 1964; French, 1968, 1973; Zajac, 1972, 1974; Dimroth and Chauvel, 1973).

Oxidation reactions play a large role in silicate–carbonate I.Fs. LaBerge (1964), Dimroth and Chauvel (1973) and Zajac (1972, 1974) presented evidence for oxidation of siderite to hematite, magnetite, or to ankerite + magnetite. Magnetite formed by this process has several aspects:

(1) Porphyrotopes and porphyrotopic aggregates of magnetite replaced siderite rhombs and siderite intraclasts.

(2) Porphyrotopes of magnetite may grow dispersed in chert.

(3) Magnetite and magnetite + ankerite form laminae.

LaBerge (1964) suggested that magnetite formed during the metamorphism. However, Dimroth and Chauvel (1973) observed that magnetite laminae reacted as competent layers during the folding and, therefore, are diagenetic. Oxidation of siderite to magnetite likely is caused by diffusion of oxygen-bearing solutions into the rock.

Reduction reactions are most important in hematite I.Fs. Two cases must be distinguished:

(1) Hematite I.F. with interbedded iron-carbonate lentils and hematite I.F. underlying carbonate I.F. tend to show intense recrystallization. Porphyrotopic and glomeroporphyrotopic magnetite, minnesotaite and carbonate (siderite and ankerite) are the most important iron-minerals in these rocks. Relicts of chert—hematite oolites and intraclasts prove the derivation of the coarse-grained iron-minerals from hematite dust. Carbonate concretions contain relict oolitic and intraclastic textures with syneresis cracks and, therefore, also replaced chert. The grey and brown cherty members of the Sokoman Formation (Gross, 1968), are type examples of this form of alteration (Chauvel and Dimroth, 1974). The mechanism of the reducing reactions is not well understood. However, the association of the "grey and brown cherty" facies with carbonate lentils may suggest that descending solutions saturated with $FeCO_3$, and perhaps carrying dissolved organic substances, might be responsible for the reduction reactions.

(2) Replacement of hematite dust by magnetite, minnesotaite and iron-carbonate took place at the contact between jasper beds and black shale. Diffusion of reducing diagenetic solutions from the shale into the jasper is the likely cause of the reducing reactions. Jasper beds in the Archean greywackes of Cadillac, Quebec, are a typical example (Dimroth, unpublished data).

The close association of hematite—magnetite layers (mesobands) and discoloration haloes in the hematite I.F. of the Sokoman Formation provides evidence for the great importance of complex redox reactions. The discoloration affects mainly the interiors of allochem grains (intraclasts, oolites), and of matrix chert laminae. Allochemical (oolitic and intraclastic) relict textures prove that metallic layers are mainly derived from allochem sands. Differential compaction features (p. 215) show that the layers formed before the cementation. Thus, it is apparent that iron preferentially migrated from matrix cherts into allochem sands. Dimroth and Chauvel (1973) proposed that organic matter reduced hematite to Fe^{2+} in the interiors of matrix chert laminae and of allochem grain: Fe^{2+} migrated into uncemented allochem sands, where it was oxidized to magnetite and/or specular hematite by oxygen-bearing solutions. The same mechanism may also explain the common replacement of the skins of allochem grains by magnetite and/or specular hematite. In this case, hematite dust has been dissolved in the interiors of the allochem grains, and has been oxidized by pore solutions at their surface.

It is relatively easy to recognize the action of the complex redox reactions discussed above, where the distance of diffusion is small. However, data presented by Zajac (1972, 1974) suggest that large-scale iron-migration might also occur. Zajac (op. cit.) correlated iron contents and textural facies of member V of the Sokoman Formation (see Fig. 7) and interpreted both as primary variations. Reduction of ferric iron to Fe^{2+} in the shallow-water domain (partly intertidal) of Zajac's "massive-bedded" facies, transport of Fe^{2+} toward the basin by saline, reducing groundwaters, and oxidation of Fe^{2+} at the sediment—water interface, is a plausible alternate interpretation.

A close relation exists between the texture and composition of I.Fs. and iron-mineral diagenesis. James (1954, 1966) investigated co-existing iron-minerals and established the

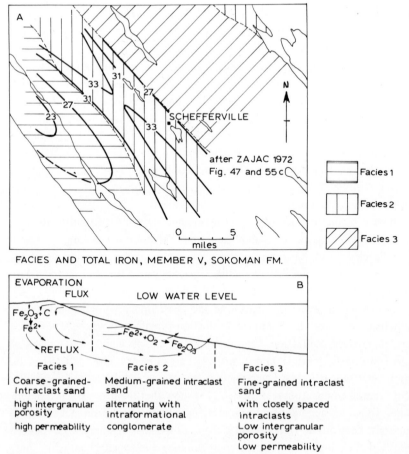

FACIES AND TOTAL IRON, MEMBER V, SOKOMAN FM.

Fig. 7. A. Relations between textural facies and iron contents of member V of the Sokoman iron-formation, Central Labrador Trough. Facies *1* = massive bedded facies (coarse-grained intraclast sands); facies *2* = conglomeratic facies (medium-grained intraclast sands alternating with intraformational conglomerate); facies *3* = "terrigenous" facies (fine-grained intraclast sand with terrigenous components). Thick lines: Cubic trend lines of average Fe content (in %). (After Zajac, 1972, fig. 47 and 55c.)

B. Interpretation of iron distribution by reflux-mobilization. Iron is mobilized by reaction of Fe_2O_3 with organic matter below intraclast banks and migrates basinward. Fe is re-precipitated at or close to the sediment−water interface within the basin.

correlation between mineral facies and texture of I.Fs. Virtually all I.Fs. that have been deposited as clean-washed sands (cemented intraclastic or oolitic cherts) belong to hematite, magnetite or silicate facies, whereas virtually all rock of the siderite and sulfide facies have been deposited as muds or as intraclastic muds. The reverse is not true; hematite I.F. (matrix chert) deposited as mud is common. James (1966) also established a correlation between the mineral facies and carbon content of I.Fs. Hematite, magnetite and silicate I.Fs. are virtually carbon-free. Most siderite I.Fs. contain a few tenth of a percent of carbon. Sulfide I.Fs. (pyritiferous graphitic shales) contain several percent carbon. Cherty pyrite I.Fs. are extremely rare. James (1954, 1966) suggested that these correlations prove that mineral facies of I.Fs. are primary, and are controlled by the physico-chemistry of the depositional environment. This conclusion does not necessarily follow; an actualistic interpretation of the observed correlations will be proposed below.

Physico-chemistry of iron-mineral diagenesis

Growth and survival of iron-metals during diagenesis is determined by the physico-chemistry of the diagenetic environment. The stability of iron-minerals is a function of many variables, in particular of Eh, pH, pCO_2 and pS^{2-} of the pore solutions. Garrels and Christ (1965) summarized the thermo-chemical data on iron-minerals, and constructed diagrams showing the stability fields of iron-minerals as functions of Eh and pH, at constant values of pS^{2-} and pCO_2. In reality, pH of marine sediments varies little (6.5 < pH < 9), whereas pCO_2, and in particular pS^{2-} and Eh, vary within extreme limits. For this reason iron-mineral diagenesis is discussed here at hand of Eh–pCO_2 and Eh–pS^{2-} diagrams (Fig. 8, after Berner, 1971). Absence of thermo–chemical data on the iron-silicates greenalite and chamosite is the main weakness of the diagrams; it is believed that the stability fields of both minerals would plot in the general vicinity of the magnetite field,

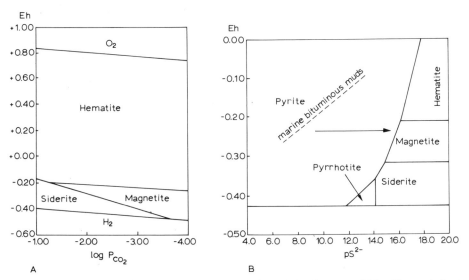

Fig. 8. A. Eh–log pCO_2 diagram for hematite, magnetite and siderite at very high pS^{2-}. $T = 25°C$; P_{tot} = 1 atm; $a_{Ca} + 2 = 10^{-2.58}$, equilibrium with $CaCO_3$ assumed. These conditions are reasonable during early diagenesis of non-sulfidic marine sediments. (After Berner, 1971, fig. 10-1.) B. Eh–pS^{2-} diagram for pyrite, pyrrhotite, hematite, magnetite and siderite. pH = 7.37; log pCO_2 = −2.40; $T = 25°C$; P_{tot} = 1 atm. (After Berner, 1971, fig. 10-2.) The broken line shows Eh–pS^{2-} in marine bituminous muds. Oversupply of iron over biogenic H_2S production in iron ores would cause an increase of pS^{2-} at constant Eh (arrow). This would stabilize magnetite or, at high pCO_2, siderite.

or between the magnetite and siderite fields (Garrels and Christ, 1965; James, 1966). Two basic relations follow from the diagrams: (1) only hematite is stable in the presence of even the smallest trace of free oxygen; (2) only pyrite is stable in the presence of traces of H_2S. Therefore the stability fields of siderite, magnetite and, presumably, the iron-silicates are extremely limited.

pH, Eh and pS^{2-} of the diagenetic pore solutions are not independent variables. The acidity is buffered by dissolved carbonate species, and is a function of the concentration of weak acids (CO_2, organic acids) in the pore-solutions. Eh and pS^{2-} are determined by dynamic equilibria. Eh and pS^{2-} are functions of the rates of organic decay and of bacterial sulfate reduction, and of the rates by which oxygen diffuses into the sediment and by which dissolved reducing substances diffuse out of the sediment. Therefore the concentration of organic matter in the sediment, and the relations between diffusion rates and other sediment properties require discussion in order to understand iron-mineral diagenesis.[1]

Most organic matter is deposited in form of finely particulate matter of low density; consequently, it accumulates with the clay fraction of the sediment. Clean washed sands universally are poor in organic matter. On the other hand, the concentration of organic matter in muds depends on the ratio of the organic and inorganic sedimentation rates. Terrigenous sedimentation rates are extremely variable. Therefore, the concentration of organic matter in marine terrigenous muds varies from practically nil (in environments with low organic productivity and high sedimentation rates), to more than 40% (in environments of high organic productivity and very low terrigenous sedimentation rates). Rates of chemical precipitation commonly are fairly high and are less variable than terrigenous sedimentation rates. Therefore, the concentration of organic matter in Phanerozoic micritic limestones varies from nil to a few percent. Chemical sediments with very high carbon contents (>5%) are extremely rare.[2]

Oxygen diffuses into the sediment from the sediment—water interface, and reducing organic substances and H_2S diffuse toward the sediment—water interface. Both also are carried in diagenetic solutions circulating in aquifers. Diffusion rates and rates of circulation in aquifers are proportional to the permeability of the sediment. They are high in clean-washed sands and low in muds or in sands with a mud matrix.

Because of these relations, oxidizing diagenetic conditions are maintained only in some clean-washed sands, and in muds with an extremely low concentration of organic matter. Therefore, hematite may be expected to form mainly in cemented allochemical iron-formations, and in matrix cherts that were deposited in environments of very low organic productivity.

Only pyrite is stable at the presence of more than traces of H_2S. Two sources of H_2S are geologically significant: (1) volcanic solfatara; and (2) sulfate-reducing bacteria. Precipitation of iron sulfides by volcanic solfatara has been studied intensely (Degens and

---

[1] For general discussion, see Chapter 2 by Duursma and Hoede, Vol. 2.

[2] See Chapter 5 by Saxby, Vol. 2, on the influence of organic matter.

Ross, 1969, and Chapter 4, Vol. 4; Bäcker and Richter, 1973; Baumann et al., 1973; Hart-mann, 1973; Puchelt et al., 1973; Wauschkuhn, 1973). It is likely that the massive vol-canogenic sulfide deposits described by Sangster (1972) and Sangster and Scott in Chap-ter 5, Vol. 6, and some of the Algoma-type I.Fs. that are directly related to volcanic cen-ters (Goodwin, 1962, 1973a, b), formed by analogous processes. However, most sulfide I.Fs. are not related to volcanic centers, and must have formed by the action of sulfate-reducing bacteria.[1]

Berner (1970, 1971, 1973) studied the formation of pyrite in Recent sediments. Sulfate-reducing bacteria produce H_2S at a rate proportional to the concentration of organic matter and to the sulfate concentration in the pore solution (Berner, 1971, p. 132; 1973). A very large amount of organic matter is required to produce a substantial concen-tration of pyrite. For example, 4% carbon would be consumed in order to produce the S^{2-} bound in 10% FeS_2, even if the reactions would take place quantitatively. Therefore, the rates of sulfate-reduction limit the amount of pyrite forming in sediments. Sulfide I.Fs. with more than 10% pyrite can be expected to form only from muds that are exceptionally rich in organic matter (>20% organic matter, at the time of deposition), and that have been deposited in environments (marine or arid-lacustrine), where sulfate is available in the diagenetic solutions. This is in agreement with the observation that most sulfide I.Fs. are carbon-rich fine-grained shales, whereas cherty sulfide I.Fs. are extremely rare.

Siderite precipitates at very low Eh and pS^{2-} (Fig. 8). Therefore, it forms during the diagenesis of Recent or ancient delta-swamp muds (Curtis and Spears, 1968; Ho and Coleman, 1969; Oertel and Curtis, 1972; Curtis et al., 1972), and in similar fresh-water deposits with high contents of organic matter. Siderite is rare in Recent marine sediments (Seibold, 1973; Puchelt et al., 1973), and the conditions of its precipitation in marine sediments are not well understood. Some siderite of cherty I.Fs. is manifestly diagenetic and may have formed by replacement of calcareous ooze (Chauvel and Dimroth, 1974).

Siderite might form in iron ores under conditions where sulfide would normally pre-cipitate in terrigenous sediments with low iron content. The Eh–pS^{2-} conditions during early diagenesis of marine bituminous muds fall in a narrow field (shown by the broken line in Fig. 8B). A large supply of iron, as is present in sedimentary iron ores, would lead to an increase of pS^{2-}, at constant Eh. Thus diagenetic Eh–pS^{2-} conditions would shift in the direction of the arrow in Fig. 8B. Therefore, siderite might form, besides some pyrite, during the diagenesis of iron-rich muds that contain enough organic matter to maintain a low Eh during diagenesis, but not enough to permit profuse proliferation of sulfate-reducing bacteria. The fact that siderite I.F. commonly contains a little carbon, and some pyrite supports this hypothesis. The carbon of siderite in I.Fs. is isotopically light (Becker and Clayton, 1972; Perry and Tan, 1973; Perry et al., 1973); this suggests that CO_2 produced by oxidation of organic matter might have been incorporated into the siderite.

---

[1] See Chapter 6 by Trudinger, Vol. 2.

Chamosite and glauconite form at present at, or close to, the sediment—water interface, by replacement of clay pellets, and as filling of the tests of foraminifera (Porrenga,
1966, 1967). Both minerals appear to form in generally aerobic environments, but at the
presence of organic matter. Greenalite and other iron-silicates might have formed under
similar conditions, but in the absence of alumina. If this is correct, one could suspect that
greenalite developed in sediments that contained a comparatively small amount of organic
matter. Magnetite of cherty I.Fs. forms by oxidation of siderite and by reduction of
hematite. There appears to be little doubt that reduction of hematite to magnetite is
caused by organic matter.

The observed replacement reactions between the various iron-minerals of cherty I.Fs.,
and the observed relations between the texture and composition of cherty I.Fs. and their
mineral facies, appear to be amenable to actualistic interpretation. The distribution of
organic matter in the sediment, and the migration rates of oxygen and of reducing
substances appear to control iron-mineral stability during diagenesis. These factors are
functions of the sediment texture, of the organic productivity in the sedimentary environment, and of the inorganic (chemical and terrigenous) sedimentation rates.

PALEOGEOGRAPHIC ANALYSIS

The classical approach to the paleogeographic analysis of cherty I.Fs. is based on
the proposal (James, 1954, 1966) that iron-mineral facies is depositional, and is a function of the physico-chemistry (notably Eh) of the environment of deposition. Furthermore, it is generally assumed that Eh decreases, more or less regulary, with basin bathymetry; this latter assumption implies deposition in density-stratified restricted marine
basins (type Baltic Sea). As a consequence, it is assumed that oxide I.Fs. were deposited
in shallow water, whereas silicate, carbonate and sulfide I.Fs. were deposited in successively deeper water. Goodwin's (1962, 1973a, b) interpretations of Algoma-type I.Fs. are
the outstanding examples based on this approach. James (1954), Goodwin (1956),
Schmidt (1963), Gross (1968, 1972), Zajac (1972, 1974), and Morey (1973) studied
Lake Superior-type I.Fs. from this viewpoint, but considered sediment textures and structures as supporting evidence.

There is no doubt that a certain correlation exists between the paleogeography and the
mineralogy of I.Fs. It is uncertain, however, whether this correlation is due to a control
of iron-mineral facies by the pH—Eh of the depositional environment, or to control of
iron-mineral facies by rock texture and carbon content, both of which are complicated
functions of the paleogeography. At present, highly-oxidized sediments may be deposited
in very deep water (e.g., red deep-sea clays and manganese nodules), and reduced sediments may form in shallow water (e.g., pyrite in peritidal muds, and siderite in delta-
swamps). Because of these uncertainties, it is preferable to base paleogeographic interpretations on rock properties that depend directly on the hydrodynamics and ecology of the
basin. The approach developed below, permits to apply actualistic models to the interpretation of the paleo-environment of Precambrian cherty I.Fs.

Lake Superior-type I.Fs.

Actualistic interpretation of the paleo-environment of Lake Superior-type I.Fs. is straightforward. These rocks show all the various textures and structures of shallow-water limestones, as they are presently deposited on the Bahama Bank and at many other localities. Consequently, it is possible to define facies by the sedimentary structures and textures. Comparison with analogous Recent limestones permits comparatively detailed paleogeographic interpretation. The facies distribution of two members of the Sokoman Iron Formation, Quebec, Canada, will be quoted here as an example (see Fig. 9 and 10 and Table IV, after Chauvel and Dimroth, 1974).

The basin model of the Sokoman Formation comprises two main environments: a marine basin, and a lagoonal platform. The lagoonal platform had a complex topography of mud and sand banks and small local basins, shifting rapidly. A domain of oolite and intraclast bars separated the lagoonal platform from the main basin.

Muds (femicrite and matrix chert) with millimetric or sub-millimetric parallel laminae, and thin to medium bedded very fine-grained sands, are the typical sediments of the basin facies. Individual members are comparatively thick, and show little lateral facies variation. Sands coarsen toward the basin margin. Sheets of oolite sand are present at the margin of the basin, close to oolite bars. Intraclastic conglomerates formed at the top of sub-tidal mud- and sand-banks close to the basin margin, in a bathymetric zone above storm-wave base.

The sediments deposited on the lagoonal platform show a radically different organization. Lateral and vertical facies transitions are extremely rapid; therefore, many sub-members can be defined in stratigraphic sections, but their lateral correlation is difficult. Sub-members composed of a single textural rock type are rare in the lagoonal platform facies, whereas they are the rule in the basin facies. Alternation of thin beds (1—10 cm) of several rock types (cemented intraclastic or oolitic chert, intraclastic conglomerate, matrix chert, femicrite, intrafemicrite), is common, and proves that quiet and turbulent hydrodynamic conditions alternated. Dune cross-beds, flaser bedding and lenticular bedding, and erosion channels are characteristic sedimentary structures. Upward coarsening cycles, 10—15 m thick, are locally present and are probably due to the gradual infilling of small lagoons. Thick units of massive or thick-bedded cemented oolite and intraclast sand represent the bars separating the lagoonal and basinal domains.

Algoma-type iron-formations

The paleogeographic interpretation of Algoma-type I.Fs. is befrayed with difficulties. Parallel laminations are their only sedimentary structures, and prove deposition in a low-energy environment. However, low-energy environments range from the sub-aerial domain to the deepest ocean basins. Other structures, like slump-folds and syn-sedimentary breccias have no bathymetric significance. Two cases must be considered separately.

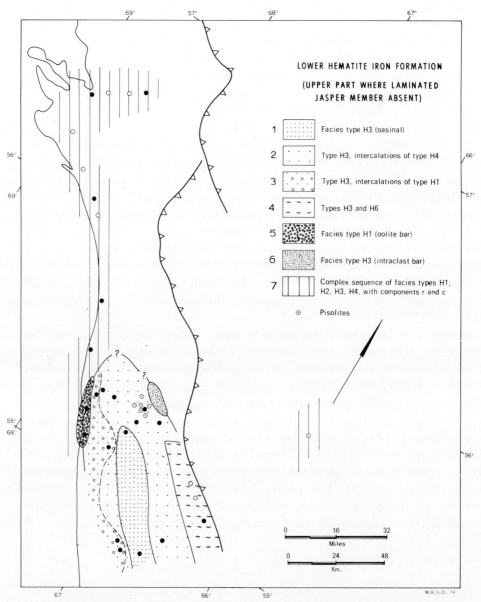

Fig. 9. Facies distribution of the lower hematite I.F. member of the Sokoman Iron-Formation, central Labrador Trough, Quebec, Canada. (After Chauvel and Dimroth, 1974. Description of facies types see Table IV.) Environments: *1* = deep basinal (below storm-wave base); *2* = basin marginal sand bank, above storm-wave base; *3* = basin margin, above wave base; *4* = basin marginal mud bank, above storm-wave base; *5* = oolite bar; *6* = intraclast bar; *7* = lagoonal platform.

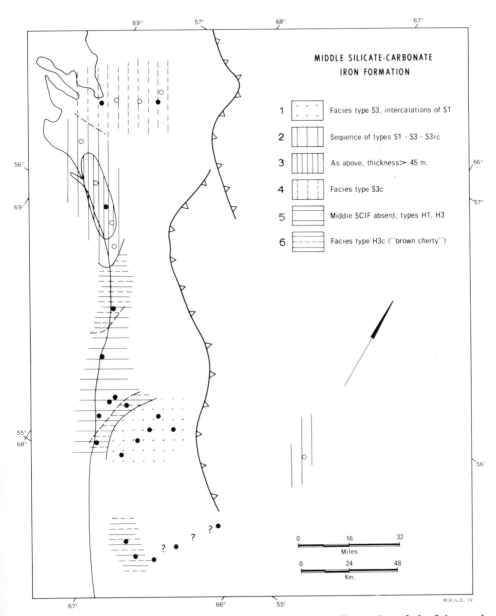

Fig. 10. Facies distribution of the middle silicate–carbonate I.F. member of the Sokoman Iron Formation, central Labrador Trough, Quebec, Canada (after Chauvel and Dimroth, 1974. Description of facies types see Table IV.) Environments: *1* = basinal; *2, 3, 4* = lagoonal platform; *5* = intraclast bar and adjoining environments; *6* = shallow lagoonal and basinal adjoining intraclast bar.

TABLE IV

Main facies types of the Sokoman Iron-Formation, central Labrador Trough (after Chauvel and Dimroth, 1974). Facies distribution see Fig. 9 and 10

Hematite iron-formation

I. Basin
a. Deep basinal zone, below storm-wave base. Facies Type (F.T.) *H3* = very fine grained cemented intraclast sand. Thin- to medium-bedded, parallel bedding. Basinal traction current deposits.
b. Basin margin, sand bank above storm-wave base: F.T. *H3* as above; intercalations of F.T. *H4* = cemented intraclastic conglomerate. Conglomerate formed by storm action.
c. Basin margin, mud bank above storm-wave base: F.T. *H3* as above; intercalations of F.T. *H6* = alternating matrix cherts (in part with mud lumps) and intraclastic conglomerate with soft pebbles. Conglomerates formed by storm action.
d. Basin margin, above wave base, subtidal. F.T. *H3*, as above, but coarser grained. Intercalations of F.T. *H1* = cemented oolite sand (oolite spill-overs sand sheet). Dune cross-bedding is common.

II. Sand Bar
a. Oolite bar: F.T. *H1* = cemented oolite sand, massive or very thick bedded.
b. Intraclast bar: F.T. *H3* = cemented coarse-grained intraclast sand, massive or very thick bedded.

III. Lagoonal platform
    Complex sequence of F.T. *H1* (= cemented oolite sand), *H2* (cemented oolitic conglomerate), *H3* (cemented, coarse-grained intraclast sand), *H4* (cemented intraclastic conglomerate), with or without interbeds of components *r* (ribboned matrix chert) and *c* (carbonate femicrite). Thin-bedded, lenticular bedding, irregular bedding, channels, cross-bedding, graded bedding. Upward coarsening cycles 10–15 m thick are present.

Silicate–carbonate iron-formation

I. Basin
a. Deep basin, below wave base: F.T. *S1* = laminated femicrite with parallel lamination. F.T. *S3* = fine-grained cemented intraclast sand; thin- to medium-bedded. Basinal traction current deposits.
b. Basin margin: F.T. *H3c* = cemented, hematite-bearing, coarse-grained intraclast sand with intercalations of carbonate femicrite lenses. Thin- to medium-bedded. Cross-bedding, lenticular bedding, channels.

II. Sand bar
    F.T. *H3* and *H1* = hematite I.F., cemented coarse-grained intraclast sand (*H3*) or oolite sand (*H1*).

III. Lagoonal platform
a. Deep lagoon, below storm-wave base: F.T. *S1* = laminated femicrite and matrix chert. Parallel laminae.
b. Lagoon, above storm-wave base, below normal wave base: F.T. *S2* = alternating femicrite and intrafemicrite. Femicrite has parallel lamination, disturbed parallel lamination and mud lumps. Intrafemicrite beds have erosional bases, and show graded bedding (content and coarse-tail grading). Intrafemicrites are storm layers.
c. Lower intertidal and upper subtidal zones: F.T. *S3rc* and *S3C* coarse-grained cemented intraclast sand alternating with carbonate femicrite and matrix chert. Lenticular bedding, flaser bedding, cross-bedding, channels.

Extensive I.Fs. of Algoma-type were deposited in the Proterozoic. These formations are thick (generally more than 100 m) and underlie very large areas (several 10,000–100,000 km^2). I.Fs. of South Africa (Beukes, 1973), Mauritania (Besnus et al., 1969), South America (Dorr, 1973), Australia (Hamersley Group, Trendall, 1973a) and Canada (Rapitan Group, Gabrielse, 1972) are examples. I.Fs. of the Hamersley Group are 1100 m thick, and were deposited in a basin covering more than 150,000 km^2. There is no evidence for high hydrodynamic energy anywhere in the I.Fs. of the Hamersley Group. Thus, these extensive Algoma-type I.Fs. unquestionably are pelagic sediments, deposited in water considerably deeper than the normal marine wave base at about 100 m.

The Algoma-type I.Fs. of volcano-sedimentary terrains, for example, the Archean I.Fs. described by Goodwin (1962, 1973a, b) and by Beukes (1973) are comparatively thin bodies (1–50 m) of small lateral extent (1–20 km), commonly intercalated between terrigenous volcanogenic sediments. It is reasonable, in this case, to assume that the I.Fs. have been deposited in the same environment as the associated terrigenous sediments. The depositional environment of the latter sediments can be established by comparison with their Recent counterparts.

Archean Algoma-type jaspers of the Rouyn-Noranda area (Dimroth et al., 1974) may serve as an example. These jaspers are intimately associated with one or several of the following rock types: (1) black or grey chert, massive or with thin parallel laminae; (2) black shale, with thin parallel laminae; (3) thin-bedded silt-laminated argillite; and (4) very fine grained, thin- to medium-bedded (1–10 cm) greywacke with graded bedding. Grading of silt upward into cherty I.F. is common, and suggests that the I.F. is a fine-grained basinal sediment component that settled from suspension. The thin-bedded grey-wackes may be distal turbidites of Walker's, R.G. (1967, 1970) type A → E. Tentatively the writer interpretes these jaspers as pelagic deposits, laid down in basin tracts (not necessarily very deep), from which terrigenous detritus has been largely excluded. Red radiolarian jaspers, and associated red micritic limestones (e.g., Garrison and Fischer, 1969), may be the closest modern analogs of these Algoma-type jaspers. Beukes (1973) described Algoma-type I.Fs. from South Africa, occurring in the same facies association. Other facies associations have been described by Goodwin (1973a, b).

Special problems of iron-formation paleogeography

Two special problems of I.F. deposition deserve further study:

(1) The suggestion that I.Fs. are lacustrine (Sakamoto, 1950; Hough, 1958; Govett, 1966; Eugster and Chou, 1973)

(2) Their relation to sulfate evaporites and red beds (Eugster and Chou, 1973; Chauvel and Dimroth, 1974). Sakamoto (1950), Hough (1958), and Govett (1966) interpreted Algoma-type I.Fs. as lacustrine deposits because of the presence of varve-like laminations. Other evidence for the lacustrine origin of these rocks has not been quoted. Eugster and Chou (1973) thought that the chert of I.Fs. is derived from magadiite. Consequently,

they also proposed a lacustrine model of I.F. deposition. I.Fs. have been deposited in large basins (Hamersley basin: 150,000 km^2; Labrador Trough: more than 1,000 km long and 70 km wide). Lakes of so large an extent are rare indeed; their deposits would be virtually indistinguishable from marine sediments. Evidence for the action of tides (tidal channels, herringbone cross-bedding, etc.), might be the only criterion by which the marine origin of cherty I.Fs. could be established beyond doubt.

Evidence for the former presence of evaporites in the Precambrian generally is circumstantial. Length-slow chalcedony (Folk and Pittman, 1971) and gypsum pseudomorphs occur in the Sokoman Formation, Labrador Trough (Dimroth and Chauvel, 1973). The Sokoman Formation overlies a gypsum solution-collapse breccia (Fleming Formation, Howell, 1954; Dimroth, 1973); red beds occur in the same sequence. The I.F. of the Rapitan Group, Mackenzie Mountains, Canada, is intercalated between red beds (Gabrielse, 1972), apparently containing gypsum (Cloud, 1973a). The Kipalu Iron Formation, Belcher Islands, is also associated with red beds (Jackson, in Dimroth et al., 1970). Evidence for association with evaporites and red beds has not been reported from other I.Fs.

Depth-control of iron-mineral facies

Bathymetric estimates of the environments of I.F. deposition, independent of their mineral facies still are rare. Chauvel and Dimroth (1974) suggested that the hematite and silicate–carbonate facies of the Sokoman I.F. range from the peritidal to the deep basinal zone, that is from sea-level down to a depth of 50–100 m. The Ruth shale, considered to be a sulfide I.F. by most authors (Gross, 1968; Zajac, 1974), has been deposited in water less than 115 m deep. Hematite, silicate–carbonate and sulfide facies of the large Algoma-type I.Fs. discussed on the preceding pages, are pelagic sediments (water depth >100 m). Pyritiferous bituminous shales (sulfide I.Fs.) were formerly thought to occur only in restricted barred basins. Recent work (Dunham, 1961; Bitterli, 1963; Hallam, 1967; Krebs, 1969) showed that they also form in very shallow and open-marine environments.

It is consequently impossible to set absolute limits to the depth-range of the various mineralogical varieties of I.F. The writer feels that the correlation between the mineral facies of I.Fs. and their paleogeography (e.g., Chauvel and Dimroth, 1974; also Zajac, 1974, in so far as based on textural criteria of environmental reconstruction) is indirect. The concentration of organic matter in the sediment, and the rock texture are functions on the paleogeography; both control the diagenesis of iron-minerals. Thus, under present day conditions, one would expect strongly reduced facies (pyrite and siderite) to form in areas of mud-deposition with high organic productivity, and weakly reduced (silicate) or oxidized (hematite) facies are expected to form in areas of sand-deposition; muds that have been deposited in areas with low organic productivity, also will give rise to hematite or silicate I.Fs.

Tectonic control of iron-formation deposition

Deposition of I.Fs. is largely controlled by tectonic factors, as is the deposition of limestones and of other chemical sediments. Chemical sedimentation requires that terrigenous detritus and volcanic material be largely excluded from the depocenter. Furthermore, chemical precipitation generally takes place in very shallow water. These requirements are fulfilled only under very quiet tectonic conditions. Therefore, the large I.Fs. were deposited on platforms, and in miogeosynclinal and parageosynclinal basins, at times of tectonic quiescence. They belong to the pre-flysch phase of miogeosynclinal deposition in the sense of Aubouin (1965). Relatively small volumes of volcanic material generally are present (for example in the Hamersley Group, Australia: Trendall, 1966; LaBerge, 1966a; South Africa: LaBerge, 1966b; Beukes, 1973; Rapitan Group, Canada: Gabrielse, 1972; Labrador Trough, Canada: Gross, 1968; Zajac, 1972, 1974). However, eruption of voluminous volcanic material is incompatible with large-scale deposition of I.Fs.

Terrigenous detritus dilutes chemical sediments in tectonically active areas, and emplacement of volcanic material interrupts chemical sedimentation in active volcanic chains. Furthermore, extensive shallow-water domains exist in miogeosynclinal and parageosynclinal basins, but not around chains of volcanic islands. Therefore, the I.Fs. of eugeosynclinal volcano-sedimentary terrains are thin and have only local extent. However, a large number of deposits is commonly present in Early Precambrian volcano-sedimentary basins, and their cumulate volume is considerable (Goodwin, 1973a, b). The present writer proposes that the limitation of high chemical precipitation rates to shallow-water domains, dilution of chemical sediment by terrigenous detritus in tectonically unstable areas, and interruption of chemical sedimentation by volcanic activity in zones of active volcanism, may be the principal tectonic controls of I.F. deposition.

ORIGIN OF CHERTY IRON-FORMATIONS

Speculations on the origin of cherty I.Fs. are limited by the following observations:

(1) Shrinkage textures, and the textures of iron-minerals suggest that I.Fs. are derived from mixed silica-iron oxide gels, mixed silica-iron silicate gels, and siderite; these substances either have been precipitated from sea- or lake-water, or have been precipitated from diagenetic pore solutions at a very early diagenetic stage. In exceptional cases their diagenetic age has been demonstrated (Chauvel and Dimroth, 1974).

(2) Varve measurements by Trendall and Blockley (1970) and by Trendall (1972, 1973b), and the general similarity of bedding structures in limestones and I.Fs. suggest that the sedimentation rates of I.Fs. have the same order of magnitude as sedimentation rates of Recent limestones.

(3) Cherty I.Fs. are commonly restricted to one or a few formations in each depositional basin, whereas dolomites are a major or minor component of most stratigraphic

units deposited in aqueous environments (e.g., Labrador Trough: Dimroth, 1973; Belcher Basin: Jackson, in Dimroth et al., 1970). Thus it appears that Ca^{2+} and Mg^{2+} have been supplied continuously to the basin, whereas the supply of iron was episodic. Therefore, cherty I.Fs. cannot be regarded as normal precipitates from Precambrian seas. They appear to be products of abnormal conditions of deposition.

Transport of iron and silica

Hematite, magnetite and pyrite are virtually insoluble at the pH of surface waters. Siderite is fairly soluble; sea-water saturated with respect to $CaCO_3$ and $FeCO_3$ may contain 3–30 ppm Fe^{2+} in solution (Holland, 1973). Therefore, transport of substantial concentrations of iron in solution is possible only at strongly reducing conditions and in the absence of H_2S (see Fig. 8). Rivers may transport several ppm of ferric hydroxide sol. Ferric hydroxide sol is flocculated with clay at the river mouth. Consequently, iron is transported essentially in two forms under present conditions; (1) in form of detrital iron minerals and as oxide films on clay and silt particles; and (2) as Fe^{2+} in reducing subsurface waters.

Present-day mean river-water contains 13 ppm dissolved silica (Livingstone, 1963) and present-day ocean-water contains 1 ppm SiO_2 (Mason, 1966, p. 194–199). Both are undersaturated with respect to amorphous silica. Organisms with siliceous tests precipitate silica from normal fresh- and sea-water. Subsurface waters and alkaline lakes may contain considerable concentrations of dissolved silica. Magadiite and other alkali silicates are less soluble than silica at pH > 7 and at normal levels of Na^+ and of CO_2 (Eugster and Chou, 1973). Therefore, magadiite is precipitated from silica-rich subsurface or lacustrine alkaline waters (Eugster, 1969; Surdam et al., 1972) and is converted to chert during diagenesis (Eugster, 1969).

Direct-precipitation hypotheses

Van Hise and Leith (1911), Gruner (1922) and James (1954, 1966) founded and developed the direct-precipitation hypothesis of cherty I.Fs. Lepp and Goldich (1964) suggested that iron was transported under non-actualistic atmospheric conditions. It is assumed that the atmosphere was reducing (Rubey, 1951, 1955; Lepp and Goldich, 1964) in the Early and Middle Precambrian, or that it contained very little oxygen (pO_2 ~ $2 \cdot 10^{-4}$ atm; Berker and Marshall, 1967; Schidlowski, 1971). Under a reducing atmosphere, iron would behave geochemically like magnesia, and would be transported in surface waters. At low atmospheric oxygen pressures iron could be transported in the ocean, provided the ocean was not polluted by H_2S.

The nature of the precipitated materials and the precipitation mechanisms are disputed. Lepp and Goldich (1964) proposed precipitation of siderite. Fryer (1972) and Holland (1973) proposed precipitation of ferric oxide in surface waters and of ferrous minerals at depth. Cloud (1968, 1972, 1973) invoked a biochemical mechanism by which ferric hydroxide is precipitated. None of these models explains the co-precipitation of iron and silica. Lepp and Goldich (1964) suggested that chert formed by replacement of carbonate, and LaBerge (1964) that silica accumulated as tests of micro-organisms. Cloud (1973a) and Holland (1973) believe in inorganic silica-precipitation from an ocean richer in SiO_2 than present-day sea-water (Siever, 1957). Eugster and Chou (1973) proposed precipitation of magadiite-type chert, and transport of iron and silica in the sub-surface.

The fact that most cherty I.Fs. are older than 1900 m.y. (Goldich, 1973) suggests a linkage between I.F. deposition and evolutionary processes. However, their age distribution does not prove that I.F. deposition is related to the evolution of the atmosphere. It also may be related to biologic evolution. Cherty I.Fs. younger than 1900 m.y. are known. The Paleozoic (Gross, 1967, Schultz, 1966) and Cenozoic (e.g., the Kosaka-tetsusekiei of Horikoshi, 1969) cherty I.Fs. are small and are the product of very special conditions. Thus, they are not directly comparable to the major Precambrian I.Fs. On the other hand, two typical cherty I.Fs. of large extent were deposited in the latest Precambrian. They are the I.Fs. of the Rapitan Group, Mackenzie Mountains, Canada (Gabrielse, 1972) and of the Jacadigo Series, Matto Grosso, Brazil and Bolivia (Dorr, 1973). Evolution of metazoans in the latest Precambrian excludes the presence of a low-oxygen atmosphere at that time.

Furthermore, Middle Precambrian and perhaps even Early Precambrian sediments contain evidence that oxidizing diagenetic reactions occurred. The oldest stromatolitic dolomites are older than 2700 m.y., and stromatolites are abundant in the Early Proterozoic. These rocks contained much organic matter at the time of their deposition. They are nearly carbon-free today, clear evidence that the organic matter has been oxidized. Red beds underlie the I.Fs. of the Circum-Ungava geosyncline (Dimroth et al., 1970; Chown and Caty, 1973). Red beds of the Labrador Trough (Dimroth, 1973) contain pebbles of andesite with red, oxidized, weathering crusts; they must have been deposited under oxidizing conditions. Hematite coatings on the surface of detrital grains must have formed after deposition, and prove that oxidizing conditions were maintained during their diagenesis, as is the case in Recent red beds (Walker, T.R., 1967a, b). The evidence for diagenetic oxidation in I.Fs. has been presented above. Precambrian volcanic rocks also may contain evidence for oxidation reactions: Sub-aerial volcanic rocks generally show higher Fe_2O_3/FeO ratios than their sub-aqueous equivalents, regardless of their Recent, Middle Precambrian (Baragar, in Dimroth et al., 1970) or Archean (Cooke and Moorhouse, 1966) age. Fossils appear to provide further evidence. Edhorn (1973) and Bell and Hofmann (1974) discovered probable eucaryotes in the Gunflint and Kipalu Iron Formations, and Edhorn (1973) suggested that green algae were present in the Gunflint microflora. Eucaryotes and green algae are obligate aerobes. Therefore, doubts may be raised against hypotheses that require an atmosphere with very low oxygen-pressure as a prerequisite of I.F. deposition.

One further remark may be in place here: there is virtually no difference between older Precambrian rocks (>1900 m.y. old) and Recent sediments. The presence of cherty I.Fs., and of presumably detrital pyrite and uraninite in three conglomerate units, are the only well documented differences. Voluminous dolomites exist in all older Precambrian suites deposited under the appropriate conditions (platform or miogeosynclinal, not deposited in glacial climate). Red beds older than 1900 m.y. appear to be present in the Transvaal Supergroup (1950 m.y.), in the Witwatersrand Supergroup (>2300 m.y.) and in the Moodies Group (>3300 m.y.). Most significantly, the carbon distribution in older Precambrian sediments appears to conform to modern patterns. Sediments deposited under a low-oxygen atmosphere should be very different: carbon should be present in all detrital sediments and, in particular, should be abundant in stromatolitic rocks. Detrital sulfide minerals should be a major component of the heavy-mineral spectrum of all sandstones. Evidence for diagenetic oxidation reactions should be absent. None of these differences have been documented.

Borchert (1952, 1960, 1965) and Braun (1964) proposed a direct-precipitation hypothesis of Minette-type iron ores that might also find application to cherty I.Fs. They assume that iron is transported in form of ferric oxihydrate films on clay and silt particles. Iron oxihydrates were reduced to Fe^{2+} by organic matter during diagenesis. In this form, iron may migrate in diagenetic waters, from which it is re-precipitated either within the sediment, or at the sediment–water interface. It may also migrate into the aqueous environment, provided the $Eh–pCO_2–pS^{2-}$ conditions are appropriate; in this case iron is re-precipitated from sea- or lake-water.

This mechanism is responsible for the precipitation of iron-minerals in Recent sediments, be it within the sediment itself (pyrite: Berner, 1970, 1971, 1973; siderite: Ho and Coleman, 1969; chamosite and glauconite: Porrenga, 1966, 1967), or at the sediment–water interface (Seibold, 1970, 1973; Lemoalle and Dupont, 1973; Monty, 1973; Müller and Förstner, 1973). Thus, Borchert's (op. cit.) mechanism provides a physicochemical basis to Cayeux (1909a, 1922) limestone-replacement hypothesis of sedimentary iron ores, discussed on the next pages. On the other hand, it is still unknown whether transport of dissolved iron into the depositional medium, and precipitation of iron-minerals from the latter actually takes place at present by this mechanism. Müller and Förstner (1973) suggested that iron-minerals are precipitated from anoxic deep waters in Lake Malawi. Conditions for iron-mineral precipitation appear to be nearly fulfilled in the Gothland basin of the Baltic Sea, where Mn^{2+} concentrations reach 900 $\mu g/l$, and where precipitation of manganiferous carbonate appears to take place (Hartmann, 1964; Seibold, 1970).

As the last possibility, precipitation of I.Fs. from hydrothermal brines must be examined. This process has been studied intensely during the last years (Degens and Ross, 1969; Bäcker and Richter, 1973; Baumann et al., 1973; Hartmann, 1973; Puchelt et al., 1973; Wauschkuhn, 1973). It plays a role only in very limited areas. The resulting ore bodies are many orders of magnitude smaller than the volcanic suites from which they are derived. Consequently, precipitation of iron ore from hydrothermal solutions may be invoked for the massive polymetallic volcanogenic sulfide deposits described by Sangster (1972) and by Sangster and Scott, Chapter 5, Vol. 6, and for a few small Algoma-type deposits associated with voluminous volcanic material (e.g., Goodwin, 1962, 1973a, b). It can play no role in the origin of the large cherty I.Fs. or of the Minette-type iron ore deposits.

Replacement hypotheses

Sorby (1856) and Cayeux (1909a, 1922) are the fathers of the replacement hypothesis of sedimentary iron ores. Sorby (1856) inferred that replacement took place during late diagenesis. Cayeux (1909a, 1922) suggested that replacement was very early diagenetic. In brief, he proposed that calcareous oolites, fossil debris and intraclasts (pseudo-oolites) were transformed to chamosite, or under appropriate conditions to iron oxihydrate during transport of the sedimentary particles. Abundant fossil debris, replaced by limonite and chamosite, is present in Minette-ores, and is evidence for replacement of $CaCO_3$. Gruner (1922) experimentally demonstrated that calcareous oolites are replaced by iron-minerals, in the presence of iron-bearing solutions. Cayeux' hypothesis is in excellent agreement with the observed growth of chamosite as replacement of pellets in Recent sediments. However, observation of Recent iron-oxide oolites by Lemoalle and Dupont (1973) suggests that limestone replacement may not be the only possible process by which iron oolites may grow. The iron-oxide oolites in Lake Chad apparently grew by direct accretion on sedimentary particles at the sediment—water interface, where diagenetic and surface waters mix. In 1911, after a brief visit to the United States, Cayeux discovered the uncanny petrographic similarity between the cherty I.Fs. of Lake Superior-type, and Minette-type ores. He thought that cherty I.Fs. were silicified Minette ores, analogous to certain Paleozoic ores he described in 1909 (Cayeux, 1909b).

In this form, the limestone-replacement hypothesis is not attractive, because chert of I.Fs. formed not later than early diagenesis. However, the petrographic similarity of Minette-type ores and cherty I.F. (and of limestone-replacement chert) doubtlessly is not accidental. Replacement of limestone by silica generally takes place during early diagenesis (silicification contemporaneous with intrabasin erosion: Cayeux, 1929; during compaction: Cayeux, 1929; Dietrich et al., 1963; before cementation of pore-space: Folk and Weaver, 1952; Folk and Pittman, 1971; Folk, 1973). Therefore, the limestone-replacement hypothesis should be more seriously considered than in the past. Kimberley (1974) and Lougheed and Mancuso (1974) recently revived the limestone-replacement hypothesis. Their proposals are not satisfactory in all respects. A great amount of work is required in order to determine whether this hypothesis is consistent with all the petrographic features of cherty I.Fs. (as it appears to be at the present state of knowledge), and whether it is conceivable from the geochemical viewpoint.

SUMMARY AND CONCLUSIONS

Fig. 11 is an attempt to analyse the formative processes in cherty I.Fs. as a process-response system (solid arrows). A conceptual model of the writer's approach to the interpretation of the origin of I.Fs. has been incorporated. This approach is based on Walther's (1893–1894) concept of comparative lithology, that is on the comparison of ancient and recent rocks. The same processes (observable in the Recent, but not accessible to observation in ancient rocks) will give rise to the same effects, independent of their age.

Sedimentary textures and structures give a clear view of the mechanical processes of sedimentation, transport, reworking, and redeposition. The hydrodynamics and ecology of the depositional basin, that is the paleogeography of the basin, control the sedimentation. Analysis of the facies distribution (as defined by the distribution of sedimentary structures and textures) permits, to a degree, reconstruction of the paleogeography. Features due to syn-sedimentary deformation, to shrinkage and compaction give evidence of mechanical diagenesis. The mechanical diagenesis is controlled by soil mechanical parameters which are indirect functions of paleogeography. Shrinkage and compaction in iron-formation are partly related to chemical reactions (dehydration, concretionary growth) and, therefore, are partly controlled by chemical parameters.

The chemical reactions during diagenesis can be interpreted at two levels of understanding. At the lower level of understanding, they are defined by the interrelations of the growing minerals: grain growth (without replacement), mineral–to–mineral replacement, concretionary replacement. These leave, in part, visible traces in form of growth textures, replacement textures and concretions. Inference at this level is straightforward, provided relicts of the pre-existing fabric remain, and assuming the resulting fabric has not been overprinted too strongly, by subsequent processes.

At a more advanced level of understanding, chemical diagenesis is analyzed in terms of two sets of reaction mechanisms:

(1) Solid-state reactions and solution–precipitation reactions (not uncommonly implying transport of material).

(2) Redox reactions and reactions not involving oxidation and reduction.

Inference on these aspects of diagenesis is based on circumstantial evidence. Geochemical and isotope data (cf., Perry and Tan, 1973; Perry et al., 1973) are important supporting evidence in addition to the petrography. Eh, pH, pS^{2-} and pCO_2 control the diagenetic reactions. These are dependent variables, determined by sediment composition (in particular organic content), texture, permeability and ground-water flow and, therefore, are functions of the paleogeographic evolution.

Is it possible to infer the processes of chemical precipitation from petrographic, and other evidence? Most workers (including the writer) thought so, and interpreted the primary-looking minerals (that is minerals not showing replacement textures, French, 1973) as precipitated particles or as derived from some closely related precursor. Observa-

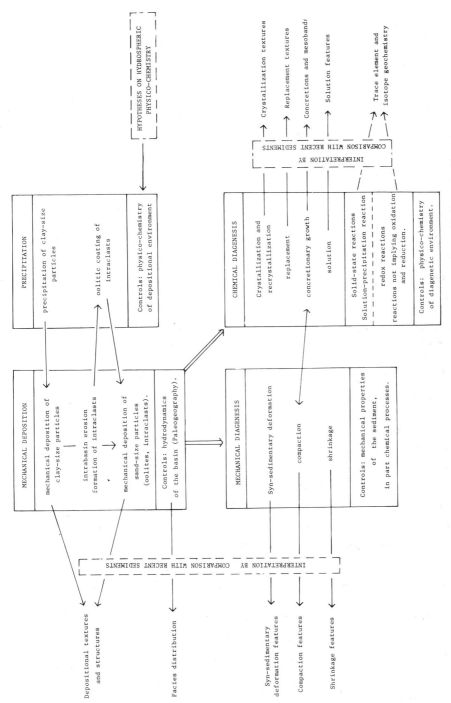

Fig. 11. Process-response model of cherty I.Fs. Interpretation of observed features by comparison with Recent sediments.

TABLE V

Selected references to photographic documentation of the most important petrographic observations
discussed in this chapter

Sedimentary features

Textural elements

pellets	D.,[1] 1968, Pl.24, fig.3, 5; DC., 1973, fig.2A
intraclasts	
pebble size	D., 1968, Pl.21, fig.3, 4; Pl.22, fig.2, 3, 4; DC., 1973, fig.1C, D, E
sand-size ("peloids")	D., 1968, Pl.22, fig.4; DC., 1973, fig.1F, 2B, E
densely set, welded	(D., 1968, fig.8)[2]; DC., 1973, fig.1F
complex	D., 1968, Pl.22, fig.4; Chauvel and Robardet, 1971, fig.4; DC., 1972
oolites, normal	D., 1968, Pl.23, Fig.2; DC, 1972
with broken oolite as core	(D., 1968, Fig.9); DC., 1972
multiple	(D., 1968, Fig.9); DC., 1972
complex	DC., 1972; Chauvel and Robardet, 1971, fig.2, 5
pisolites	D., 1968, Pl.23, fig.1; Gross, 1972, fig.6, 12; DC., 1972; Zajac, 1972, fig.26
porosity (chert-filled) inter-particle	D., 1968, Pl.24, fig.4; DC., 1973, fig.2E, F, G
laminar-fenestral	Dimroth and Dressler, in preparation
gas bubbles	[DC., unpublished][3]
internal sediment in	Folk, 1973, fig.7, 8, 9, 10 in cherts

Sedimentary structures

lamination in matrix chert	Trendall, 1972, Pl.15, 16, 17; 1973B, fig.2,3,4,5,6
in femicrite	D, 1968, Pl.21; fig. 1, 2, 4; Zajac, 1974, fig.23
bedding (thin to thick)	Zajac, 1974, fig.37, 46, 47, 50, 54, 56, 58, 63
cross-lamination (ripple)	Gross, 1972, fig.9
cross-bedding (mega-ripple and dune)	Zajac, 1974, fig.48 (large ripple)[2], 49, 62, 63
channels	D., 1968, fig.7, Pl.22, fig.1
distribution grading	DC., 1973, fig.1F; measurements fig.4A
coarse-taile and content grading	D., 1968, Pl.21, fig.4

Organo-sedimentary structures
pisolites see *sedimentary textures*

stromatolites	
morphology	Hofmann, 1969, Pl.1–5, 7–13; Cloud and Semikhatow, 1969, Pl.3, fig.1–3; Gross, 1972, fig.1; Walter, 1972, fig.1A, C; Zajac, 1974, fig.60
lamination of	Hofmann, 1969, Pl.6; Walter, 1972, fig.1E
pillar texture in	Hofmann, 1969, Pl.8
in chert	Walter, 1972, fig. 1B, D, F, 2, 6; Walter et al., 1972, fig.1, 2
in manganese nodules	Monty, 1973, Pl.1–3

TABLE V (continued)

Mottling of chert at 10–30μ scale (probably diagenetic)

chalcedony spherulites — DC., 1973, fig.7B; Mukhopadhyay and Chanda, 1972, fig.2; Zajac, 1974, fig.24

micropolygonal quartz — DC., 1973, fig. 7C

siderite spheres — LaBerge, 1973, fig.8, 9, 10

other types — LaBerge, 1967; LaBerge, 1973

Textural rock types

all types of table III — D., 1968; DC., 1972; DC., 1973

Diagenic features

Syn-sedimentary deformation features

load casts[2] — Gross, 1972, fig.15, 16

faulting — Gross, 1972, fig.8

folding — Gross, 1972, fig.21A–D, fig.23, 24

brecciation — Gross, 1972, fig.17, 18, 19, 20, fig.17, note stylolitic contacts of fragments

Syneresis textures

in oolites and pisolites — D., 1968, fig.9, Pl.23, fig.2; DC., 1973 fig.2B; Gross, 1972, fig.12

septaria — Gross, 1972, fig.10, 11

Compaction

spastolites — DC., 1972; DC., 1973, fig.2C

spastolites in other rocks — Laugier, 1959, Pl.II, fig.3, 4, 7, 8, 9, 10; Chauvel and Robardet, 1970, fig.1, 2

folding of chert veins — Gross, 1972, fig.13; DC., 1972; DC., 1973, fig.7G

differential compaction around concretions — Trendall, 1972, fig.6, Pl.17A; DC., 1973, fig.8A, B, 10; Gross, 1972, fig.5[4]; Zajac, 1974, fig.48[4,5]

Concretionary bodies

carbonate concretions — (DC, 1973, fig.11D)

  replaced chert-hematite oolites in — (DC., 1973, fig.11E)

  replaced chert intraclasts in — DC., 1973, fig.8E

chert nodules (pods) — Trendall, 1972, fig.14, Pl.17A; Gross, 1972, fig.5[4]; DC., 1973, fig.8A, B, 10; Zajac, 1974, fig.48

  lamination discordant to — Trendall, 1972, fig.6, Pl.17A; DC., 1973, fig.8A, B, 10

magnetite layers (mesobands) — Trendall, 1972, Pl.14, Pl.17; Trendall, 1973, fig.4, 5, 6; DC., 1973, fig.8A, B, 10

  laminations discordant to — Trendall and DC, as magnetite layers

  compacted oolites in — DC, 1973, as magnetite layers

TABLE V (continued)

Solution porosity (chert-filled)

intraclast moldic	[Dimroth, unpublished]
oolite-moldic	[Dimroth, unpublished]
carbonate-moldic	Mukhopadhyay and Chanda, 1972, fig.11
vugs	DC., 1973, fig.2H
autobrecciation (solution-collapse?)	Mukhopadhyay and Chanda, 1972, fig.3

Stylolites   (D., 1968, fig.12); DC., 1973, fig.7E,F

Crystallization textures

Quartz of matrix cherts

microcrystalline	Mukhopadhyay and Chanda, 1972, fig.1
nucleating on iron ore	Mukhopadhyay and Chanda, 1971, fig.7; DC., 1973, fig.7A
chalcedony spherulites	Mukhopadhyay and Chanda, 1972, fig.2
nucleating on iron ore	DC., 1973, fig.7B
micro-polygonal	DC., 1973, fig.7C
recrystallized	Mukhopadhyay and Chanda, 1973, fig.5; DC., 1973, fig.7D
grain size guided by dust inclusions	no documentation?
grain shape guided by dust inclusions	DC., 1973, fig.7D

Cement textures

overgrowth of chalcedony	D., 1968, Pl.24, Fig.4; DC., 1973, fig.2E, H
columnar encrustation	D., 1968, Pl.24, fig.7; DC., 1973, fig.26
quartz overgrowth	(Mukhopadhyay and Chanda, 1972, fig.6)
multi-mineral cements	Braun, 1964, fig.5, 6, 29, 33[4]; Edwards, 1958, fig.11, 12, 18; Cochrane and Edwards, 1960, Pl.13,14; DC., 1973, fig.2F, 3B

Replacement of very early diagenetic iron-minerals

greenalite → hematite dust	[Goodwin, 1968]
hematite → greenalite	[Dimroth, unpublished]
greenalite → micro-granular siderite	[Dimroth, unpublished]
leaching of hematite dust	D., 1968, Pl.22, fig.2 (DC., 1973, fig.9) Trendall, 1972, 1973, see silica pods
leaching of greenalite	[Dimroth, unpublished]
leaching of graphite	Hofmann, 1969, Pl.8, fig.1

Allochemical replacement, mainly without oxidation or reduction

greenalite → minnesotaite	French, 1973, fig.4; Klein, 1973, fig.8A
greenalite → ankerite	French, 1973, fig.6
siderite → ankerite	DC., 1973, fig.11A, B

many others see French, 1973, Table I for references

TABLE V (continued)

Oxidation reactions	
siderite → magnetite	LaBerge, 1964; Zajac, 1974, fig.71, 72
greenalite → magnetite	French, 1973, fig.9
Others, see French, 1973	
Reducing reactions	
hematite oolites → silicate, carbonate oolites	(DC., 1973, fig.11E)
chert-hematite intraclasts, carbonate intraclasts	DC., 1973, fig.8E
Redox reactions	
See leaching of hematite dust, chert pods, magnetite mesobands	

[1] D. = Dimroth, DC. = Dimroth and Chauvel.
[2] Reference in brackets = drawing.
[3] Reference in [] brackets = described, but not documented, or unpublished.
[4] Feature not mentioned in legend of photograph.
[5] in top set of cross beds shown in photograph.

tion of primary-looking siderite and greenalite in some rocks deposited in strongly oxidizing environments (Chauvel and Dimroth, 1974) forced the author to abandon this concept. Comparison of primary-looking minerals in ancient chemical sediments (for example, Precambrian limestone, dolomite, limestone-replacement chert) with their probable precursor (aragonite) is not encouraging. Therefore, no window to the process of precipitation is shown in Fig. 11. Extrapolation to the precipitation of iron-formations is based on physico-chemical hypotheses.

ACKNOWLEDGEMENTS

The concepts of this paper are based on work done and published jointly with Dr. J.J. Chauvel, Rennes, France. It is a pleasure to acknowledge my debt of gratitude to those who donated or loaned material for comparison and helped with pre-prints: Drs. J.J. Chauvel, H.P. Eugster, A.M. Goodwin, H.D. Holland, H. Gabrielse, M.M. Kimberley, E.C. Perry, Jr., R.G. Schmidt. The Department of Natural Resources of Quebec funded field trips to the Biwabik, Gunflint and Témiskamie Iron Formations. Dr. K.H. Wolf read the manuscript at two stages of drafting; his constructive criticism, proved very helpful during the preparation of the final version of this paper.

REFERENCES

Alexandrov, E.A., 1973. The Precambrian banded iron ores of the Soviet Union. *Econ. Geol.*, 68: 1035–1063.

Amstutz, G.C. and Bubenicek, L., 1967. Diagenesis in sedimentary mineral deposits. In: G. Larsen and G.V. Chilingar (Editors), *Diagenesis in Sediments. Dev. Sedimentol.*, 8: 417–476.

Aubouin J., 1965. *Geosynclines*. Elsevier, Amsterdam.

Ayres, D.E., 1972. Genesis of iron-bearing minerals in banded iron-formation mesobands in the Dales Gorge Member, Hamersley Group, Western Australia. *Econ. Geol.*, 67: 1214–1233.

Bäcker, H. and Richter, H., 1973. Die rezente hydrothermal-sedimentäre Lagerstätte Atlantis – II – Tief im Roten Meer. *Geol. Rundsch.*, 62: 697–741.

Bathurst, R.G.C., 1958. Diagenetic fabrics in some British Dinantian limestones. *Liverp. Manch. Geol. J.*, 2: 11–36.

Bathurst, R.G.C., 1971. *Carbonate Sediments and their Diagenesis. Dev. Sedimentol.*, 12: 1–620.

Baumann, A., Richter, H. and Schoell, M., 1973. Suakin Deep: brines and hydrothermal sediments in the deepest part of the Red Sea. *Geol. Rundsch.*, 62: 697–741.

Bayley, R.W. and James, H.L., 1973. Precambrian iron-formations of the United States. *Econ. Geol.*, 68: 934–959.

Becker, R.H. and Clayton, R.N., 1972. Carbon isotopic evidence for the origin of a banded iron-formation in Western Australia. *Geochim. Cosmochim. Acta*, 36: 577–595.

Bell, R.T. and Hofmann, H.J., 1974. Investigations of the Belcher Group (Aphebian), Belcher Islands, N.W.T. *Geol. Assoc. Can., Abstracts G.A.C./M.A.C.* Meeting, May 19–22, 1974, St-Johns, Newfoundland, p. 8.

Bergeron, R., 1954. *A Study of the Quebec-Labrador Iron Belt between Derry Lake and Larch River*. Thesis, Univ. Laval, Que., 230 pp.

Berker, L.V. and Marshall, L.C., 1967. The rise of oxygen in the earth's atmosphere with notes on the Martian atmosphere. *Adv. Geophys.*, 12: 309–331.

Berner, R.A., 1970. Sedimentary pyrite formation. *Am. J. Sci.*, 268: 1–23.

Berner, R.A., 1971. *Principles of Chemical Sedimentology*. McGraw-Hill, New York, N.Y., 240 pp.

Berner, R.A., 1973. Pyrite formation in the ocean. In: *Proceeding of Symposium on Hydrogeochemistry and Biogeochemistry, Sept. 7–9, 1970, Tokyo, Japan.* The Clarke Co., Washington, 1: 402–417.

Besnus, Y., Bronner, G., Mosser, C. and Oksengorn, S., 1969. Etudes géochimiques et minéralogiques sur la province ferrifère du Tiris (Precambrien de la dorsale Reguibat, Fort-Gouraud, Mauritanie). *Bull. Serv. Carte Géol. Alsace Lorraine*, 22: 311–328.

Beukes, N.J., 1973. Precambrian iron-formations of southern Africa. *Econ. Geol.*, 68: 960–1004.

Bitterli, P., 1963. Aspects of the genesis of bituminous rock sequences. *Geol. Mijnbouw*, 42: 183–201.

Blake, R.L., 1965. Iron phyllosilicates of the Cuyuna District in Minnesota. *Am. Mineral.* 50: 149–169.

Borchert, H., 1952. Die Bildungsbedingungen marin-sedimentärer Eisenerze. *Chem. Erde*, 16: 49–74.

Borchert, H., 1960. Genesis of marine sedimentary iron ores. *Trans. Inst. Min. Metall., Lond.*, 69: 261–679.

Borchert, H., 1965. Formation of marine sedimentary iron ores. In: J.P. Riley and G. Kirow (Editors), *Chemical Oceanography*. Academic Press, London and New York, 2: 159–204.

Braun, H., 1964. Zur Entstehung der marin-sedimentären Eisenerze. Clausthaler Hefte, 2: 1–133.

Burst, J.F., 1965. Subaqueously formed shrinkage cracks in clay. *J. Sediment. Petrol.*, 35: 348–353.

Carozzi, A.V., 1961. Distorted oolites and pseudo-oolites: *J. Sediment. Petrol.*, 31: 262–274.

Carozzi, A.V., 1963. Half-moon oolites. *J. Sediment. Petrol.*, 33: 633–645.

Carozzi, A.V., 1964. Complex ooids from Triassic lake deposits, Virginia. *Am. J. Sci.*, 262: 231–241.

Cayeux, L., 1909a. Evolution minéralogique des minerais de fer oolithiques primaires de France. *C.R. Acad. Sci. Fr.*, 149: 1388–1390.

Cayeux, L., 1909b. Le quartz secondaire des minerais de fer oolithiques du silurien de France et son remplacement en profondeur par du fer carbonaté. *C.R. Acad. Sci. Fr.*, 149: 1095–1097.

Cayeux, L., 1911. Comparaison entre les minerais de fer huroniens des Etats-Unis et les minerais de fer oolithiques de France. *C.R. Acad. Sci. Fr.*, 153: 1188–1190.

Cayeux, L., 1922. *Les Minerais de Fer Oolithiques de France II. Minerais de Fer Secondaires. Etudes des Gîtes Minéraux de France.* Paris, Serv. Carte Géol. Impr. Natl., 1052 pp.

Cayeux, L., 1923. Le phénomène dit de l'impression dans les minerais de fer mésozoiques de France. *C.R. Acad. Sci. Fr.*, 176: 1334–1337.

Cayeux, L., 1929. *Les Roches Sédimentaires de France – Roches Siliceuses.* Mém. Carte Géol. Fr., Paris. Impr. Natl., 778 pp.

Cayeux, L., 1935. *Les Roches Sédimentaires de France – Roches Carbonatées (Calcaires et Dolomies).* Masson, Paris, 463 pp.

Chauvel, J.J., 1968. *Contribution à l'Etude des Minerais de Fer de l'Ordovicien Inférieur en Bretagne.* Thèse, Univ. Rennes, 245 pp.

Chauvel, J.J. and Dimroth, E., 1974. Facies types and depositional environment of the Sokoman Iron Formation, Central Labrador trough, Quebec, Canada. *J. Sediment. Petrol.*, 44: 299–327.

Chauvel, J.J. and Robardet, M., 1970. Le minerais de fer de Saint-Sauveur-le-Vicomte (Manche): position stratigraphique, étude pétrographique, signification paléogéographique. *Bull. Soc. Géol. Minéral. Bretagne, Ser. C*, 2: 61–71.

Chilingar, G.V., Bissel, H.J. and Wolf, K.H., 1967. Diagenesis of carbonate rocks. In: G. Larsen and G.V. Chilingar (Editors), *Diagenesis in Sediments. Develop. Sedimentol.*, 8: 179–322.

Chilingarian, G.V. and Wolf, K.H. (Editors), 1975–1976. *Compaction of Coarse-Grained Sediments*, Vol. I and II. Elsevier, Amsterdam, I: 522 pp, II: in press.

Choquette, P.W., 1955. A petrographic study of the State College siliceous oolite. *J. Geol.*, 63: 337–347.

Choquette, P.W. and Pray, L.C., 1970. Geologic nomenclature and classification of porosity in sedimentary carbonates. *Bull. Am. Assoc. Petrol. Geol.*, 54: 207–250.

Chown, E.H. and Caty, J.L., 1973. Stratigraphy, petrography, and paleocurrent analysis of the Aphebian clastic formations of the Mistassini–Otish basin. *Geol. Assoc. Can., Spec. Pap.*, 12: 49–71.

Cloud Jr., P.E., 1968. Atmospheric and hydrospheric evolution of the primitive earth. *Science*, 160: 729–736.

Cloud Jr., P.E., 1972. A working model of the primitive earth. *Am. J. Sci.*, 272: 537–548.

Cloud Jr., P.E., 1973a. Paleoecological significance of banded iron-formation. *Econ. Geol.*, 68: 1135–1143.

Cloud Jr., P.E., 1973b. Pseudofossils: a plea for caution. *Geology*, 1: 123–126.

Cloud Jr., P.E. and Semikhatow, M.A., 1969. Proterozoic stromatolite zonation. *Am. J. Sci.*, 267: 1017–1061.

Cochrane, G.W. and Edwards, A.B., 1960. The Roper River oolitic ironstone formation. *Mineragr. Invest. Tech. Pap. No. 1. Commonw. Sci. Ind. Res. Org.*, Aust., Melbourne, p. 1–28.

Cooke, D.L. and Moorhouse, W.W., 1966. Temiskaming volcanism in the Kirkland Lake area, Ontario, Canada. *Can. J. Earth Sci.*, 6: 117–132.

Courtois, C., 1974. *Les Terres Rares dans quelques Minerais de Fer.* Thèse, Univ. Paris-sud (Centre d'Orsay), 141 pp.

Curtis, C.D. and Spears, D.A., 1968. The formation of sedimentary iron minerals. *Econ. Geol.*, 63: 257–270.

Curtis, C.D., Petrowski, C. and Oertel, G., 1972. Stable carbon isotope ratios within carbonate concretions: a clue to place and time of formation. *Nature*, 235: 98–100.

Davies, G.R., 1970. Algal-laminated sediments, Gladstone embayment, Shark Bay, Western Australia. *Am. Assoc. Petrol. Geol., Mem.*, 13: 169–205.

Degens, E.T. and Ross, D.A., 1969, Editors. *Hot Brines and Recent Heavy Metal Deposits in the Red Sea.* Springer, New York, N.Y., 600 pp.

Dietrich, R.V., Hobbs Jr., C.R.B. and Lowry, L.D., 1963. Dolomitization interrupted by silicification. *J. Sediment. Petrol.*, 33: 646–663.

Dimroth, E., 1968. Sedimentary textures, diagenesis and sedimentary environment of certain Precambrian ironstones. *Neues Jahrb. Geol. Paläontol., Abh.,* 130: 247–274.

Dimroth, E., 1973. *Stratigraphy of the Central Labrador Trough between lat. 56°30′ and the Height-of-Land.* Que. Dept. Nat. Resour., open-file document No. GM 28691, 280 pp.

Dimroth, E. and Chauvel, J.J., 1972. Petrographie des minerais de fer de la fosse du Labrador. *Geol. Rundsch.,* 61: 97–115.

Dimroth, E. and Chauvel, J.J., 1973. Petrography of the Sokoman Iron Formation in part of the Central Labrador trough, Quebec, Canada. *Geol. Soc. Am. Bull.,* 84: 111–134.

Dimroth, E. and Dressler, B., in prep. Iron-mineral formation in sediments of the Labrador trough.

Dimroth, E., Baragar, W.R.A., Bergeron, R. and Jackson, G.D., 1970. The filling of the Circum-Ungava Geosyncline. In: A.J. Baer (Editor), *Symposium on Basins and Geosynclines of the Canadian Shield. Geol. Surv. Can., Pap.,* 10–40: 45–142.

Dimroth, E., Rocheleau, M., Boivin, P., Larouche, M. and Côté, R., 1974. Preliminary report on stratigraphic and tectonic work in Rouyn-Noranda area, Counties of Rouyn-Noranda, Abitibi-West and Témiscamingue. *Que. Dept. Nat. Resour., Open-file rep.,* D.P. 246, 40 pp.

Donaldson, J.A., 1963. Stromatolites in the Denault Formation, Marion Lake, Coast of Labrador, Newfoundland. *Geol. Surv. Can. Bull.,* 102: 33 pp.

Dorr, J.V.N., 1973. Iron-formation in South America. *Econ. Geol.,* 68: 1005–1022.

Duff, P.M., Hallam, A. and Walton, E.K., 1967. *Cyclic Sedimentation. Dev. Sedimentol. 10.* Elsevier, Amsterdam, 280 pp.

Dunham, K., 1961. Black shale, oil and sulfide ore. *Adv. Sci.,* 18: 284–299.

Dunham, R.J., 1969. Vadose pisolite in the Captain Reef (Permian), New Mexico and Texas. In: G.M. Friedman (Editor), *Depositional Environments in Carbonate Rocks. Soc. Econ. Palaeontol. Mineral., Spec. Pap.,* 14: 182–191.

Edhorn, A.S., 1973. Further investigations of fossils from the Animikie, Thunder Bay, Ontario. *Geol. Assoc. Can., Proc.,* 25: 37–65.

Edwards, A.B., 1958. Oolitic iron-formation in Northern Australia. *Geol. Rundsch.,* 47: 668–682.

Eugster, H.P., 1969. Inorganic bedded cherts from the Magadi area, Kenya. *Contrib. Mineral. Petrol.,* 22: 1–31.

Eugster, H.P. and Chou, I. Ming, 1973. The depositional environment of Precambrian banded iron-formations. *Econ. Geol.,* 68: 1144–1168.

Folk, R.L., 1959. Practical petrographical classification of limestones. *Bull. Am. Assoc. Petrol. Geol.,* 43: 1–38.

Folk, R.L., 1962. Spectral subdivision of limestone types. In: W.E. Ham (Editor), *Classification of Carbonate Rocks. Am. Assoc. Petrol. Geol., Mem.,* 1: 62–84.

Folk, R.L., 1965. Some aspects of recrystallization in ancient limestones. In: L.C. Pray and R.C. Murray (Editors), *Dolomitization and Limestone Diagenesis: a symposium. Soc. Econ. Palaeontol. Mineral., Spec. Pub.,* 13: 14–48.

Folk, R.L., 1968. *Petrology of sedimentary rocks.* Hemphill's Book Store, Austin, Texas.

Folk, R.L., 1973. Evidence for peritidal deposition of Devonian Caballos Novaculite, Marathon Basin, Texas. *Am. Assoc. Petrol. Geol. Bull.,* 57: 707–725.

Folk, R.L. and Pittman, J.S., 1971. Length-slow chalcedony: a new testament for vanished evaporites. *J. Sediment. Petrol.,* 41: 1045–1058.

Folk, R.L. and Weaver, C.E., 1952. A study of the texture and composition of chert. *Am. J. Sci.,* 250: 498–510.

Franklin, J.M., Kustra, C., Loubat, H., Mackasey, W. and Mudler, D., 1972. Excursion C34: The Precambrian rocks of the Atikokan–Thunder Bay–Marathon area. *Int. Geol. Congr., 24th, Montreal,* p. 1–74.

French, B.M., 1968. Progressive contact metamorphism of the Biwabik Iron-Formation, Mesabi Range, Minnesota. *Minn. Geol. Surv. Bull.,* 45.

French, B.M., 1973. Mineral assemblages in diagenetic and low-grade metamorphic iron-formation. *Econ. Geol.,* 68: 1063–1074.

Friedman, G.M., 1965. Terminology of crystallization textures and fabrics in sedimentary rocks. *J. Sediment. Petrol.*, 36: 263–267.

Fryer, B.J., 1972. Age determinations in the Circum-Ungava geosyncline and the evolution of Precambrian iron-formation. *Can. J. Earth Sci.*, 9: 652–663.

Gabrielse, H., 1972. Younger Precambrian of the Canadian Cordillera. *Am. J. Sci.*, 272: 521–536.

Garrels, R.M. and Christ, C.L., 1965. *Solutions, Minerals and Equilibria.* Harper and Row, New York, N.Y., 450 pp.

Garrels, R.M., Perry Jr., E.A. and Mackenzie, F.T., 1973. Genesis of Precambrian iron-formations and the development of atmospheric oxygen. *Econ. Geol.*, 68: 1173–1179.

Garrison, R.E. and Fischer, A.G., 1969. Deep-water limestones and radiolarites of the Alpine Jurassic. In: G.M. Friedmann (Editor), *Depositional Environments in Carbonate Rocks. Soc. Econ. Paleontol. Mineral., Spec. Publ.*, 14: 20–56.

Goldich, S.S., 1973. Ages of Precambrian iron-formations. *Econ. Geol.*, 68: 1126–1134.

Goodwin, A.M., 1956. Facies relations in the Gunflint iron-bearing formation. *Econ. Geol.*, 51: 687–728.

Goodwin, A.M., 1962. Structure, stratigraphy and origin of iron-formations, Michipicoten area, Algoma district, Canada. *Geol. Soc. Am. Bull.*, 73: 561–586.

Goodwin, A.M., 1973a. Archean iron-formation and tectonic basins of the Canadian Shield. *Econ. Geol.*, 68: 915–933.

Goodwin, A.M., 1973b. Archean volcanogenic iron-formation of the Canadian Shield. In: *Genesis of Precambrian Iron and Manganese Deposits. Proc. Kiev Symp. 1970, UNESCO., Earth Sci.*, 9: 23–34.

Goodwin, A.M. and Ridler, R.H., 1970. The Abitibi orogenic belt. In: A.J. Baer (Editor), *Symposium on Basins and Geosynclines of the Canadian Shield. Geol. Surv. Can., Pap.*, 70–40: 1–30.

Govett, G.J.S., 1966. Origin of banded iron-formations. *Geol. Soc. Am. Bull.*, 77: 1191–1212.

Gross, G.A., 1965. Geology of iron deposits in Canada. I. General geology and evaluation of iron deposits. *Geol. Surv. Can. Econ. Geol., Rep.*, 2: p. 1–181.

Gross, G.A., 1967. Geology of iron deposits in Canada. II. Iron deposits of the Grenville and Appalachian Provinces. *Geol. Surv. Can. Econ. Geol., Rep.*, 22.

Gross, G.A., 1968. Geology of iron deposits in Canada. III. Iron ranges of the Labrador Geosyncline. *Geol. Surv. Can. Econ. Geol., Rep.*, 22: 1–179.

Gross, G.A., 1972. Primary features in cherty iron-formations. *Sediment. Geol.*, 7: 241–261.

Grubb, P.L.C., 1971. Silicates and their paragenesis in the Brockman Iron-Formation. *Econ. Geol.*, 66: 281–292.

Gruner, J.W., 1922. Origin of sedimentary iron-formations. *Econ. Geol.*, 17: 408–460.

Hallam, A., 1967. The depth significance of shales with bituminous laminae. *Mar. Geol.*, 5: 481–493.

Han, T.M., 1972. Diagenetic–metamorphic replacement features in the Negaunee formation of the Marquette iron range, Lake Superior district. *Soc. Min. Geol. Japan, Spec. Issue*, 3: 430–438.

Hartmann, M., 1964. Zur Geochemie von Mangan und Eisen in der Ostsee. *Meyniana, Kiel*, 14: 3–20.

Hartmann, M., 1973. Untersuchungen von suspendiertem Material in den Hydrothermallaugen des Atlantis – II – Tiefs. *Geol. Rundsch.*, 62: 742–753.

Ho, Clara and Coleman, J.M., 1969. Consolidation and cementation of recent sediments in the Atchafalaya Basin. *Geol. Soc. Am. Bull.*, 80: 183–192.

Hofmann, H.J., 1969. Stromatolites from the Proterozoic Animikie and Sibley Groups, Ontario. *Geol. Surv. Can. Pap. 68–69.*

Holland, H.D., 1973. The oceans: a possible source of iron in iron-formations. *Econ. Geol.*, 68: 1169–1172.

Horikoshi, E., 1969. Volcanic activity related to the formation of the Kuroko-type deposits in the Kosaka district, Japan. *Miner. Deposita*, 4: 321–345.

Hough, J.L., 1958. Fresh-water environment of deposition of Precambrian banded iron-formations. *J. Sediment. Petrol.*, 28: 414–430.

Howell, J.E., 1954. *Silicification in the Knob Lake Group of the Labrador Iron Belt.* Ph.D. thesis, Univ. Wisconsin, Madison, Wisc., unpublished.

James, H.L., 1954. Sedimentary facies of iron formation. *Econ. Geol.*, 49: 251–266.

James, H.L., 1966. Chemistry of the iron-rich sedimentary rocks. *U.S. Geol. Surv., Prof. Pap.*, 440-W: 1–61.

Jüngst, H., 1934. Zur geologischen Bedeutung der Synärese. Ein Beitrag zur Entwässerung der Kolloide im werdenden Gestein. *Geol. Rundsch.*, 25: 312–325.

Kimberley, M.M., 1974. Origin of iron ore by diagenetic replacement of calcareous oolite. *Nature*, 250: 319.

Klein, C.J., 1973. Changes in mineral assemblages with metamorphism of some banded Precambrian iron-formation. *Econ. Geol.*, 68: 1075–1089.

Krebs, W., 1969. Über Schwarzschiefer und bituminöse Kalke im mitteleuropäischen Variscikum. *Erdöl Hohle*, 22: 2–6 and 62–67.

LaBerge, G.L., 1964. Development of magnetite in iron-formations of the Lake Superior region. *Econ. Geol.*, 59: 1313–1343.

LaBerge, G.L., 1966a. Altered pyroclastic rocks in iron-formation in the Hamersley Range, Western Australia. *Econ. Geol.*, 61: 147–161.

LaBerge, G.L., 1966b. Altered pyroclastic rocks in South African iron-formation. *Econ. Geol.*, 61: 572–581.

LaBerge, G.L., 1967. Microfossils and Precambrian iron-formations. *Geol. Soc. Am. Bull.*, 78: 331–342.

LaBerge, G.L., 1973. Possible biologic origin of Precambrian iron-formations. *Econ. Geol.*, 68: 1098–1109.

Laugier, R., 1959. Observations pétrographiques sur les niveaux salifères du Trias moyen de Lorraine. *Bull. Soc. Géol. Fr., Ser. 7*, 1: 31–39.

Lemoalle, J. and Dupont, B., 1973. Iron-bearing oolites and the present conditions of iron sedimentation in Lake Chad (Africa). In: G.C. Amstutz and A.J. Bernard (Editors), *Ores in Sediments*. Springer, Berlin, pp. 167–178.

Lepp, H. and Goldich, S.S., 1964. Origin of Precambrian iron-formations. *Econ. Geol.*, 59: 1025–1061.

Livingstone, D.A., 1963. Data of cheochemistry, Chapter G. Chemical composition of rivers and lakes. *U.S. Geol. Surv., Prof. Pap.*, 440-G, 64 pp.

Logan, B.W., Rezak, R. and Ginsburg, R.N., 1964. Classification and environmental significance of algal stromatolites. *J. Geol.*, 72: 68–83.

Lougheed, M.S. and Mancuso, J.J., 1974. The origin of magnetite in iron-formation. *Inst. Lake Superior Geol., Abstr., Meeting 1974, Sault. Ste-Marie, Ont.*, p. 19–20.

Mason, B., 1966. *Principles of Geochemistry*. Wiley, New York, N.Y., 3rd ed., 329 pp.

Mengel, J.T., 1963. *The Cherts of the Lake Superior Iron-Bearing Formations*. Ph.D. thesis, Univ. Wisconsin, Oshkosh, Wisc., unpublished.

Mengel, J.T., 1973. Physical sedimentation in Precambrian cherty iron-formations of the Lake Superior Type. In: G.C. Amstutz and A.J. Bernard (Editors), *Ores in Sediments*. Springer, Berlin, pp. 179–194.

Milton, C. and Eugster, H.P., 1959. Mineral assemblages of the Green River Formation. In: P.H. Abelson (Editor), *Researches in Geochemistry*. Wiley, New York, N.Y., pp. 118–150.

Monty, C.L.V., 1972. Recent algal stromatolitic deposits, Andros Island, Bahamas. Preliminary report. *Geol. Rundsch.*, 61: 742–783.

Monty, C.L.V., 1973. Les nodules de manganèse sont des stromatolithes océaniques. *C.R. Acad. Sci. Paris*, 276 (série D): 3285–3288.

Morey, G.B., 1973. Stratigraphic framework of Middle Precambrian rocks in Minnesota. In: G.M. Young (Editor), *Huronian Stratigraphy and Sedimentation*. *Geol. Assoc. Can., Spec. Publ.*, 12: 211–250.

Mukhopadhyay, A. and Chanda, S.K., 1972. Silica diagenesis in the banded hematite jasper and bedded chert associated with the Iron Ore Group of Jamda–Koira valley, Orissa, India. *Sediment. Geol.*, 8: 113–135.

Müller, G. and Förstner, U., 1973. Recent iron ore formation in Lake Malawi, Africa. *Miner. Deposita*, 8: 278–290.

Oertel, G. and Curtis, C.D., 1972. Clay ironstone concretions preserving fabrics due to progressive compaction. *Geol. Soc. Am. Bull.*, 83: 2597–2606.

Oldershaw, A.E., 1960. Electron microscopic examination of Namurian bedded cherts, North Wales (Great Britain). *Sedimentology*, 10: 255–272.

Panella, G., 1972. Precambrian stromatolites as paleontological clocks. *Int. Congr., 24th, Montreal, Sec. 1*, p. 50–57.

Park, W.C. and Schot, E.K., 1968. Stylolites: their nature and origin. *J. Sediment. Petrol.*, 38: 175–191.

Perry, E.C. and Tan, F.C., 1973. Significance of carbon isotope variations in carbonates from the Biwabik Iron Formation. In: *Genesis of Precambrian Iron and Manganese Deposits. Proc. Kiev. Symp. 1970, UNESCO, Earth Sci.*, 9: 299–305.

Perry, E.C., Tan, F.C. and Morey, G.B., 1973. Geology and stable isotope geochemistry of the Biwabic Iron Formation, Northern Minnesota. *Econ. Geol.*, 68: 1110–1125.

Pettijohn, F.J., Potter, P.E. and Siever, R., 1972. *Sand and Sandstone*. Springer, New York, N.Y., 618 pp.

Porrenga, D.H., 1966. Glauconite and chamosite as depth indicators in the marine environment. *Mar. Geol.*, 5: 495–501.

Porrenga, D.H., 1967. *Clay Mineralogy and Geochemistry of Recent Marine Sediments in Tropical Areas*. Stolk, Dordrecht, 145 pp.

Puchelt, H., Schock, H.H., Schroll, E. and Hanert, H., 1973. Rezente marine Eisenerze auf Santorin, Griechenland. *Geol. Rundsch.*, 62: 786–811.

Purser, B.H. and Loreau, J.P., 1973. Aragonitic, supratidal encrustations on the Trucial Coast, Persian Gulf. In: B.H. Purser (Editor), *The Persian Gulf – Holocene Carbonate Sedimentation and Diagenesis in a Shallow Epicontinental Sea*. Springer, New York, N.Y., p. 279–328.

Rubey, W.W., 1951. The geologic history of sea water. *Bull. Geol. Soc. Am.*, 62: 1111–1147.

Rubey, W.W., 1955. Development of the hydrosphere and atmosphere with special reference to probable composition of the early atmosphere. *Geol. Soc. Am., Spec. Pap.*, 62: 631–650.

Sakamoto, T., 1950. The origin of the Precambrian banded iron ores. *Am. J. Sci.*, 248: 449–474.

Sander, B., 1936. Beiträge zur Kenntnis der Anlagerungsgefüge (rhytmische Kalke und Dolomite aus der Trias). *Mineral. Petrol. Mitt.*, 48: 27–209, (English translation 1951, *Am. Assoc. Petrol. Geol.*, 207 pp.).

Sangster, D.F., 1972. Precambrian volcanogenic massive sulphide deposits in Canada: a review. *Geol. Surv. Can. Pap.*, 72-22: 1–44.

Sarkar, B., 1973. Deformed oolites in the Precambrian Bhander limestone, India. *J. Sediment. Petrol.*, 43: 636–693.

Schidlowski, M., 1971. Probleme des atmosphärischen Evolution in Präkambrium. *Geol. Rundsch.*, 60: 1351–1383.

Schmidegg, O., 1928. Über geregelte Wachstumsgefüge. *Jahrb. Geol. Bundesanst., Austria*, 78: 1–52.

Schmidt, R.G., 1963. Geology and ore deposits of the Cuyuna North Range, Minnesota. *U.S. Geol. Surv., Prof. Pap.*, 407, 96 pp.

Schopf, J.W., 1972. Precambrian paleobiology. In: C. Ponnamperuma (Editor), *Exobiology*. North-Holland, Amsterdam, pp. 16–61.

Schultz, R.W., 1966. Lower carboniferous cherty ironstone at Tynagh Ireland. *Econ. Geol.*, 61: 311–342.

Seibold, E., 1970. Nebenmeere im humiden und ariden Klimabereich. *Geol. Rundsch.*, 60: 73–105.

Seibold, E., 1973. Rezente submarine Metallogenese. *Geol. Rundsch.*, 62: 641–683.

Siever, R., 1957. Silica budget in the sedimentary cycle. *Am. Mineral.* 42: 821–841.

Sorby, H.C., 1856. On the origin of the Cleveland Hill ironstone. *Proc. Yorks. Geol. Soc.*, 3: 457–461.

Spencer, E. and Percival, F.G., 1952. The structure and origin of the banded hematite jaspers of Singhbhum, India. *Econ. Geol.*, 47: 365–383.

Spry, A., 1969. *Metamorphic Textures*. Pergamon, Oxford, 350 pp.

Stewart, F.H., 1965. The mineralogy of the British Permian evaporites. *Mineral. Mag.*, 34: 460–470.

Surdam, R.C., Eugster, H.P. and Mariner, R.H., 1972. Magadi-type chert in Jurassic and Eocene–Pleistocene rocks, Wyoming. *Geol. Soc. Am. Bull.*, 83: 2261–2266.

Swineford, A., Leonard, A.B. and Frye, D.C., 1958. Petrology of the Pliocene pisolitic limestone in the Great Plains. *Kansas Geol. Surv. Bull.*, 130 (2): 97–116.

Trendall, A.F., 1966. Altered pyroclastic rocks in iron-formation in the Hamersley Range, Western Australia. *Econ. Geol.*, 61: 1451–1458.

Trendall, A.F., 1972. Revolution in earth history. *J. Geol. Soc. Austr.*, 19: 289–311.

Trendall, A.F., 1973a. Precambrian iron-formations of Australia. *Econ. Geol.*, 68: 1023–1034.

Trendall, A.F., 1973b. Warve cycles in the Weeli Wooli Formation of the Precambrian Hamersley Group, Western Australia. *Econ. Geol.*, 68: 1089–1097.

Trendall, A.F. and Blockley, J.G., 1970. The iron-formation of the Precambrian Hamersley Group, Western Australia, with special reference to the associated crocidolite. *Geol. Surv. West. Aust., Bull.*, 119: 1–336.

Van Hise, C.R. and Leith, C.K., 1911. Geology of the Lake Superior Region. *U.S. Geol. Surv., Mem.*, 53, 641 pp.

Voll, G., 1960. New work on petrofabrics. *Liverp. Manch., Geol. J.*, 2: 503–567.

Walker, R.G., 1967. Turbidite sedimentary structure and their relationship to proximal and distal depositional environments. *J. Sediment. Petrol.*, 38: 1120–1154.

Walker, R.G., 1970. Review of the geometry and facies organization of turbidites and turbidite-bearing basins. In: J. Lajoie (Editor), Flysch Sedimentology in North America. *Geol. Assoc. Can., Spec. Pap.*, 7: 219–251.

Walker, T.R., 1962. Reversible nature of chert–carbonate replacement in sedimentary rocks. *Geol. Soc. Am. Bull.*, 73: 237–242.

Walker, T.R., 1967a. Formation of red beds in modern and ancient deserts. *Geol. Soc. Am. Bull.*, 78: 917–920.

Walker, T.R., 1967b. Colour of recent sediments in tropical Mexico: a contribution to the origin of red beds. *Geol. Soc. Am. Bull.*, 78: 917–920.

Walter, M.R., 1972. A hot spring analog for the depositional environment of Precambrian iron-formation of the Lake Superior region. *Econ. Geol.*, 67: 965–972.

Walter, M.R., Bauld, J. and Brock, T.D., 1972. Siliceous algal and bacterial stromatolites in hot spring and geyser effluents of Yellowstone National Park. *Science*, 178: 402–405.

Walther, J., 1893–1894. *Einleitung in die Geologie als historische Wissenschaft*. Gustav Fischer Verlag, Jena, 3 vol., 1055 pp.

Wauschkuhn, A., 1973. Rezente Sulfidbildung in vulkanischen Seen auf Hokkaido. *Geol. Rundsch.*, 62: 774–785.

Wolf, K.H., 1965a. Gradational sedimentary products of calcareous algae. *Sedimentology*, 5: 1–37.

Wolf, K.H., 1965b. "Grain diminution" of algal colonies to micrite. *J. Sediment. Petrol.*, 35: 420–427.

Zajac, I.S., 1972. *The Stratigraphy and Mineralogy of the Sokoman Formation in the Knob Lake Area, Quebec and Newfoundland*. Ph.D. thesis, Univ. Michigan, unpublished.

Zajac, I.S., 1974. The stratigraphy and mineralogy of the Sokoman Formation in the Knob Lake area, Quebec and Newfoundland. *Geol. Surv. Can. Bull.*, 220: 1–159.

Chapter 6

GENETIC PROBLEMS AND ENVIRONMENTAL FEATURES OF VOLCANO–SEDIMENTARY IRON-ORE DEPOSITS OF THE LAHN–DILL TYPE

HORST QUADE

INTRODUCTION

The "volcano–sedimentary iron ores" are represented in a most characteristic way by a group of predominantly hematite iron-ore deposits which occur in the Devonian and Lower Carboniferous of the Central European Variscan system, but which are known from other regions too. The ore bodies form syngenetic horizons within eugeosynclinal sequences and are bound to submarine volcanics of the keratophyric–spilitic group. The geotectonic and paleogeographic position of this ore type (frequently cited as "Lahn–Dill type"), as well as the sedimentation features and the spectrum of trace elements, are quite different from those of other iron-formations, especially compared to the itabiritic and oolitic ones. The comparatively small deposits have highly variable iron contents, reaching nearly up to the grade of pure hematite, and then representing the highest iron concentration in a sedimentary environment. The reserves of an isolated ore body rarely exceed 5 million tons, but a volcanic arch with more than one eruption center (and consequently more than one ore body) may contain up to 100 million tons.

During the past, the economic importance of mining of volcano–sedimentary iron ores of the Lahn–Dill type has not been great and has depended predominantly on the requirements of local blast furnaces. During the first decades of this century, more than a hundred mines have been operating in Germany, Poland and Czechoslovakia, predominantly producing a calcareous type of hematite ore. However, the intensive tectonic deformation of the ore-bearing sequences and the great variance of ore facies within an ore horizon, even over extremely low distances, prevented the winning of high quantities of chemically and physically uniform ore. Today, only a special ore type rich in silica is used as a raw material for technological processes (e.g., in tempering processes) and as an additional charge in blast furnaces to meliorate the composition of slag.

Though the interest in future prospection of volcano–sedimentary iron ores is low, considerable scientific work has been done during the last two decades in order to establish a genetic concept of these ore deposits which may serve as a conceptual model or prototype for the interrelationship between marine sedimentation and syngenetic sub-marine volcanism in geosynclinal furrows, inasmuch as they represent a "type" of the eugeosynclinal mineralization cycle. Up to now, there does not exist a genetic idea generally accepted by all authors. The main difficulty seems to be the lack of precisely corresponding actualistic equivalents or analogues. Nevertheless, the model of the Lahn–Dill type of ore formation is cited, whenever a syngenetic volcanic source is needed (as a genetic "deus ex machina") to explain an extraordinary metal concentration in sedimentary sequences.

The present chapter is a review of the comprehensive literature on this subject and of the main results of studies made by the author. It tries to give a review of the geolog-ical, geochemical and petrographical features of the volcano–sedimentary iron ores and the ore-bearing sedimentary and volcanic rock assemblages, as well as to demon-strate the complexity of the ore-forming processes deduced from these phenomena and from observations in areas of present-day actual volcanic activity. The author is aware of the fact that some of the conclusions drawn refer to idealized conditions and con-sequently contain a high degree of ambiguity resulting from personal preferences in in-terpreting the available information.

GENERAL DIAGNOSTIC STATEMENT

Because of the lack of a clear and generally valid definition of the volcano–sedimen-tary iron-ore type, some diagnostic information will be given as a basis for further dis-cussions of phenomenal features and genetic aspects of this style of mineralization. The following data primarily refer to the "classical" Lahn–Dill type as first mentioned by Harbort (1903) and Schneiderhöhn (1941).

(1) The iron ores occur as syngenetic, conformable layers and lenticular bodies within sedimentary, volcanic and/or mixed sequences of eugeosynclinal furrows.

(2) The ore bodies are bound to areas with volcanic rocks of the spilitic–keratophyric group, predominantly with spilitic tuffs, belonging to the pre-flysch period of geosyn-clines ("initial magmatic episode", sensu Stille, 1940).

(3) Ore deposits of temporary economic importance only occur in the zones with the maximum accumulation of spilitic tuffs within a volcanic arch, i.e., near to the volcanic eruption centres.

(4) The ore bodies are normally underlain by spilitic tuffs, sometimes by pillow lavas and are overlain by pelagic limestones or shales with intercalations of clastic material. Transgressions of ore sediments on nearby reef complexes have also been observed.

(5) The ore horizons are well bedded and internally laminated, showing features of rapid sedimentation as well as of erosion, transport and redeposition.

(6) The ore sediments are rhythmic sequences of extremely varied iron contents, with a general tendency from silica-rich at the bottom to calcareous at the top.

(7) The iron contained in these ores may be present in primary and secondary mineral phases including hematite, magnetite, siderite, limonite, iron chlorite, stilpnomelane, specularite, and melnikovite—pyrite. Quartz, calcite, dolomite, and chlorite are the main accessory components. Clastic fragments and pyroclastic particles, limestone lenses and argillaceous bands are common impurities.

(8) Small-scale variation of ore facies and ore quality is a typical feature of this type of ore deposit.

(9) Because of their position on the top of volcanic rises, the ore bodies only occur in or on anticlinal structures. This is the consequence of a preferential tectonic deformation controlled by lithology, earlier structures and paleogeomorphical features.

(10) The ore reserves of a single deposit are low; they rarely exceed 5 million tons. The highest accumulation of ore has been determined in the still operating Fortuna mine in the Lahn area, with about 10 million tons of ore or about 3.5 million tons of iron content. The reserves of an ore district which corresponds to a volcanic arch with several eruption centres may, however, be as much as 100 million tons.

These descriptive and diagnostic statements are valid for all volcano—sedimentary iron-ore occurences of Central Europe which, without exception, are of Devonian age. The same type has been reported, however, for instance, from the Devonian of the Taurus Mountains in Turkey (Vaché, 1966). There is only sparse information about analogous mineralizations in other geosynclinal systems, possibly because of lack of economic interest in prospecting this ore type. From regional geological mapping in many areas of the world, it is known that the most common types of iron mineralization in volcanic sequences are incrustations and vein-fillings of hematite, magnetite and/or pyrite within pillow lavas of spilitic and keratophyric composition, thus corresponding to the Central European Variscan, but which are not precisely analogues to the Lahn—Dill type sensu stricto in some other respects.

GEOLOGICAL SETTING

Regional and stratigraphic distribution

The volcano—sedimentary iron ores of the Lahn—Dill type are principally confined to eugeosynclinal furrows of the Central European Variscan system. The map (Fig. 1) shows the distribution of these structural units: the Rheno-Hercynian zone with the Rheinisches Schiefergebirge (unit 1 in Fig. 1), the major part of the Harz (unit 2) and the Flechtinger Höhenzug (unit 3), the Saxo-Thuringian zone with the Thüringer Wald, Frankenwald (unit 4) and the southernmost part of the Harz (= Unterharz) and the Sudeten—Moravia zone with the Ostsudeten and the Devonian of Moravia (unit 5). The most important mining districts have been:

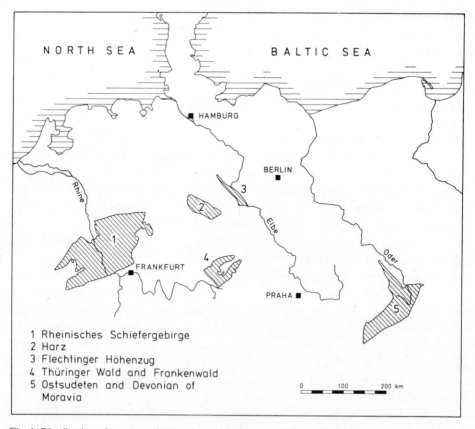

1 Rheinisches Schiefergebirge
2 Harz
3 Flechtinger Höhenzug
4 Thüringer Wald and Frankenwald
5 Ostsudeten and Devonian of
   Moravia

Fig. 1. Distribution of eugeosynclinal units within the Central European Variscan system.

(1) the eastern Sauerland anticline (northeastern part of unit 1); (2) the Dill and Lahn synclines (southern part of unit 1); (3) the Kellerwald (southeastern section of unit 1); (4) the Harz with the Elbingerode complex and the Oberharz diabase belt (unit 2); (5) the Thüringer Wald with the Pörmitz fold belt (northern portion of unit 4); (6) the Frankenwald (southern part of unit 4); and (7) the Ostsudeten (eastern Sudetes = northern part of unit 5) with the Altvatergebirge and Hohes Gesenk and the Devonian of the upper Moravia valley (central section of unit 5).

The important iron-ore occurrences form stratigraphically characteristic horizons on the tops of the principal spilitic tuff sequences at the Givetian/Frasnian boundary between the Middle and Upper Devonian (Rheinisches Schiefergebirge and Harz). In the Thüringer Wald and the Frankenwald they belong to the Upper Frasnian and in the Sudetic Mountains and the Moravia valley, they are bound to the Eifel stage of the Lower Middle Devonian (Fig. 2). Less important iron mineralizations occur within the tuffs and, beyond this, together with Upper Devonian tuffs in the northern Lahn

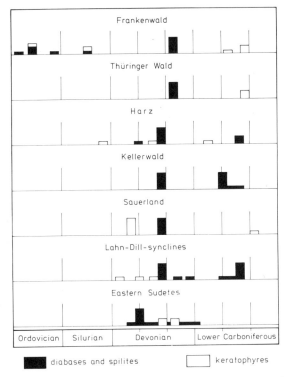

Fig. 2. Stratigraphic position of syngenetic spilitic, diabasic and keratophyric rocks of the ophiolitic suite within eugeosynclinal furrows of the Central European Variscan system.

syncline and as hematite incrustations and vein-fillings in Lower Carboniferous effusive diabases ("Deckdiabas") of the Lahn—Dill area.

It will be demonstrated that this regional and stratigraphic ore distribution pattern in the eugeosynclinal zones is indicated by certain paleogeographic and structural controls which characterize the favorable areas for the development of syngenetic volcano—sedimentary iron-ore deposits. In the past, these characteristics have been used as an exploration guide.

Geotectonic and paleogeographic framework

The Central European Variscan system may be taken as a model of complex geosynclinal sedimentation and structural development of geosynclines (Aubouin, 1965). The area of main interest in this paper covers the northern branch of the Variscan Europe (Aubouin's "extra-Alpine Hercynian Europe") between the old northern continental shield "Laurasia" and the mobile Alpine chain in the south. In terms of paleogeography and magmatic activity, a great variety of geotectonic units may be distinguished with regularly arranged zones of littoral, neritic and pelagic sedimentation in Devonian and Lower Carboniferous time (Kossmat, 1927; Brinkmann, 1948; Aubouin, 1965; for further details, see Rösler, 1960; Krebs, 1968; Dvorak and Paproth, 1969; Quade, 1970; Meischner, 1971):

(1) the Moldanubian zone with its type area, the Bohemian Massif, in the south: a shelf area of neritic sedimentation on a folded pre-Variscan basement (= intermediate massif between the Alpine and extra-Alpine Variscan geosyncline branches);

(2) the Saxo-Thuringian zone north of the Moldanubian, divided into an internal (southern) eugeosynclinal ridge (Fichtelgebirge, Erzgebirge, western Sudetes) with a neritic Devonian facies and an external (northern) eugeosynclinal furrow (Thüringisches Schiefergebirge, Thüringer Wald, southernmost part of the Harz) with a predominantly pelagic Devonian facies and a conformable Lower Carboniferous flysch sequence;

(3) the synsedimentary cordillera (Meischner, 1971) of the "Mitteldeutsche Schwelle": an uplift in the axial zone of divergence between the two eugeosynclinal furrows of the Saxo-Thuringian and Rheno-Hercynian zones, supplying large amounts of coarse detritus to the adjacent basins in the north and the south, represented by the Lower Carboniferous flysch (i.e., greywacke) facies;

(4) the Rheno-Hercynian zone north of the "Mitteldeutsche Schwelle", divided into an internal (southern) eugeosynclinal furrow of great complexity (Lahn and Dill synclines, Kellerwald, major part of the Harz) with a terrigenous to pelagic facies in the Devonian concordantly overlain by the Lower Carboniferous flysch sequence and a miogeosyncline-like shelf of terrigenous and pelagic sedimentation, separated from the southern furrow by the mid-geosynclinal ridge of the Siegerland; and

(5) the Sudetes–Moravia zone bordering the Bohemian zone in the northeast, divided into a northern eugeosynclinal furrow with terrigenous to pelagic facies of Middle Devonian age (eastern Sudetes and northern part of the Devonian of Moravia) and a southern shelf area with terrigenous sediments and pelagic limestones (southern part of the Devonian of Moravia and the Drahaner Plateau).

In these Variscan units the eugeosynclinal furrows are the main distribution zones of spilitic, diabasic and keratophyric lavas and tuffs which characterize the geosynclinal extrusive ophiolitic suite. They are confined to areas of the highest relative mobility between subsiding troughs and more stable blocks which probably were bordered initially by faults. Despite certain differences related to the chronological and spatial pattern and to the intensity of volcanic activity and tectonic deformation, the main paleogeographic and structural features are quite similar in the Lahn and Dill synclines, eastern Sauerland, Harz, Thuringer Wald, Frankenwald, Sudetes, and Moravia. A historic outline is given below.

The *evolution of the geosynclines* started in the Devonian with the subsidence of broad shelf areas at the dipping borders of Variscan uplifts (e.g., the northern continent, the mid-geosynclinal cordillera of the "Mitteldeutsche Schwelle", the Moldanubian zone). In the Rheno-Hercynian zone sediments older than Devonian are widely scattered in a few anticlines. In the Saxo-Thuringian zone Ordovician and Silurian units are known in more complete sequences which include volcanic rocks of the ophiolitic type. But there is no evidence of an independent geosynclinal stage. Where exposed, the Silurian to Devonian boundary is not marked by a disconformity or a change of the sedimentary facies, so that the older formations are integrated into the latter Variscan development.

The *generative stage* of the geosynclines starts in the Lower Devonian of the Rheno-Hercynian zone and the Sudetes—Moravia zone and in the Middle Devonian of the Saxo-Thuringian zone with the deposition of shales, sandstones and sub-greywackes of littoral to neritic facies with transitions to pelagic conditions in the deeper basins and with a condensed sediment sequence on exposed intra-geosynclinal rises (e.g., in the Hörre between the Lahn and Dill synclines). These depositional features are encountered continuing during the lower Middle Devonian, but with a steadily decreasing supply of terrestrial material. The pelagic facies extends over the margins of the restricted basins, thus covering vast areas with black goniatite shales and well-sorted sandstones which are considered to be turbidites in some cases.

This *initial phase of geosynclinal sedimentation* has been accompanied by the *first volcanic activity,* producing the major part of the keratophyric lavas and tuffs (e.g., western Sauerland, Lahn syncline, eastern Sudetes and Moravia). Though there is no doubt about the syngenetic nature and submarine emplacement of these rocks, it should be stressed that some of the tuff horizons show attitudes of an aerial transport and are regionally widespread like key-beds, even if of low thickness; e.g., the main keratophyric sequence in the western Sauerland covers an area of about 2000 km^2 (Rippel, 1953) and has accumulated up to a maximum thickness of more than 200 m.

The *geosynclinal development stage of high mobility* started with the *subsidence* of long and narrow troughs within the hitherto more or less uniform pelagic areas. This first epeirogenic phase in the lower Middle Devonian (Eifel stage) in the Sudetes—Moravia zone, in the upper Middle Devonian of the Rheno-Hercynian zone and the Frasnian in the Saxo-Thuringian zone, is characterized by the most intensive explosive volcanism of the Variscan period bound to the margins of the subsiding troughs. The volcanic eruptions supplied large quantities of spilitic tuffs and minor amounts of pillow lavas accumulated to form volcanic rises with steep slopes. These build-ups covered parts of the troughs as well as the adjacent more stable blocks. Large reefs grew on elevated areas of the shelf and along the flanks of the rises. The furrows in between were occupied by thin pelagic sediments (shales and limestones) intercalated with detrital material derived from the reefs and the volcanic rises. Thus, a pronounced geomorphological surface relief was established along which smaller-scale local ecological units occurred which, in time, increased the differences between eugeosynclinal and shelf zones (= miogeosynclinal zones) and led to a distinct geosynclinal polarity.

The *succeeding transgression* of Upper Devonian in the Rheno-Hercynian and Saxo-Thuringian zones initiated pelagic accumulation of ostracod shales in the deeper-water environments and of goniatite limestones in the shallow-water milieu of reefs and volcanic rises. Arenite and greywacke turbidites extended into the basins from both the shelf and the synsedimentary cordillera of the "Mitteldeutsche Schwelle", but were still restricted to certain areas (Meischner, 1968). Syngenetic volcanic rocks of this time are only known from some localities of the northern Lahn syncline (spilitic tuffs and lavas).

The end of the Devonian and the Lower Carboniferous of the Variscan system are characterized by *a second epeirogenic phase of high tectonic mobility*. The pre-Variscan geoanticlinal cordilleras emerged and the adjacent geosynclinal basins were filled up with flysch (i.e., greywacke) sediments masking the remaining pelagic facies of black alum shales and cherts. Large masses of diabasic lavas extruded in some regions of the Rheno-Hercynian zone near the intra-geosynclinal rises (e.g., the Hörre between the Lahn and Dill synclines) and thin keratophyric tuff bands are known as key-beds within shale sequences of the upper Lower Carboniferous. The youngest volcanic rocks known are intrusive diabases and keratophyres penetrating even folded Devonian and Carboniferous successions.

In contrast to the mobile zones, the stable shelf areas (e.g., the northwestern part of the Rheinisches Schiefergebirge and the Drahaner Plateau in Moravia) are the domain of shallow-water sedimentation interrupted by local turbidity currents; they became basins of rapid subsidence after the folding of the internal zones, i.e., in the Upper Carboniferous.

The *orogenesis* of the Central European Variscan system seems to have been a continuous process starting with the first uplifts of pre-Variscan cordilleras and culminating with a remarkable climax at the end of the Lower Carboniferous, followed by a second main phase in the upper part of the Upper Carboniferous when the coal-bearing paralic (molasse-type) series of the Ruhrgebiet and the eastern Sudetes were also folded.

Depositional environment of the volcano–sedimentary iron ores

It has been mentioned already that the volcano–sedimentary iron formation is bound to volcanic rocks of the keratophyric-spilitic assemblage within the Variscan eugeosynclinal areas of Central Europe. Though iron mineralisations frequently are encountered in keratophyric, spilitic and diabasic lavas of various geological systems and periods, larger economic ore concentrations only occur as syngenetic lenticular layers on the tops of submarine volcanic rises formed by spilitic tuffs within the Rheno-Hercynian, Saxo-Thuringian and Sudetes–Moravia zones. These tuffs are the products of the main phase of explosive volcanism accompanying the subsidence of eugeosynclinal furrows. Therefore, they are characteristically restricted to distinct fault zones separating different structural blocks (e.g., between "epeirogenic basins" and "epeirogenic uplifts"; see Schönenberg, 1956) or to narrow troughs with short distances between the bordering faults. Extremely great thicknesses of tuffs have been observed in junction zones of crossing faults, thus forming transversal rises (Schönenberg, 1951; Krebs, 1960).

Due to the subsidence of eugeosynclinal furrows and the eruption of tuffs, the paleo-geographic conditions within the hitherto more or less uniform pelagic environment changed rapidly. The volcanites were confined to isolated seamounts or continuous arches, thus transforming distinctive zones of the basins into shallow-water rises. They occasionally were covered on the flanks by stromatoporoid and coral reefs, most of which underwent penecontemporaneous reworking by the turbulent surface water. The organic limestone build-up, however, persisted as reef debris and lesser occurrences of autochthonous reef per se. These morphologically prominent zones are the distribution areas of the volcano—sedimentary iron ores and are characterized by a succeeding sedimentation of thin, partly condensed goniatite limestones. The more stable and hitherto uplifted blocks without volcanic activity ("epeirogenic uplifts" and vast "epeirogenic basins") became comparatively deeper basins with a much lower rate of sediment accumulation ("relief inversion"). Ostracod shales and dark impure limestones with intercalations of reef debris and epiclastic material eroded from nearby rises are the indicative sediments of these zones.

These differences between iron-ore-bearing rises and basins without primary ore facies persisted for a long time. It is known, for example, from the western Dill syncline (Kegel, 1923; Krebs, 1960) that tuff rises of Middle Devonian age do not have any Upper Devonian cover and were transgressed directly by the Lower Carboniferous (see also Gräbe, 1962: examples from the Pörmitz fold belt).

The contrasting rock facies on rises and within basins, as well as the phenomena of "relief inversion", have been used as a prospecting guide for the localization of iron-ore bodies, especially in areas with great thicknesses of the covering sediment sequences (Kegel, 1934).

Sedimentary facies of the volcano—sedimentary iron ores

The sedimentary facies of the volcano—sedimentary iron ores depend in a characteristic way on the small-scale morphology of the volcanic rises or ridges and associated reef complexes, which influenced the vertical and lateral distribution of the ore horizons, as well as the oxidation—reduction potential of the environment. The latter controlled the oxidation state of the iron minerals. Turbulent-water erosion along the tops of the rises and reefs resulted in erosional channels and depressions which subsequently were filled by detritus and/or iron sediments. Therefore, both the erosion and the primary thickness variations of sediments (see section below) resulted in a weakly to profoundly developed unconformity at the base of the ore bodies.

As to the depositional conditions of the volcano—sedimentary iron ores, one may distinguish between a primary and a secondary ore-facies type. The former facies is the product of immediate precipitation of iron sediments from the volcanic solutions pouring into the sea water; this facies is bound to the zones of maximum thickness of tuffs which are interpreted as being the centres of volcanic eruption. The secondary or

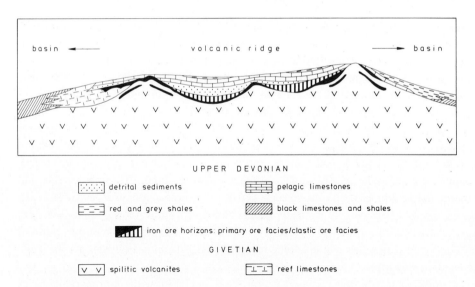

Fig. 3. Schematic section through a complex reef-bearing volcanic ridge with three eruption centres showing different types of sedimentary facies and the vertical and lateral distribution of the main facies types of volcano–sedimentary ores.

clastic ore facies results from sedimentary reworking and redeposition on the flanks of these centres with local transportation to adjacent basins or depressions (see Fig. 3).

The interrelation of paleomorphological, stratigraphic, and sedimentological aspects permits the classification of three main types of ore deposits:

(1) Deposits on the tops of prominent volcanic rises with transitions to reef complexes within the oxidation zone of sea water, characterized by predominantly hematite ore types and overlain by pelagic goniatite limestones. The majority of the characteristic Lahn–Dill deposits belongs to this type.

(2) Deposits on the tops of volcanic rises overlain by grey to dark shales and impure limestones. This type contains primary hematite ores which are totally or partly reduced diagenetically to magnetite ores; within these deposits primary pyrite and siderite ore bands may occasionally be encountered.

(3) Deposits on the tops and flanks of volcanic rises overlain by thick sequences of grey to black shales, containing primary hematite ores with intercalations of iron silicate bands. This type is restricted to areas with a cover of basin sediments.

The volcano–sedimentary iron ores cover the volcanic rocks of the rises and the organo-detrital limestones of the reefs with a tendency to level out the pre-existing surface morphology. Therefore, the well-developed bedding planes of the ore successions are unconformable with respect to the upper surface of the strata below. Occasionally, a slight unconformity is also evident at the top of the ore bodies, especially when these consist of primary ore types.

The most distinctive sedimentary features of the iron ores are the internal textures and fabrics of layers, depending on the respective ore type and the paleotopographical position of the ore succession. The most important of these structures are:

(1) contorted lamination, within layers of primary silica-rich hematite ore (frequently in the lower part of the succession) with flame-like fabrics of pale-red jasper inclusions, poor in iron; (2) irregular cross-lamination within layers of nearly pure compact hematite ore and chloritic "green ironstone"; (3) thin banding when pyroclastic or sedimentary material is intercalated; (4) graded bedding within layers of clastic hematite ore with a calcitic matrix; (5) clastic textures in calcareous iron-ore layers with reworked fragments of other ore types or sediments; (6) curved lamination above and beneath buried blocks of organic limestones; (7) scour-and-fill structures within calcareous hematite layers covering karst cavities in organic limestones; (8) internal cavities within calcareous hematite layers filled in the lower part by red clay and in the upper part by recrystallized calcite; and (9) oolitic textures are not typical for this genetic ore type and have been reported only from iron silicate ores of the eastern Sudetes (Skacel, 1966).

The development of different sedimentary facies of volcano-sedimentary iron ores has been influenced by two processes: (a) the outpouring of the volcanic "solution" into the sea water, and (b) the sedimentation and crystallization under sedimentary conditions.

Though it is very difficult to define exactly the participation of each factor in the process of ore formation, some criteria may be stated:

(1) The principal "volcanic" components of the iron ores are silica, iron and partly calcium, besides tuffaceous fragments and fine-grained chloritic material.

(2) The outpour of the tuffs has been interrupted when the "solution" were exhaled. From almost all deposits it is known that the ore bodies overlie the tuff sequences with a sharp boundary. Pyroclastic fragments within iron ores have been observed only in basinal (clastic) ore facies types and may be interpreted as being derived from the adjacent volcanic rise.

(3) The "solutions" must have had high concentrations of silica and iron. The silica-rich hematite ore which is regarded as being the most characteristic primary ore facies is confined to the vicinity of the eruption centres and always occurs in the lower part of the ore successions. The latter have accumulated to form wave-resistant masses without considerable lateral transport of the precipitation products (Lippert, 1951). Probably the "solutions" may be defined as colloidal systems of high viscosity which became extremely unstable when entering the sea water.

(4) Other primary ore types indicating a great volcanic influence are compact, pure hematite layers with iron contents above 60% (see Bottke, 1965) and chloritic "green ironstones" which frequently are the main components of the lowermost layer of an ore sequence.

(5) The internal fabrics of the primary ore types indicate that the first precipita-

tion products have been colloidal mixtures of amorphous silica and Fe(III)-hydroxides or iron silicates (e.g., colloform banding, round gel particles with shrinking fissures).

(6) The distribution pattern of primary ore facies frequently show a concentric arrangement around the eruption centres (Bottke, 1965) with downward transitions to sedimentary facies (see also Fig. 3).

(7) The first reworking occurred immediately after the precipitation of iron sediments. In nearly all penecontemporaneous sedimentary ore facies, "amoeba-shaped" unrounded particles of cryptocrystalline intergrowths of quartz and hematite have been observed, which are typical for the silica-rich hematite ore facies.

(8) The volcanic support of ore "solutions" has not been uninterrupted. The bedding planes within the primary ore layers may be interpreted as marking quieter periods of volcanic emanations. Occasionally, these planes are covered by thin sediment bands, even with fossils (e.g., styliolines in the lower ore body of the Waldhausen mine in the Lahn area and goniatites in the upper part of the ore sequences reported from several other mines).

(9) Depending on the paleotopographical position of the ore accumulations, after a certain time the influence of sedimentary processes overwhelmed those of the volcanic mechanisms. Primarily precipitated iron sediments and partly recrystallized ores were reworked, eroded and transported. The ore successions on the flanks of the rises and in the nearby basins, both of which lack primary ore facies, indicate an intensive lateral transport of ore fragments. The resulting sedimentary ore types contain hematite ore fragments embedded in calcareous and argillaceous material.

(10) These "secondary" ore facies types may also be encountered as transgressive sediments on the tops of the rises, thus covering the primary ore facies types.

(11) The sedimentary process of reworking has rarely been interrupted by new volcanic eruptions. Only a few examples of occurrences of pyroclastic beds or pillow lavas within or above the upper parts of the ore sequences are known.

(12) The "normal" marine sedimentation continued after the deposition of ore sediments with a characteristic clastic sequence consisting of detrital material eroded from the volcanis rises (e.g., pebbles of spilite, diabase, tuff, ore, and reef limestone), thus indicating a transgressive phase with a succeeding pelagic sedimentation of goniatite limestones and shales.

Mineralogical facies of the volcano—sedimentary iron ores

The ore-forming processes of the volcano—sedimentary Lahn—Dill-type of deposits may be subdivided into six phases due to the interrelationship of volcanic and sedimentary agents:

(1) the volcanic emanation of ore "solutions" and the rapid precipitation of ore sediments while pouring into the sea water; (2) the first diagenetic phase of crystallization of the newly precipitated sediments ("primary ore facies"); (3) the reworking

of iron-ore sediments and the redeposition on the flanks of the volcanic rises and in the nearby basins; (4) the second diagenetic phase represented by the crystallization of the redeposited ore sediments ("secondary ore facies"); (5) the hydrothermal (epigenetic) alteration of iron ores by intruded diabases and associated hydrothermal phases; and (6) the supergene alteration of iron ores when exposed surficially.

Though it is very difficult to distinguish these six phases exactly by petrographic examination, a combined analysis of ore fabrics, mineral components and sedimentary rock facies may lead to a paragenetic scheme as proposed in Fig. 4. It should be stressed that the different mineralogical ore types are commonly intergradational and that "pure" paragenetic phases are not developed.

Nearly nothing is known about the composition of the ore "solutions" resulting from volcanic emanations. They exhaled *at the end* of the tuff eruption phase, but in some cases iron-ore layers also occur *within* the tuff sequences. The concentric arrangement of the primary ore sediments as obviously wave-resistant masses around the eruption centers near the summit of the volcanic rises, suggest that these "solutions" have been colloidal systems with high concentrations of silica and iron rather than dispersal liquids. There is no evidence that would indicate that the type and amount of the precipitates have been controlled by processes other than or in addition to volcanic-exhalative mechanisms and the rate(s) thereof. These colloidal systems must have been

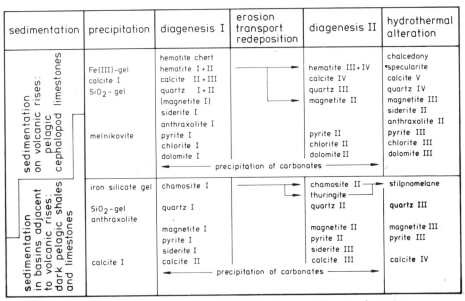

Fig. 4. Schematic representation of mineral formation in volcano–sedimentary iron ores.

nearly free of accessory elements because of the chemical "purity" of the primary sediments. As the normal marine sedimentation continued even in the more immediate
vicinity of these centers, it may be concluded that the colloidal systems had a positive
oxidation potential (i.e., +Eh) and lacked gas phases, the latter of which could have
modified the Eh and pH of the environment. The primary ore types have to be derived
from gels of iron (III)-hydroxide and amorphous silica.

Commonly, the ore sequences begin with a thin layer of iron-silicate ore (chamosite
ore or "green ironstone") which seems to be a chloritic transition facies between the
volcanic rocks below and the iron ore sensu stricto. Only a few examples are known
of primary iron(II)-types (e.g., melnikovite—pyrite and siderite) which occur in deposits
with transgressive black or dark-grey shales of a sedimentary environment of low or
negative oxidation potential (e.g., deposits in the southern Lahn syncline and in the
Pörmitz fold belt).

While the influence of the sedimentary environment on the formation of primary
iron sediments in general has been low, the first diagenetic phase of crystallization (and/
or recrystallization) depended on the marine pH and Eh conditions. As stressed by
several authors (e.g., Garrels and Christ, 1965), the variation of pH and Eh in normal
marine environments ranges from pH 8.4/Eh + 0.4 to pH 7.5/Eh + 0.1. Thus, the principal primary ore types contain hematite as the main iron mineral. Microgranular chalcedony or quartz, occasionally with well-developed fibrous textures, forms the groundmass of the silica-rich ore types (pale red hematite chert) with heamatite as the coloring
pigment which may be so abundant that the groundmass becomes practically opaque.[1]
Gelatinous spherulites of iron-stained silica with shrinking fissures are very common
in these cherty ore types (see Cissarz, 1924). Cryptocrystalline needles of hematite in
quartz grains have also been reported from many occurrences. A second primary ore
type is that of compact hematite ore with a fine-grained hematite cement and minute
particles of quartz or calcite.

Chamosite ores are rarely well crystallized. Diagenetic magnetite, siderite and pyrite
on the other hand, may form ideal blasts within the siliceous groundmass, but they
have been observed only in transitional facies types along the border of deep basins
or in ore bodies buried by dark shales.

The phases of reworking, transportation and redeposition of ore particles by turbulent
surface waters can only be reconstructed from data of detailed stratigraphic correlations
supported by faunal investigations, especially using conodonts as guide fossils. It is known
that these processes already started soon after the accumulation of the primary ore
sediments and continued up to the deposition of the younger pelagic limestones. Detrital ore types are partly contemporaneous with the upper primary ore beds and also
cover them in some cases. The clastic fragments may be rounded pebbles, unrounded

---

[1] For detailed discussion on textures in iron ores, see the chapter by Dimroth.

debris or "amoeba-shaped" particles, in the latter case indicating an erosional activity before the crystallization of the ore sediments began. The eroded material has only been transported over shorter distances and is almost totally absent in basin sequences without underlying volcanic rocks.

The second phase of diagenetic crystallization occurred under the same conditions as the first. Calcite and argillaceous material are the embedding groundmass, in near-reef deposits intermixed by reef debris. The principal ore types formed are calcareous hematite and detrital ("speckled") calcite-hematite ores. Hematite shales with rounded particles of cherty hematite ore in a groundmass of fine-grained hematite occur, as a special facies, only on the tops of volcanic rises.

Oolitic ore types have been reported only from the eastern Sudetes by Skacel (1966) who described thuringite oolites in a calcareous basin sequence adjacent to a typical volcano-sedimentary ore body.

As a result of the influence of the sedimentary environment, primary iron minerals may be transformed to a more stable mineral state: hematite replacing primary magnetite, magnetite recrystallized from hematite or chamosite, etc. Generally the groundmass consists of coarser grains than that of the first diagenetic phase.

In some deposits, the epigenetic alteration of the mineral paragenesis has been distinct. A lot of diabase and spilite intrusions are also known to penetrate the ore bodies. These are obviously sometimes pre-dating the main deformation of the rock units. Where cutting hematite sequences, these intrusions gave rise to the formation of compact magnetite and siderite ores. Well-examined occurrences in the Fortuna mine in the Lahn syncline indicate that near the contacts of dikes, the iron has been totally reduced to magnetite and that with increasing distance the proportion of magnetite decreases in favour of siderite and pyrite. The groundmass, whether silica or carbonate, has been recrystallized to form holocrystalline cement of interlocking coarse grains with scattered aggregates of iron minerals. Intermixtures of iron chlorites are abundant, occasionally forming "green ironstones" within the "hydrothermal haloes" of the dikes. The strongest influence of the intrusions encountered is the crystallization of coarse-grained specularite. Within the whole reaction zone, an inorganic amorphous form of carbon (anthraxolite II) may be recognized as little black spots, even penetrating the contact zone in the diabase or spilite.

The Devonian and Carboniferous sequences of the Central European Variscan system have undergone a low-grade regional metamorphism (anchimetamorphism). The only case of greenschist to amphibolite facies has been reported from parts of the eastern Sudetes (Altvater Mountains), where the hematite ores were altered to a banded hematite-magnetite ore which resembles certain itabiritic types, but without the so perfect separation of iron minerals and silica (see Skacel, 1966).

Due to weathering processes, the iron-ore bodies near to the surface have been altered to earthy masses of limonite, occasionally with high concentrations of manganese and, sometimes, phosphorous.

Chemical composition of volcano–sedimentary iron ores

Due to the different processes of ore formation, the chemical composition of the volcano–sedimentary iron ores varies in wide ranges. Therefore, it is impossible to establish representative analyses for this type of deposit as a whole. Table II gives some analyses

TABLE I

Comparative mineral assemblages in volcano–sedimentary iron-ore types

Ore type	Oxides	Silicates	Carbonates	Sulfides	Fe-content (%)
(1) Primary ore types:					
(a) red hematite chert	hematite	Fe-SiO$_2$ gels (cryptocrystalline) chalcedony quartz			up to 43
(b) compact hematite ore	hematite	quartz chalcedony (iron silicate)	calcite (ankerite)		up to 68
(c) melnikovite–pyrite ore	magnetite	quartz chalcedony (iron silicate)	calcite	melniko-vite–pyrite	up to 31
(d) siderite ore	(hematite) (magnetite)	(quartz) (chalcedony) (iron silicate)	siderite calcite (ankerite) (dolomite)	(pyrite)	up to 30
(e) "green ironstone"	(magnetite)	chamosite quartz (chalcedony; thuringite)		pyrite	15–25
(2) Secondary ore types:					
(a) detrital calcite-hematite ore ("speckled ore")	hematite	(quartz)	calcite (ankerite; dolomite)		up to 38
(b) calcareous hematite ore	hematite	(quartz) (iron silicate)	calcite (ankerite) (dolomite)		up to 42
(c) hematite shale	hematite	(quartz) Al-silicate	(calcite)		up to 41
(d) magnetite ore	magnetite (hematite)	quartz (iron silicate)	(calcite) (dolomite)	pyrite	up to 52
(e) thuringite ore	(magnetite)	thuringite	calcite (siderite)	pyrite	up to 25
(3) Epigenetic ore types:					
(a) magnetite ore	magnetite (hematite)	quartz iron silicate	calcite siderite	pyrite	up to 65

TABLE I (continued)

Ore type	Oxides	Silicates	Carbonates	Sulfides	Fe-content (%)
(b) siderite ore	(magnetite) (hematite)	quartz iron silicate	siderite calcite (ankerite; dolomite)	pyrite	up to 40
(c) iron silicate ore	magnetite (hematite)	iron silicate quartz stilpnomelane	calcite (siderite)	pyrite	up to 30
(d) limonite ore	limonite (hematite)	(quartz)	(calcite)		up to 40

TABLE II

Comparative chemical analysis (in %) of different iron-ore facies types in volcano–sedimentary deposits of the Lahn area (compiled after Quade, 1968)

	Fe	FeO	Fe$_2$O$_3$	Mn	P	CaO	SiO$_2$	Al$_2$O$_3$
Silica-rich	16.61	2.18	21.35	0.10	0.071	0.20	74.98	–
hematite ore	18.30	2.16	23.76	0.10	0.042	0.17	72.10	–
(jasper ore)	32.61	1.39	45.08	0.06	0.064	0.17	51.84	–
from the	36.07	1.29	50.14	0.12	0.032	0.20	46.28	–
Waldhausen mine	41.38	0.44	56.68	0.08	0.044	0.18	36.30	–
	42.52	1.71	58.89	0.10	0.114	0.19	37.40	–
Compact hematite	65.98	2.51	91.55	0.07	0.088	0.94	2.94	–
ore from the	60.41	3.22	82.80	0.10	0.030	0.37	8.08	–
Fortuna mine	67.03	0.35	95.45	0.07	0.012	0.22	2.94	–
	65.84	1.13	92.88	0.12	0.220	1.18	2.11	0.34
	60.25	1.70	84.26	0.16	0.042	1.27	9.16	0.86
Clastic hematite	40.75	1.53	56.56	0.14	0.095	13.66	10.32	6.18
ore ("Scheckenerz")	38.15	1.60	52.77	0.12	0.088	16.91	10.40	3.22
from the Fortuna	34.20	1.99	46.68	0.10	0.101	0.15	33.28	13.56
mine	34.19	1.90	46.78	0.12	0.110	0.15	33.64	13.20
Epigenetic magnetite	63.00	34.74	–	0.22	0.055	0.38	0.75	0.28
ore from the	63.92	33.31	–	0.13	0.073	0.69	1.26	0.67
Waldhausen mine	51.43	22.69	–	0.10	0.084	0.60	10.52	3.52
	39.40	19.59	–	0.10	0.100	0.57	33.48	1.76
Epigenetic	35.12	43.77	1.57	0.11	0.112	10.76	3.04	1.96
siderite ore from	32.70	41.50	0.63	0.19	0.114	10.10	4.76	0.66
the Fortuna mine	33.20	41.50	1.34	0.16	0.126	10.54	5.74	1.32
	38.65	47.15	2.86	0.16	0.412	7.28	1.78	0.13
Melnikovite–pyrite	27.72	10.33	–	0.13	0.031	0.58	30.10	22.44
ore from the	27.50	6.09	–	0.12	0.044	0.52	34.34	24.11
Lindenberg mine	30.90	6.79	–	0.10	0.030	0.38	27.80	26.07
	28.05	8.21	–	0.10	0.063	0.66	33.12	23.24

of different ore types in order to illustrate the variability of ore composition, even within the same type. The composition of the ores depends on the volcanic supply of ions as well as on the sedimentary processes of deposition, erosion, transport, and redeposition. From the intimate interrelationship of these agents there resulted a lot of different ore types; only the most extreme types are listed in Table I.

In all ore types, of course, silica, calcite and iron are the chief constituents while the other elements make up the balance, though occurring in small amounts. The alumina contents in primary iron-ore types are generally very low and increase only in distinct facies of iron-silicate ores or reworked ore types and in epigenetic varieties resulting from secondary influences of intruded diabases or spilites. Fig. 5 gives an example of two drill-hole sequences of the Fortuna mine in order to demonstrate the variation of alumina (Al_2O_3) over a distance of 35 m within the same ore body: the drill hole Fo 20 cuts a hematite ore series between underlying tuffs and transgressive detrital sediments

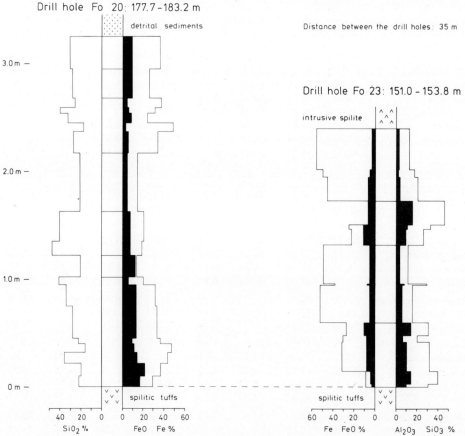

Fig. 5. Chemical analysis of two adjacent ore sequences of the Fortuna mine in the Lahn syncline, demonstrating the modification of ore composition over short distances: Fo 23 influenced by an intrusive spilite.

and the drill hole Fo 23 shows the same series, but influenced by an intrusive spilite, showing Al_2O_3-contents of up to 18%. Though stratigraphically complete chemical analyses of alkalies are lacking, it may be deduced from balance calculations that these elements are extremely low, rarely exceeding 1%.

Figure 6 gives an example of stratigraphically-lithologically continuous analyses of an ore body of the Waldhausen mine near Weilburg/Lahn illustrating the high grade of variability of the chemical composition. Each ore layer begins with silica-rich parts at the base and shows a relative enrichment of iron near the top. $Fe_2O_3 + Fe_3O_4 + SiO_2$ amount to 96% or more. The small-scale variation of chemical composition may be observed vertically and laterally in all deposits and is one of the most characteristic aspects of the Lahn–Dill type iron ore. Even average analyses of complete ore sequences do not correspond. The only general trend to be registered is the increase of CaO-contents from the base to the top of a sequence and the decrease of SiO_2 from the eruption centers of the volcanic rises to the adjacent basins. Though the ratio of iron to silica varies in wide ranges, the amount of iron has the tendency to diminish in the same direction as silica, due to the influence of sedimentary processes. The only enrichment of iron encountered till now beyond the volcanic rises is that in karst holes along the top of reef limestones which functioned as collecting depressions or pools for the fine hematite debris derived from the areas of primary ore facies.

Base metals (e.g., Cu, Zn, Pb, Co, Ni) belong to the trace elements with an uncharacteristic variability that does not permit of giving representative data for this genetic ore type. Even phosphorus and in primary ores also manganese, are components without

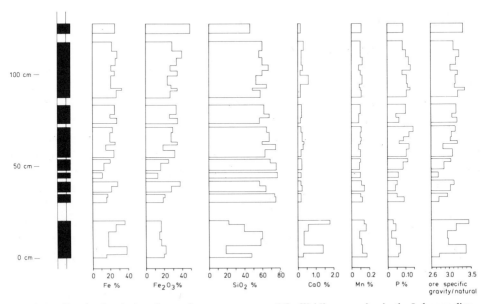

Fig. 6. Small-scale chemical analyses of an ore sequence of the Waldhausen mine in the Lahn syncline.

TABLE III

Trace-element spectra (ppm) in hematite and magnetite minerals separated from iron ores of the Lahn–Dill type (hematite from primary silica-rich ore, diagenetic magnetite from chloritic ore, epigenic magnetite formed by hydrothermal alteration of calcareous hematite ore)

	Primary hematite from silica-rich ore	Diagenetic magnetite from chloritic ore	Epigenetic magnetite from calcareous hematite ore
Al	10–10000	10–5000	200–10000
Mg	10–5000	10–3000	200–10000
Mn	0–4500	0–600	trace –9000
Ti	10–4500	0–4500	10–10000
V	0–2200	10–1000	10–300
Cu	10–1000	0–200	10–280
Pb	0–50	0–1500	0–300
Zn	0–5000	10–800	0–100
Sn	0–50	10–250	0–300
Ni	0–5100	0–30	0–10
Co	0–100	0–100	–

abnormal enrichment, when compared with marine sediments. Therefore, it is very difficult to draw any conclusion as to the genetic significance of these elements (see Table III).

THE ORIGIN OF VOLCANO–SEDIMENTARY IRON ORES

The origin of volcano–sedimentary iron ores has been discussed since the beginning of mining in the district of the Middle European Variscan. In spite of vast geologic, petrographic and geochemical researches, there is no one theory of origin which could be generally accepted to explain all observations. The monotonous mineral paragenesis of the ore deposits, the lack of "critical" mineral-indicators and the undiagnostic chemical composition do not permit the deduction of a model generally valid neither for the source and composition of "ore solutions" nor for the conditions of precipitation of the primary ore sediments. Moreover, diagenetic and epigenetic processes altered the mineral components and the fabrics of the ores in such a way that almost every deposit seems to represent a special genetic model, or at least sub-model. As there is no individual deposit which can be regarded as "characteristic" for the whole genetic type, the generalization and overemphasis of singular aspects must lead to a great variety of controversial theories. Consequently, almost every author proposes another concept of origin, due to his particular observations and experiences. Another reason for the lack of a uniform concept may have been in the past the difficulty of citing actualistic comparisons for the described features of the volcano–sedimentary iron ores.

Hypotheses of origin

In order to understand the controversial theories of the origin of volcano–sedimentary iron ores which were published in the first decades of systematical geological research, it should be stressed that in the 18th century and in the first half of the 19th century only deposits with superficial outcrops were mined, i.e., almost exclusively anticlinal structures of the volcanic rises with siliceous hematite, magnetite and limonite ores. But it was already known that with increasing depth the composition changed to calcareous types poorer in iron. Therefore, many authors (e.g., Sandberger, 1847; Bischoff, 1854; Riemann, 1878; Denckmann, 1901) proposed a supergene origin and silification by descending waters, enriched with iron while circulating in volcanites and replacing nearby sedimentary rocks. The primary ores were interpreted as sideritic and limonitic ores, altered to hematite and magnetite ores by dynamic metamorphism.

With the progress of paleontological stratigraphy and the possibility of correlating ore and sediment sequences, it became generally known that the ore layers are syngenetic conformable/strata-bound horizons within the volcano–sedimentary suites, especially *at the contact* between tuffs and limestones or shales, but also *within* the tuff sequences, (see, e.g., Lotz, 1902; Harbort, 1903; Ahlburg, 1917; Kegel, 1934; Lippert, 1951). This concept is generally accepted today. The change in ore and sediment facies was proved by detailed stratigraphy using conodonts as guide fossils (see, e.g., Krebs, 1960; Bottke, 1965; Quade, 1968) and the differences in ore composition could be explained by sedimentary differentiation, diagenetic and epigenetic alteration (see, e.g., Rösler, 1960; Knauer, 1960; Dave, 1963; Steinike, 1963; Bottke, 1965; Skacel, 1966; Quade, 1970).

Schneiderhöhn (e.g., 1941) was the first to integrate the volcano–sedimentary iron-ore type into a global genetic model of ore formation, citing Harbort (1903) as the author of a volcanic source of iron. He gave the definition of the "Lahn–Dill type" as a "submarine exhalative–sedimentary" and syngenetic product of the initial ophiolite–magmatic stage of geosynclinal development (sensu Stille, 1940), resulting from chloridic emanations in the final stage of volcanic activity. The majority of later authors accepted this idea as a general concept (see Borchert, 1957, 1960; Amstutz, 1959; Cissarz, 1956; and others). However, Oftedahl (1958) contradicted the existence of metal-rich vapors in connection with basic volcanism and postulated an acid magma as a source of iron and silica, a theory which is not ascertainable for the Devonian eugeosynclinal troughs with Lahn–Dill-type ores. Hentschel (1960) and Rösler (1962) believed in wall-rock leaching and "pseudo-hydrothermal" phases. Gräbe (1962) cited again the idea of Harrassowitz (1921) deriving iron and silica from lateritic processes. Without being able to discuss in detail all theories, Fig. 7 illustrates the great variety of opinions published about the complex problem of the origin of volcano–sedimentary iron ores.

Any further attempt to explain the genesis of Lahn–Dill-type deposits has to be based on some irrevocable statements which should be definitive (see section "General

syngenetic – contemporaneous				epigenetic	
volcano–sedimentary		sedimentary		metasomatic	
exhalative	hydrothermal	supergene-lateritic	submarine-halmyrolitic	pneumatolytic-hydrothermal	supergene-oxidative
primary magmatic differentiation		decomposition or weathering of volcanites		magmatic differentiation	weathering
syn-volcanic to late-volcanic pre-orogenic		post-volcanic pre-orogenic		syn-orogenic	post-orogenic
HARBORT 1903 MICHELS 1921 CISSARZ 1924 SCHNEIDER-HÖHN 1941 LIPPERT 1951 BORCHERT 1957 1960 BOTTKE 1965	LOTZ 1907 AHLBURG 1917 KEGEL 1923 QUADE 1970	HENTSCHEL 1960 RÖSLER 1962	HARRASSOWITZ 1921 GRABE 1962	HUMMEL 1922	RICHTER 1930 LEHMANN 1941	SANDBERGER 1847 BISCHOFF 1854 RIEMANN 1878 DENCKMANN 1901

Fig. 7. Metallogenetic concepts of the Lahn–Dill-type volcano–sedimentary iron ores.

diagnostic statement"). The principal points still to be considered are the following: (1) actualistic examples of the formation of iron-rich sediments by volcanic processes; (2) similarities and differences between the Lahn–Dill and other types of sedimentary iron formations; (3) the relation of volcano–sedimentary iron ores to other syngenetic metal mineralizations in geosynclinal environments; and (4) possible source of iron and silica in ophiolitic geosynclinal volcanism.

Actualistic examples of the formation of iron-rich sediments by volcanic processes

Based on reports by Silvestri and Bergeat about fumaroles of the Etna and Stromboli volcanoes, Italy, Harbort (1903) was the first to cite actualistic examples in order to explain the conditions of volcano–sedimentary ore formation. He proceeded on the assumption that acid halide gases containing Fe(II)-irons supplied the necessary silica and metals, which rapidly oxidized when entering open air or sea water. This idea has been introduced into the global concept of ore genesis by Schneiderhöhn (1941) and seems to be proved by a substantial amount of subsequent investigations (see, e.g., Tatsumi, 1970).

Of great importance have been the results of a vast research program carried out by Russian scientists since 1935 in the volcanic area of the Kamchatka and Kuril Islands east of the Sea of Okhotsk. Gorshkov (1958), Naboko (1959, 1960) and Selenov (1960) published a considerable amount of analyses and observations about the interrelationship of lava effusions and eruptions of vapors, especially about the modification of the chemical composition of the emanations. They distinguished high-temperature gases, hydrothermal phases and low-temperature waters which supply large amounts of iron, alumina and silica, and smaller amounts of other metals. A number of small streams derived from acid fumaroles precipitate iron-hydroxide muds along their watercourse or when entering sea water. It has been calculated, for instance, that the river Yuryeva descending from the Ebeko volcano, yearly furnishes about 35 tons of iron and 65 tons of aluminium to the ocean water of the Okhotsk sea. It is an important fact that in this area the amount of metals in the juvenile exhalations is obviously very low. Chlorine, sulphur and carbon monoxide escape together with water vapor and oxygen, and not as a chemical compound with metals. Only if sulphuric acid is produced by oxidation of hydrogen sulphide will a leaching process attack the wall-rock (in this case: volcanites), giving rise to the formation of metal-rich hydrothermal phases. Therefore, the above-mentioned authors proposed a direct correlation between acidity as well as temperature and metal content; they accepted a colloidal medium transported by gas and vapor rather than dilute ionic solutions.

One of the rare cases directly observed of the submarine formation of iron-bearing sediments by volcanic processes is that of the Santorini caldera, Greece, which has been described by Behrend (1934), Lippert (1953), Harder (1960), Butuzova (1966, 1968) and Bonatti et al. (1971). The most systematic research in this area, however, has been carried out by Puchelt (1973) who provided a mass of chemical analyses of sediment cores from the Kameni Islands (see Table IV). Thus, it could be proved that the sources of iron are warm submarine springs discharging iron and manganese as sulfate or hydrocarbonate complexes in a solution oversaturated with respect to carbon dioxide. The factors influencing the precipitation in sea water are interpreted as being pH and Eh changes for all compounds sensitive to differences in these two parameters and to the decrease of temperature and change of ionic strength for silica. The resulting sediment is a mixed mass of gel of iron hydroxide and amorphous silica with a ratio near to that of chamosite. The striking fact of small amounts of alumina in nearly all samples is explained by special physico-chemical conditions: "... since $Al(OH)_3$ is less soluble than $Fe(OH)_2$, it will be the compound which is precipitated prior to $Fe(OH)_2$. $Al(OH)_3$-rich layers should occur in deeper parts of the sediments not sampled so far" (Puchelt, 1973, pp. 240–241).

In the last few years, highly saline and metal-rich subsurface brines have been observed in basins on the floor of the Red Sea (Degens and Ross, 1969; see also their Chapter 4, Vol. 4), in deep drill holes under the Salton Sea geothermal area of·California (White, 1968) and in the Matupi Harbor, New Britain, T.P.N.G. (Ferguson and Lambert, 1972), among others (see Table V). These three types of brines seem to have obtained their high metal contents from leaching underlying sedimentary and/or volcanic rocks without a direct participation of volcanic processes, though the Matupi example suggests the influence of fumaroles of the Tavurvur volcano at least in respect to the alkali compounds.

TABLE IV

Quantitative chemical analyses of a sediment core (core GK) from the Kameni Islands, Santorini, Greece (after Puchelt, 1973)

Depth (in cm) below sediment/water interface	pH (%)	CO_2 (%)	Fe_2O_3 (%)	MnO (%)	CaO (%)	MgO (%)	TiO_2 (%)	P_2O_5 (%)	SiO_2 (%)	Na_2O (%)	K_2O (%)	Cl^- (%)	SO_3 (%)	Org. C (%)	Cu (ppm)	Pb (ppm)
0–10	5.9	13.10	46.2	0.08	1.35	2.19	0.17	0.57	23.65	5.25	0.36	4.50	0.86	0.82	12	<1
10–19	6.1	23.30	44.5	0.10	1.82	2.07	0.12	0.45	20.34	3.77	0.482	3.24	0.69	0.67	28	2
10–27	5.8	23.16	45.4	0.09	2.04	2.19	0.13	0.52	21.12	2.82	0.349	3.07	0.56	0.56	9	<1
27–30	5.6	25.4	42.9	0.09	1.76	1.96	0.18	0.53	21.29	3.64	0.325	4.02	1.07	n.d.	16	<1
30–38	5.7	15.40	44.2	0.10	2.22	2.17	0.23	0.48	24.10	3.10	0.301	4.24	1.54	0.74	15	<1
38–44	5.5	4.54	26.2	0.07	1.49	1.65	0.30	0.31	39.10	5.65	0.820	6.73	1.37	1.37	35	5
44–52	5.6	0.75	23.6	0.17	0.78	1.25	0.29	0.20	42.29	5.38	0.663	4.48	2.79	2.35	2	4
52–60	5.7	<0.10	27.2	0.19	0.42	0.39	0.29	0.19	43.39	5.38	0.325	6.13	3.17	3.16	1	1.5
60–70	5.6	1.62	22.4	0.18	0.45	0.78	0.11	0.16	43.44	4.65	0.277	6.46	3.66	2.66	<0.5	3.5
70–80	5.9	0.16	28.5	0.17	1.07	0.30	0.19	0.29	26.98	5.19	0.28	5.55	3.20	2.62	21	5
80–90	5.8	0.19	31.8	0.06	0.76	0.28	0.15	0.25	34.09	4.45	0.39	4.86	3.35	1.93	n.d.	n.d.
90–100	6.0	<0.10	25.0	0.07	0.76	1.04	0.24	0.22	41.60	5.73	0.615	8.46	2.74	0.86	0.5	n.d.
100–110	5.6	0.19	25.0	0.09	0.00	1.15	0.12	0.19	40.72	5.32	0.277	6.01	3.61	1.96	5	2
110–120	5.6	1.19	21.0	0.14	1.18	1.06	0.30	0.25	43.87	4.85	0.735	6.30	2.89	1.32	2	<1
120–130	5.6	<0.10	33.1	0.03	0.37	0.73	0.15	0.25	35.14	3.97	0.253	5.45	3.28	2.26	4	<1
130–140	5.6	<0.10	36.2	0.02	0.37	0.20	0.16	0.26	27.52	5.59	0.43	4.54	3.11	1.81	4	2
140–150	5.6	<0.10	38.0	0.05	0.39	0.65	0.30	0.31	29.07	4.78	0.313	7.18	2.68	1.63	6	<1
150–160	5.8	0.42	28.5	0.07	0.46	0.84	0.17	0.25	32.43	4.58	0.481	5.40	3.10	0.26	3	1
160–170	5.8	0.72	30.3	0.04	1.15	1.02	0.25	0.24	33.87	3.37	0.723	4.30	1.28	0.58	11	5

TABLE V

Composition of metal-rich subsurface brines from the Red Sea Deeps (after Brewer and Spencer, 1969), Salton Sea geothermal area (after White, 1968), and Matupi Harbor, New Britain, T.P.N.G. (after Ferguson and Lambert, 1972)

| | Red Sea Brines | | | Salton Sea Brines | | Matupi Harbor Thermal Waters | |
| | Discovery Deep | Atlantis II Deep | | | | | |
		56°C brine	44°C brine				
Fe (ppm)	0.27	88	0.20	2,290	2,000	108	97
Mn (ppm)	54.60	82	82	1,400	1,370	20	111
Zn (ppm)	0.77	5.40	0.15	540	500	1.35	0.05
Pb (ppm)	0.17	0.06	0.01	8	3	0.05	0.09
Cu (ppm)	0.08	0.26	0.02	102	80	0.06	0.05
Ca (ppm)	5,120	5,120	2,470	28,000	28,000	475	395
Mg (ppm)	810	----	----	54	10	700	1,340
Na (ppm)	93,050	92,600	46,900	50,400	53,000	1,930	13,600
K (ppm)	2,140	1,870	1,070	17,500	16,500	130	756
Cl (ppm)	155,300	156,030	80,040	155,000	155,000	1,760	22,500
SO$_4$ (ppm)	695	840	2,260	5.4	---	5,820	5,420
pH (20°C)	6.2	5.3	---	5.2	4.64	3.4	3.7
Temp. °C	44.9	56	44	340	300	44	65

TABLE VI

Variation of chemical analyses (in %) of Red Sea deposits (selected samples from the Atlantis II Deep and the Discovery Deep, after Bischoff, 1969)

Oxides	119K90	119K151	119K262	119K355	120K50	120K100	120K125	120K167	120K282
SiO_2	18.00	15.00	7.20	25.00	32.00	21.00	21.00	24.00	32.00
TiO_2	0.05	0.23	0.23	0.48	0.17	0.09	0.14	0.14	0.03
Al_2O_3	2.20	4.70	1.50	6.30	1.20	1.50	3.40	3.30	0.20
Fe_2O_3	38.00	8.30	57.00	4.50	38.00	32.00	42.00	39.00	46.00
Mn_3O_4	0.74	0.31	0.43	0.39	1.23	5.58	5.40	5.74	2.13
MgO	2.10	3.00	1.10	4.40	1.60	1.30	1.30	1.40	1.20
CaO	8.70	37.60	6.20	25.50	6.10	4.00	2.30	2.30	2.10
Na_2O	3.80	2.50	3.20	2.40	1.60	2.00	2.10	2.90	2.10
K_2O	0.40	0.69	0.18	0.74	0.35	0.46	0.60	1.10	0.73
ZnO	0.36	0.17	0.14	0.09	1.66	3.88	0.42	0.37	0.09
CuO	0.03	0.02	0.17	0.02	0.64	0.67	0.04	0.04	0.42
PbO	0.04	0.02	0.04	0.02	0.08	0.20	0.05	0.05	0.08

The Salton Sea hot brines have extremely high concentrations of metal ions and it seems to be evident that such "solutions", while ascending, become diluted and cooled, so that outpouring thermal springs of the Red Sea and Matupi types may be the submarine equivalents. They are only slightly acid due to small amounts of H_2S, CO_2, HCl or HF and their metal content seems to be related to the considerably concentrated chloride ions forming soluble metal complexes. The resulting sediment is a cyclically bedded sequence of colloidal precipitation products accumulated in submarine depressions or pools with a low rate of deposition (see Bischoff, 1969, p. 394: about 40 cm per thousand years). The process of precipitation may be the result of an increase in Eh and/or pH when the thermal springs enter into the sea water (see Ferguson and Lambert, 1972, p. 34). The variation of composition of the different layers (see Table VI) could be explained by fluctuating physico-chemical conditions and changes of the chemistry of the brines as demonstrated by Bischoff (1969, p. 395) in the case of the Red Sea deposits: "Today the brine is an iron hydroxide-silicate producer as evidenced by the iron-montmorillonite facies; in the past it has been an iron hydroxide, iron-manganese carbonate and base-metal sulfide producer as evidenced by the succession of facies."

As to the ore formation by thermal springs, it is likely that certain stratiform metal deposits could form under the described conditions, especially deposits of iron and manganese with variable amounts of base metals as, for instance, zinc, copper and lead. These conditions include percolating waters with significant metal contents and a sedimentary environment suitable for the separation and precipitation of metal ions or gels inclusive of a continuous sedimentation in submarine depressions or pools without an influx of detritus. However, for ore-grade enrichment to occur in this fashion it appears probable that the circulating fluids would have to leach considerable thicknesses of rocks over a long period of time. However, up to now, there is no example known of an actualistic mono-metal deposit as represented by the Paleozoic Lahn–Dill iron-ore type.

Similarities and differences between the Lahn–Dill type and other types of sedimentary iron formations

In the last decades, several concepts have also been published related to a volcanic–sedimentary source of the iron in the presently considered ores in comparison with other sedimentary iron ore deposits, even in cases where there is an absence of evidence for a contemporaneous volcanism. Formozova (1964) proposed explaining the genesis of all iron-formations by volcanic processes which are strata-bound within sedimentary sequences with intercalated volcanic rocks. She distinguished three types: (1) the banded iron-formation in Precambrian greenstone belts; (2) the chert-iron-formation with oolitic iron ores; and (3) the calcareous iron-formation of the Lahn–Dill type.

Harder (1963) restricted this generalization to itabirites with small amounts of alumina. But others (e.g., Epprecht, 1946; Cissarz, 1954, 1956; Jancovic, 1962) included certain chamosite, siderite and iron-manganese ore types (see also, Derry et al., 1964; Schultz, 1966; Egorov and Timofeieva, 1970; Shkolnik, 1970).

The majority of itabirites occur as banded iron ores in a miogeosynclinal sedimentary suite without close association to volcanism in time and space. There are, however, some examples of ore deposits occurring in Archean eugeosynclinal basins with contemporaneous greenstone volcanites (lavas and pyroclastics), as for instance the Algoma-type on the Canadian Shield (see discussion by Sangster/Scott, Chapter 6, Vol. 6, and, on Brazilian ores, by Eichler, this volume, Chapter 4), or parts of the Kola–Ukraine Belt in Russia. There is no evidence as to whether, in these cases, the iron and silica may be derived directly from a volcanic source or from sub-aquatic leaching of iron-rich volcanic rocks. Though it is beyond doubt that also in Precambrian time, syngenetic volcanic processes have supplied certain chemical compounds to the sedimentary environment, there are no geochemical and mineralogical indications left that this influence has been of great importance, as Eichler demonstrates.

The differences between the banded iron-formation and the Lahn–Dill-type ore are obvious: the extent and the volume of an itabiritic ore body exceed those of the Lahn–Dill deposits by several dimensions. They are typical basin sediments with a textural cyclicity, associated with coarse clastics, quartzites, conglomerates, dolomites, and black shales, rarely with pyroclastics and lavas. There is no evidence that itabirites are intimately bound to eruption centers of volcanic rises.

The same aspects may be cited in respect to oolitic iron-ore types. Based on the discovery of small occurrences of oolitic chamosite-thuringite particles in the eastern Sudetes, associated with a basin facies of a Lahn–Dill-type ore body, Cissarz (1954)

suggested this to be indicative of a volcano—sedimentary genesis of iron-silicate oolites in general. Cissarz applied his arguments especially to the Silurian chamosite-ore
deposits in southeastern Macedonia, Jugoslavia, though it is well-known that oolites
are characteristically rare in the Lahn—Dill ore types. Quite apart from this fact, there
is a great difference as to the chemical composition of the two ore types: most of the
oolitic oxide and silicate ores have considerably higher amounts of alumina and phosphorus as well as clastic debris which are, for example, quite common in the Minette
iron-stones.

    Another iron-ore type explained as being of volcano—sedimentary origin is that of
Vares in Bosnia, Jugoslavia (see Cissarz, 1956; Jankovic, 1962). The ore body represents a sequence of sideritic and hematitic ore with underlying layers of pyrite, sphalerite and chalcopyrite, embedded in a sedimentary succession of Upper Triassic limestones and cherty slates. The average chemical composition of this ore, as mentioned
by Jankovic, is: 33% Fe, 3% Mn and 18—20% SiO_2, with 0.06% Cu, 0.03% Sb, 0.04%
Zn, 0.04% Pb and average amounts of $BaSO_4$ of 2—3% (see also, Table VII). The ore
body is limited by faults so that there is no certainty about its syngenetic nature; possibly it has been formed by epigenetic metasomatic processes. Contemporaneous volcanites of considerable thickness have not been observed in the nearest vicinity of the mined
deposit.

    An interesting mineralization type is that of the iron-manganese deposit of the Gon-
zen in Sargans, Switzerland, which has been described by Epprecht (1946). Within
Upper Jurassic limestones several ore bodies of hematite, manganese and mixed layers
with textures similar to those of certain Lahn—Dill-type ores but with characteristic
chemical differences occur (see Table VIII). As there is no evidence of a contemporaneous volcanism, Epprecht thought of a telethermal origin for the ore-forming solutions, without citing a volcanic source of the metal ions. Schneiderhöhn (1955), however, took it as a typical example of volcano—sedimentary ore formation, as he did
also in respect to the Vares type.

    The layers of hematite ore within the lead- and zinc-bearing sedimentary suite of the
Lower Carboniferous of Tynagh, County Galway, Ireland (see Derry et al., 1964; Schultz,

TABLE VII

Chemical composition (in %) of selected ore types of the Vares deposit, Bosnia/Jugoslavia (after Jancovic,
1962)

Ore types	Fe	MnO	SiO_2	Al_2O_3	CaO	MgO
Blue grey hematite ore	49.50	3.02	10.85	3.90	2.39	0.51
Red hematite ore	39.35	8.90	5.91	4.90	8.35	1.74
Siderite ore	37.70	4.83	3.95	2.35	1.14	3.04
Barite-siderite ore	39.15	5.10	3.05	2.03	1.23	2.22
Limonite-siderite ore	47.80	2.87	8.13	4.79	0.28	0.36

TABLE VIII

Chemical composition (in %) of selected ore types of the Gonzen deposit, Sargans/Switzerland (after Epprecht, 1946)

Ore types	Fe	Mn	SiO$_2$	Al$_2$O$_3$	CaO	MgO
Hematite ore	57.41	0.26	7.40	0.35	1.20	0.85
Hematite ore	65.48	0.19	1.50	0.20	0.25	0.50
Hematite ore	55.45	0.19	13.50	0.75	3.50	1.45
Poor hematite ore	31.52	5.60	3.50	–	–	24.60
Poor hematite ore	41.12	0.85	4.35	–	–	17.20
Hausmannite ore	4.80	37.50	1.40	0.51	–	28.20
Hausmannite ore	1.90	53.72	1.05	0.45	–	16.90
Mn-carbonate ore	8.15	31.77	2.50	0.41	–	30.90
Fe–Mn ore	11.50	20.77	1.10	1.55	22.50	1.20

1966) and the iron-manganese ores of the Pb–Zn deposit of Atasu, Kazakhstan, Russia seem to be quite similar to the Gonzen-type deposit.

In spite of some lithological, sedimentological and geochemical similarities between the above-mentioned sedimentary deposit types and the Lahn–Dill iron-ore type, there exist considerable differences. Whether volcanic agents participated in the formation of these deposits or not, the most striking fact is that there is no evidence of an intimate relation between volcanic activity and ore sediment precipitation near to eruption centers. The sedimentary environment of these deposits is that of a shallow-marine shelf rather than an eugeosynclinal trough, and the deposition of ore sediments took place in large but restricted basins. Apart from this, it should be stressed, the banded itabiritic formation and the non-banded oolitic deposits are extensively distributed in space and time, while the other types, including the Lahn–Dill type, seem to be metallogenetic and non-corresponding rarities.

The relation of volcano–sedimentary iron ores to other syngenetic metal mineralizations in geosynclinal environments

When Schneiderhöhn started to develop his global genetic concept (1941), he based it on the geosyncline theory of Stille (1940). Though there could rise some doubt, today, about the general validity of this theory, it may still serve as a conceptual model for the classification of subsiding and stable blocks within a vast sedimentation area of high tectonic and magmatic mobility. The main phase of syngenetic ore formation in a geosynclinal environment is that of the initial magmatic period (sensu Stille) which includes the generative and development stages (sensu Aubouin). During this period ophiolitic volcanites poured out onto the sea floor, forming volcanic build-ups around the eruption centers or along eruption fissures.

The volcano–sedimentary iron ores of the Lahn–Dill type have been interpreted as being the most characteristic mineralizations of this phase of geosynclinal develop- ment, because of their regional restriction to the volcanic rises and the ubiquitous in- timate interrelationship between volcanism and sedimentation during the ore-forming process. This concept has been generally accepted, especially by Borchert (1957, 1960) and Amstutz (1959) who have in recent years amplified and re-classified the group of related rock and ore types.

Schneiderhöhn (1955) cited three groups of marine exhalative–sedimentary ore deposits: apart from that of Lahn–Dill-type, he mentioned the "exhalative–sedimen- tary manganese" (see Chapter 9 by Roy, this volume) and the "exhalative–sedimentary sulphide ores" (see, e.g., Chapter 5 by Sangster/Scott, Vol. 6), some itabiritic and other iron ores, the genesis as well as the geology of which is still under discussion (see above). Borchert (1957, p. 569) explained the relationship between the different geosynclinal mineralizations by changing depths of the juvenile "basaltic" magma centers beneath the sea floor. The Lahn–Dill-type iron ores, the poly-sulphide types of Meggen and Rammels- berg and Ergani Maden (Turkey) and the manganese-chert formation of the Alps are referred to one and the same genetic realm with decreasing magmatic and structural mobility: the Lahn–Dill-type formed during the most mobile geosynclinal phase and the manganese-chert formation originated during a relatively late and quiet period with a deep-seated magmatic source. Amstutz (1959) gave a more descriptive classification of the initial magmatic mineralizations using the term "spilitic deposits": "sulpho-spilitic deposits" with sulphide metal occurrences, "oxy-spilitic-deposits" with oxides of iron and titanium and "spilitic deposits of native metals". Rösler (1964) postulated the definition of an "enlarged Lahn–Dill type" including all syngenetic marine mineralizations related more or less directly to contemporaneous volcanic or generally magmatic processes. The "ore solutions" of most of the deposits in question would have to be deduced from frequently unknown intrusive magmas and even from fictitious, laterally very remote, sources (Rosler 1964, p. 451).

Without discussing this complex problem to the fullest deserved extent, some exam- ples of metal mineralizations will be given cited by several authors as being of volcano– sedimentary origin (apart from that already mentioned):

(1) Iron- and copper-sulphide deposits within or near spilitic sequences (e.g., occur- rences in Norway, the Mediterranean area, the Urals, western Tasmania and the Lake Superior district; see Oftedahl, 1958; Amstutz, 1959; Anger, 1966; among others).

(2) Poly-metallic sulphide deposits within sedimentary sequences without significant contemporaneous volcanites (e.g., strata-bound lead–zinc–copper deposits of the north- ern Caucasus, the Altai Mountains, the Mount Isa in Queensland and the Kupferschiefer of Central Europe as well as lead–zinc occurrences of the eastern Alps and Silesia; see Stanton, 1958; Amstutz, 1959; Smirnov, 1960; Schneider, 1964; among others).

(3) Sulphide deposits with gold–pyrite mineralizations in basic volcanites (e.g., oc- currences on the Canadian Shield, the Japanese Kuroko-type, and the Gold Coast, see Amstutz, 1959).

(4) Iron-oxide deposits as intrusive equivalents (e.g., the Kiruna ore body in northern Sweden, the Mount Iron and Pea Ridge in Missouri and the magmatite flow of El Laco in Chile; see Amstutz, 1959).

(5) Manganese-ore occurrences, often associated with banded iron-ore formations (e.g., Kriwoi Rog in Russia, Urucúm near Corumbá/Brazil and Cerro Bolivar in Venezuela; see Amstutz, 1959, and Chapter 9 by Roy, this volume).

Whatever the reason and purpose of such a global and undifferentiated generalization may be, among these examples only the Lahn–Dill-type ores and, at most, some sulphidic metal deposits are undoubtedly of geosynclinal origin and syngenetically "volcanic", i.e., integrated into volcanic processes with eruptions of lavas and tuffs of the geosynclinal realm sensu stricto. However, continuous genetic transitions between these mineralization types were not known, until recently (see, for example, Chapter 4 by Gilmour, Vol. 1). Even in the cases of the polysulphide–barite deposits of Meggen and Rammelsberg, which are penecontemporaneous with the iron-ore horizons of the Lahn–Dill area (but without the significant eruptive rocks), there is no evidence of a missing link to the volcano–sedimentary iron-ore type, neither with respect to the geotectonic position and geological environment nor to the chemical and mineralogical composition.

At the present, one has to be aware of the possibility that there is a general tendency to unquestionably accept the volcanic source of metal ions rather than to establish criteria that would assist in proving this hypothesis. The geosynclinal model of syngenetic volcanic ore formation often regarded to be an omnivalent concept which permits of citing volcanism as a genetic "deux ex machina" whenever desired or necessary in order to explain extraordinary metal concentrations within marine sedimentary sequences. There is no doubt, however, that the differences between the phenomena of syn-volcanic ore formation and epi-volcanic metal enrichment in percolating waters, with or without late-volcanic additives, are metallogenetic criteria of the first order. The sedimentary environment of ore deposition, the facies of the intercalating sediments and the geotectonic position of the ore-bearing rock units should all be integrated into the genetic model, in addition to geochemical, mineralogical and textural aspects. Whether the Lahn–Dill-type ore formation may serve as a model for all strata-bound metal deposits in a geosynclinal or generally marine environment, or has to be regarded as a "mineralogical rarity", seems to be of subordinate importance, though it should not be ignored that it is the most characteristic one as to interrelationship between volcanism, sedimentation and ore formation under geosynclinal conditions. In this respect, it is feasible that the majority of the other metal deposits cited above have been formed by thermal waters as exemplified by, for example, the recent occurrences of the Red Sea and the Salton Sea.

Possible source of iron and silica in ophiolitic geosynclinal volcanism

One of the critical aspects of genetic discussions about the Lahn–Dill deposit type is that of the source of iron and silica in basic volcanics belonging to the ophiolitic association. The overwhelming majority of iron ores in the Central European Variscan area is bound to tuffs and lavas of spilitic to diabasic composition, though incrustations and vein-fillings of hematite are also known from keratophyric rocks (see Lehmann, 1941).

Without entering into a fundamental discussion about the complex spilite-diabase problem, some general statements can be made. Among the basic rocks encountered in the Variscan geosynclines of Central Europe, four main types of rocks may be distinguished (see Table IX):

(1) Primary spilites or "weilburgites" (sensu Lehmann, 1941) with "continuously varied ratios and high totals of K_2O and Na_2O, but low content in CaO" (Lehmann, 1972, p. 249) and primary albite and/or orthoclase with carbonate (up to 30%, rarely more), chlorite and a "general deficiency in epidote, pumpellyite and prehnite" (Lehmann in Amstutz, 1974, p. 30).

(2) Secondary spilites with albitized feldspar, chloritized pyroxene, epidote and mostly decomposed amphibole (rarely present).

(3) Diabases with ("basaltic") An-contents in the plagioclase of between 20% and 30% in intrusive types or up to 50% in extrusive types, usually in ophitic intergrowths with pyroxene or its chloritized derivates.

(4) Picrites as ultrafemic intrusive equivalents of nearly peridotitic composition.

Though the genesis of these rock types with "magmatic textures" and "metamorphic paragenesis" gave rise to a lot of controversial theories (see contributions in Amstutz, 1974), nearly all authors well acquainted with the detailed geologic and petrographic features of the Variscan volcanites in eugeosynclinal areas of Central Europe agree on a primary magmatic origin of these rock types without significant epigenetic alterations

TABLE IX

Composition (in %) of spilites, diabases and picrites from the Lahn–Dill area (after Lehmann, 1972)

Basic rocks	Locali-ties	Si	Al	Fe^{3+}	Fe^{2+}	Mg	Ca	Na + K	Ti	CO_2
Weilburgites	1	48.57	18.62	1.87	4.97	5.43	3.03	14.31	2.22	1.36
	2	50.90	14.67	5.55	5.25	3.65	5.15	12.78	1.19	nil
	3	42.59	18.35	1.51	8.34	5.59	9.21	11.70	2.17	5.00
Diabases	4	36.55	19.83	2.35	8.46	18.34	7.37	4.86	1.84	nil
	5	49.77	14.32	2.97	8.72	3.62	6.28	11.24	2.12	nil
	6	45.67	18.53	2.22	7.35	13.48	6.12	4.92	1.44	0.41
Picrites	7	39.13	7.66	2.71	9.58	34.24	3.75	1.68	0.31	>0.1
	8	37.29	6.83	2.32	8.80	38.74	4.61	0.81	0.46	nil

Localities: 1 = Northwest of Ernsthausen/Lahn; 2 = road Niederbiel–Leun/Lahn; 3 = Schellhofs Kopf/ Lahn; 4 = Königszug mine/Dill; 5 = Wasenbach valley/Dill; 6 = east of Schelder Hütte/Dill; 7 = south of Tiefenbach/Lahn; 8 = Frechenhausen--Bottenhorn/Dill.

(for further details, see Lehmann, 1941; Barth, 1960; Rösler, 1960; Hentschel, 1960). As a striking example, Hentschel described a drill-hole core from the southern Lahn syncline which contained a complete intrusive suite of spilitic and diabasic rock varieties in continuous transition. A calculation of the mean normative mineral composition of this sill results in the following values (%) (Quade, 1970, p. 51):

quartz	0.64
orthoclase	4.89
albite	21.98
anorthite	17.64
oligoclase	13.35
orthopyroxene	19.99
diopside	10.96
hypersthene	12.55
magnetite	4.56
ilmenite	2.40
pyrite	0.43
apatite	0.35
calcite	1.28
H_2O	5.50

In spite of the differentiation into considerably differing rock types, these values demonstrate that the sill as a total has the mean composition of basalts with fem = 54.60 and sal/fem = 0.55 and an An-content in the plagioclase of 46%. Comparable results have also been obtained by Rösler (1960).

The concept of deducing the ophiolitic spilite-diabase association from a primary "basaltic" magma has been approved by several authors and is one of the criteria for the initial magmatic period in terms of the geosyncline theory of Stille (1940); see Borchert, 1957, 1960; Aubouin, 1965. The obvious differentiation and spilitization (albitization, chloritization) of the magma, due to the influence of water and alkalis, may occur prior to the development of extrusive lavas and intrusive sills, as demonstrated by Lehmann (1972), or when pouring out onto the sea floor or intruding into water-filled sediments. "Transformation of originally dry basaltic magma as a result of the taking up of water and alkalis from the adjacent rocks can occur during the upsurge of the magma through tectonic fissures or even in the upper part of the magmatic chamber. If the magma was affected by such a transformation before starting crystallization or during its initial phases, the resulting magma is the same as if the rock originated from a primary differentiation from the original magma" (Fiala in Amstutz, 1974, p. 18). But, such a "hydro-magma" can also form when an effusive submarine lava flow is cooling rapidly at its marginal contacts with the sea water and floor, while its still liquid interior reacts with water entering through fissures and pores (for further details, see Fiala).

As to the formation of volcano–sedimentary iron ores, it is of great importance that spilitic tuffs are the most abundant volcanic rock type in the eugeosynclinal troughs and that these tuffs are accumulated in thick sequences with small intercalations of lava bodies near to local eruption centers or fissures, thus forming volcanic rises. Due to high amounts of volatiles in the "spilitic" magma, probably mixed with hot water and steam, the main phase of volcanism has been specifically explosive. "Supply in volatiles from outside and/or release of the outer pressure (orogenic effect) gave rise to ascent, and sudden upward transport is to be concluded from the abundance of pyroclastics interspersed with a multitude of relatively small bodies of weilburgite" (Lehmann, 1972, p. 267).

The iron-ore "solutions" poured out when the tuff eruption decreased or ended, but a certain controversy still exists as to the temperature and composition of the metal-bearing gases or liquids. The geological features of the areas of accumulation indicate that the influence of these volcanic phases on the sedimentary environment has been low: limestone sedimentation could continue even near to the eruption centers and calcitic fossils are encountered within the iron-ore sequences. Thus, the pH and Eh values must have been almost the same as those of sea water. High-temperature acid exhalations, as proposed by Harbort (1903) and Schneiderhöhn (1941), are unlikely. Therefore, Hentschel (1960) and Rösler (1962) suggested that circulating hot ("pseudo-hydrothermal") waters enriched in iron and silica by wall-rock leaching could have been the ore solutions, mobilized and heated by intrusive spilite-diabase bodies. But:

(1) most of the intrusives are rather younger than the iron-ore horizons;

(2) hundreds of meters of drill holes into the depositional areas have proved that the volcanic rocks predominantly intruded into basinal sedimentary sequences, rarely into the volcanic rises;

(3) the release of heat and degassing of intrusives is a relatively short and non-recurring process, but the intercalating sediment layers within the ore sequences make it likely that the ore "solutions" poured out with a certain cyclicity;

(4) there is no evidence of decomposition and leaching nor of a loss of iron and silica in the tuff sequences beneath or in the vicinity of iron-ore deposits, as is evidenced by drill holes;

(5) even if pseudo-hydrothermal phases would be accepted, there is no explanation given as to why such dilute thermal waters should not percolate into the basins, but ascend into the volcanic rises of greatest rock thicknesses, thus giving rise to ore deposition in the bathymetric zone of strongest water agitation.

Though the lack of geochemical indications may be regarded as the weak point in this concept, the only possible conclusion to be drawn from all information given up to now is to see an intimate connection between spilitization, tuff eruption and ore formation. There is no doubt that the physico-chemical conditions of the sedimentary ore accumulation have been extraordinary. High amounts of iron and silica, probably in a colloidal state, have to be accepted for the ore "solutions", as well as a high viscosity of the first precipitates, which must have been able to resist strong water agitation along the tops of the volcanic rises. The erosion and redeposition occurring under sedimentary influences are of secondary importance as to the principal genetic problem.

Lehmann (1972) discussed the possibility of an enrichment of iron within the "spilitic" magma chamber and pointed out that, even in spite of the separation of iron compounds from the *basic* magma, the resulting volcanic rocks are still comparatively rich in iron. The contradictory theory of Oftedahl (1958) that significant iron concentrations could only be affiliated to *acid* eruptives is not maintainable since the magnetite flow of El Laco, Chile, has been discovered. Some aspects of the Misi iron-ore province in northern Finland (Nuutilainen: for reference, see Lehmann, 1972, p. 267) may be of interest in this respect: magnetite ore bodies, poor in titanium and phosphorous, are embedded in quartzite, but it is noteworthy that the occurrence is in a magmatic province of plutonic rocks comprising amphibolite, gabbro, albite-gabbro, and albitite. Though the albitite amount is less than 10% of the gabbro, it may be concluded "that the albite gabbros and albitites are plutonic equivalents to the volcanic spilites and keratophyres" (Nuutilainen). Whether the Lahn–Dill-type iron ores are related to spilitic-diabasic associations only or, as Lehmann (1972) supposed, to spilitic-diabasic-keratophyric associations, may be of interest, but cannot be a matter of discussion, as there is no evidence of a continuous transition between spilites and keratophyres nor a significant iron-ore concentration in keratophyric rocks occurring in the described Paleozoic areas.

CONCLUSIONS

(1) The volcano–sedimentary Lahn–Dill type of iron ores is regarded as a model of syngenetic geosynclinal ore formation.

(2) The Lahn–Dill-type iron ores are represented by a group of predominantly hematite accumulations which occur in the Devonian and Lower Carboniferous of the Central European Variscan system, but which are also known from other areas.

(3) The small individual ore bodies form strata-bound layers at the top of volcanic rises of thick masses of spilitic tuffs and lavas which are affiliated to eugeosynclinal furrows or troughs. The ore horizons are underlain by volcanites and overlain by pelagic limestones or shales. Transgression of ore sediments on nearby reef complexes have also been observed.

(4) The ore sequences are well bedded and internally laminated, showing features of rapid precipitation, erosion, transport, and redeposition. A general tendency exists in each deposit for silica-rich deposits to occur at the bottom and calcareous ones at the top, with *horizontal* stratigraphic transitions from the upper part of volcanic build-ups (= eruption centers) to calcareous accumulations along the slopes.

(5) The iron minerals may be related to a primary and a secondary ore facies and their origin to the influence of volcanic and sedimentary processes. The minerals recorded include hematite, specularite, magnetite, siderite, iron chlorite, stilpnomelane, and melnikovite–pyrite. Quartz, calcite, dolomite, and chlorite are the main accessory components. Clastic fragments, pyroclastic particles, limestones lenses and argillaceous

bands are common impurities. Small-scale variation of ore facies and ore quality is a typical feature of this type.

(6) As to the genetic problem of this ore type, actualistic examples of formation of iron-rich sediments in volcanic environments and similarities with other iron formations and marine metal deposits are discussed. The volcano–sedimentary iron ores are a typical, but not a representative, example of metal precipitates derived from active volcanism and deposited under marine conditions.

A differentiated and spilitized "basaltic" magma enriched in water has to be considered as a source for the iron and silica. The ascending ore "solution" is likely to be a colloidal system rich in iron and silica rather than a dispersal ionic solution. The primary ore sediment seems to have been a rapidly precipitated gelationous mud of high viscosity, which was able to resist the strong waves and currents along the top of the volcanic rises.

ACKNOWLEDGEMENT

This paper is an abstract of a "Habilitationsschrift" presented at the Technical University of Clausthal. The author wishes to thank the Deutsche Forschungsgemeinschaft which supported the work by a grant.

REFERENCES

Ahlburg, J., 1917. Über die Eisenerze und Eisen-Manganerze des Lahngebietes und ihre Beziehungen zu Eruptivgesteinen. *Z. Prakt. Geol.*, 25: 29–38; 49–56.

Albrecht, F., 1952. *Zur Geochemie der oxydischen Eisenerze, insbesondere des Typus Lahn–Dill.* Dissertation Univ. München (unpublished).

Amstutz, G.C., 1959. Syngenese und Epigenese in Petrographie und Lagerstättenkunde. *Schweiz. Mineral. Petrogr. Mitt.*, 39: 1–84.

Amstutz, G.C. (Editor), 1964. *Sedimentology and Ore Genesis. Develop. Sedimentol.* Elsevier, Amsterdam, 184 pp.

Amstutz, G.C. (Editor), 1974. *Spilites and Spilitic Rocks.* Springer, Heidelberg, 482 pp.

Amstutz, G.C. and Bernard, A.J. (Editors), 1973. *Ores in Sediments.* Springer, Heidelberg, 350 pp.

Anger, G., 1966. Die genetischen Zusammenhänge zwischen deutschen und norwegischen Schwefel-kieslagerstätten unter besonderer Berücksichtigung der Ergebnisse von Schwefelisotopen-Untersuchungen. *Clausthaler Hefte Lagerstättenk. Geochem. Miner. Rohst.*, 3: 115 pp.

Aubouin, J., 1965. *Geosynclines.* Elsevier, Amsterdam, 335 pp.

Barth, V., 1960. Devonský vulkanismus sternberskohornobenesovskeho pasma v Nizkem Jeseniku. *Acta Mineral. Palack. Olomuc.*, 1: 1–131.

Barth, V., 1966. The initial volcanism in the Devonian of Moravia. In: *Paleovolcanites of the Bohemian Massif*, pp. 115–125.

Behrend, F., 1934. Rezenter Vulkanismus und die Bildung von Eisenerzen. *Z. Dtsch. Geol. Ges.*, 86: 360–367.

Bischoff, J.L., 1969. Red Sea geothermal brine deposits: their mineralogy, chemistry, and genesis. In: E.T. Degens and D.A. Ross (Editors), *Hot Brines and Recent Heavy-Metal Deposits in the Red Sea.* Springer, Berlin/Heidelberg/New York, pp. 368–406.

Bonatti, E., Honnorez, J. and Joensu, O., 1971. Submarine iron deposits from the Mediterranean Sea. (Paper presented at the 8th Int. Sedimentol. Congr., Heidelberg, 1971.)

Borchert, H., 1957. Der initiale Magmatismus und die zugehörigen Lagerstätten. Neues Jahrb. Mineral. Abh., 91: 541–572.

Borchert, H., 1960. Geosynklinale Lagerstätten, was dazu gehört und was nicht dazu gehört, sowie deren Beziehungen zu Geotektonik und Magmatismus. Freiberg. Forschungsh. C, 79: 7–61.

Boström, K., 1970. Submarine volcanism as a source for iron. Earth Planet. Sci. Lett., 9: 348–354.

Bottke, H., 1962. Der Roteisenstein des östlichen Sauerlands und seine Beziehungen zur Stratigraphie und Fazies des Oberen Givets und der Adorf-Stufe. Roemeriana, 6: 15–96.

Bottke, H., 1965. Die exhalativ–sedimentären devonischen Roteisensteinlagerstätten des Ostsauerlandes. Geol. Jahrb., Beih., 63: 147 pp.

Brause, H., Gotte, W. and Douffet, H., 1968. Gesetzmässigkeiten in der saxothuringischen Zone des Variszikums und ihre Beziehungen zu älteren Orogenen. Rep. 23rd Int. Geol. Congr., 3: 199–212.

Brewer, P.G. and Spencer, D.W., 1969. A note on the chemical composition of the Red Sea brines. In: E.T. Degens and D.A. Ross (Editors), Hot Brines and Recent Heavy-Metal Deposits in the Red Sea. Springer, Berlin/Heidelberg, New York, pp. 174–179.

Butuzova, G.Y., 1966. Iron-ore sediments of the fumarole field of the Santorini volcano, their composition and origin. Dokl. Akad. Sci. U.S.S.R., Earth Sci. Sect., 168: 215–217.

Butuzova, G.Y., 1968. Recent volcano–sedimentary iron-ore process in the Santorini volcano-caldera (Aegean Sea) and its effect on the geochemistry of sediments. Acad. Sci. U.S.S.R., Geol. Inst. Trans., 194: 215–217.

Cissarz, A., 1924. Mineralogisch-mikroskopische Untersuchung der Erze und Nebengesteine des Roteisensteinlagers der Grube Maria bei Braunfels a.d. Lahn. Mitt. Kaiser-Wilhelm Inst. Eisenforsch. Düsseldorf, 5: 109–125.

Cissarz, A., 1954. Zur Petrographie und Genesis südwestmazedonischer Eisensilikatlagerstätten. Bull. Serv. Geol. Geophys. Serbie, 11.

Cissarz, A., 1956. Lagerstätten und Lagerstättenbildung in Jugoslavien in ihren Beziehungen zu Vulkanismus und Geotektonik. Razpr. Zav. Geol. Geoliz. Istraz. Srbije, 6 (6).

Dave, A.S., 1963. Paragenetischer und geochemischer Aufbau der Eisenerzlagerstätte Braunesumpf bei Hüttenrode im Harz. Freiberg. Forschungsh. C, 146: 110 pp.

Davidson, C.F., 1964. Uniformitarianism and ore genesis. Min. Mag., 1964: 1–12.

Degens, E.T. and Ross, D.A. (Editors), 1969. Hot Brines and Recent Heavy-Metal Deposits in the Red Sea. Springer, Heidelberg, 612 pp.

Denckewitz, R., 1952. Verbandsverhältnisse und Gefügeanalyse von Erz und Nebengestein des Eisensteinvorkommens Lindenberg und Südwestrand der Lahnmulde. Hess. Lagerstättenarch., 2: 1–87.

Derry, D.R., Clark, G. and Gillat, N., 1964. The Northgate base-metal deposit at Tynagh, County Galway, Ireland. Econ. Geol., 59: 1622.

Dvorak, J. and Paproth, E., 1969. Über die Position und die Tektogenese des Rhenoherzynikums und des Sudetikums in den mitteleuropäischen Variszide. Neues Jahrb. Geol. Paläontol. Monatsh., 2: 65–88.

Egorov, E.W. and Timofeieva, M.W., 1970. Effusive iron-silica formations and iron deposits of the Maly Khingan. Proc. Kiev Symp., UNESCO, Earth. Sci., 9: 181–185.

Ehrenberg, H., Pilger, A. and Schröder, F., 1954. Das Schwefelkies–Zinkblende–Schwerspatlager von Meggen (Westfalen). Geol. Jahrb., Beih., 12.

Epprecht, W., 1946. Die Eisen- und Manganerze des Gonzen. Beitr. Geol. Schweiz, Geotech. Ser., 24.

Ferguson, J. and Lambert, I.B., 1972. Volcanic exhalations and metal enrichment at Matupi Harbor, New Britain, T.P.N.G. Econ. Geol., 67: 25–37.

Formozova, L.N., 1964. Vergleichende Charakteristik der effusivsedimentären Eisenerzformation. Ber. Geol. Ges. D.D.R., 9 (4/5): 479–485.

Gaertner, H.R., 1942. Die geologische Stellung der oberdevonischen Eisenerzlager in Thüringen und Oberfranken. Jahrb. Reichsstelle Bodenforsch., 62: 81–108.

Garrels, C.D. and Christ, Ch.L., 1965. *Solutions, Minerals, and Equilibria.* Harper and Row, New York, N.Y., 450 pp.

Götz, H., 1937. Die Keratophyre der Lahnmulde. *Mineral. Petrogr. Mitt.,* 49: 168–215.

Goodwin, A.M., 1973. Archean iron-formations and tectonic basins of the Canadian Shield. *Econ. Geol.,* 68: 915–933.

Gräbe, R., 1956. Ausbildung und Entstehung der oberdevonischen Roteisenerze und ihre Nebengesteine im Schleizer Trog. *Ber. Geol. Ges. D.D.R.,* 1: 155–198.

Gräbe, R., 1962. Beziehungen zwischen der tektonischen und faziellen Entwicklung des Oberdevons und Unterkarbons sowie zur Genese der Eisenerze vom Lahn–Dill Typus am NW-Rand des Bergaer Sattels (Thüringisches Schiefergebirge). *Freiberg. Forschungsh., C,* 140.

Griggs, R.E., 1922. *The Valley of the 10000 Smokes.* Nat. Geogr. Soc., London, 340 pp.

Harbort, E., 1903. Zur Frage der Entstehung gewisser devonischer Roteisenlagerstätten. *Neues Jahrb. Mineral. Geol. Paläontol.,* 1: 179–192.

Harder, H., 1954. Beiträge zur Petrographie und Genese der Hämatiterze des Lahn–Dill-Gebietes. *Heidelb. Beitr. Mineral. Petrogr.,* 4: 54–66.

Harder, H., 1960. Rezente submarine vulkanische Eisenausscheidungen von Santorin, Griechenland. *Fortschr. Mineral.,* 38 (2): 187–189.

Harder, H., 1963. Zur Diskussion über die Entstehung der Quarzbändererze (Itabirite). *Neues Jahrb. Mineral. Monatsh.,* 1963: 303–314.

Harder, H., 1964. Untersuchungen rezenter vulkanischer Eisenausscheidung zur Klärung der Erze vom Lahn–Dill Typus. *Ber. Geol. Ges. D.D.R.,* 9 (4/5): 439–623.

Harder, H., 1964. Geochemische Unterscheidung genetisch verschiedener marin-sedimentärer Eisenerzlagerstätten. *Ber. Geol. Ges. D.D.R.,* 9 (4/5) 475–478.

Harrassowitz, H., 1927. Anchimetamorphose, das Gebiet zwischen Oberflächen- und Tiefenumwandlung der Erdrinde. *Ber. Oberhess. Ges. Natur- Heilk. Giessen,* 12: 9–15.

Hegemann, R., 1948. Über sedimentäre Lagerstätten mit submariner vulkanischer Stoffzufuhr. *Fortschr. Mineral.,* 27: 54–55.

Henningsen, D., 1963. Zur Herkunft und Unterscheidung der sandigen Gesteine am Südostrand des Rheinischen Schiefergebirges. *Neues Jahrb. Geol. Paläontol. Monatsh.,* 2: 49–67.

Henningsen, D., 1966. Die paläozoischen Grauwacken bei Giessen und ihre Fortzetzung unter der südlichen Hessischen Senke. *Ber. Oberhess. Ges. Natur- Heilk., Giessen, Naturwiss. Abt.,* 34: 19–31.

Hentschel, H., 1960. Zur Frage der Bildung der Eisenerze vom Lahn–Dill Typ. *Freiberg. Forschungsh., C,* 79: 82–105.

Hesemann, J., 1927. Die devonischen Eisenerze des Mittelharzes. *Abh. Prakt. Geol. Bergwirtsch. lehre,* 10.

Jankovic, S., 1962. Rudna lezista, metalogenetske epohe imetalogenetska produrcja gvozdija u Jugoslaviji. *Rudarski Glasn.,* 4: 68–97.

Karrenberg, H. and Quitzow, H.W., 1942. Die Erze des schlesischmährischen Devons. *Arch. Lagerstättenforsch.,* 75: 155–166.

Kegel, W., 1923. Zur Kenntnis der devonischen Eisenerzlager in der südlichen Lahnmulde. *Z. Prakt. Geol.,* 31: 1–6; 20–29; 36–41.

Kegel, W., 1934. Geologie der Dillmulde. *Abh. Preuss. Geol. Landesamt, Neue Folge,* 160.

Knauer, E., 1960. Quantitativ-mineralogisch-petrographische Untersuchungen an den mitteldevonischen Roteisenerzen vom Büchenberg bei Elbingerode im Harz. *Geologie, Beih.,* 9 (29).

Kraume, E. and co-workers, 1955. Die Erzlager des Rammelsberges bei Goslar. *Geol. Jahrb., Beih.,* 118.

Krauskopf, K.B., 1957. Separation of manganese from iron in sedimentary processes. *Geochim. Cosmochim. Acta,* 12: 61–84.

Krebs, W., 1960. Stratigraphie, Vulkanismus und Fazies des Oberdevons zwischen Donsbach und Hirzenhain (Rheinisches Schiefergebirge, Dill–Mulde). *Abh. Hess. Landesamt Bodenforsch.,* 33.

Krebs, W., 1968. Zur Frage der bretonischen Faltung im östlichen Rhenoherzynikum. *Geotekton. Forsch.*, 28: 1–71.

Lange, H., 1957. Paragenetische und genetische Untersuchungen an der Schwefelkieslagerstätte "Einheit" bei Elbingerode (Harz), *Freiberg, Forschungsh., C,* 33.

Lehmann, E., 1941. *Eruptivgesteine und Eisenerze im Mittel- und Oberdevon der Lahnmulde.* Techn.-Pädagog. Verlag Scharfes, Wetzlar, 391 pp.

Lehmann, E., 1972. On the source of the iron in the Lahn–Dill deposits. *Miner. Deposita,* 7: 247–270.

Lippert, H.J., 1951. Zur Gesteins- und Lagerstättenbildung in Roteisensteingruben des östlichen Dill-Gebietes. *Abh. Senckenberg. Naturforsch. Ges.,* 485: 1–30.

Lippert, H.J., 1953. Bericht über eine Studienfahrt nach Santorin in der südlichen Ägäis. *Z. Dtsch. Geol. Ges.,* 105: 586–587.

Lotz, H., 1902. Über die Dillenburger Rot- und Magneteisenerze. *Z. Dtsch. Geol. Ges.,* 54: 139–142.

Maucher, A., 1957. Die Deutung des primären Stoffbestandes der kalkalpinen Pb–Zn-Lagerstätten als syngenetisch-sedimentäre Bildung. *Berg- Hüttenmänn. Monatsh. Montau. Hochsch. Leoben,* 102: 226–229.

Meischner, D., 1971. Clastic sedimentation in the Variscan geosyncline east of the River Rhine. *8th. Int. Sedimentol. Congr., Sedimentol. Parts Centr. Europe, Guidebook,* pp. 9–43.

Michels, Fr., 1921. Das Roteisensteinvorkommen der Grube "Neuelust" bei Nanzenbach (Dillkreis). *Senckenbergiana,* 3 (3/4).

Naboko, S.I., 1959. Volcanic exhalations and products of their reactions as exemplified by the Kamchatka–Kuriles volcanoes. *Bull. Volc., Ser. II,* 20: 121–136.

Nieder, R., 1931. Zusammenhang zwischen Tektonik und Lagerausbildung in Roteisensteinlagern an der Lahn. *Arch. Lagerstättenforsch.,* 51.

Oftedahl, Chr., 1958. A theory of exhalative–sedimentary ores. *Geol. Fören Stockh. Förhandl.,* (80) 1: 1–19.

Pauly, E., 1958. Das Devon der südwestlichen Lahnmulde und ihrer Randgebiete. *Abh. Hess. Landesamt Bodenforsch.,* 25.

Pilger, A., 1951. Die tektonischen Probleme des initialen Magmatismus. *Geol. Jahrb.,* 65: 1–30.

Pilger, A., 1957. Über den Untergrund des Rheinischen Schiefergebirges. *Geol. Rundsch.,* 46: 197–212.

Puchelt, H., 1973. Recent iron sediment formation at the Kameni Islands, Santorini (Greece). In: G.C. Amstutz and A.J. Bernard (Editors), *Ores in Sediments.* Springer, Heidelberg, pp. 227–245.

Quade, H., 1963. *Entstehung und Ausbildung der Roteisensteinlagerstätte Eisenfeld bei Philippstein im Oberlahnkreis.* Thesis, Univ. Giessen, 246 pp.

Quade, H., 1965. Zur paläogeographischen Entwicklung des Mittel- und Oberdevons im Bereich der Lagerstätte Eisenfeld. *Notizbl. Hess. Landesamt Bodenforsch.,* 93: 207–228.

Quade, H., 1968. *Die Entwicklung des initialen Geosynklinalmagmatismus und die Bildung der exhalativ–sedimentären Eisenerzlagerstätten im mitteleuropäischen Variszikum.* Habilitationsschrift, Univ. Clausthal-Zellerfeld, 318 pp.

Quade, H., 1970. Der Bildungsraum und die genetische Problematik der vulkano-sedimentären Eisenerze. *Clausthaler Hefte Lagerstättenk. Geochem. Miner. Rohst.,* 9: 27–65.

Richter, H., 1930. Beitrag zur geologischen Kenntnis der Lahn–Dillmulde mit besonderer Berücksichtigung der Schalsteine, Diabase und Roteisenerze. *Z. Int. Bergwirtsch. Bergtech.,* 23: 65–80; 85–101.

Riemann, W., 1894. Das Vorkommen der devonischen Eisen- und Manganerze in Nassau. *Z. Prakt. Geol.,* 2: 50–57.

Rietschel, S., 1966. Die Geologie des mittleren Lahntroges. *Abh. Senckenb. Naturforsch. Ges.,* 509: 58 pp.

Rippel, G., 1953. Räumliche und zeitliche Gliederung des Keratophyrvulkanismus im Sauerland. *Geol. Jahrb.,* 68: 401–456.

Rösler, H.J., 1960. Zur Petrographie, Geochemie und Genese der Magmatite und Lagerstätten des Oberdevons und Unterkarbons in Ostthüringen. *Freiberg. Forschungsh., C,* 92: 1–275.

Rösler, H.J., 1962. Zur Entstehung der oberdevonischen Eisenerze von Typ Lahn–Dill in Ostthüringen. *Freiberg. Forschungsh., C,* 138: 1–79.

Rösler, H.J., 1964. Genetische Probleme der Erze des sogenannten erweiterten Lahn–Dill Typus. *Ber. Geol. Ges. D.D.R.,* 9: 445–454.

Sandberger, F., 1847. *Übersicht über die geologischen Verhältnisse des Herzogtums Nassau.*

Scherp, A., 1961. Der Initialmagmatismus im ostrheinischen Schiefergebirge und seine Lagerstätten. *Erzmetall,* 14 (7): 328–335.

Schneider, H.J., 1964. Facies differentiation and controlling factors for the depositional lead–zinc concentration in the Ladinian geosyncline of the eastern Alps. In: C.G. Amstutz (Editor), *Sedimentology and Ore Genesis.* Elsevier, Amsterdam, pp. 29–45.

Schneiderhöhn, H., 1923. Schichtige Erzlagerstätten von strittiger Entstehung. *Geol. Rundsch.,* 14: 60–68.

Schneiderhöhn, H., 1941. *Lehrbuch de Lagerstättenkunde, 1.* Fischer, Jena, 858 pp.

Schneiderhöhn, H., 1955. *Erzlagerstätten, Kurzvorlesungen.* Fischer, Stuttgart, 3rd ed., 375 pp.

Schönenberg, R., 1951. Initialer Magmatismus und Tektonik in Ostthüringen. *Geol. Rundsch.,* 39: 119–121.

Schönenberg, R., 1956. Oberdevonische Tektonik und kulmischer Magmatismus im nordöstlichen Dilltrog. *Geol. Jahrb.,* 71: 595–616.

Schtscherba, G.N., 1967. Mestorojdenija atasuiskogo tipa. *Geol. Rudn. Mest.,* 9 (5): 106–114.

Schultz, R.W., 1966. Lower Carboniferous cherty ironstones at Tynagh, Ireland. *Econ. Geol.,* 61 (2): 311–342.

Seibold, E., 1973. Rezente submarine Metallogenese. *Geol. Rundsch.,* 62 (3): 641–684.

Selenov, K.K., 1960. Transportation and accumulation of iron and aluminium in volcanic provinces of the Pacific. *Izv. Akad. Nauk S.S.S.R., Ser. Geol.,* 1960: 47–59.

Shkolnik, E.L., 1970. Effusive jasper iron-formation and iron ores of the Uda area. *Proc. Kiev Symp., UNESCO, Earth Sci.,* 9: 187–189.

Skacel, J., 1966. Zelezorudna loziska moravskoslezskeho devonu. *Rozpr. Ceskoslov. Akad. Ved.,* 76 (11): 59 pp.

Smirnov, W.I., 1960. Über die möglichen exhalativen und exhalativ-sedimentären Kiesvorkommen in der Sowjetunion. *Freiberg. Forschungsh., C,* 79: 63–66.

Stanton, R.L., 1958. Abundances of copper, zinc, and lead in some sulfide deposits. *J. Geol.,* 66: 484–502.

Steinike, K., 1963. Quantitativ-mineralogische Untersuchungen an den Eisenerzen vom Typus Lahn–Dill aus Pörmitz bei Schleiz (Ostthüringen). *Freiberg. Forschungsh., C,* 142: 123 pp.

Stifft, C.E., 1831. *Geognostische Beschreibung des Herzogtums Nassau in besonderer Beziehung auf die Mineralquellen dieses Landes.*

Stille, H., 1940. *Einführung in den Bau Nordamerikas.* Borntraeger, Berlin, 717 pp.

Stützel, H., 1933. Die Erze der Grube Theodor bei Aumenau und ihr Verhältnis zum Nebengestein. *Neues Jahrb. Mineral. Geol. Paläontol., Monatsh.,* 67: 155–195.

Tatsumi, T. (Editor), 1970. *Volcanism and Ore Genesis.* Univ. Tokyo Press, Tokyo, 448 pp.

Tatsumi, T., Sekine, Y. and Kanehira, K., 1970. Mineral deposits of volcanic affinity in Japan: metallogeny. In: T. Tatsumi (Editor), *Volcanism and Ore Genesis.* Univ. Tokyo Press, Tokyo, pp. 3–47.

Vaché, R., 1966. Zur Geologie der Varisziden und ihrer Lagerstätten im südanatolischen Taurus. *Miner. Deposita,* 1: 30–42.

Watanabe, T., 1970. Volcanism and ore genesis. In: T. Tatsumi (Editor), *Volcanism and Ore Genesis.* Univ. Tokyo Press, Tokyo, pp. 423–432.

White, D.E., 1957. Thermal waters of volcanic origin. *Bull. Geol. Soc. Am.,* 68: 1937–1957.

White, D.E., 1968. Environments of generation of some base metal ore deposits. *Econ. Geol.,* 63: 301–335.

Williams, D., 1965. Vulkanismus und Erzlagerstätten. *Bergakademie,* 17: 591–599.

Chapter 7

DEEP-SEA MANGANESE NODULES

G.P. GLASBY and A.J. READ

HISTORICAL INTRODUCTION

Deep-sea manganese nodules were first recovered from the ocean floor on 18 February 1873, 160 miles southwest of the island of Ferro in the Canary Group during the voyage of the H.M.S. *Challenger* (Murray and Renard, 1891). The results of this cruise were unique inasmuch as they were to dominate thinking on manganese nodules for over 80 years. Large quantities of nodules displaying a wide range of morphologies and internal structures were recovered from both the Atlantic and Pacific Oceans (Fig. 1). The nodules were shown to consist of concentric bands of ferromanganese oxides around such diverse nuclei as pumice, coral, phosphorite nodules, volcanic ash, palagonite, sharks' teeth and glacial erratics. A slow growth rate for the nodules was established and some of the nodules were shown to have broken in situ and subsequently accreted manganese around the broken surfaces. Great diversity in appearance in the nodules was noted but generally nodules from a single site were similar in appearance and differed in size, form and internal appearance from those at another station: "so much so that now, after a detailed study of the collections, it is usually possible for us to state at sight from which *Challenger* station any particular nodule had been produced". In many cases, the external form of the nodule depended on the shape of the nucleus and was often complicated by the incorporation of multiple nuclei into the nodule.

Basically, four major hypotheses of nodule formation were presented.

(1) "The manganese of the nodules is chiefly derived from the decomposition of the more basic volcanic rocks and minerals with which the nodules are nearly always associated in deep-sea deposits. The manganese and iron of these rocks and minerals are at first transformed into carbonates, and subsequently into oxides, which on depositing from solution in the watery ooze, take a concretionary form around various kinds of nuclei."

(2) "They are formed under the reducing influence of organic matters on the sulphates of seawater, sulphides being produced and subsequently oxidised."

(3) "They arise from the precipitation of manganese contained in the waters of submarine springs at the bottom of the ocean."

(4) "They are formed from the compounds of manganese dissolved in seawater in the form of bicarbonates, and transformed at the surface of the sea into oxides, which are precipitated in a permanent form on the bottom of the ocean."

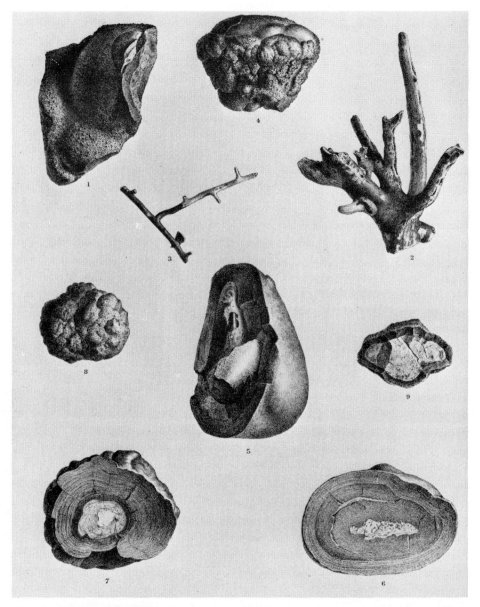

Fig. 1. Line drawing of manganese-iron nodules collected during the H.M.S. *Challenger* Expedition (1872–1876), (Murray and Renard, 1891, plate III).

With the exception of 2, each of these hypotheses has been refined and discussed by modern proponents, although Murray and Renard (1891) themselves accepted the first interpretation.

Following this, work on nodules was sporadic. More extensive collections of nodules from the Pacific were made during the "Albatross" Expedition of 1899–1900 and the limits of nodule distribution in the equatorial Pacific were mapped (Agassiz, 1902, 1906). In particular, the E–W trending zone of high nodule concentration lying off the west coast of the United States between the latitudes 6°30′N and 20°N was recognised (cf., Horn et al., 1972a). Fossil manganese nodules from Timor, Indonesia, were also discovered and shown to have deposited initially on the deep-sea floor on a red clay substrate and subsequently uplifted to their present position (Molengraaf, 1916, 1922). The nodules are remarkable for their excellent state of preservation. Recent studies have shown that the distribution of these deposits is controlled by tectonic uplift following the northward migration of Australia (Audley-Charles, 1972).

Following the Second World War, an extensive collection of deep-sea sediment cores was acquired as a result of the 1947–1948 Swedish Deep-Sea Expedition. Geochemical investigations of fifteen of these cores showed a marked interrelationship between Mn, Ni and Co which was attributed to the scavenging of Ni and Co by the manganese oxides (Landergren, 1964). Goldberg (1954) also put forward a colloidal scavenging hypothesis of nodule formation and showed that the incorporation of trace elements into manganese nodules could be explained in terms of the scavenging of the elements from seawater by manganese and iron oxides. It was not until 1965, however, that coherent hypotheses of nodule formation began to appear. In that year, Mero (1965) for the first time collated data on the regional variation of nodule composition throughout the Pacific, and Manheim postulated the influence of diagenetic processes on the formation of nodules from shallow-water, continental margin environments. Since that time, there has been considerable expansion in the literature on manganese nodules and they have been the subject of such esoteric studies as the search for transuranic elements (Otgonsuren et al., 1969), eletric monopoles (Fleischer et al., 1968) and cosmic spherules (Finkelman, 1970, 1972; Jedwab, 1970, 1971). Current ideas accept that any hypothesis of nodule formation must be multifaceted, i.e., a number of possible mechanisms may contribute to manganese deposition and trace element uptake any one of which may be dominant in a given situation.

The realisation that manganese nodules may be a potential ore resource led the International Decade of Oceanography (I.D.O.E.) to sponsor a conference "Ferromanganese Deposits on the Ocean Floor" at the Lamont-Doherty Geological Observatory in January 1972. This served to co-ordinate all existing data on nodules (Horn, 1972) and as a considerable stimulus to the further study of the geological, economic, legal, environmental and technological problems associated with the development of an incipient nodule industry. At the present time, four countries (the United States, Japan, W. Germany and France) are expressing active interest in nodule mining and in November 1972, the *Hughes Glomar Explorer* was launched as the first nodule mining ship.

DISTRIBUTION OF MANGANESE NODULES IN THE.WORLD'S OCEANS

Regional distribution

Manganese nodules are found in all the major oceans and in many different types of sedimentary environment (e.g., Ewing et al., 1971; Horn, 1972; Horn et al., 1972a, b, c, 1973a, b, c, d) (Fig. 2). Cronan (in press) has classified the principal types of environment in which nodules occur into seven categories: oceanic seamounts, plateaux, active mid-ocean ridges, inactive ridges, continental borderlands, marginal topographic elevations, and the deep ocean floor between about 2000 and 6000 m. Several factors may be considered important in controlling the overall distribution of nodules throughout the world's oceans.

Sedimentation rate

Undoubtedly the major factor influencing nodule distribution is the sedimentation rate. In the Pacific, for example, two major belts of nodule occurrence, one lying E—W off the west coast of the United States and one in the southwestern Pacific Basin, are associated with regions of extremely low sedimentation rate (i.e., red clay and siliceous ooze areas). In general, the surface concentration of nodules in the Pacific is higher than in the Atlantic or Indian Oceans, reflecting the much lower influx of continental detritus. The relationship of nodule distribution to sedimentation rate is well illustrated in the diagram of Horn et al. (1972a) for nodule distribution in the North Pacific (Fig. 3). From this, it is apparent that nodule distribution is closely related to sediment type; nodules being abundant in regions of red clay and siliceous ooze, less abundant in regions of calcareous ooze and almost completely absent in regions of biogenic ooze, ice-rafted

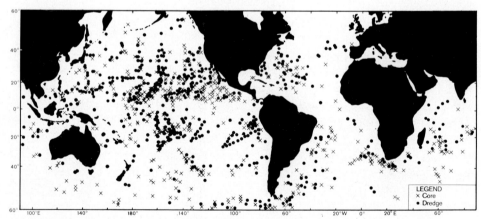

Fig. 2. Known occurrences of manganese nodules on the sea floor. Crosses indicate positions of nodules obtained by cores, circles those obtained by dredge. Data from Horn et al. (1973a).

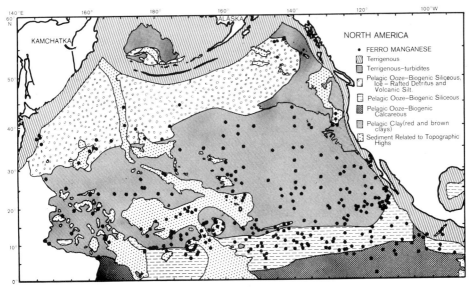

Fig. 3. Chart showing the relationship between nodule distribution (black dots) and sedimentary province in the North Pacific. Data from Horn et al. (1972a).

sediment and volcanic silt, hemipelagites and turbidites. Locally, exceptions do exist to this general principle. Moore and Heath (1966) and Moore, T.C. (1970), for example, have noted that manganese nodules are most abundant on the steepest slopes of an equatorial seamount where Quaternary sediments are thickest. According to these authors, this results from the trapping of downward moving sediments and nodules on relatively flat portions of the slope. In such cases, nodules will be associated with regions of apparently higher sedimentation rate.

Availability of potential nucleating agents

Manganese nodules generally form around a central nucleus. The availability of a potential nucleating agent on which the manganese nodule can accrete is therefore of importance in controlling both the regional and local distribution of nodules and may influence the overall character and morphology of the nodule. In regions of extremely low sedimentation rate well away from land such as the red clay areas of the Pacific, for example, fossil material such as whales' earbones or sharks' teeth may be an important source of nodule nuclei. In regions where volcanism has been important, volcanic weathering products may be an important source of nuclei. Glacial erratics may serve as nodule nuclei in high latitudes and phosphorite nodules have been observed as nodule nuclei in plateau regions such as the Blake Plateau (Pratt and McFarlin, 1966), the Campbell Plateau (Summerhayes, 1967) and the Aghulas Bank (Summerhayes and Willis, 1973). In regions where potential nucleating agents are widely distributed on the sea-floor, coalescence of nodules may occur during incipient stages of nodule growth to give highly distorted nodules. Because of the importance of nucleating agents in nodule formation, the localised distribution of nodules may be strongly dependent on this factor. On the flanks of the Carlsberg Ridge, for example, Glasby (1973a) has shown that massive manganese crusts are formed in regions of steeper topographic gradient where outcropping of strata can be expected, whereas nodules are formed in intervening regions of flatter topography where smaller volcanic debris has accumulated by erosion. In regions characterised by the complete absence of potential nucleating agents, micronodules may form in the sediment column. Similar relationships between nodule distribution and availability of potential nucleating agents have been demonstrated by Ewing et al. (1973a) for an abyssal hill province in the North Atlantic and Horn et al. (1973d) have emphasised the importance of "seeding" in controlling nodule distribution between the Clipperton and Clarion Fracture Zones in the equatorial Pacific.

Andrews and Meylan (1972) have suggested an interesting scheme for the development of nodule nuclei in an area of the central Pacific: (1) extrusion of lava on to the sea floor; (2) polygon-like jointing of the flow surface; (3) enlargement of the joints, especially at joint intersections, by degradation and removal of the newly exposed volcanic material (possibly with assistance from benthic organisms); this produces separate slabs; (4) shattering of some slabs; (5) formation of nodule clusters from the shattered slabs, in some cases within depressions on the pavement surface; (6) rounding of the irregularly shaped nodules by further deposition of manganese and iron oxides.

Brundage (1972) has suggested that on the Blake Plateau undercutting by current scouring may be responsible for breaking the pavement into slabs. Although this scheme is by no means generalised, it does indicate the possible complexity in the development of manganese crustal growth on a central nucleus.

Age

An important factor in controlling nodule distribution is the age of the nucleus on which the manganese is accreting. In the Pacific, for example, there is evidence that the manganese crustal thickness increases with age along certain seamount chains such as the Revillagigedo Island region off the coast of Mexico (Moore, J.G., 1970) and in the Hawaiian chain (Moore, J.G., 1965, 1966; J.E. Andrews, personal communication). In the Carlsberg Ridge, Glasby (1973a) has shown that thick encrustations of manganese are found on highly weathered volcanic nuclei on the flanks of the mid-ocean ridge whereas only a thin veneer of manganese overlying fresh, brecciated lava flows of Pliocene or Pleistocene age is found on the axis of the ridge. In the Northeast Pacific, Dietz (1955) has noted different thicknesses of manganese crusts on adjacent seamounts (the Erben and Fieberling Guyots); the difference in thickness probably reflecting differences in the age of the seamounts. The length of time the nodule nucleus has been in contact with seawater may also influence the nodule morphology. Glasby (1972a), for example, has shown that in the South Tasman Basin, highly distorted nodules with multiple nuclei are a result of the youth of the nodules; insufficient time being allowed for a thick coating of manganese to develop and mask distortions in the nodule structure due to the presence of multiple nuclei.

Bottom current velocity

Another important factor in controlling nodule distribution is the bottom current velocity (e.g., Lister, 1971; Andrews, 1972; Andrews and Meylan, 1973; Kennett and Brunner, 1973). Watkins and Kennett (1971, 1972) have attributed the high concentration of nodules in the vicinity of the Indian/Antarctic mid-ocean ridge to the onset of a high bottom-current velocity which has resulted in erosion of the sediment and an effective lowering of the sedimentation rate. Similar conclusions have been drawn by Hollister and Heezen (1967) for nodule distribution in the Bellingshausen Sea and by Goodell et al. (1971) for nodule distribution in the Southern Ocean and by Hollister et al. (1974) for nodule distribution in the Samoan Passage (see also MacDonald and Hollister, 1973). In the South Atlantic, Horn et al. (1972b) have interpreted differences in the distribution of nodules in the eastern and western side of the ocean as being influenced primarily by the free flow of water on the western side. Lonsdale et al. (1972) have shown that the distribution of manganese nodules over the Horizon Guyot is controlled by erosional processes and the distribution of manganese deposits over plateau regions such as the Blake Plateau, Campbell Plateau and Aghulas Bank has been shown to be dependent on the high bottom-current velocity required to sweep sediment away from the region and create conditions favourable for manganese accretion. It is of interest that Summerhayes and Willis (1973) note a sequence for manganese deposition on the Aghulas Bank.

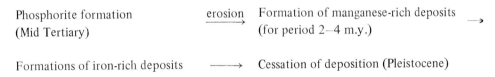

Phosphorite formation   erosion   Formation of manganese-rich deposits
(Mid Tertiary)   ———→   (for period 2–4 m.y.)   ———→

Formations of iron-rich deposits   ———→   Cessation of deposition (Pleistocene)

According to Summerhayes and Willis (1973) "the deposits lie beneath the swift flowing Aghulas Current which, during times of lowered sea-level in the Pleistocene, would probably have swept vigorously along the upper continental slope much as the Gulf Stream sweeps the Blake Plateau today". It is probable that cessation of manganese deposition is a result of changes in bottom current velocity (and hence sediment transport) in this region due to changes in sea level during the Pleistocene.

On a local scale, bottom currents may be responsible for both uncovering and covering nodules with sediment. Mero (1965) has noted examples of underwater photographs where nodules are concentrated in troughs of sediment-waves with the crest of the sediment-wave essentially devoid of nodules. Since ripple markings are not a static feature on the sea floor, alternate covering and uncovering of manganese nodules might be expected in certain restricted localities where bottom currents are in the range to permit ripple marking to occur on the sea floor.

Although high bottom currents may favour nodule formation by scouring of bottom sediments and thereby decreasing the effective sedimentation rate, they may inhibit manganese crustal growth at the very highest current velocities. Heezen and Hollister (1971), for example, note that Lower Cretaceous limestones recovered from the Blake Escarpment at 5000 m beneath a swift current have a layer of manganese much thinner than that covering the much younger Pliocene and Miocene sediments on the Plateau.

Biological activity

There is some evidence that activity of benthic organisms is responsible for both keeping nodules at the sediment surface and for causing some localised variations in nodule distribution on the sea floor (cf., Mero, 1965; A. Bruun in Arrhenius, 1967). Andrews and Meylan (1972) have recently examined a series of underwater photographs from the Central Pacific and suggested that bottom-feeder activity may be responsible for some unusual barren areas within otherwise rich nodule fields. Presumably the main influence of these bottom feeders is in disturbing nodules during burrowing in search of food. As Mero (1965) notes, nodule growth rate is so low that animal activity would not have to be particularly great to keep nodules at the sediment surface.

Redox conditions

Nodules form preferentially in well oxygenated regions where high redox potentials prevail. Nodules are therefore not generally found in stagnant waters or regions of high organic productivity. Diagenetic remobilisation of manganese oxides in sediments will occur where reducing conditions develop below the sediment—water interface, and nodules are either not found in such areas or occur only in the upper layers of the sediment column where oxidising conditions prevail (Lynn and Bonatti, 1965; Wangersky and Joensuu, 1967; Li et al., 1969; Ericson and Wollin, 1973).

In less oxidising environments such as freshwater lakes, lochs and fjords, the factors controlling the genesis of nodules are complex but include such parameters as the redox characteristics of the sediment—water interface (which in turn is controlled by the annual pattern of thermal stratification in the case of lakes), the energy of the environment (wave action and turbulence), and the diagenetic remobilisation of manganese and iron in the sediment column. In even less oxidising conditions, manganese carbonate may form as the principal phase (see e.g., Calvert and Price, 1970; Callender, 1973). The redox characteristics of the environment are therefore of the greatest importance in determining the occurrence and type of manganese nodules and in limiting the distribution of manganese oxides to moderately oxidising environments.

The above comments give some idea of the complexity of factors controlling nodule distribution on a regional scale. It should be noted that they are not incompatible with the suggestion of Bender et al. (1966, 1970) of a rather uniform "rain" of manganese over the entire ocean floor and that nodule and sediment manganese accumulation rates are very similar. According to this hypothesis, manganese nodules exist not because of some unusual ability to attract available manganese but rather because some mechanism prevents objects like sharks' teeth and volcanic nuclei from being covered with sediment. They remain on the surface and accumulate manganese at roughly the same rate as the surrounding sediment. It should be recognised, however, that the distribution of manganese can manifest itself in different ways depending on the nature of the sedimentary environment. In regions of high sedimentation rate where potential nucleating agents are absent, micronodules may form instead of the more typical deep-sea nodules. In regions of high organic productivity, the redox potential of the sediment may be so low that extensive remobilisation of manganese takes place within the sediment column and prevents the deposition of manganese from external sources. Because of this, a more generalised hypothesis of nodule genesis than the one presented by Bender et al. (1966, 1970) is required.

One of the major problems in nodule genesis lies in relating the observed distribution of nodules to major structural features of the sea floor as revealed by currently accepted ideas of plate tectonics. It has already been stated that manganese crustal-thickness increases with distance away from the axis of certain active mid-ocean ridge systems, and that there is some evidence of increasing thickness with age along certain seamount chains in the Pacific, such as the Hawaiian chain and the Revillagigedo Island region off Mexico. There is also increasing evidence of ferruginous sedimentation in the vicinity of the axis of certain centres of sea-floor spreading such as the East Pacific Rise. It seems probable that the former situation is related to the time-dependent direct deposition of manganese and associated ferride elements from seawater, whereas the latter represents the more sporadic influence of volcanic exhalites at the axis of the ridge analogous to the Red Sea Brine situation (see also Bonatti et al., 1972; Blissenbach and Fellerer, 1973; Tarling, 1973). In regions of descending lithospheric plates, such as the deep oceanic trenches, sedimentation rates are generally too high to permit extensive nodule formation. Recent evidence suggests an increasing age of basement and sediment thickness away from the axis of the Mid-Atlantic Ridge (Ewing et al., 1973b) and across the Pacific from west to east (Winterer, 1973), and it will be of interest to examine the effect of this on the regional distribution of nodules and their distribution in the sediment column in situ. This will give an insight into the role of sedimentary facies on nodule formation. The most spectacular effects of plate tectonics are to be found in the distribution of fossil nodules in Timor. As stated previously, these were initially deposited on a red clay substrate and uplifted to their present position following the northward migration of Australia (Audley-Charles, 1972).

Localised distribution

One of the major problems in assessing manganese nodules as an ore resource is their extreme variability in distribution over localised areas. Areas where such localised variation has been observed include the Blake Plateau (Hawkins, 1969; Brundage, 1972), the Manihiki Plateau (Bezrukov, 1973), Hawaiian Archipelago (Andrews, 1972; Morgenstein, 1972a; Landmesser and Morgenstein, 1973), Central Pacific (Moore and Heath, 1966; Hubred, 1970; Andrews and Meylan, 1972; Kaufman and Siapno, 1972; Schultze-Westrum, 1973), North Atlantic seamounts (Aumento et al., 1968; Ewing et al., 1973a), Carlsberg Ridge, Indian Ocean (Laughton, 1967; Glasby, 1973a) and the South Tasman Basin (Glasby, 1972a, 1973b). Several factors may influence this variability; these include erosion or scour by bottom currents locally removing sediment and exposing nodules to leave a "lag deposit" (Hawkins, 1969), the availability of potential nucleating agents in a region of strong topographic contrast (Moore and Heath, 1966; Glasby, 1973a), or where different populations of nuclei are introduced by different processes (e.g., ice-rafting vs. submarine volcanism) (Glasby, 1972a), or burrowing by benthic organisms (Mero, 1965; Heezen and Hollister, 1967; Andrews and Meylan, 1972). Andrews (1972) has commented that in the Hawaiian Archipelago the thickest and richest deposits of manganese occur where the following environmental criteria are met: (1) good supplies of iron-rich volcanogenic sediments (sands and silts) from the islands; (2) terraces to trap these sediments; and (3) exposure to the flow of currents around the islands, particularly where they are accelerated through channels between the islands, or over shallow peaks. Clearly, the localised variability of nodule distribution on the sea floor is of extreme importance if nodules are to be mined commercially because it considerably complicates any assessment of the ore grade of a resource (cf., Barten and Shaw, 1969; Anon., 1973).

Distribution with depth

The distribution of manganese nodules with depth in the sediment column has been studied mainly in gravity and piston cores, and is therefore restricted to the upper few metres of the sediment column. Essentially, nodules occur dominantly at the sediment surface, although they do occur to a lesser extent within the sediment column (Cronan and Tooms, 1967a; Goodell et al., 1971; Horn, 1972; Ewing et al., 1973a; Horn et al., 1973c). Some evidence suggests that this distribution of nodules with depth in the sediment column is fairly regular (Cronan and Tooms, 1967a) and that the composition and mineralogy of the nodules does not vary markedly with depth in a given locality (Cronan and Tooms, 1969; Goodell et al., 1971). It must be emphasised, however, that the major problem in studying the depth distribution of nodules within the sediment column lies in the relatively small probability of recovering nodules of appreciable size in a core barrel of restricted diameter (Goodell et al., 1971). For this reason, knowledge of the depth distribution of manganese nodules throughout the complete sedimentary column (and hence their potential for retention in marine sequences on land) is not well understood.

Several hypotheses have been invoked to account for the observed depth distribution of nodules. Cronan and Tooms (1967a), for example, suggested that distribution of nodules within the sediment column implies that nodules were formed at the sediment surface or at depth within the sediment and then concentrated at the surface, either by selective erosion of the surrounding sediment or by the action of various benthic organisms. Horn et al. (1973c), on the other hand, note that a large proportion of nodules occurring below the sediment surface occur at hiatuses or unconformities, suggesting that they were formed at the sediment surface during a period of lowered sedimentation and subsequently buried (see also Kobayashi et al., 1971; Pimm et al., 1972). From a study of the distribution of micronodules in a series of sediment cores, Ericson and Wollin (1973) concluded that the distribution of the micronodules is independent of the palaeoclimatic zones and that there is a well defined lower boundary below which there is no trace of micronodules.

One of the most interesting developments is the observations of manganese nodules in J.O.I.D.E.S. deep drill holes (Fig. 4). Although manganese nodule distribution has not been documented routinely as part of this project, Margolis (1973) noted the occurrence of manganese deposits at large-scale unconformities in sediments from the Campbell Plateau during Leg 29 on the Deep-Sea Drilling Project. The unconformities were assumed to indicate the onset of intense bottom currents associated with the western boundary current which were able to scour away sediment and permit the formation of extensive manganese deposits. On the Macquarie Ridge, the distribution of manganese micronodules in the core increased with the amount of volcanic ash and with lower sedimentation rate but there was no evidence of decreasing amounts of micronodules with depth in the sediment column as suggested by Ericson and Wollin (1973). From this it appears that the accumulation rate of manganese throughout the sediment column is constant with time. At unconformities, the concentration of manganese deposits increases merely because the manganese is continuing to accrete whereas sedimentation has temporarily ceased. The form of metals at depth within the sediment column also appears to depend on the nature of the bottom currents; at low bottom currents, pyrite forms whereas at higher bottom currents manganese nodules and micronodules form. From S.E.M. measurements, Margolis (1973) also showed that as more dissolution of siliceous ooze takes place incipient manganese micronodule formation occurs. The dissolution of forams and siliceous organisms on the sea floor provides sites for the replacement by manganese oxides. This explains why areas of high biological productivity are areas of manganese nodule formation. It must be emphasised, however, that one of the major problems in interpretation of the origin of manganese nodules found in J.O.I.D.E.S. deep-sea drill cores is the possibility of the nodule having fallen down the drill hole from the sediment

Fig. 4. Manganese nodule from J.O.I.D.E.S. deep-sea drill hole 274 (68°59.81'S 173°25.64'E, 3326 m) taken at a depth of 91.7 m in the sediment in a matrix of diatom detrital silty clay containing pebbles and manganese nodules. The nodule contains multiple nuclei interpenetrated to varying degrees by manganese oxide.

surface (cf., Cronan, 1973a). It is therefore customary to date the sediment surrounding the nodule palaeontologically before making any detailed assessment of its origin. Other related studies of J.O.I.D.E.S. drill cores have been concerned with the origin of ferruginous sediments from hydrothermal and other sources (cf., Drever, 1971; Von der Borch and Rex, 1970; Von der Borch et al., 1971; Cook, 1971, 1972; Cronan, 1973b; Natland, 1973).

GEOCHEMISTRY

Manganese nodules are very heterogeneous and large-scale variations in composition are observed both within individual nodules and between nodules from adjacent areas of the sea floor. Because of the importance of this factor in assessing the grade of these depositions as an ore resource, the unusual procedure of discussing compositional variations within individual nodules and between nodules from adjacent areas of the sea floor before discussing regional variations in nodule composition is adopted (see also Friedrich et al., 1973).

Compositional variations within individual nodules

Compositional variations within individual nodules were first studied, using standard analytical techniques, by Cronan and Tooms (1967b). At the 95% confidence level, Ni, Ba, Mn and Co were shown to be at a significantly higher concentration 2–6 mm from the nodule surface than adjacent to the nodule nucleus, whereas Si and Cr were at much higher concentrations nearer the nucleus. These variations were interpreted as reflecting mainly variations in the amount of detrital volcanic material present in the sample; higher concentrations of siliceous detrital material being found nearer the nucleus of the nodule. More detailed studies of a series of Pacific nodules by Raab (1972) showed that externally many of these nodules are characterised by a smooth surface (most recently exposed to seawater) and a gritty, lumpy surface (most recently exposed to sediment). These two surfaces are markedly different in composition from each other and from the interior of the nodule. In general, it was found that the in situ upper-surface of the nodule is enriched in Fe, Co and Pb and depleted in Cu, Ni, Mo, Zn and Mn with respect to the in situ underside of the nodule. The Al-content is generally as high or higher in the gritty layer as in the smooth layer indicating that dilution due to admixed clay is not responsible for these variations. In contrast to the surface layers, individual layers within nodules tend to be more uniform in composition. From these data, Raab (1972) suggests that nodules from this particular part of the Pacific grow at the sediment—water interface and that accretion of components such as Cu, Ni, Mn, Co, Pb and Zn takes place predominantly from the underlying sediment. The high concentrations of Cu, Ni, Mo, Zn and Mn and low concentrations of Co, Pb and Fe, in the surfaces last exposed to the sediment compared with the surface last exposed to seawater suggest that, at least in some parts of the Pacific, certain phases in nodules are unstable in contact with seawater and that seawater is undersaturated with respect to Cu, Ni, Mn, Zn and Mn phases.

A powerful technique in studying inter-element relationships in deep-sea nodules is electron microprobe analysis. From a study of fourteen nodules, Burns and Fuerstenau (1966) showed that there is a distinct correlation between certain elements within the nodule structure indicative of stoichiometric substitution of the minor elements for manganese and iron. On this basis, Ni^{2+}, Cu^{2+}, Zn^{2+}, Mg^{2+}, K^+ and Ba^{2+} were assumed to substitute for Mn^{2+} in the "manganite" phase and Co III of Fe III in the hydrated iron-oxide phase. By contrast, Cronan and Tooms (1968) were able to show that the inter-element relationships in nodules were highly variable and paritcular that the correlation between Ca and Zn with Mn and between Co and Fe as proposed by Burns and Fuerstenau (1966) were not a characteristic feature of all nodules. Further, beta coefficients calculated for 187 random points on microprobe profiles showed that inter-element relation-ships were not as marked as previously anticipated (Burns and Brown, 1972). Other studies have emphasised the need to consider the distribution of trace elements in the nodule structure in terms of a three-component system, consisting of an iron-rich phase, a manganese-rich phase and a silicate-rich phase, and have demonstrated the marked differ-ence in trace-element assemblage and distribution pattern between deep-sea nodules and shallow water, continental-margin nodules (Dunham and Glasby, 1974). Similarly, it has been established that submarine weathering leaches several elements, notably SiO_2, Al_2O_3, Na_2O, CaO and MnO, from the hydrated glass surrounding the basaltic nuclei of nodules (Fein and Morgenstein, 1972). The manganese bands formed on the altered glass are further depleted in SiO_2 and Al_2O_3 but are similar to the hydrated glass in Na_2O and CaO. These results taken together emphasise the chemical heterogeneity of manganese nodules and the need to consider this factor in assessing the compositional variability between nodule samples.

Localised variations in composition

Localised variations in nodule composition were first reported for nodules from the western flanks of the Carlsberg Ridge, Indian Ocean, by Cronan and Tooms (1967b). Variations of up to a factor of three were noted in the composition of certain elements in nodules from a single sampling site. This was only slightly greater than compositional variations observed within a single nodule from the same site. Variations in nodules between adjacent sites, 15–25 km apart, however, varied by a much larger degree. Cu and Ni for example, varied by factors of 7/1 and 5/1, respectively. Other elements showed a lesser, but statistically significant difference in composition. Although suggestions on the origin of this variation were tentative, it was proposed that such localised variations in nodule composition could reflect either differences in environmental conditions at the different sampling sites during nodule formation (e.g., redox gradients or rates of advec-tion of dissolved oxygen in seawater), or the possible influence of submarine geothermal activity.

More recently, Glasby et al. (1971) have demonstrated the marked variation in compo-sition of manganese crusts from two sites 33 km apart in the central region of the Gulf of Aden. Basically, samples from the median valley of the Gulf of Aden were found in cavities on the underside of fresh basalt lava flows and were significantly enriched in Mn and depleted in Fe and a number of trace elements, particularly Co, Pb and V, compared with massive manganese encrustations found on more weathered basalts taken at a greater distance away from the median valley. The formation of manganese on the underside of basalts at the median valley coupled with the presence of an organic-rich mud in the vicinity of the sampling site suggests that diagenetic processes might be contributing to the compositional variations; whereas the trace-element enriched manganese crusts formed away from the median valley are deposited directly from seawater, those formed in the organic-rich sediments in the vicinity of the median valley are subject to the enrichment of manganese, and the corresponding depletion if Fe and other tracemetals, resulting from diagenetic processes within the sediment column.

Finally, Glasby (1972a) has demonstrated a variation of a factor of 6—8 in the composition of Cu, Ni and Co in manganese nodules and encrustations taken from two sites 17 km apart in the South Tasman Basin. The origin of this variation is not known but is not related to variations in nodule morphology or the nature of the nodule nucleus. Hubred (1970) has similarly observed a severalfold variation in the elemental composition of nodules from a single dredge haul in an abyssal hill in the eastern Pacific and Grant (1967) has noted a severalfold variation in composition in nodules within individual dredge hauls from the southern oceans. Meyer (1973a, b) has shown a dependence of trace-metal content on nodule morphology in nodules from the equatorial Pacific.

It must be emphasised that the above data are based on the analyses of only a limited number of samples using analytical techniques of only moderate precision ($\pm 25\%$ at the 95% confidence level). They do, however, indicate the possibility of large-scale variations in composition, particularly in the ore metals, Cu, Ni and Co, over very limited areas of the sea floor. Further substantial studies on the origins of localised variations in nodule composition are therefore essential if either the statistics of sampling of these deposits on the ocean floor are to be fully evaluated or the regional geochemistry of manganese nodules put in proper perspective.

Regional variations in composition

Regional variations in the composition of deep-sea nodules were first systematically documented by Mero (1965) based on the analysis of 166 nodules sampled throughout the Pacific Basin. Basically, four major types of nodules were recognised:

(1) Iron-rich nodules (A-type) found in the South Pacific and thought to have formed by the preferential deposition of iron relative to manganese from a water mass moving towards Tahiti.

(2) Manganese-rich nodules (B-type) found mainly around the continental borderland of the United States, particularly in or near the Gulf of California. These nodules are generally depleted in Cu, Ni and Co and it was suggested that this reflects the rapid formation of these nodules, insufficient time being available for the incorporation of trace metals on to the manganese-rich colloids.

(3) Copper- and nickel-rich (C-type) found in the central parts of the Pacific farthest from land and thought to reflect the importance of biological activity particularly associated with the high-productivity zone of the equatorial divergence and

(4) Cobalt-rich (D-type) centred on topographic highs in the central parts of the Pacific. The areas of topographic rises are generally characterised by highly oxidising environments, resulting from the high water current velocity over these features and it was suggested that this factor might be responsible for the incorporation of Co into these nodules.

TABLE I

Average composition of surface nodules from different areas within the Pacific Ocean. Data from Cronan (1972) in weight percent, air-dried weight

	Southern borderland seamount province	Continental borderland of Baja California	Northeast Pacific	Southwest Pacific	Central Pacific	South Pacific	West Pacific	Mid-Pacific Mountains	North Pacific
Mn	15.85	33.98	22.33	19.81	15.71	16.61	16.87	13.96	12.29
Fe	12.22	1.62	9.44	10.20	9.06	13.92	13.30	13.10	12.00
Ni	0.348	0.097	1.080	0.961	0.956	0.433	0.564	0.393	0.422
Co	0.514	0.0075	0.192	0.164	0.213	0.595	0.395	1.127	0.144
Cu	0.077	0.065	0.627	0.311	0.711	0.185	0.393	0.061	0.294
Pb	0.085	0.006	0.028	0.030	0.049	0.073	0.034	0.174	0.015
Ba	0.306	0.171	0.381	0.145	0.155	0.230	0.152	0.274	0.196
Mo	0.040	0.072	0.047	0.037	0.041	0.035	0.037	0.042	0.018
V	0.065	0.031	0.041	0.031	0.036	0.050	0.044	0.054	0.037
Cr	0.0051	0.0019	0.0007	0.0005	0.0012	0.0007	0.0007	0.0011	0.0044
Ti	0.489	0.060	0.425	0.467	0.561	1.007	0.810	0.773	0.634
L.O.I.	24.78	21.96	24.75	27.21	22.12	28.73	25.50	30.87	22.52
Depth (m)	1146	3003	4537	4324	5049	3539	5001	1757	4990

The geochemical classification of Pacific nodules was subsequently refined and extended by Cronan and Tooms (1969 – see also Cronan, 1972) (Table I). Basically, these authors found a similar pattern of distribution of trace metals in Pacific nodules to that reported by Mero (1965). Certain elements were shown to be depth dependent. Cu and Ni concentrations in nodules, for example, were shown to be positively correlated with depth. This was thought to reflect variations in nodule mineralogy; todorokite-rich nodules being enriched in Cu and Ni and impoverished in Co and Pb relative to birnessite-rich nodules. The overall regional variations in composition of Pacific nodules was thought to reflect a number of factors such as:

(1) The proximity of the nodules to continental or volcanic sources of elements.

(2) The chemical environment of deposition, including the degree of oxygenation.

(3) Local factors such as the upward migration of reduced manganese in sediments from certain areas and

(4) Regional variations in the depth of deposition and mineralogy of the nodules.

In the continental borderland region, upward migration of manganese is probably the most important factor in determining the composition of nodules and leads to an enrichment of manganese in the sediments. Elsewhere, with the possible exception of iron, there is little correlation between the composition of nodules and the composition of their associated sediments.

In an attempt to synthesise these data, Price and Calvert (1970) suggested the dominant role of diagenesis in controlling the composition of manganese nodules and concretions throughout the Pacific Basin. According to this hypothesis, the Mn/Fe ratio of the nodule varies systematically throughout the Pacific Basin and becomes the key to interpreting the overall compositional variations in the nodules. Thus, the highest values in the Mn/Fe ratios of nodules are found in the eastern marginal areas of the Pacific extending westwards along the north equatorial region. The values decrease westwards towards the centre of the ocean, and the lowest values are seen in a large area of the Southwestern Pacific and in a small area in the Northwest Pacific. This systematic variation in the Mn/Fe ratio of nodules suggests that the diagenetic mobility of manganese occurs on an ocean-wide basis. Thus, the highest Mn/Fe ratios occur in those areas where maximal diagenetic remobilisation of manganese relative to iron takes place (such as marginal environments). Conversely, the ratio in the nodules approaches the value in the oxidate fraction of the pelagic sediment in those areas where minimal remobilisation occurs. The depletion of trace metals in nodules characterised by high Mn/Fe ratios also reflects the diagenetic remobilisation of manganese within the sediment column, leading to the effective fractionation of manganese relative to iron and trace metals within the nodule.

Trace metals were also thought to be subject to diagenetic processes. In particular, Price and Calvert (1970) note that the concentrations of minor metals in marginal manganese nodules correlate with the order of stability of water-soluble, organic-rich metal complexes Ni > Co > Cu > Zn > V, Mo. It was therefore suggested that marginal manganese nodules contain less, Ni, Co and Cu relative to their availability in the sediments because they form stable chelates, whereas Mo and V, and to some extent Zn, are precipitated because their chelates are not stable, particularly in the presence of iron and manganese oxides. Subsequent work has, however, shown that the order of solubility of metals depends on both the nature of the chelating agent and the nature of the sediment substrate (Rashid 1971, 1972a, b; Rashid and Leonard 1973). The general order of solubility for carbonates appears to be Ni > Co > Cu > Zn > Mn (i.e., as listed by Price and Calvert, 1970) whereas for sulphides it is Cu > Co > Mn > Ni > Zn. Thus, the role of chelation in controlling the composition of manganese nodules is largely dependent on the nature of the sediment substrate. Its importance has, however, been inferred for certain shallow marine environments (Presley et al., 1972).

The idea, that diagenesis is the major factor controlling nodule composition throughout the Pacific Basin, is extremely important in as much as it implies that variations in nodule composition can be interpreted on a broad scale and not on an ad hoc basis as before. Thus, Price and Calvert (1970) effectively demolished the submarine volcanicity hypothesis of nodule formation proposed by Arrhenius et al. (1964), Arrhenius and Bonatti (1965) and Bonatti and Nayudu (1965) (see also Glasby, 1973c). It must be emphasised, however, that the above data were all based on the analysis of a relatively small number of samples spread throughout the Pacific Basin, with only a limited knowledge of the interrelation between the chemistry of the nodules and the underlying sediments.

Perhaps the most significant advance in understanding the origin of compositional variations of nodules comes from the work of Horn et al. (1973b). Here, trace-metal data for manganese nodules are superimposed directly on detailed sediment charts of the North Pacific. From this, it is apparent that Cu and Ni are considerably enriched in nodules from the band of siliceous radiolarian ooze south of Hawaii (average composition Cu 1.16%, Ni 1.28%, Mn 24.6% and Co 0.23%), compared with nodules from the red clay area to the north (average composition Cu 0.49%, Ni 0.76%, Mn 18.2% and Co 0.25%). Cu and Ni are therefore nearly twice as high in nodules from the siliceous ooze compared with those from the red clay area and Mn is consistently 6% higher. Co does not follow the trends of Cu, Ni and Mn. It is approximately the same concentration in both types of deep-water environment but is enriched in elevated regions such as in the vicinity of the Hawaii Islands and the Manihiki Plateau. These data are of utmost importance as they demonstrate unequivocally the detailed interrelationship of nodule composition, sediment type and submarine topography (see also Horn et al., 1973e). Similar conclusions have been drawn for the South Pacific (Glasby, in press) and the oceanic basins of southern Africa (Summerhayes and Willis, 1975).

In order to demonstrate the diagenetic control of Cu and Ni enrichment in nodules from the siliceous ooze area, a series of calculations have been carried out based on the data of Hurd (1972) (Table II). Essentially the results show a rough balance between the rate of incorporation of Cu into manganese nodules in this area and the rate of diffusion of Cu across the sediment--water interface as a result of the dissolution of siliceous

TABLE II

Semi-quantitative estimate of rate of copper uptake into manganese nodules vs. rate of upward migration of copper from underlying siliceous sediments, assuming conditions relevant to the central equatorial Pacific

Rate of uptake of copper in manganese nodules		Rate of upward migration of copper from siliceous sediments	
Assume surface density of nodules on sea-floor	100 kg/m^2 (10 g/cm^2)	Mean flux of dissolved silica across the sediment–water interface in central equatorial Pacific	$4.1 \cdot 10^{-3}$ moles/cm^2/10^3 yr* = 246 g/cm^2/10^6 yr
Cu content	1%		
Rate of accretion of nodules	1 cm/10^6 yr	Assume Cu content of sediments	100 ppm
Mn thickness on nodules	2 cm		
∴ Rate of accretion of Cu in nodules	$10 \times 0.01 \times 0.5$ g/cm^2/10^6 yr = 0.05 g/cm^2/10^6 yr	∴ Mean flux of Cu across sediment water interface	= 0.02 g/cm^2/10^6 yr

* Data from Hurd (1972, p. 42, table 6).

organisms on the sea floor. From this, it is not unreasonable to suggest the role of diagenesis in accounting for the higher Cu contents of nodules from areas of siliceous ooze compared with nodules from red clay areas. It must be emphasised, however, that these calculations are intended only as a semi-quantitative guide and that other interpretations may be possible.

Other studies have demonstrated that the high Cu and Ni input into the equatorial region results primarily from the influx of organisms (Greenslate et al., 1973). According to these authors, the high abundance of nodules and the high content of Cu and Ni in nodules from the siliceous ooze province results from a combination of factors; namely, the low sedimentation rate at depths below the carbonate compensation depth which permits the formation of a large quantity of nodules, and the high pore volume of the siliceous sediments which greatly facilitates the migration of Cu and Ni through the sediment and the subsequent incorporation of these elements into the nodules. This process of incorporation of Cu and Ni into the nodules is continuous throughout the lifetime of the nodules which from their size and growth rate is estimated to be of the order of 10^6-10^7 years.

These data indicate the possible role of diagenesis in controlling nodule composition and show that the nodules most enriched in copper and nickel are to be found in the siliceous ooze area south of Hawaii, whereas the nodules most enriched in cobalt are associated with topographic highs. This conclusion is of the utmost importance in the selection of nodule mining sites as the three metals, copper, nickel and cobalt, constitute the potential ore metals in manganese nodules. It should be noted that, whereas the copper—nickel rich nodules are generally associated with regions of rolling topography, the cobalt-rich nodules are generally associated with regions of rugged topography. This factor may play a dominant role in the selection of nodule mining sites, since large scale recovery of nodules from the deep-sea floor would be technically much easier in a region of smooth topography.

MINERALOGY

Because of the extremely fine particle size of nodular material, study of the mineralogy of marine manganese nodules by standard techniques, such as X-ray diffraction and infra-red spectroscopy, has proved most difficult (e.g., Elderfield and Glasby, 1973). Typically, X-ray diffraction profiles are diffuse and characterised by low peak intensities. This in turn has led to considerable confusion regarding the terminology and structure of manganese oxide minerals in the natural environment. One problem of particular importance is the preparation of samples for mineralogical analysis. Brown (1972) has noted the marked improvement in X-ray diffraction patterns of nodules on crushing under liquid nitrogen and the marked dehydration of nodules which have been sealed in plastic bags immediately on collection and then exposed to the air is well known. This suggests the possibility of mineralogical change in the nodules, unless particular care is taken with storage and they are kept in a cool, sealed environment.

Basically, two major schools of thought have developed concerning mineralogical nomenclature. Whereas Buser and Grütter (1956) identified the minerals occurring in manganese nodules as 10 Å manganite, 7 Å manganite and δ MnO_2, subsequent authors have referred to these minerals as todorokite (Straczek et al., 1960), birnessite (Jones and Milne, 1956) and δ MnO_2, respectively. This situation is complicated by the recent assertion of Giovanoli et al. (1970), that the mineral nomenclature should be revised to include the mineral buserite (named after the Swiss mineralogist W. Buser). According to these authors, two groups of manganite are identified, the birnessite family and the buserite family. The birnessite group can be recognised by a strong X-ray reflection near 7 Å and its second order, while the buserite group can be identified by a strong reflection near 9.6 Å and its second order. The mineral species are both non-stoichiometric with respect to the water content, the oxidation state and the content of some of the cations. Both are assumed to have a layer lattice and its is concluded that synthetic buserite differs from birnessite in that another water or OH^- layer is inserted in the layer structure thereby expanding the layer separation from 7.09 Å to 9.6 Å. This conclusion is supported by the fact that a synthetic sequence buserite → birnessite → random-stacked birnessite is observed in controlled dehydration. At present, no universal agreement exists on this question of nomenclature.

From a structural standpoint, Buser and Grütter (1956) suggested, on the basis of a comparison with the synthetic manganous manganites, lithophorite [$3MnO_2$. (Zn,Mn)-$0.3H_2O$] and chalcophanite [$(Al, Li)MnO_2(OH)_2$] (cf., Wadsley, 1952, 1953), that manganese nodules consist principally of irregular layered sheets of manganese oxides in which Mn^{4+} ions are octahedrally coordinated by O^{2-}. The structure is assumed to be stabilised by the incorporation of species such as Mn^{2+}, Fe^{3+} and Na^+ in the interlayer positions, and goethite (α-FeOOH) is assumed to occur in nodules containing iron in concentrations greater than can be accommodated in the layered structure. More recent work on the structure of manganese minerals by R.J. Davis (personal communication) indicates that the 7 Å and 3.5 Å lines of 7 Å manganite may be attributed to (0, 0, ℓ) reflections and the 2.4 and 1.4 Å lines to (h, k, 0) reflections. This suggests the existence of an ideal mineral showing (h, k, ℓ) reflections of which birnessite is the form showing stacking disorder. 7 Å manganite may therefore be considered to be a layer mineral which loses its lines on heating to 120°C to become δ MnO_2. A structure is postulated by Davis in which double layers of close packed oxygen atoms are present with Mn ions in octahedral holes between them. These layers are interleaved with layers of water molecules and alkalies and possibly Mn between these and the oxygen layers. This is similar to the situation in chalcophanite described by Wadsley (1953). The interstitial alkalies prevent the 7 Å manganite from dehydrating smoothly and the basal spacings are lost on heating because the dehydrated material has no regularity in the c-direction.

10 Å manganite is interpreted by Davis as a similar structure having triple layers of close packed oxygens (or hydroxyls), with two layers of intervening octahedrally coordinated manganese ions. These triple layers are interleaved with layers of water as before.

Todorokite is therefore the perfect form of 10 Å manganite, showing (h, k, ℓ) reflections. Electron-diffraction studies on todorokite indicates that it is orthorhombic or monoclinic- and the powder pattern shows multiplets in the position of the (h, k, 0) reflections of 10 Å manganite. There is thus some interest in the effect of heating of 10 Å manganite and todorokite on their X-ray powder patterns and it is possible that a form of δ MnO$_2$ may be produced with layers of symmetry lower than hexagonal, giving multiplets where δ MnO$_2$ gives single lines. There appears to be no evidence that 7 Å manganite and δ MnO$_2$ are compositionally and mineralogically identical with differences in powder pattern resulting from differences in grain size as suggested by Bricker (1965).

These conclusions indicating the interrelation of 10 Å manganite and 7 Å manganite have subsequently been discussed by Burns and Brown (1972). According to these authors, X-ray powder photographs indicate that nodules when formed contained only one distinct authigenic ferromanganese oxide phase "10 Å manganite", which has a 9.8–9.9 Å basal (0, 0, 1) plane. Oxidation of some Mn^{2+} and loss of structural water results in the formation of minute δ MnO$_2$ platelets together with exsolved hydrated iron oxide from the "10 Å manganite". So-called "7 Å manganite" is just the (1, 0, 1) plane in the manganite structure. The "10 Å manganite" was successfully reconstructed from δ MnO$_2$ in laboratory studies under-water pressures of 12,000 psi.

The paragenetic sequence of manganese minerals has been investigated by a number of authors (Bricker, 1965, fig. 29, p. 1338; McKenzie, 1971, fig. 2, p. 501; Givanoli et al., 1970, fig. 7, p. 18a) (e.g., Fig. 5). Several differences exist in the three interpretations, depending on the mineralogical nomenclature employed and the reaction pathways stud- ied. Generally, however, Mn(OH)$_2$ is the first-formed precipitate in the precipitation of manganese oxides in the marine environment. This is then immediately oxidised, giving the appearance of direct precipitation of the more highly oxidised compounds. Glasby (1972b) has discussed the ageing sequence of marine manganese minerals and proposed a

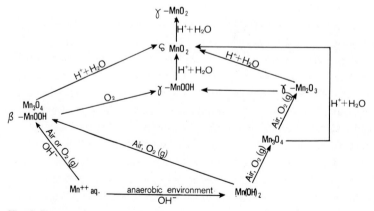

Fig. 5. Paragenetic sequence in the system Mn–O$_2$–H$_2$O at 25°C and 1 atm total pressure. Data from Bricker (1965).

sequence 10 Å manganite → 7 Å manganite → δ MnO_2. The high activation energy for such a phase conversion would probably preclude the above ageing sequence in the marine environment, although Cronan and Tooms (1968) find some evidence for post-depositional migration of manganese within the nodule structure.

So far, no discussion of the mineralogy of the iron oxide phase of nodules has been presented. This is principally because the extremely fine grain size of the iron dioxide phase of nodules precludes its identification by X-ray diffraction techniques. The only examples where identification of the iron oxide phase of nodules by X-ray diffraction has been reported, is in certain Pacific nodules following recrystallisation of the iron oxide phase with hydroxylamine hydrochloride (Arrhenius, 1963; Burns, 1965) and in iron-rich nodules from the Nares Abyssal Plain (Smith et al., 1968) (see also Glasby, 1972c). Johnson and Glasby (1969) therefore investigated the iron oxide mineralogy, using Möss-bauer spectroscopy. The spectra were consistent with the nodules containing iron in the high spin, octahedrally coordinated Fe^{3+} state either as a mixture of α- and γ-FeOOH, or some other combination of iron and manganese oxides. From the hyperfine splitting of the spectrum at low temperatures, Johnson and Glasby (1969) were able to calculate a mean particle diameter for the iron oxide phase to be of the order 100 Å. This corresponds to approximately 10 unit cells and emphasises the cryptocrystallinity of the iron oxide phase of nodules. From electron microprobe analyses, Burns and Brown (1972) were able to show, that iron oxides coat the boundary of the incipient nucleating agent of the nodules before the deposition of manganese oxide occurs. This suggests the possible importance of iron oxides in the formation of manganese nodules, i.e., nodule formation may involve flocculation and deposition of colloidal iron oxides in seawater on to suitable nuclei in cavities under conditions of locally high pH. This is followed by the deposition of manganite by autocatalytic partial oxidation of dissolved Mn II ions or complexes in seawater by the precipitated Fe III oxide.

From a genetic standpoint, there is strong evidence to suggest that the mineralogy of manganese nodules is controlled by the redox characteristics of the sedimentary environment, rather than the kinetics of nucleation or mineralogical ageing phenomena (Glasby, 1972b). Basically, manganese nodules from shallow-water, continental margin environments, such as Loch Fyne, Scotland, the Jervis Inlet, British Columbia, contain 10 Å manganite as the principal mineral phase, whereas those from well oxygenated deep-sea environments, such as the Carlsberg Ridge contain δ MnO_2. The implication is that 10 Å manganite was formed in less oxidising near-shore environments, whereas δ MnO_2 is formed in the more oxygenated deep-sea environments. The boundary conditions for the transition between the various mineralogical phases are, however, imperfectly understood. Cronan (in press), for example, notes the common occurrence of todorokite (10 Å manganite) in Blake and Campbell Plateau nodules compared with the occurrence of highly oxidised birnessite in nodules from seamount provinces. Obviously, therefore, subtle variations in redox characteristics can be responsible for marked changes in nodule mineralogy.

INTERNAL STRUCTURE

It has long been recognised that manganese nodules are heterogeneous, structurally, mineralogically and chemically. The concentric growth structure of nodules was, for example, first recognised by Murray and Renard (1891). These authors leached whole sections of nodules in strong hydrochloric acid and showed that the concentric banding pattern was retained in the silicate minerals incorporated within the nodule structure. At higher magnifications, more detailed structure is visible. Sorem (1967), for example, recognised that the various concentric bands within a single nodule represent ancient outer surfaces of the nodule. Textural differences between the major growth zones within the nodule suggest that the nodule growth rate was not uniform with time. Erosion occurred at certain periods and clastic grains and fossils were incorporated in an ancient outer surface of the nodule at least once. The environmental and growth histories of the nodule were therefore recognised as being complex.

Sorem and Foster (1972a) extended these observations and showed that five distinctive textural patterns can be recognised in the sequences of laminae; these zones are classified as: massive, mottled, compact, columnar and laminated, respectively. The columnar and mottled zones are the most abundant, the massive, compact and columnar zones being less common. Using X-ray macroprobe analysis, the same authors were able to show marked variations in trace-metal contents throughout individual nodules and correlate these with individual growth layers within the nodule (Sorem, 1973; Sorem and Foster, 1972b). From a petrographic study of both the nodule crust and core, Cronan and Tooms (1968) were able to show evidence of manganese replacement of the nodule core. It was therefore suggested that two processes are operative in nodule formation: (1) the leaching and reprecipitation of elements within the original volcanic core; and (2) the processive replacement and coating of these cores by elements derived from seawater. The former gives rise to the isolated segregations within the nodule core, while ageing of the material precipitated from seawater is responsible for the close packed segregation in the nodule crusts. It will be recognised that this hypothesis envisages a certain amount of post-depositional ageing and remobilisation of manganese within the nodule structure.

Dunham and Glasby (1974) described in more detail the concentric growth cusps within the nodule (Fig. 6). Crystallisation of these cusps begins at nuclei perhaps 0.05 mm apart. Growth then continues as shown in Fig. 7. As the cusps grow upwards, they also grow sideways but leave delta-shaped areas between the cusps. Here, clay minerals, possibly of clastic origin, collect. Finally, the cusps coalesce. When the cusps reach some critical size, two or more new nucleating centres form, causing the cusps to bifurcate. At any stage during this process, a continuous layer running across the ends of all the cusps may form. The cusp size is probably a function of the relative rates of nucleation, which in turn is dependent on the variation of some external environmental parameter, such as bottom temperature or redox conditions of the environment. The cusp size and shape can vary considerably both within a single nodule and between nodules from different sampling sites as shown by Glasby (1972a).

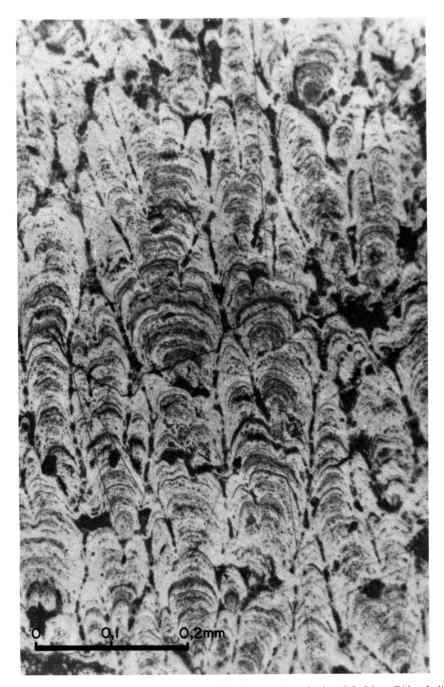

Fig. 6. Photomicrograph of manganese nodules from western flanks of Carlsberg Ridge, Indian Ocean (2°56.5′N 60°02.3′E–2°56.5′N 60°03.3′E; 4259–3926 m). Magnification 75X.

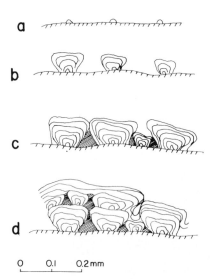

Fig. 7. Suggested mode of formation of growth cusps of deep-sea nodules. Reproduced from Dunham and Glasby (1974, fig. 12).

Fig. 8. Scanning electron photomicrograph of an ethched polished section of a nodule from the Indian—Antactic Ridge (54°56′S 154°46′E–55°00′S 115°00′E; 4060–4279 m) showing details of cusp lamination structure. Note irregularity in lamellae thickness. Magnification: 320 X. Reproduced from Margolis and Glasby (1973, fig. 3F, p. 3605).

A considerable advance in the study of nodule structure has recently been made by the use of scanning electron microscopy (Margolis and Glasby, 1973). Using this technique, these authors were able to show the presence of microfine laminae 0.25–10 μm thick, which appear to be a characteristic growth feature of deep-sea nodules (Fig. 8). These laminae are the smallest discrete limit of nodule structure so far resolved and individual laminae can be traced for considerable distances throughout the nodule. These laminae may represent one of two possibilities; either discontinuous growth at the nodule surface or recrystallisation phenomena. Tentatively, it was suggested that these laminae are a function of the discontinuous growth of the nodule on a time scale of 25–10,000 y and possibly represent the influence of long-term fluctuations in bottom current velocities. Whatever their origin, recognition of these laminae is of the utmost importance in understanding the genesis of nodules. Other scanning electron microscope studies of manganese nodules have been made by Fewkes (1973) and Woo (1973).

DETERMINATION OF VALENCY STATES

Manganese and iron exist in manganese nodules predominantly in tetra- and trivalent states, respectively (Manheim, 1965; Johnson and Glasby, 1969). Because of their low concentrations in nodules, however, the valency states of other transition metals have not been well documented and are the subject of considerable speculation. This has led to considerable uncertainty in the mechanism of removal of these trace metals from seawater by marine manganese oxides. Among the elements for which this problem is important are: cerium (Goldberg, 1965; Ehrlich, 1968; Glasby, 1973d); cobalt (Burns, 1965; Goldberg, 1965); nickel (Burns and Fyfe, 1967; Burns, 1970); lead (Goldberg, 1965); vanadium and uranium (Glasby, 1970) Basically, the problem of whether these elements are oxidised to a higher valency state during their incorporation in manganese nodules.

For manganese itself, Andermann (1972) has suggested the possible use of high resolution X-ray photo emission and X-ray photon induced photoelectron emission spectroscopy for determining the orbital characteristics of manganese and the relative abundances of Mn^{2+} and Mn^{4+} in the nodule structure. Neither technique is capable of solving this technique by visual inspection of spectra but require the use of sophisticated curve fitting techniques to achieve the necessary results. For the less abundant transition elements, electron spin resonance (E.S.R.) spectroscopy appears to be a useful technique for determining the number of unpaired electrons, and hence valency state, of transition metals and was investigated as a possible solution to this problem.

E.S.R. spectra were determined on nodules from three different localities and the spectra of salts of a series of transition metals were determined for comparative purposes (A.F. Ward and G.P. Glasby, unpublished data) (Fig. 9). For each nodule, broad spectra were obtained and no fine structure was observed due to the line broadening caused by the very high concentrations of paramagnetic ions. Differences were, however, apparent

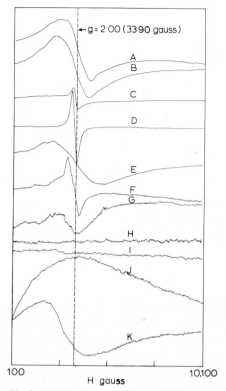

Fig. 9. E.S.R. spectra of: *A* nodule 6269, Carlsberg Ridge, Indian Ocean: *B* nodule Z2139A, South Tasman Basin; *C* nodule, Loch Fyne, Scotland; *D* $MnSO_4$. $4H_2O$; *E* MnO_2; *F* $FeSO_4$. $7H_2O$; *G* Fe_2O_3; *H* black CuO; *I* mixture NiO and Ni_2O_3; *J* grey cobalt oxide CoO; and *K* black cobalt oxide Co_2O_3. The spectra were taken at room temperature on a Varian V4502-15 X-band E.S.R. spectrometer using 100 kHz modulation.

between the spectra of deep-sea nodules from the Carlsberg Ridge, Indian Ocean, and the South Tasman Basin and that of a shallow-water nodule from Loch Fyne, Scotland. Basically, the deep-sea nodules showed a characteristic broad-line spectrum similar to MnO_2, whereas the Loch Fyne nodule displayed a narrow-line spectrum with a line width approximately 1/7th of that of the deep-sea nodules. The Loch Fyne spectrum correlated closely with that of $MnSO_4$ and suggests, that the Loch Fyne nodule contains a proportion of divalent manganous ion in agreement with the findings of Manheim (1965) that shallow-water manganese nodules show appreciably lower oxidation states (and hence higher manganous ion contents), than deep-sea nodules. These preliminary results suggest that E.S.R. spectra may be used to identify qualitatively the presence of the divalent manganous ion in manganese nodules and thus to evaluate the redox characteristics of the depositional environment of the nodule. Quantitative evaluation of the results would, however, require detailed computer simulation of the powder spectra of artificial standards.

Comparison of the nodules spectra with those of the transition metal salts indicates some similarity in the spectra of deep-sea nodules with that of the trivalent cobalt oxide but no similarity with the spectra of divalent copper or nickel oxides. The application of E.S.R. spectroscopy to the determination of transition metal-valency states therefore appears to be less suitable than anticipated. A fuller account of the E.S.R. spectra of nodules has recently been presented by Wakeham and Carpenter (1973, 1974).

RATES AND MECHANISMS OF ACCRETION OF NODULES

Rates of accretion of deep-sea manganese deposits have traditionally been determined by radiometric dating techniques (e.g., Bender et al., 1966, 1970; Sackett, 1966; Somaya-julu, 1967; Ku and Broecker, 1969; Somayajulu et al., 1971; Krishnaswamy and Lal, 1972; Krishnaswamy et al., 1972; Schornick, 1972; Bertine and Turekian, 1973; Bhat et al., 1973; Heye and Beiersdorf, 1973; Moore, W.S., 1973; Ku, in press). Of these, the ionium/thorium method has found the most widespread application. Basically, this technique involved the determination of the content of ionium (^{230}Th) relative to a stable reference isotope of thorium (^{232}Th) at a series of depths within the nodule.* From a knowledge of the half-life of the ^{230}Th, the age of a particular horizon within the nodule can be determined and the mean rate of accretion of the nodule calculated. Because of the low content of uranium relative to thorium in the nodule compared with normal seawater, the contribution of uranium-supported thorium is generally small and a correction factor can be applied to allow for this.

Using this technique, Ku and Broecker (1969) were able to show that deep-sea manganese deposits accrete at an extremely slow rate of the order $1-6$ mm/10^6 year and that the distribution of ^{230}Th and ^{231}Pa on the surface of a given nodule is not uniform. Higher concentrations of these isotopes are observed on the upper surface of the nodule rather than the underside, suggesting that these nuclides are precipitated only on those portions of the nodule in contact with seawater. From a consideration of the relative enrichment of these nuclides on the upper and lower surfaces of tabular and rounded nodules, it was concluded that nodules must overturn on the sea floor with overturn times as long as tens or hundreds of thousands of years. Further studies revealed that in shallow water, continental margin environments, such as lochs or fjords where diagenetic remobilisation of manganese can occur within the sediment column, rates of accretion of manganese nodules were at least two orders of magnitude higher than in the deep sea (Ku and Glasby, 1972; Dean et al., 1973; Krishnaswamy and Moore, 1973).

In spite of the apparent success of these dating techniques in determining the rates of accretion of manganese nodules, one disturbing feature remains; why is the measured rate

---

* Uranium is stabilised in seawater as the soluble tricarbonate uranyl ion $UO_2(CO_3)_3^{4-}$ whereas the thorium ion Th^{4+} is easily hydrolysed in seawater.

of accretion of manganese nodules so much lower than the measured rate of deposition of the surrounding sediment? If this is indeed so, it would be anticipated that nodules would become rapidly buried by sediment. This is contrary to all observations which show conclusively that nodules occur predominantly at the sediment—water interface.

Several criticisms may be levelled at the radiometric dating technique. For example, petrographic evidence shows the existence of sharp discontinuities within certain deep-sea nodules (Glasby, 1970). Since both the $^{230}Th/^{232}Th$ and $^{230}Th/^{231}Pa$ methods of dating rely on the determination of the radiometric decay in the upper 1 mm of the nodule for the assessment of average growth rate (cf., Ku and Broecker, 1969), the existence of a sharp break in the banding structure of the nodule suggests a possible hiatus in growth rate, which would invalidate any attempt to extrapolate the measured growth rate over a considerable period of time. This effect may not be as critical in nodules from shallow-water, continental environments where such discontinuities have not been observed (Glasby, 1970), but other factors, such as the resolution of manganese with changing sedimentary conditions (Murray and Irvine, 1895), could invalidate measured growth rates in this type of environment. In addition, the concentration of manganese in concentrically banded growth structures, having a mean period of formation of the order of 50,000 years, poses severe sampling problems for isotope methods involving nuclides having half-lives of the order 80,000 and 34,000 years, respectively. As a minimum requirement, therefore, all future radiometric determinations of nodule growth rates should be accompanied by a detailed petrographic analysis of the nodule.

One serious criticism of the radiometric determination of slow growth rates of nodules has recently been presented by Lalou and her coworkers (Lalou and Brichet, 1972; Lalou et al., 1973a, b, c). These authors established the presence of "excess" ^{14}C and ^{230}Th in the nuclei of certain nodules and sought to interpret this in terms of the recent "epigenisation" of the nuclei of the nodules and, hence, the rapid growth of the surrounding manganese oxide layers. This hypothesis is very attractive when compared with the slow growth rate hypothesis in so much as it apparently overcomes the problem of the difference in growth rate of the nodule compared with that of the surrounding sediment. Two major objections may be raised against Lalou's arguments, however: firstly, the implicit assumption that the nodule nucleus represents a closed system so that no post-depositional diagenetic changes can occur to incorporate these isotopes (i.e., ^{14}C and ^{230}Th) in the nucleus *after* the onset of deposition of manganese, and secondly, the assumption that nodule formation is a world-wide phenomenon which occurred over a geologically short period of time and ceased approximately 5,000 years ago. To assume that nodules formed in this way as a result of a catastrophic change in seawater chemistry due to some agent, such as submarine volcanism, has no other geological supporting evidence from studies of sediment cores; does not explain the formation of manganese nodules in many different types of environments (such as lakes and lochs); does not explain the discrete stratigraphic horizons observed in sections of nodules (e.g., Sorem and Foster, 1972a, b) and assumes a geologic event of such magnitude as to be unreasonable. Much further work needs to be carried out on the natural occurrence of "excess" ^{14}C and ^{230}Th in material occurring on the sea floor which has nct been coated by manganese oxides before this hypothesis can be accepted. Thus, although radiometric dating is an invaluable tool in dating nodules, it does possess certain inherent deficiencies which have previously not been well documented by its proponents.

A second technique that has recently been developed for nodule dating is the hydration rind dating technique (Morgenstein, 1972b). In this method, it is assumed that under conditions of constant temperature, availability of water, and glass composition, sideromelane (and other mafic glasses) will hydrate to palagonite at a constant rate and that this rate is linear with time. Rates of palagonite hydration have been determined through corresponding radiogenic and palaeontologic dating of glass, both in the marine and terrestrial environments, and from this ages of unknown samples can be calculated from a determination of hydration rind thickness. Using this technique, Morgenstein (1972b) was able to show that the rates of accretion of manganese nodules on the Waho Shelf, Hawaii, are about 2–3 times faster than those reported from the deep sea, and that the growth rates are not constant but vary considerably with time within a given nodule. Of particular interest is the observation that the average diameter of manganese botryoids within the nodule increases almost linearly with increasing manganese accretion rate. This is in direct contradiction to the suggestion of Dunham and Glasby (1974) that slow accretion rates should lead to large botryoid size. The results do, however, confirm the extremely low rates of accretion of deep-sea manganese deposits determined by radiometric techniques, but again this method depends upon standards whose age has been determined by radiometric or foraminiferal dating. Thus, there is a fundamental inconsistency in our present understanding of nodule genesis; why are nodules found dominantly at the sediment–water interface? Perhaps the action of bottom currents or burrowing of benthic organisms or even seismic activity (Olausson and Uusitalo, 1964; Emiliani and Milliman, 1966) is involved in uncovering the nodule at the sediment–water interface, or perhaps the dilemma is an artifact resulting from limitations inherent in present methods of determination of nodule accretion rate. The fact that the bulk density of manganese nodules (1.96 g/cm^3; Ku, in press) does not greatly exceed that of deep-sea sediments, such as radiolarian clay from the equatorial Pacific (1.20–1.47 g/cm^3; Shumway, 1960; Keller and Bennett, 1972) suggests that the upward force required to maintain nodules at the sediment surface must be relatively small and that it must be well within the capability of benthic organisms to do this given the time scale available. However, this remains one of the most perplexing and unresolved problems in the study of nodule genesis.

Several mechanisms of accretion of marine manganese deposits have been postulated. Perhaps the most widely accepted is the colloidal scavenging hypothesis of Goldberg (1954). According to this author, the observed inter-element relations in manganese nodules (i.e., Fe–Ti–Co–Zr; Mn–Cu–Ni) can be interpreted in terms of the adsorption of anionic species of titanium, cobalt and nickel from seawater by the positively charged colloidal

iron oxide, and of cationic species of copper and nickel by the negatively charged colloidal manganese oxide. Although this hypothesis has been substantially modified by
modern developments in electrochemical theory, its basic statement of the role of sorption in controlling incorporation of trace metals into manganese nodules is still valid (cf.,
Glasby, 1974).

More recently, several interesting ideas have been presented regarding the precise
manner of nucleating of the manganese and iron oxides in manganese nodules. Burns and
Brown (1972) have examined the boundaries of detrital material within manganese nodules, using the electron microprobe and shown that iron coats the incipient nucleating
agent before the deposition of manganese plus trace metals can occur. This suggests the
possibility that the initial formation of manganese nodules takes place by flocculation
and deposition of colloidal iron oxides in seawater on to suitable nuclei under conditions
of locally high pH. This is then followed by the deposition of manganite by autocatalytic
partial oxidation of dissolved manganous ions by the precipitated iron oxides. Morgenstein and Felsher (1971) have proposed that in nodules containing palagonite as the
nucleus, the process of palagonitisation is the principal catalytic agent in the promotion
of ferromanganese oxide deposition. According to this hypothesis, leaching of iron and
manganese takes place during the diagenetic solution of palagonite. The volume increase
associated with the palagonite formation results in fracturing of the palagonite and the
iron and manganese are then able to interpenetrate the pores of the palagonite and form
ferromanganese oxide coatings. Obviously, this process ceases when the process of palagonitisation is complete and is replaced by the normal autocatalytic oxidation of manganese
from seawater by the ferromanganese oxides already incorporated in the nodule. Although this hypothesis is clearly restricted to nodules containing palagonite as the nucleus, it does perhaps explain the efficacy of palagonite as a nucleating agent for manganese nodules compared with other material found in the deep sea.

THERMOCHEMICAL CONSIDERATIONS

In considering the deposition of manganese nodules from a thermodynamic viewpoint,
their formation is often described by the oxidation of manganous ions to $\delta \, MnO_2$ (e.g.,
Crerar and Barnes, 1974):

$$Mn^{2+}_{aq} + \tfrac{1}{2} \, O_2(aq) + 2 \, OH^-_{aq} \rightarrow \delta \, MnO_2(s) + H_2O \, (l) \tag{1}$$

In order to decide whether ocean waters are far removed from equilibrium with respect to
manganous ions, the equilibrium constant at 2°C, 500 atm has been calculated, using
standard free energy data and the result compared with the equilibrium constant calculated from analytical values appropriate to a depth of 5,000 m (2°C, 500 atm).

Using the self-consistent data listed in Table III, the free energy change is calculated to

TABLE III

Summary of thermodynamic data (1 atm, 25°C) used in the calculations*

	ΔG_f° (kcal mol^{-1})	ΔH_f°(kcal mol^{-1})	S° (cal deg^{-1} mol^{-1})	C_p° (cal deg^{-1} mol^{-1})
MnO_2 (s)	−111.18	−124.29	12.68	12.94
H_2O (l)	− 56.687	− 68.315	16.71	17.995
OH_{aq}^-	− 37.594	− 54.970	− 2.57	−35.5
Mn_{aq}^{2+}	− 54.5	− 52.76	−17.6	12
O_2(aq)	3.9	− 2.8	26.5	7.16

* The data in this table were compiled from Wagman et al. (1968, 1969) and Khodakovskiy et al. (1968).

be:

$$\Delta G \text{ (1 atm, 25°C)} = -40.13 \text{ kcal mol}^{-1} \quad \{K_1(1 \text{ atm, 25°C}) = 10^{29.4}\}$$

From the standard thermodynamic relationships:

$$\Delta G = \Delta H - T \Delta S$$

$$\left(\frac{\partial \Delta H}{\partial T}\right)_p = \Delta C_p$$

$$\Delta S = \Delta C_p \int d\ln T$$

Assuming that ΔC_p is independent of temperature, the free energy change for reaction (1) at 2°C and 1 atm is then calculated from the date in Table III to be −39.13 kcal mol^{-1} $\{K_1$ (1 atm, 2°C) = $10^{31.1}\}$. However, if the free energy of formation of δ MnO_2 determined by Bricker (1965) (−108.3 kcal mol^{-1}) is used ΔG (1 atm, 2°C) is then calculated to be −36.29 kcal mol^{-1} $\{K_1$ (1 atm, 2°C) = $10^{28.8}\}$.

To estimate the pressure effect on reaction (1), it is better to use partial molar volumes for seawater (Millero, 1969) rather than values referring to infinite dilution. The pressure effect is not large (Glasby, 1972d). Using the data listed in Table IV, the free energy change is calculated by means of the relationship:

$$\left(\frac{\partial \Delta G}{\partial P}\right)_T = -\Delta V$$

to be 0.43 kcal mol^{-1} for an increase in pressure of 500 atm giving ΔG (500 atm, 2°C) = −35.86 kcal mol^{-1} and K_1 (500 atm, 2°C) = $10^{28.5}$. In this calculation, the compressibility change of reaction (1) and the effects of temperature on the volume change have

TABLE IV

Summary of molar volumes, and partial molar ionic volumes in seawater used in the calculations*

	$V/cm^3\ mol^{-1}$	Reference
MnO_2	16.6	Robie et al. (1967)
H_2O	17.6**	Keenan et al. (1969)
OH^-_{aq}	1.2	Millero (1969)
Mn^{2+}_{aq}	−18.8	Millero (1969, 1971)
$O_2(aq)$	30.0	Tiepel and Gubbins (1972)

* These values refer to 25°C.
** The effect of salt concentration on this value is minor (Lewis and Randall, 1961).

been neglected. Clearly, manganous ions are unstable with respect to oxidation to δ MnO_2 in oxygenated seawater under the conditions encountered in the deep-sea environment.

A comparison of the equilibrium constant estimated above with that calculated from experimental values at depth is hampered by a lack of precise experimental details of the manganous, oxygen and hydroxyl ion activities relevant to conditions of nodule growth, i.e., immediately adjacent to the sediment–water interface. The concentrations of total soluble manganese in seawater have been carefully determined by Riley and Taylor (1968), using a rigorously tested method. For the present calculation we take the soluble manganese concentration at depth to be 3.5 μgl^{-1} (6.5 · 10^{-8} mol l^{-1}). This value represents an upper limit to the concentration of free manganous ions and reactions leading to a reduction of the free ion concentration must be considered. Activity coefficients used in the following calculations were estimated (where possible) by the mean salt method (Garrels and Christ, 1965) and are listed in Table V. Hydrolysis of manganous ions at a pH of 8 is of little consequence (Perrin, 1962). Complexing with bicarbonate may also be neglected (Gamsjager et al., 1970) (see also Hem, 1963a), and, while data on

TABLE V

Summary of activity coefficient data used in the calculations*

Cl^-	0.64	CO_3^{2-}	0.20
HCO_3^-	0.68	SO_4^{2-}	0.12
$MnHCO_3^+$	0.68	$MnCO_4^0$	1.13
$MnCl^+$	0.68	$MnCO_3^0$	1.13
Mn^{2+}	0.28	$O_2(aq)$	1.2

* The data in this table were obtained from Garrels and Christ (1965).

the formation of $MnCO_3^0$ ion pairs is not available, the correlation of data for the formation of carbonate ion pairs for other divalent ions suggests that 5–10% of the total manganese may be present as $MnCO_3^0$ ion pairs (Garrels and Christ, 1965; see also Garrels and Thompson, 1962). The ion pair formation constant for manganous sulphate ion pairs determined by Fisher and Davis (1965) at $5 \cdot 10^{-4}$ mol l^{-1} $MnSO_4$ and at 500 atm is 209. Using this figure and data from Table V, we estimate the concentration ratio $(MnSO_4^0)/(Mn_{aq}^{2+})$ to be 0.09. A similar calculation for ion pairing with chloride yields the ratio $(MnCl_{aq}^+)/(Mn_{aq}^{2+}) = 0.2$ (Masterton and Berka, 1966). In making these calculations, association by chloride and sulphate with other cations has been taken into account using data from Garrels and Christ (1965), but the effects of pressure and temperature on the association constants and activity coefficients have not been included. It is therefore estimated that soluble manganese concentration contains about 25% as ion pairs with inorganic species and the free manganese ion concentration is taken to be $4.9 \cdot 10^{-10}$ mol l^{-1}. Data on the complexing with organic ligands is not available and has not been considered.

The pH immediately above the sediment–water interface is not available from in situ measurements and must be estimated from shipboard determinations, making the appropriate adjustments for temperature and pressure. There has been much discussion over the origin of the oceanic buffer capacity and Sillen (1967) considers heterogeneous aluminosilicate reactions to be important in controlling pH. On the other hand, the evidence provided by Culberson and Pytkowicz (1968) supports the commonly held view that it is the ionization of carbonic acid which is predominant in determining the pH of seawater. In these calculations, the methods of Culberson and Pytkowicz (1968) are followed and the pH at 2°C and 500 atm is estimated to be 8.0. The effect of decreasing the temperature from 25°C to 2°C is to increase the pH by 0.2 and increasing the pressure to 500 atm decreases the pH by a similar amount, thereby compensating the effect due to the temperature change. To obtain the activity of hydroxyl ions from this figure, the ionic activity product of water at 2°C, 500 atm is estimated to be $2.4 \cdot 10^{-15}$ (Harned and Owen, 1958) giving $a_{OH^-} = 2.4 \cdot 10^{-7}$. The concentration of dissolved oxygen at depth is taken to be 4 m l^{-1} at N.T.P. ($1.78 \cdot 10^{-4}$ mol l^{-1}) (Richards, 1957). The activities of water and δ MnO_2 are taken as unity. Using the above figures and data from Table V the "equilibrium" constant of reaction (1) is found to be $K_1' = 10^{24.3}$. This value is much smaller than that calculated from the free energy change ($K_1 = 10^{28.5}$). So if we accept the pH and oxygen concentration given above as applying to the conditions of nodule growth and providing there is no extensive complexing of manganous ions by reactions not considered above, then clearly (since $K_1/K_1' = 10^{4.2}$) seawater is supersaturated with manganous ions by several orders of magnitude.

This conclusion rests on the assumption (and others) that the bulk oxygen fugacity is also that in contact with the δ MnO_2 phase. Now it is well known that the surface of δ MnO_2 in an aqueous solution of pH 8 is negatively charged (Healy et al., 1966) facilitating the adsorption of manganese and other cations. The autocatalytic nature of the oxidation of manganous ions is also well known (see for example, Morgan, 1967) and in conjunction with the reasonable suggestions by Bricker (1965), regarding reaction paths for the oxidation of Mn_{aq}^{2+} to δ MnO_2, it seems likely that during oxidation the δ MnO_2 core will be covered with a film of manganese oxide containing Mn III. If this is so, then the fugacity of oxygen to be substituted in the equilibrium expression describing the reaction:

$$Mn_{aq}^{2+} + \tfrac{1}{2} O_2(g) + 2\, OH_{aq}^- \rightleftarrows \delta\, MnO_2\, (s) + H_2O\, (l) \tag{2}$$

at 1 atm and $25°C$ is not 0.2 atm (neglecting the fugacity coefficient) but is that at the δ MnO_2 surface as described by reactions such as

$$Mn_2O_3 + \tfrac{1}{2} O_2 \rightarrow \delta\, MnO_2 \tag{3}$$

$$K_3 = 1/P_{O_2}^{\frac{1}{2}} = 10^{4.4}$$

and

$$Mn_3O_4 + O_2 \rightarrow 3\, MnO_2 \tag{4}$$

$$K_4 = 1/P_{O_2} = 10^{13.3}$$

A description along similar lines for the "stationary state" existing for the oxidation of copper in aerated solution has been noted by Read (1972).

Assuming that Mn_2O_3 is the phase in contact with the δ MnO_2 core, then $P_{O_2}^{\frac{1}{2}} = 10^{-4.4}$ at the δ MnO_2 surface, and the ratio $K_2(0.2\ atm)/K_2\ (10^{-4.4}\ atm) = 10^{-4.05}$. Provided this ratio is largely independent of temperature, pressure and salinity effects, the comparison of this value with the value for the ratio K_1/K_1' $(10^{4.5})$ suggests that seawater may not be far removed from equilibrium as described by reactions (1) and (2), perhaps less than an order of magnitude, and that the phase in contact with δ MnO_2 may be Mn_2O_3.

It should be noted in passing, that the inference to be drawn from the Eh–pH measurements of Baas Becking et al. (1960) in conjunction with the Eh–pH diagram published by Bricker (1965) is, that seawater is undersaturated with manganous ions by several orders of magnitude. This conclusion is not supported by the Eh–pH measurements of Hem (1963b) (from studies of the oxidation of manganous ions), which correspond to the Eh–pH diagrams when oxidation was commenced at pH values rather higher than those for seawater. The manganous ion concentrations used in these experiments was quite high (10 ppm). Is is now generally realised that Eh measurements in natural systems such as seawater represent mixed potentials and cannot, at present, provide reliable evidence on individual redox reactions (see e.g., Morris and Stumm, 1967). This is particularly the case when individual reaction components are present in very low concentrations and where electrochemical reversibility is not attained and indicates the limitations of experimentally measured Eh values in describing redox equilibria in seawater (see also Riley and Chester, 1971; Liss et al., 1973).

ACKNOWLEDGEMENTS

The authors would like to thank Mr A.F. Ward, Physics and Engineering Laboratory, Lower Hutt, New Zealand, for permission to publish the previously unpublished E.S.R. spectra of manganese nodules.

REFERENCES

Agassiz, A., 1902. Reports on the scientific results of the expedition to the tropical Pacific, in charge of Alexander Agassiz, by the U.S. Fish Commission Steamer "Albatross", from August 1899, to March 1900, Commander Jefferson F. Moser, U.S.N., Commanding. I. Preliminary report and list of stations. *Mem. Mus. Comp. Zool. Harv.*, 26: 1–108.

Agassiz, A., 1906. Reports on the scientific results of the expedition to the eastern tropical Pacific, in charge of Alexander Agassiz, by the U.S. Fish Commission Steamer "Albatross", from October 1904, to March 1905, Lieut. Commander L.M. Garrett, U.S.N., Commanding. V. General report of the expedition. *Mem. Mus. Comp. Zool. Harv.*, 33: 1–75.

Andermann, G., 1972. An evaluation of analytical techniques to obtain spectroscopic characterization of molecular properties of manganese nodules. *Hawaii Inst. Geophys. Rep., HIG–72–23:* 113–125.

Andrews, J.E., 1972. Distribution of manganese nodules in the Hawaiian Archipelago. In: *Manganese Nodule Deposits in the Pacific Symposium/Workshop Proceedings Honolulu, Hawaii, October 16–17, 1972.* State Cent. Sci. Policy Technol. Assess., Dep. Plann. Econ. Dev., State of Hawaii, pp. 61–65.

Andrews, J.E. and Meylan, M.A., 1972. Results of bottom photography: Kana Keoki cruise Manganese '72. *Hawaii Inst. Geophys. Rep., HIG–72–23:* 83–111.

Andrews, J.E. and Meylan, M.A., 1973. Bathymetry and manganese accretion in a region of the Equatorial Pacific. *EOS, Trans. Am. Geophys. Union,* 54 (4): 339 (Abstract).

Anonymous, 1973. Mining: U.S. project to scoop ores from the seabed. *The Times,* April 23: 8.

Arrhenius, G., 1963. Pelagic sediments, In: M.N. Hill (Editor), *The Sea.* Interscience, New York, N.Y., 3: 665–727.

Arrhenius, G., 1967. Deep-sea sedimentation: A critical review of U.S. work. *Trans. Am. Geophys. Union,* 48: 604–631.

Arrhenius, G. and Bonatti, E., 1965. Neptunism and vulcanism in the ocean. *Prog. Oceanogr.* 3: 7–22.

Arrhenius, G., Mero, J. and Korkisch, J., 1964. Origin of oceanic manganese minerals. *Science,* 144: 170–173.

Audley-Charles, M.G., 1972. Cretaceous deep-sea manganese nodules on Timor: implications for tectonics and Olistostrome development. *Nature Phys. Sci.,* 240: 137–139.

Aumento, F., Lawrence, D.E. and Plant, A.G., 1968. The ferro-manganese pavement on San Pablo Seamount. *Geol. Surv. Pap. Can.,* 68–32: 1–30.

Baas Becking, L.G.M., Kaplan, I.R. and Moore, D., 1960. Limits of the natural environment in terms of pH and oxidation–reduction potential. *J. Geol.,* 68: 243–284.

Barten, K.S. and Shaw, J.L., 1969. A Monte Carlo simulator for predicting the feasibility of deep ocean mining operations. *Oceanol. Int. Conf., Session D.,* 10 pp.

Bender, M.L., Ku, T-L. and Broecker, W.S., 1966. Manganese nodules: their evolution. *Science,* 151: 325–328.

Bender, M.L., Ku, T-L. and Broecker, W.S., 1970. Accumulation rates of manganese in pelagic sediments and nodules. *Earth Planet. Sci. Lett.,* 8: 143–148.

Bertine, K.K. and Turekian, K.K., 1973. Molybdenum in marine deposits. *Geochim. Cosmochim. Acta,* 37: 1415–1434.

Bezrukov, P.L., 1973. On the sedimentation in the northern part of the South Pacific. In: R. Fraser (Editor). *Oceanography of the South Pacific 1972,* N.Z. Nat. Comm. UNESCO, Wellington, pp. 217–219.

Bhat, S.G., Krishnaswamy, S., Lal, D., Rama and Somayajulu, B.L.K., 1973. Radiometric and trace-element studies of ferro-manganese nodules. *Proc. Symp. Hydrogeochem. Biogeochem., Tokyo,* 1: 443–462.

Blissenbach, E. and Fellerer, R., 1973. Continental drift and the origin of certain mineral deposits. *Geol. Rundsch.,* 62: 812–840.

Bonatti, E. and Nayudu, Y.R., 1965. The origin of manganese nodules on the ocean floor. *Am. J. Sci.,* 263: 17–39.

Bonatti, E., Kraemer, T. and Rydell, H., 1972. Classification and genesis of submarine iron-manganese deposits. In: D.R. Horn (Editor), *Ferromanganese Deposits on the Ocean Floor.* Nat. Sci. Found., Washington, D.C., pp. 149–166.

Bricker, O.P., 1965. Some stability relations in the system $Mn-O_2-H_2O$ at 25°C and one atmosphere total pressure. *Am. Miner.,* 50: 1296–1354.

Brown, B.A., 1972. A low-temperature crushing technique applied to manganese nodules. *Am. Miner.,* 57: 284–287.

Brundage, W.L., 1972. Patterns of manganese pavement distribution on the Blake Plateau. In: D.R. Horn (Editor), *Ferromanganese Deposits on the Ocean Floor.* Nat. Sci. Found., Washington, D.C., pp. 221–250.

Burns, R.G., 1965. Formation of cobalt (III) in the amorphous $FeOOH \cdot nH_2O$ phase of manganese nodules. *Nature,* 205: 999.

Burns, R.G., 1970. *Mineralogical Applications of Crystal Field Theory.* Cambridge Univ. Press, London, 224 pp.

Burns, R.G. and Brown, B.A., 1972. Nucleation and mineralogical controls on the composition of manganese nodules. In: D.R. Horn (Editor), *Ferromanganese Deposits on the Ocean Floor.* Nat. Sci. Found., Washington, D.C., pp. 51–61.

Burns, R.G. and Fuerstenau, D.W., 1966. Electron-probe determinations of inter-element relationships in manganese nodules. *Am. Miner.,* 51: 895–902.

Burns, R.G. and Fyfe, W.S., 1967. Crystal-field theory and the geochemistry of transition elements. In: P.H. Abelson (Editor), *Researches in Geochemistry.* Wiley, New York, N.Y., 2: 259–285.

Buser, W. and Grütter, A., 1956. Über die Natur der manganknollen. *Schweiz. Miner. Petrogr. Mitt.,* 36: 49–62.

Callender, E., 1973. Geochemistry of ferromanganese crusts, manganese carbonate crusts, and associated ferromanganese nodules from Green Bay, Lake Michigan. In: *Inter-University Program of Research on Ferromanganese Deposits of the Ocean Floor, Phase I Report.* Nat. Sci. Found., Washington, D.C., pp. 105–120.

Calvert, S.E. and Price, N.B., 1970. Composition of manganese nodules and manganese carbonates from Loch Fyne, Scotland. *Contrib. Miner. Petrol.,* 29: 215–233.

Cook, H.E., 1971. Iron and manganese rich sediments overlying oceanic basaltic basement, Equatorial Pacific, Leg 9, D.S.D.P. *Prog. Geol. Soc. Am.,* 3: 530–531 (Abstract).

Cook, H.E., 1972. Stratigraphy and sedimentation. In: *Initial Reports of the Deep Sea Drilling Project.* U.S. Gov. Print. Off., Washington, D.C., 9: 933–943.

Crerar, D.A. and Barnes, H.L., 1974. Deposition of deep-sea manganese nodules. *Geochim. Cosmochim. Acta,* 38: 279–300.

Cronan, D.S., 1972. Regional geochemistry of ferromanganese nodules in the world ocean. In: D.R. Horn (Editor), *Ferromanganese Deposits on the Ocean Floor*. Nat. Sci. Found., Washington, D.C., pp. 19–30.

Cronan, D.S., 1973a. Manganese nodules in sediments cored during Leg 16, Deep Sea Drilling Project. In: *Initial Reports of the Deep Sea Drilling Project*. U.S. Gov. Print. Off., Washington, D.C., 9: 605–608.

Cronan, D.S., 1973b. Basal ferruginous sediments cored during Leg 16, Deep Sea Drilling Project, In: *Initial Reports of the Deep Sea Drilling Project*. U.S. Gov. Print. Off., Washington, D.C. 16: 601–604.

Cronan, D.S., in preparation. Deep-sea manganese nodules: distribution and geochemistry. In: G.P. Glasby (Editor), *Marine Manganese Deposits*. Elsevier, Amsterdam.

Cronan, D.S. and Tooms, J.S., 1967a. Sub-surface concentrations of manganese nodules in Pacific sediments. *Deep-Sea Res.*, 14: 117–119.

Cronan, D.S. and Tooms, J.S., 1967b. Geochemistry of manganese nodules from the N.W. Indian Ocean. *Deep-Sea Res.*, 14: 239–249.

Cronan, D.S. and Tooms, J.S., 1968. A microscopic and electron probe investigation of manganese nodules from the Northwest Indian Ocean. *Deep-Sea Res.*, 15: 215–223.

Cronan, D.S. and Tooms, J.S., 1969. The geochemistry of manganese nodules and associated pelagic deposits from the Pacific and Indian Oceans. *Deep-Sea Res.*, 16: 355–359.

Culberson, C. and Pytkowicz, R.M., 1968. Effect of pressure on carbonic acid, boric acid and the pH in seawater. *Limnol. Oceanogr.*, 13: 403–417.

Dean, W.E., Ghosh, S.K., Krishnaswami, S. and Moore, W.S., 1973. Chemistry and accretion rates of freshwater ferromanganese nodules. In: M. Morgenstein (Editor), *The Origin and Distribution of Manganese Nodules in the Pacific and Prospects for Exploration*. A symposium organised by the Valdivia Manganese Explor. Group and the Hawaii Inst. Geophys., Honolulu, Hawaii, pp. 13–20.

Dietz, R.A., 1955. Manganese deposits on the Northeast Pacific sea-floor. *Calif. J. Mines Geol.*, 57: 209–220.

Drever, J.I., 1971. Chemical and mineralogical studies, site 66. In: *Initial Reports of the Deep Sea Drilling Project*. U.S. Gov. Print. Off., Washington, D.C., 7: 965–968.

Dunham, A.C. and Glasby, G.P., 1974. A petrographic and electron microprobe investigation of some deep- and shallow-water manganese nodules. *N.Z. J. Geol. Geophys.*, 17: 929–953.

Ehrlich, H.L., 1968. Bacteriology of manganese nodules, II. Manganese oxidation by cell-free extract from a manganese nodule bacterium. *Appl. Microbiol.*, 16: 197–202.

Elderfield, H. and Glasby, G.P., 1973. Infrared spectra of manganese nodules and ferromanganese sediments. *Chem. Geol.*, 11: 117–122.

Emiliani, C. and Milliman, J.D., 1966. Deep-sea sediments and their geological record. *Earth-Sci. Rev.*, 1: 105–132.

Ericson, D.B. and Wollin, G., 1973. Precipitation of manganese oxide in deep-sea sediments. In: *Inter-University Program of Research on Ferromanganese Deposits of the Ocean Floor, Phase I Report*. Nat. Sci. Found., Washington, D.C., pp. 99–103.

Ewing, M., Horn, D., Sullivan, L., Aitken, T. and Thorndike, E., 1971. Photographing manganese nodules on the ocean floor. *Oceanol. Inst.*, 6 (12): 26–27, 30–32.

Ewing, M., Shipley, T.H. and Conary, S.D., 1973a. Intensive survey of a manganese nodule region in the North Atlantic Ocean. In: *Inter-University Program of Research on Ferromanganese Deposits of the Ocean Floor, Phase I Report*. Nat. Sci. Found., Washington, D.C., pp. 187–215.

Ewing, M., Carpenter, G., Windisch, C. and Ewing, J., 1973b. Sediment distribution in the oceans: the Atlantic. *Bull. Geol. Soc. Am.*, 84: 71–88.

Fein, C.D. and Morgenstein, M., 1972. Microprobe analysis of manganese crusts from the Hawaiian Archipelago. *Hawaii Inst. Geophys. Rep., HIG–72–23*: 41–58.

Fewkes, R.H., 1973. External and internal features of marine manganese nodules as seen with the SEM and their implications in nodule origin. In: M. Morgenstein (Editor), *The Origin and Distribution of Manganese Nodules in the Pacific and Prospects for Exploration*. A symposium organised by the Valdivia Manganese Explor. Group and the Hawaii Inst. Geophys., Honolulu, Hawaii, pp. 21–29.

Finkelman, R.B., 1970. Magnetic particles extracted from manganese nodules: suggested origin from stony and iron meteorites. *Science*, 167: 932–934.

Finkelman, R.B., 1972. Relationship between manganese nodules and cosmic spherules. *Mar. Technol. Soc. J.*, 6 (4): 34–39.

Fisher, F.H. and Davis, D.F., 1965. The effect of pressure on the dissociation of manganese sulphate-ion pairs in water. *J. Phys. Chem.*, 69: 2595–2598.

Fleischer, R.L., Jacobs, I.S., Schwarz, W.M., Price, P.B. and Goodell, H.G., 1968. Search for multiply charged Dirac magnetic poles. *Gen. Electr. Res. Dev. Cent. Tech. Inf., Ser. 68–C–356:* 19.

Friedrich, G.H., Kunzendorf, H. and Plüger, W.L., 1973. Geochemical investigation of deep-sea manganese nodules from the Pacific on board R/V Valdivia – an application of the EDX-technique. In: M. Morgenstein (Editor), *The Origin and Distribution of Manganese Nodules in the Pacific and Prospects for Exploration.* A symposium organised by the Valdivia Manganese Explor. Group and the Hawaii Inst. Geophys., Honolulu, Hawaii, pp. 31–43.

Gamsjager, H., Kraft, W. and Schindler, P., 1970. Potentiometrische Untersuchungen am System Mn^{++}–CO$_2$–H$_2$O. *Helv. Chim. Acta*, 53: 290–299.

Garrels, R.M. and Christ, C.L., 1965. *Solutions, Minerals and Equilibria.* Harper and Row, New York, N.Y., 450 pp.

Garrels, R.M. and Thompson, M.E., 1962. A chemical model for sea water at 25°C and one atmosphere total pressure. *Am. J. Sci.*, 260: 57–66.

Giovanoli, R., Feitknecht, W. and Fischer, F., 1970. Buserite, birnessite, and the reduction of birnessite. *Interim. Rep. No. 27a* (Univ. Berne), 26 pp.

Glasby, G.P., 1970. *The Geochemistry of Manganese Nodules and Associated Pelagic Sediments from the Indian Ocean.* Thesis, Univ. London, 674 pp., unpublished.

Glasby, G.P., 1972a. Manganese deposits in the Southwest Pacific. *Hawaii Inst. Geophys. Rep. HIG–72–23:* 59–82.

Glasby, G.P., 1972b. The mineralogy of manganese nodules from a range of marine environments. *Mar. Geol.*, 13: 57–72.

Glasby, G.P., 1972c. The nature of the iron oxide phase of marine manganese nodules. *N.Z. J. Sci.*, 15: 232–239.

Glasby, G.P., 1972d. Effect of pressure on deposition of manganese oxides in the marine environment. *Nat. Phys. Sci.*, 237: 85–86.

Glasby, G.P., 1973a. Distribution of manganese nodules and lebensspuren in underwater photography from the Carlsberg Ridge, Indian Ocean. *N.Z. J. Geol. Geophys.*, 16: 1–17.

Glasby, G.P., 1973b. Manganese deposits of variable composition from north of the Indian–Antarctic Ridge. *Nat. Phys. Sci.*, 242: 106–108.

Glasby, G.P., 1973c. The role of submarine volcanism in controlling the genesis of marine manganese nodules. *Oceanogr. Mar. Biol., Ann. Rev.*, 11: 27–44.

Glasby, G.P., 1973d. Mechanisms of enrichment of the rarer elements in marine manganese nodules. *Mar. Chem.*, 1: 105–125.

Glasby, G.P., 1974. Mechanisms of incorporation of manganese and associated trace elements in marine manganese nodules. *Oceanogr. Mar. Biol., Ann. Rev.*, 12: 11–40.

Glasby, G.P., in press. Exploitation of manganese nodules in the South Pacific. *Proc. Circum Pac. Energy Min. Resour. Conf., Hawaii, Aug. 1974.*

Glasby, G.P., Tooms, J.S. and Cann, J.R., 1971. The geochemistry of manganese encrustations from the Gulf of Aden. *Deep-Sea Res.*, 18: 1179–1187.

Goldberg, E.D., 1954. Marine geochemistry, I. Chemical scavengers of the sea. *J. Geol.*, 62: 249–265.

Goldberg, E.D., 1965. Minor elements in sea water, pp. 163–196. In: J.P. Riley and G. Skirrow (Editors), *Chemical Oceanography.* Academic Press, London, 1: 712 pp.

Goodell, H.G., Meylan, M.A. and Grant, B., 1971. Ferromanganese deposits of the South Pacific Ocean, Drake Passage, and Scotia Sea. In: J.L. Reid (Editor), *Antarctic Oceanology. Antarct. Res. Ser. Am. Geophys. Union*, Baltimore, Md., 1: 27–92.

Grant, J.B., 1967. A comparison of the chemistry and mineralogy with the distribution and physical aspects of marine manganese concretions of the Southern Oceans. *Contrib. Sediment. Res. Lab., Fla State Univ.*, 19: 99 pp.

Greenslate, J.L., Frazer, J.Z. and Arrhenius, G., 1973. Origin and deposition of selected transition metals in the seabed. In: M. Morgenstein (Editor), *The Origin and Distribution of Manganese Nodules in the Pacific and Prospects for Exploration.* A symposium organised by the Valdivia Manganese Explor. Group and the Hawaii Inst. Geophys., Honolulu, Hawaii, pp. 45–60.

Harned, H.S. and Owen, B.B., 1958. *The Physical Chemistry of Electrolytic Solutions.* Reinhold Publ. Corp., New York, N.Y., 803 pp.

Hawkins, L.K., 1969. Visual observations of manganese deposits on the Blake Plateau. *J. Geophys. Res.,* 74: 7009–7017.

Healy, T.W., Herring, A.P. and Fuerstenau, D.W., 1966. The effects of crystal structure on the surface properties of a series of manganese dioxides. *J. Colloid. Interf. Sci.,* 21: 435–444.

Heezen, B.C. and Hollister, C.D., 1971. Ion by ion. In: *The Face of the Deep.* Oxford Univ. Press, New York, N.Y., pp. 423–444.

Hem, J.D., 1963a. Manganese complexes with bicarbonate and sulfate in natural water. *J Chem. Eng. Data,* 8: 99–101.

Hem, J.D., 1963b. Chemical equilibria and rates of manganese oxidation. *U.S.G.S. Water Supply Pap, 1667–A:* 64 pp.

Heye, D. and Beiersdorf, H., 1973. Radioactive and magnetic investigations on manganese nodules in order to determine the accumulation rate and/or the age. *Z. Geophys.,* 39: 703–726 (In German; English Abstr.).

Hollister, C.D., and Heezen, B.C., 1967. The floor of the Bellingshausen Sea. In: J.B. Hersey (Editor), *Deep-Sea Photography. The John Hopkins Oceanogr. Stud.,* 3: 177–189.

Hollister, C.D., Johnson, D.A. and Lonsdale, P.F., 1974. Current-controlled abyssal sedimentation. Samoan Passage, Equatorial West Pacific. *J. Geol.,* 82: 275–300.

Horn, D.R. (Editor), 1972. *Ferromanganese Deposits on the Ocean Floor.* Nat. Sci. Found., Washington, D.C., 293 pp.

Horn, D.R., Horn, B.M. and Delach, M.N., 1972a. Ferromanganese deposits of the North Pacific. *Tech. Rep. Off. Int. Decade Ocean Explor.,* 1: 78 pp.

Horn, D.R., Ewing, M., Horn, B.M. and Delach, M.N., 1972b. Worldwide distribution of manganese nodules. *Ocean Ind.,* 7 (1): 26–29.

Horn, D.R., Horn, B. and Delach, M.N., 1972c. Worldwide distribution and metal content of deep-sea manganese deposits. In: *Manganese Nodule Deposits in the Pacific Symposium/Workshop Proceedings Honolulu, Hawaii, October 16–17, 1972.* State Center Sci. Policy Technol. Assess. Dep. Plann. Econ. Dev., State of Hawaii, pp. 46–60.

Horn, D.R., Horn, B.M. and Delach, M.N., 1973a. *Surface Distribution Ferromanganese Deposits on the Ocean Floor.* Chart compiled by Lamont-Doherty Geol. Obs., Columbia Univ., Palisades, New York.

Horn, D.R., Delach, M.N. and Horn, B.M., 1973b. Metal content of ferromanganese deposits of the oceans. *Tech. Rep. Off. Int. Decade Ocean Explor.,* 3: 57 pp.

Horn, D.R., Horn, B.M. and Delach, M.N., 1973c. Ocean manganese nodules metal values and mining sites. *Tech. Rep. Off. Int. Decade Ocean Explor.,* 4: 57 pp.

Horn, D.R., Horn, B.M. and Delach, M.N., 1973d. Factors which control the distribution of ferromanganese nodules and proposed research vessel's track North Pacific. *Tech. Rep. Off. Int. Decade Ocean Explor.,* 8: 20 pp (plus 20 profiles).

Horn, D.R., Horn, B.M. and Delach, M.N., 1973e. Copper and nickel content of ocean ferromanganese deposits and their relation to properties of the substrate. In: M. Morgenstein (Editor), *The Origin and Distribution of Manganese Nodules in the Pacific and Prospects for Exploration.* A symposium organised by the Valdivia Manganese Explor. Group and the Hawaii Inst. Geophys., Honolulu, Hawaii, pp. 77–83.

Hubred, G.L., 1970. Relationship of morphology and transition metal content of manganese nodules to an abyssal hill. *Hawaii Inst. Geophys. Rep. HIG–70–18:* 38 pp.

Hurd, D.C., 1972. Intersections of biogenic opal, sediment and sea-water in the Central Equatorial Pacific. *Hawaii Inst. Geophys. Rep. HIG–72–22:* 81 pp.

Jedwab, J., 1970. Les sphérules cosmiques dans les nodules de manganese. *Geochim. Cosmochim. Acta,* 34: 447–457.

Jedwab, J., 1971. Particules de materière carbonée dans les nodules de manganèse des grandes fonds océaniques. *C.R. Hebd. Seance Acad. Sci., Paris,* 272D: 1968–1971.

Johnson, C.E. and Glasby, G.P., 1969. Mössbauer Effect determination of particle size in microcrystalline iron–manganese nodules. *Nature,* 222: 376–377.

Jones, L.H.P. and Milne, A.A., 1956. Birnessite, a new manganese oxide mineral from Aberdeenshire, Scotland. *Mineralog. Mag.,* 31: 283–288.

Kaufman, R. and Siapno, W.D., 1972. Variability of Pacific Ocean manganese nodule deposits. In: D.R. Horn (Editor), *Ferromanganese Deposits on the Ocean Floor.* Nat. Sci. Found., Washington, D.C., pp. 263–269.

Keenan, J.H., Keyes, F.G., Hill, P.G. and Moore, B.S., 1969. *Steam Tables.* Wiley, New York, N.Y., 162 pp.

Keller, G.H. and Bennett, R.H., 1972. Sediment mass physical properties – Panama Basin and Northeastern Equatorial Basin. In: *Initial Reports of the Deep-Sea Drilling Project, Leg 16.* U.S. Gov. Print. Off., Washington, D.C., pp. 499–512.

Kennett, J.P. and Brunner, J.P., 1973. Antarctic Late Cenozoic glaciation: evidence for initiation of ice rafting and inferred increased bottom-water activity. *Bull. Geol. Soc. Am.,* 84: 2043–2052.

Khodakovskiy, I.L., Ryzhenko, B.N. and Naumov, G.B., 1968. Thermo-dynamics of aqueous electrolyte solutions at elevated temperatures. *Geochim. Int.,* 5 (6): 1200–1219.

Kobayashi, K., Kitazawa, K., Kanaya, T. and Sakai, T., 1971. Magnetic and micropaleontological study of deep-sea sediments from the west-central equatorial Pacific. *Deep-Sea Res.,* 18: 1045–1062.

Krishnaswamy, S. and Lal, D., 1972. Manganese nodules and budget of trace solubles in oceans. In: D. Dyrssen and D. Jagner (Editors), *The Changing Chemistry of the Oceans. Proc. 20th Nobel Symp.,* pp. 307–320.

Krishnaswamy, S. and Moore, W.S., 1973. Accretion rates of fresh-water manganese deposits. *Nat. Phys. Sci.,* 243: 114–116.

Krishnaswamy, S., Somayajulu, B.L.K. and Moore, W.S., 1972. Dating of manganese nodules using beryllium–10, In: D.R. Horn (Editor), *Ferromanganese Deposits on the Ocean Floor.* Nat. Sci. Found., Washington, D.C., pp. 117–122.

Ku, T.L., in preparation. Rates of accretion. In: G.P. Glasby (Editor), *Marine Manganese Deposits.* Elsevier, Amsterdam.

Ku, T.L. and Broecker, W.S., 1969. Radiochemical studies on manganese nodules of deep-sea origin. *Deep-Sea Res.,* 16: 625–637.

Ku, T.L. and Glasby, G.P., 1972. Radiometric evidence of rapid growth rates of shallow-water, continental margin manganese nodules. *Geochim. Cosmochim. Acta,* 36: 699–703.

Lalou, C. and Brichet, E., 1972. Signification des mesures radio-chimiques dans l'évaluation de la vitesse de croissance des nodules de manganèse. *C.R. Hebd. Séance Acad. Sci., Paris,* 275D: 815–818. (English Abstract in: *Aquat. Sci. Fish. Abstr.,* 3 (1): 10, 1973.)

Lalou, C., Brichet, E. and Gressus, C.L., 1973a. Etude d'un nodule de manganèse au microscope electronique à balayage et par microanalyse X Implications dans le mode de formation des nodules. *Ann. Inst. Oceanogr., Monaco,* 49 (1): 5–17.

Lalou, C., Brichet, E. and Ranque, D., 1973b. Certains nodules de manganèse trouvés en surface des sédiments sout-ils des formation contemporaines de la sédimentation? *C.R. Hebd. Séance Acad. Sci., Paris,* 276D: 1661–1664.

Lalou, C., Delibrias, G., Brichet, E. and Labeyrie, J., 1973c. Existence de carbone-14 au centre de deux nodules de manganèse du Pacifique: ages carbone-14 et thorium-230 de ces nodules. *C.R. Hebd. Séance Acad. Sci., Paris,* 276D: 3013–3015 (English Abstr. In: *Aquat. Sci. Fish. Abstr.,* 3 (12): 19, 1973.)

Landergren, S., 1964. On the geochemistry of deep-sea sediments. *Rep. Swed. Deep-Sea Exped.,* 10: 61–154.

Landmesser, C.W. and Morgenstein, M.E., 1973. Survey and mapping of manganese deposits in the Hawaiian Archipelago. In: M. Morgenstein (Editor), *The Origin and Distribution of Manganese Nodules in the Pacific and Prospects for Exploration.* A symposium organised by the Valdivia Manganese Explor. Group and the Hawaii Inst. Geophys., Honolulu, Hawaii, pp. 93–101.

Laughton, A.S., 1967. Underwater photography of the Carlsberg Ridge. In: J.B. Hersey (Editor), *Deep-Sea Photography. The John Hopkins Oceanogr. Stud.,* 3: 191—206.

Lewis, G.N. and Randall, M., 1961. *Thermodynamics.* McGraw-Hill, New York, N.Y., 723 pp. (Revised by Pitzer, K.S. and Brewer, L.)

Li, Y-H., Bischoff, J.L. and Mathieu, G., 1969. The migration of manganese in the Arctic Basin sediment. *Earth Planet. Sci. Lett.* 7: 265—270.

Liss, P.S., Herring, J.R. and Goldberg, E.D., 1973. The iodide/iodate system in seawater as a possible measure of redox potential. *Nat. Phys. Sci.,* 242: 108—109.

Lister, C.R.B., 1971. Crustal magnetization and sedimentation near two small seamounts west of the Juan de Fuca Ridge, Northeast Pacific. *J. Geophys. Res.,* 76: 4824—4841.

Lonsdale, P.F., Normark, W.R. and Newmann, W.A., 1972. Sedimentation and erosion on Horizon Guyot. *Bull. Geol. Soc. Am.,* 83: 289—316.

Lynn, D.C. and Bonatti, E., 1965. Mobility of manganese in diagenesis of deep-sea sediments. *Mar. Geol.,* 3: 457—474.

MacDonald, K.C. and Hollister, C.D., 1973. Near botton thermocline in the Samoan Passage, West Equatorial Pacific. *Nature,* 243: 461—462.

McKenzie, R.M., 1971. The synthesis of birnessite, cryptomelane, and some other oxides and hydroxides of manganese. *Mineral. Mag.,* 38: 493—502.

Manheim, F.T., 1965. Manganese-iron accumulations in the shallow marine environment. In: *Symposium on Marine Geochemistry. Occas. Publ. Univ. Rhode Island,* 3: 217—278.

Margolis, S.V., 1973. Manganese deposits encountered during Deep-Sea Drilling Project Leg 29 in Subantarctic waters, p. 109—113. In: M. Morgenstein (Editor), *The Origin and Distribution of Manganese Nodules in the Pacific and Prospects for Exploration.* A symposium organised by the Valdivia Manganese Explor. Group and the Hawaii Inst. Geophys., Honolulu, Hawaii, 175 pp.

Margolis, S.V. and Glasby, G.P., 1973. Microlaminations in marine manganese nodules as revealed by scanning electron microscopy. *Bull. Geol. Soc. Am.,* 84: 3601—3610.

Masterton, W.W. and Berka, L.H., 1966. Evaluation of ion-pair association constants from osmotic coefficients. *J. Phys. Chem.,* 70: 1924—1929.

Mero, J.L., 1965. *The Mineral Resources of the Sea.* Elsevier, Amsterdam, 312 pp.

Meyer, K., 1973a. Surface sediment and manganese nodules facies, encountered on R/V Valdivia cruises 1972/73. In: M. Morgenstein (Editor), *The Origin and Distribution of Manganese Nodules in the Pacific and Prospects for Exploration.* A symposium organised by the Valdivia Manganese Expl. Group and the Hawaii Inst. Geophys., Honolulu, Hawaii, pp. 125—130.

Meyer, K., 1973b. Surface sediment- and manganese nodules facies, encountered on R/V Valdivia cruises 1972/73. *Meerestechnik Mar. Technol.,* 4: 196—199.

Millero, F.J., 1969. The partial molal volumes of ions in seawater. *Limnol. Oceanogr.,* 14: 376—385.

Millero, F.J., 1971. The molal volumes of electrolytes. *Chem. Rev.,* 71:147—176.

Molengraaf, G.A.F., 1916. On the occurrence of nodules of manganese in Mesozoic deep-sea deposits from Borneo, Timor and Rotti, their significance and mode of formation. *Proc. Acad. Sci. Amst.,* 18: 415—430.

Molengraaf, G.A.F., 1922. On manganese nodules in Mesozoic deep-sea deposits of Dutch Timor. *Proc. Acad. Sci. Amst.,* 23: 997—1012.

Moore, J.G., 1965. Petrology of deep-sea basalt near Hawaii. *Am. J. Sci.,* 263: 40—52.

Moore, J.G., 1966. Rate of palagonitization of submarine basalt adjacent to Hawaii. *U.S. Geol. Surv., Prof. Pap.,* 550D: 163—171.

Moore, J.G., 1970. Submarine basalt from the Revillagigedo Islands region, Mexico. *Mar. Geol.,* 9: 341—355.

Moore, T.C., 1970. Abyssal hills in the central equatorial Pacific: sedimentation and stratigraphy. *Deep-Sea Res.,* 17: 573—593.

Moore, T.C. and Heath, G.R., 1966. Manganese nodules, topography and thickness of Quaternary sediments in the Central Pacific. *Nature,* 212: 983—985.

Moore, W.S., 1973. Accumulation rates of manganese crusts on rocks exposed on the sea floor. In: *Inter-University Program of Research on Ferromanganese Deposits of the Ocean Floor, Phase I Report.* Nat. Sci. Found., Washington, D.C., pp. 93—97.

Morgan, J.J., 1967. Applications and limitations of chemical thermodynamics in natural water systems. In: R.F. Gould (Editor), *Equilibrium Concepts in Natural Water Systems. Adv. Chem. Ser.,* 67: 1–27.

Morgenstein, M., 1972a. Manganese accretion at the sediment–water interface at 400–2400 m depth, Hawaiian Archipelago. In: D.R. Horn (Editor), *Ferromanganese Deposits on the Ocean Floor.* Nat. Sci. Found., Washington, D.C., pp. 131–138.

Morgenstein, M., 1972b. Sedimentary diagenesis and rates of manganese accretion on the Waho Shelf, Kauai Channel, Hawaii. *Hawaii Inst. Geophys. Rep., HIG–72–23:* 1–40.

Morgenstein, M. and Felsher, M., 1971. The origin of manganese nodules: a combined theory with special reference to palagonitization. *Pac. Sci.,* 25: 301–307.

Morris, J.C. and Stumm, W., 1967. Redox equilibria and measurements of potentials in the aquatic environment, p. 270–285. In: R.F. Gould (Editor), *Equilibrium Concepts in Natural Water Systems. Adv. Chem. Ser.,* 67: 270–285.

Murray, J. and Irvine, R., 1895. On the manganese oxides and manganese nodules in marine deposits. *Trans. R. Soc. Edinb.,* 37: 721–742.

Murray, J. and Renard, A.F., 1891. Deep sea deposits. *Rep. Sci. Results Explor. Voyage Challenger,* 525 pp.

Natland, J.H., 1973. Basal ferromanganoan sediments at DSDP site 183, Aleutian Abyssal Plain, and site 192, Meiji Guyot, Northwest Pacific, Leg 19. In: *Initial Reports of the Deep Sea Drilling Project.* U.S. Gov. Print. Office, Washington, D.C., 19: 629–636.

N.E.L., 1964. *Steam Tables.* H.M.S.O., 147 pp.

Olausson, E. and Uusitalo, S., 1964. On the influence of seismic vibrations on sediments. *Bull. Comm. Geol. Finl.,* 35: 101–114.

Otgonsuren, O., Perelygin, V.P. and Flerov, G.N., 1969. The search for remote transuranium elements in iron–manganese concretions. *Dokl. Akad. Nauk SSSR,* 189: 1200–1203.

Perrin, D.D., 1962. The hydrolysis of the manganous (II) ion. *J. Chem. Soc.,* 1962: 2197–2200.

Pimm, A.C., Burroughs, R.H. and Bunce, E.T., 1972. Oligocene sediments near Chain Ridge, Northwest Indian Ocean: structural implications. *Mar. Geol.,* 13: M14–M18.

Pratt, R.M. and McFarlin, P.F., 1966. Manganese pavements on the Blake Plateau. *Science,* 151: 1080–1082.

Presley, B.J., Kolodny, Y., Nissenbaum, A. and Kaplan, I.R., 1972. Early diagenesis in a reducing fjord, Saanich Inlet, British Columbia – II. Trace element distribution in interstitial waters and sediment. *Geochim. Cosmochim. Acta,* 36: 1073–1090.

Price, N.B and Calvert, S.E., 1970. Compositional variation in Pacific Ocean ferromanganese nodules and its relationship to sediment accumulation rates. *Mar. Geol.,* 9: 145–171.

Raab, W., 1972. Physical and chemical features of Pacific deep-sea manganese nodules and their implications to the genesis of nodules. In: D.R. Horn (Editor), *Ferromanganese Deposits on the Ocean Floor.* Nat. Sci. Found., Washington, D.C., pp. 31–49.

Rashid, M.A., 1971. Role of humic acids of marine origin and their different molecular weight fractions in complexing di- and tri-valent metals. *Soil. Sci.,* 111: 298–306.

Rashid, M.A., 1972a. Role of quinone groups in solubility and complexing of metals in sediments and soils. *Chem. Geol., 9:* 241–247.

Rashid, M.A., 1972b. Amino acids associated with marine sediments and humic compounds and their role in solubility and complexing of metals. *Proc. Int. Geol. Congr., 24th, Montreal,* 10: 346–353.

Rashid, M.A. and Leonard, J.D., 1973. Modifications in the solubility and precipitation behaviour of various metals as a result of their interaction with sedimentary humic acid. *Chem. Geol.,* 11: 89–97.

Read, A.J., 1972. Dissolution of copper in weakly acidic solutions. *J. Phys. Chem.,* 76: 3656–3663.

Richards, F.A., 1957. Oxygen in the ocean. *Geol. Soc. Am., Mem.,* 67 (1): 185–238.

Riley, J.P. and Chester, R., 1971. *Introduction to Marine Chemistry.* Academic Press, London, 465 pp.

Riley, J.P. and Taylor, D., 1968. The determination of manganese in seawater. *Deep-Sea Res.,* 15: 629–632.

Robie, R.A., Bethke, P.M. and Beardsley, K.M., 1967. Selected X-ray crystallographic data molar volumes and densities of minerals and related substances. *U.S. Geol. Surv. Bull*, 1248: 1–87.

Sackett, W.M., 1966. Manganese Nodules: Thorium-230/Protactinum-231 ratios. *Science*, 154: 646–647.

Schornick, J.S., 1972. Uranium and thorium isotope geochemistry in ferromanganese concretions from the Southern Ocean. *Contrib. Sedim. Res. Lab. Fla. State Univ.*, 34: 161 pp.

Schultze-Westrum, H-H., 1973. The station and cruise pattern of the R/V Valdivia in relation to the variability of manganese nodule occurrences. In: M. Morgenstein (Editor), *The Origin and Distribution of Manganese Nodules in the Pacific and Prospects for Exploration*. A symposium organised by the Valdivia Manganese Explor. Group and the Hawaii Inst. Geophys., Honolulu Hawaii, pp. 145–149.

Shumway, G., 1960. Sound speed and absorption studies of marine sediments by a resonance method, Part I. *Geophysics*, 25: 451–467.

Sillen, L.G., 1967. The ocean as a chemical system. *Science*, 156: 1189–1197.

Smith, R.E., Gassaway, J.D. and Giles, H.N., 1968. Iron–manganese nodules from Nares Abyssal Plain: geochemistry and mineralogy. *Science*, 161: 780–781.

Somayajulu, B.L.K., 1967. Berryllium-10 in a manganese nodule. *Science*, 156: 1219–1220.

Somayajulu, B.L.K., Heath, G.R., Moore, T.C. and Cronan, D.S., 1971. Rates of accumulation of manganese nodules and associated sediment from the equatorial Pacific. *Geochim. Cosmochim. Acta*, 35: 621–624.

Sorem, R.K., 1967. Manganese nodules: nature and significance of internal structure. *Econ. Geol.*, 62: 141–147.

Sorem, R.K., 1973. Manganese nodules as indicators of long-term variations in sea floor environment. In: M. Morgenstein (Editor), *The Origin and Distribution of Manganese Nodules in the Pacific and Prospects for Exploration*. A symposium organised by the Valdivia Manganese Explor. Group and the Hawaii Inst. Geophys., Honolulu, Hawaii, pp. 151–164.

Sorem, R.K. and Foster, A.R., 1972a. Marine manganese nodules: importance of structural analysis. *Int. Geol. Congr., 24th, Montreal*, 8: 192–200.

Sorem, R.K. and Foster, A.R., 1972b. Internal structure of manganese nodules and implications to beneficiation. In: D.R. Horn (Editor), *Ferromanganese Depositis on the Ocean Floor*. Nat. Sci. Found., Washington, D.C., pp. 167–181.

Straczek, J.A., Horen, A., Ross, M. and Warshaw, C.M., 1960. Studies of the manganese oxides. IV. Todorokite. *Am. Miner.*, 45: 1174–1184.

Summerhayes, C.P., 1967. Manganese nodules from the Southwestern Pacific. *N.Z. J. Geol. Geophys.*, 10: 1372–1381.

Summerhayes, C.P. and Willis, J.P., 1973. Manganese encrustations from the Agulhas Bank. *Tech. Rep. Mar. Geol. Program It. Geol. Surv. Univ. Cape Town*, 5: 121–126.

Summerhayes, C.P. and Willis, J.P., 1975. Geochemistry of manganese deposits in relation to environment of the sea-floor around Southern Africa. *Mar. Geol.*

Tarling, D.H., 1973. Metallic ore deposits and continental drift. *Nature*, 243: 193–196.

Tiepel, E.W. and Gubbins, K.E., 1972. Partial molal volumes of gases in dissolved electrolyte solutions. *J. Phys. Chem.*, 76: 3044–3049.

Von der Borch, C.C. and Rex, R.W., 1970. Amorphous iron oxide precipitates in sediments cored during Leg 5, Deep Sea Drilling Project. In: *Initial Reports of the Deep Sea Drilling Project*. U.S. Gov. Print. Office, Washington, D.C., 5: 541–544.

Von der Borch, C.C., Nesteroff, W.D. and Galehouse, J.S., 1971. Iron-rich sediments cored during Leg 8 of the Deep Sea Drilling Project. In: *Initial Reports of the Deep Sea Drilling Project*. U.S. Gov. Print. Office, Washington, D.C., 8: 829–833.

Wadsley, A.D., 1952. The structure of lithiophorite, $(Al, Li) MnO_2(OH)_2$. *Acta Crystallogr.*, 5: 676–680.

Wadsley, A.D., 1953. Interstitial atoms in the layer structure $ZnMn_3O_7 3H_2O$ (chalcophanite). *Nature*, 172: 1103–1104.

Wagman, D.D., Evans, W.H., Parker, V.B., Halow, I., Bailey, S.M. and Schumm, R.H., 1968. *Selected Values of Thermodynamic Properties*. NBS Tech. Note 270–3, 264 pp.

Wagman, D.D., Evans, W.H., Parker, V.B., Halow, I., Bailey, S.M. and Schumm, R.H., 1969. *Selected Values of Thermodynamic Properties. NBS Tech. Note* 270–4, 141 pp.

Wakeham, S. and Carpenter, R., 1973. Electron spin resonance spectra of manganese nodules. *EOS, Trans. Am. Geophys. Union,* 54 (4): 339.

Wakeham, S. and Carpenter, R., 1974. Electron spin resonance spectra of marine and fresh-water manganese nodules. *Chem. Geol.,* 13: 39–47.

Wangersky, P.J. and Joensuu, O.I., 1967. The fractionation of carbonate deep-sea cores. *J. Geol.,* 75: 148–177.

Watkins, N.D. and Kennett, J.P., 1971. Antarctic bottom water: major change in velocity during the Late Cenozoic between Australia and Antarctica. *Science,* 173: 813–818.

Watkins, N.D. and Kennett, J.P., 1972. Regional sedimentary disconformities and Upper Cenozoic changes in bottom water velocities between Australasia and Antarctica. *Antarct. Res. Sci.,* 19: 273–295.

Winterer, E.L., 1973. Sedimentary facies and plate tectonics of Equatorial Pacific. *Bull. Am. Assoc. Petrol. Geol.,* 57: 265–282.

Woo, C.C., 1973. Scanning electron micrographs of marine manganese micronodules, marine pebble-sized nodules, and fresh water manganese nodules. In: M. Morgenstein (Editor), *The Origin and Distribution of Manganese Nodules in the Pacific and Prospects for Exploration.* A symposium organised by the Valdivia Manganese Explor. Group and the Hawaii Inst. Geophys., Honolulu, Hawaii, pp. 165–171.

Chapter 8

FRESHWATER FERROMANGANESE DEPOSITS

EDWARD CALLENDER and CARL J. BOWSER

INTRODUCTION

Deposits of freshwater iron and manganese have long been known in Europe, Asia, and North America. Until the valuable deposits of iron from much older sediments were discovered late in the 20th century, these types of deposits served as the most important economic sources of iron. The deposits in Canada alone have been known since 1670, fully 200 years before the discovery of ocean ferromanganese nodules on the "Challenger" expedition. Eurasian iron deposits have been known even longer. The deposits of the Three Rivers area in Quebec are of particular note inasmuch as the first iron was mined here in 1730 and operated continuously until the 1880's. At that time the nearby Radnor forges had the oldest operating blast furnace on the North American continent (Bartlett, 1893; Griffin, 1893).

Commonly referred to in earlier literature as "bog ores" a review of the articles on these deposits clearly indicates a whole range of occurrences that include: soils, springs and bogs, rivers, and lake bottom deposits. These iron-rich deposits vary greatly in form as well; ranging from cemented soils and stream sediments to lake and stream bottom crusts to encrusted sands to boulder-cored nodules. Although these "bog ores" vary greatly in form and occurrence, they seem to have in common the fact that the deposits are found mainly in the glaciated, crystalline shield areas characterized by poor drainage and heavily vegetated podzolic soils. A list of some of the better known deposits of freshwater ferromanganese in the Northern Hemisphere is tabulated in Table I.

It is apparent that the term "bog iron" used in most of the older literature covered a whole range of types of occurrences and forms. Most recently the term "freshwater ferromanganese" has been used, and strictly speaking, would include all the types of deposits that had previously been known as "bog ores." However, because these types of deposits are no longer major economic sources of iron and because recent attention seems to have shifted to the relatively "glamorous" deep-ocean nodules, the current work on freshwater deposits is restricted mainly to the lake types of deposits. Thus, freshwater ferromanganese in the modern context has come to be associated mainly with lake deposits. Because the current interest lies with the lake deposits of freshwater ferromanganese, these will be dealt with almost exclusively in this chapter. In any event, it seems

TABLE I

Location of freshwater ferromanganese deposits

Continent	Location	Type of deposit	References
North America	Canada		
	Ontario		
	Thunder Bay	concretions, bog iron	Moore (1909);
	Kingston	concretions	Kindle (1936); Terasmae (1971); Harriss and Troup (1969)
	Quebec		
	St. Lawrence R.		
	Three Rivers	"bog ore"	Griffen (1893)
	Middlesex County	"ochre ore"	Moore (1909)
	Ste. Anne Montmorenci		Gadd et al. (1972)
	Nova Scotia		
	Ship Harbor Lake	concretions (nodular, disk)	Kindle (1932)
	Grand Lake, Daniel Lake	concretions (disk, crusts)	Kindle (1935)
	Kedgemakooge Lake,	conglomerate	Kindle (1936)
	Christopher Lake	conglomerate	Beals (1966)
	Misc. N.S. lakes		Chalmers (1884)
	New Brunswick		
	United States		
	Minnesota		
	Lake Superior	"hardpan" layers	Mothersill and Shegelski (1973)
	Wisconsin		
	Trout Lake	concretions (disk, crusts)	Twenhofel et al. (1945)
	Tomahawk Lake	concretions (crusts, rims)	Bowser and Travis (1970)
	Green Bay (L. Michigan)	concretions, coatings	Rossmann and Callender (1969); Callender (1970); Moore and Meyer (1969); Hall (1969)
	Michigan		
	Lake Michigan	concretions, coatings	Rossmann and Callender (1969); Callender (1970); Edgington and Callender (1970); Rossmann et al. (1972)

TABLE I (continued)

Continent	Location	Type of deposit	References
North America	United States New York (and Ontario, Canada) Lake Ontario	concretions, coatings	Cronan and Thomas (1970, 1972)
	Oneida Lake	concretions (disk, crusts)	Gillette (1961); Dean (1970)
	Lake George	concretions (nodular, disk)	Schoettle and Friedman (1971)
	Vermont Lake Champlain	concretions (disk, nodular)	Johnson (1969)
Europe	Finland (lakes)	"bog ore", concretions	Aarnio (1918); Landergren (1948); Vaasjoki (1956)
	Sweden (lakes)	"bog ore", concretions	Naumann (1922); Ljunggren (1953, 1955a,b)
	England English Lake District	"oxidate" crusts	Gorham and Swaine (1965)
	Scotland Loch Fyne	concretions (nodular)	Buchanan (1878); Calvert and Price (1970)
Eurasia	Russia Karelian lakes	concretions	Inostrantsev (1877); Kurbatov (1936, 1937)
	Lake Pinnus-Yarvi	manganese carbonate	Shterenberg et al. (1966)
	miscellaneous occurrences	ferromanganese ores and sediments	Semenovitch (1958); Strakhov (1966); Varentsov (1972)

clear that all types of freshwater ferromanganese deposits originate from similar processes and thus knowledge gained from the study of one type should apply in one way or another to the whole spectrum of types.

In spite of the fact that such deposits are widespread in both North America and Eurasia they have received little attention until only recently. In North America, aside from the excellent descriptions of the early exploited Canadian deposits by Bartlett (1893) and Griffin (1893) and the more or less descriptive papers on Canadian Lakes by Moore (1909), Kindle (1932, 1935, 1936) and Twenhofel et al. (1945), not much was published on these deposits until after 1960. The record of studies of European and Asian localities is similar (Aarnio, 1918, on Finnish lakes; Vogt, 1915, on Norwegian lakes; and Naumann, 1922, on Swedish lakes).

Following a series of geochemical and mineralogical papers by Ljunggren (1953, 1955a,b) and a now classic analysis of the low-temperature geochemical processes for the separation of iron and manganese by Krauskopf (1957), published studies of freshwater ferromanganese deposits are much more numerous, particularly those that have emphasized the geochemical processes involved. Most notable papers of this sort are: Gorham and Swaine (1965) on the English lakes; Rossmann and Callender (1968, 1969), Callender (1969, 1970), Edgington and Callender (1970) on Lake Michigan; Harriss and Troup (1969) on Nova Scotia lakes; Cronan and Thomas (1970, 1972) on Lake Ontario; Sevastyanov and Volkov (1966) and Strakhov (1966) on Russian lakes.

Morphologically similar to many of the freshwater ferromanganese nodules are those that have been described from the shallow-marine environment, particularly those from the Barents, Kara, and White and Baltic Seas. Although these deposits will not be described in detail in this chapter, much of the published work on the localities is pertinent to the understanding of the freshwater deposits. Papers on shallow-marine nodules of particular interest include the studies on the Gulf of Bothia (Winterhalter and Siivola, 1967; Winterhalter, 1968), the White, Kara, and Barents Sea deposits; (Klenova and Pakhomova, 1940; Strakhov, 1966) and the review article by Manheim (1965).

GEOLOGIC SETTING

Sedimentary manganese deposits, especially lacustrine ferromanganese concretions and bog-ores, have a widespread occurrence throughout North America, Europe, and parts of Asia. Generally, these deposits occur at more northernly latitudes and are often associated with glacial debris. Glaciated regions of the Northern Hemisphere are generally poorly drained and contain glacial sediment derived from Precambrian crystalline rocks. Thus, there exists an abundant source of manganese in the freshly exposed, igneous/metamorphic minerals that constitute the bulk of glacial debris. This ground-up glacial material is very permeable and thus easily weathered under the cool, temperate climatic conditions. Soil development in this climatic region is minor with podzols and gray-brown podzols the predominant soil types. These northern temperate regions are characterized by hardwood and mixed hardwood/deciduous forests which result in abundant leaf litter and humus. The combination of a humid, cold-temperate climate and abundant vegetation results in acid humus which has a significant effect on the chemistry of water percolating through the soil. Consequently, soil ground water in this climatic region is characterized by acid pH (<pH 6) and abundant dissolved organic matter (predominantly humic/fulvic acids) which both favor the rapid release of manganese and iron from exposed, permeable glacial debris. As a result, the streams have a brown "tea" color, exhibit pH values between 6 and 7, and contain up to several parts per million of "dissolved" iron and manganese.

Many lakes and bogs that occupy depressions in the glaciated regions of North America and Europe contain deposits of ferromanganese oxides. The lakes are all relatively young (less than 11,000 years) and contain abundant sand and gravel deposits located generally in shallow areas. Waters in contact with these "coarser" sediments are well-oxygenated. Ferromanganese nodules and concretions are generally found in these sandy and gravelly sediments which exhibit very low rates of sedimentation (lag deposits) but are not broken up by intense wave action close to shore. Near-shore sediments contain abundant nuclei for nodule accretion, i.e., sand grains, pebbles, cobbles, clay fragments, and occasional wood fragments. The source of "dissolved" metals for ferromanganese oxide precipitation can be interstitial water driven by a hydraulic groundwater gradient (near-shore sands), stream discharge at the mouth of rivers, overlying lake water, and pore water of muds and clays whose metal "ions" are driven upward by diffusion/advection which results in enrichment of near-bottom water.

OCCURRENCE AND MORPHOLOGY OF FRESHWATER FERROMANGANESE OXIDES

The occurrence of ferromanganese oxides in freshwater ferromanganese deposits is represented by four major categories: (1) coatings; (2) crusts; (3) concretions or nodules; and (4) dispersed ferromanganese oxides. A complete description of these different types is presented in the following sections.

Coatings

The upper limit for the thickness of a coating is arbitrarily placed at a few tens of microns. The most widespread occurrence of ferromanganese oxide coatings in North America is illustrated by the northern Lake Ontario deposit where coatings of a few microns in thickness are found on sand grains (Cronan and Thomas, 1970). The percentage of sand grains coated varies considerably, but generally is highest in areas of clean, medium-to-coarse, well-sorted sand.

Ferromanganese-oxide- coated sands (Fig. 1) are also widespread in northern Green

Fig. 1. A. Underwater photograph showing occurrence of ferromanganese oxides in Green Bay, Lake Michigan. Undisturbed flocculent silty clay overlying a sandy bottom. (Scale: 1 inch = 1½ inches.)

Bay, Lake Michigan (Callender, 1970). The distinction here between coatings and micronodules is a difficult one since the thickness of the coating varies from a few microns to 200 microns. In northern Green Bay, the ferromanganese oxides typically coat medium-to-coarse sands comprised of quartz and feldspar. However, coated limestone cobbles and boulders have also been dredged from Green Bay. Generally, the coatings are black in color when wet and dark-brown when dry.

Coatings of ferromanganese oxides have been reported from all five of the St. Lawrence Great Lakes (R.L. Thomas, personal communication). They occur on sand grains, cobbles, boulders, and glacial clay in localities where the sedimentation rate is very low and/or currents keep the sediment swept clean of finer material. Ferromanganese coatings on rocks in the beds of streams are a common occurrence in northern Maine and Colorado (Hem, 1964) and in Sweden (Ljunggren, 1953).

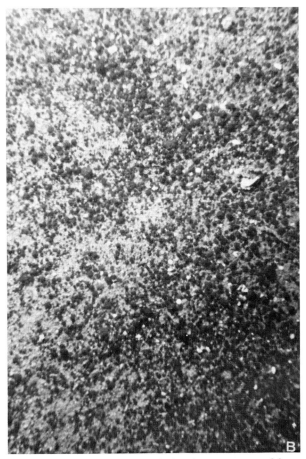

Fig. 1. B. Underwater photograph showing occurrence of ferromanganese oxides in Green Bay, Lake Michigan. Medium sand containing ferromanganese concretions (dark spots). (Scale: 1 inch = 1½ inches.)

Crusts

A much more common mode of occurrence of freshwater ferromanganese is in the form of crusts. Pebbles, cobbles, and boulders resting on the sediment surface are surrounded by a rim-like crust composed of ferromanganese oxides. In most cases, rocks exposed at the sediment—water interface show some degree of crust development (Dean, 1970). The ferromanganese oxide rim forms around the nucleus in a plane parallel to the sediment surface. In Grand Lake, Nova Scotia, the ferromanganese oxide rim begins at the sediment—water interface and attains its maximum width approximately 1.2 cm above the interface (Harriss and Troup, 1970). It has been observed from several North American Lakes that cobbles exhibit multiple oxide rims oriented at different angles, suggesting that the cobbles have been disturbed during concretion development (C.J. Bowser, unpublished data; Harriss and Troup, 1970).

Fig. 1. C. Underwater photograph showing occurrence of ferromanganese oxides in Green Bay, Lake Michigan. Ferromanganese-oxides encrusted boulders resting on medium sand. (Scale: 1 inch = 1½ inches.)

The pebbles and cobbles that constitute nuclei for these crusts are of varying lithology, ranging from slate, sandstone, or granite in Canadian lakes to limestone in Green Bay, Lake Michigan. Oxidate crusts from the Canadian lakes and Lake Oneida, New York tend to develop a saucer shape with the convex side upward (Dean, 1970). Many crusts show a coarse concentric banding in both horizontal and vertical sections (Harriss and Troup, 1970; Dean, 1970). Detailed examination of broken cross sections of these crusts show that the ferromanganese oxide rims consist of alternating rust-colored bands of iron oxide and dark-brown bands of manganese oxide (Harriss and Troup, 1970).

Similar deposits have been noted in Trout Lake, Wisconsin, by Bowser and Travis (1970). The extensive 2–4 cm crusts of ferromanganese oxides from Lake Tomahawk are deposited around glacial boulders and cobbles in areas where the sedimentation rate is relatively low. In some localities these crusts have coalesced to form sheets 3–5 m in diameter. Maximum development of the ferromanganese crusts occur 1–2 cm above the sandy sediment–water interface. The iron/manganese ratio of oxide layers below the zone of maximum growth is generally higher than the same layer traced above the zone of maximum growth (Bowser, unpublished data).

Ferromanganese crusts, other than those that form rims about pebbles and cobbles, occur in lakes. Oxidate crusts occur in abundance from several lakes in the English Lake District (Gorham and Swaine, 1965). Although some of these crusts resemble the Oneida Lake pancakes (Dean, 1970), others occur as fragments in oxidized surface muds. In Lake Windermere, small pieces of oxidate crust were found embedded in this mud adjacent to the underlying clay; soft, friable pieces of incipient crust were recovered from a sample of rust-colored clay beneath the surficial mud (Gorham and Swaine, 1965). In Green Bay, Lake Michigan, orange-brown oxidate crusts occur in sands that generally contain ferromanganese nodules (Callender, 1973). These oxidate crusts appear to represent cementation of the sand by iron-rich ferromanganese oxides and in several cases underly manganese-rich nodules.

Nodules

Although concretions of ferromanganese oxides may be represented by a variety of shapes (spherical, subspherical, discoidal, flattened, sheets), nodules are restricted to those that exhibit spherical or subspherical shapes. Nodules appear to be the most commonly reported occurrence of ferromanganese oxides in the oceans (Mero, 1965; Manheim, 1965). Nodules are the most noticeable morphological form of ferromanganese in lakes, but their occurrence is probably not equal to that of coatings and oxidate crusts. However, the distinction between oxidate crusts and flattened, saucer-shaped, or discoidal concretions is not clear so that our classification of freshwater ferromanganese oxide deposits is somewhat arbitrary.

Freshwater ferromanganese nodules range in diameter from 1 mm in northern Green Bay, Lake Michigan (Rossmann and Callender, 1969), to several centimeters in Lake Champlain (Johnson, 1969). Since only a few freshwater localities have been studied in detail, a more complete description of these nodule localities is given below.

Ferromanganese nodules from Lake Michigan (specifically Green Bay) vary in diameter from less than 1 mm to greater than 2 cm. The nodules are black when wet and orange-brown to black when dry (Rossmann, 1973). Many of the smaller nodules appear to be agglomerates of micro-nodules. Microscopic examination of nodule cross-sections reveals the typical concretionary structure (Figs. 2 and 3) of alternating iron- and manganese-rich bands about a nucleus. The nodules commonly have a nucleus of quartz and/or feldspar but other nuclei, such as stiff glacial clay, limestone–dolostone, and wood, have been observed (Callender, 1970; Rossmann, 1973). In northern Green Bay, nodules averaging 1 mm in diameter commonly exhibit a dark band (manganese oxide) immediately adjacent to a nucleus of quartz or feldspar. This dark band is surrounded by an orange, iron-rich band (Callender, 1970). Medium-sized nodules (2–10 mm in diameter) from

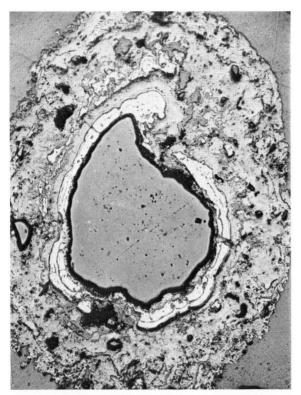

Fig. 2. Reflected-light photomicrograph of a Green Bay ferromanganese nodule cross-section. Note highly reflective material (iron oxide) around nucleus and detrital grains "floating" in iron-manganese oxide matrix. (Scale: 1 cm = 70 μm).

middle Green Bay show a distinct concentric structure of finely-laminated, alternating iron- and manganese-rich bands. Small detrital grains are commonly dispersed throughout the nodule.

Other important localities of freshwater nodules from North American lakes are Lake Champlain (Johnson, 1969) and Lake George (Schoettle and Friedman, 1971), both situated in northeastern New York State. The Lake George nodules consist of dark brown spherical types with alternating concentric layers of porous and dense material; and flat or disk-shaped brown concretions which are somewhat lighter than the spherical variety (Schoettle and Friedman, 1971). The spherical nodules range between 1 mm and 1 cm in diameter with nuclei consisting of quartz grains, feldspar grains, or clay minerals similar to the Green Bay (Lake Michigan) spherical nodules. The Lake George spherical nodules are of two types: those with porous surfaces and a well-developed internal concentric structure; and those with smooth surfaces and a less well-developed concentric structure. The discoidal nodules vary in thickness from 2 mm to 1 cm and exhibit a diameter of up to 6 cm. The outer rim tends to exhibit the darkest shade of brown color and these discoidal nodules commonly consist of aggregates or crusts that are cemented together to

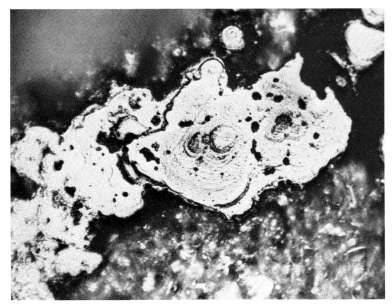

Fig. 3. Reflected-light photomicrograph of psilomelane in a ferromanganese nodule from Green Bay, Lake Michigan. (Scale: 1 cm = 20 μm).

form irregular masses with hard upper surfaces and soft lower surfaces (Schoettle and Friedman, 1971). The Lake Champlain nodules are similar to those from Lake George. The concretions vary in diameter from a few millimetres to several centimetres, and in color from light brown to dark brown or black (Johnson, 1969). When dry, the nodules are lightweight and friable. The surface of many Lake Champlain nodules tends to be covered with fine sand and silt. Cross-sections of the concretions show concentric layers of ferromanganese oxides alternating with layers of loosely oxide-cemented, agglutinated detrital grains consisting predominantly of quartz (Johnson, 1969). Many larger concretions have discoidal shapes with thicknesses ranging from 1 to 2 cm and diameters ranging from 4 to 8 cm. Cross-sections show multiple centers of nucleation suggesting that they have been formed by cementing together of several adjacent concretions.

Dispersed ferromanganese oxides

Surficial concentrations of fine-grained ferromanganese oxides are common in Lake Superior (Mothersill and Shegelski, 1973; Nussmann, 1965), Lake Michigan (Callender, 1969), and from lakes in the English Lake District (Gorham and Swaine, 1965). In western Lake Superior, an upper dark yellowish-brown oxidized layer ranges in thickness from 50 cm around the margins of basinal areas to less than 1 cm in central parts of basins in Thunder Bay (Mothersill and Shegelski, 1973). Thin limonitic-colored layers (up to 0.5 cm thick) occur within the surficial oxidized unit and these are commonly overlain by thin, black layers usually less than 0.1 cm in thickness. Moderate yellowish-brown crusts containing high concentrations of manganese have been found at several other localities in Lake Superior (Nussmann, 1965). The crusts are thin (several millimetres thick) and are found within the surficial brown sediment. The crusts are probably sediment enriched with hydrous manganese oxides which have been deposited slowly. Surficial muds from several English lakes show this phenomenon of ferromanganese oxide-enriched layers consisting of dark-brown muds, associated oxidate crusts, and underlying rusty-colored clay (Gorham and Swaine, 1965).

Sediment types associated with ferromanganese nodules

Whichever sediment type is associated with freshwater nodules, it must have a very low sedimentation rate relative to the accretion of the nodules. Otherwise the nodules could become buried and either not form as nodules or reprecipitate as dispersed oxides. The most common nodule sediment type in the Northern Hemisphere is a lag deposit consisting of glacial cobbles, granules, and sands. Generally, the ferromanganese is present as an oxide coating. This sediment type is very prominent in North American lakes including the St. Lawrence Great Lakes. Although the sediment surface needs to be swept clean of fine sediment, too intense wave action will cause mechanical erosion of precipitated oxides, such as occurs in the shallower areas of Lake Erie. Occasionally, ferromanganese nodules and coated sands have been found associated with muddy sands. Nodules associated with this sediment type usually have a corroded appearance as if the oxides were undergoing some dissolution. Another sediment type associated with ferromanganese oxides is stiff glacial clay. This too represents a lag deposit where no active sediment accumulation is presently occurring. Sometimes a bleb of clay will form the nucleus for a ferromanganese oxide concretion.

CHEMICAL COMPOSITION OF FRESHWATER FERROMANGANESE OXIDES

Iron/manganese ratios

The iron/manganese ratio in ferromanganese oxides varies greatly for specific aquatic environments. Chemical analyses of many freshwater and shallow-marine nodules (bulk material) yield ratios above 1, while deep-sea nodules give ratios below 1. Ferromanganese concretions from Swedish lakes (Ljunggren, 1955; Manheim, 1965) and those from Lake Champlain (Johnson, 1969) and Lake George (Schoettle and Friedman, 1971) in New York State (see Table IV) give ratios that range from 3 to 9. Ferromanganese oxides from the Great Lakes vary between 1 and 3 with the oxide-coated sands from Lake Ontario having the lowest iron/manganese ratio (Cronan and Thomas, 1970). Ferromanganese concretions from several Nova Scotian lakes (Canada) have ratios (Harriss and Troup,

1969) that average 0.55 (Table IV), a value comparable to deep-sea nodules (Manheim, 1965).

Chemical analysis of several groups of nodules sampled on a ½-mile grid pattern at three sites in Green Bay, Lake Michigan (Rossmann, 1973) illustrates the variability that can be expected in any one deposit (see Table V). Nodules from the northern-most area (Fig. 4, area I) have the highest ratios (abundant iron), while nodules adjacent to the Menominee River (Fig. 4, area III) contain significantly higher concentrations of manganese. Proximity to and chemistry of the source of metals are major factors controlling the ferromanganese chemistry of nodules at these sites (Rossmann, 1973). Cronan and Thomas (1972) plotted the distribution of Fe and Mn in the Lake Ontario ferromanga-

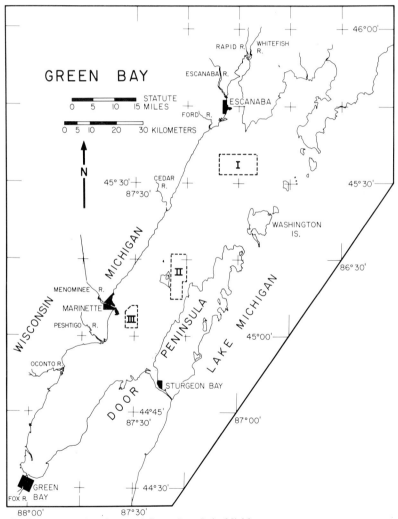

Fig. 4. Outline cultural map of Green Bay, Lake Michigan.

nese oxide deposit. Manganese is most abundant in the north-central part of the deposit where iron is lowest (Fe/Mn < 0.7), and least abundant in the southwest part where iron is highest in concentration (Fe/Mn > 1.7). Cronan and Thomas' (1972) data show a fairly regular increase in the Fe/Mn ratio of oxide coatings from 0.4 in the north to 11 in the south. Cronan and Thomas postulate that this variation in iron and manganese is a result of the differential solubility of Fe and Mn oxides (Krauskopf, 1957) which precipitate in response to redox variations in the lake sediments. Similar variations are seen in the Fe/Mn ratios of Green Bay surficial sediments (Fig. 5).

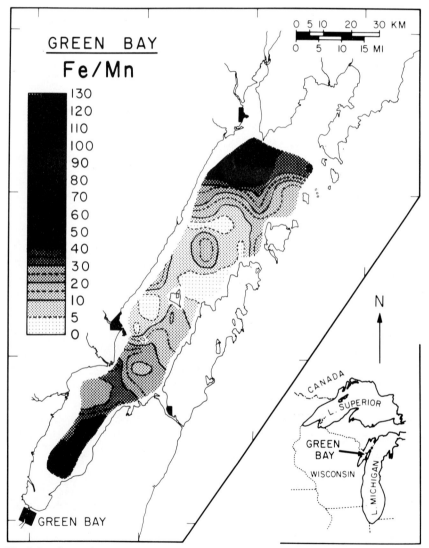

Fig. 5. Iron/manganese ratio map for surficial sediments in Green Bay, Lake Michigan.

Major-element chemistry

Table II presents the most complete set of available chemical data for freshwater ferromanganese nodules (includes crusts). Although many authors do not distinguish between weight percent soluble and weight percent total, a glance at the data leaves one with the impression that most data are expressed in total weight percentage. Major elements, as defined here, are those that occur in concentrations above 0.5 wt.% (5000 ppm).

The alkaline–alkaline earth elements (Na, K, Ca, Mg, Ba) show large variability among freshwater nodule localities. Sodium is much lower in freshwater and shallow-marine nodules than in deep-sea nodules. On the other hand, K–Ca–Mg exhibit concentrations similar to marine nodules with the exception that potassium in ferromanganese oxides from the English Lake District and magnesium from Lake Ontario ferromanganese oxides are significantly higher than average freshwater values. These differences may reflect local geological sources of detrital material that constitute nuclei. In virtually every case, the barium content of freshwater nodules is higher than that of marine nodules. Barium in seawater is buffered by the mineral barite ($BaSO_4$) and thus is not available for incorporation into manganese oxides. Freshwater does not contain sufficient concentrations of sulfate to cause precipitation of barite and thus barium is available for ionic substitution in several manganese oxide mineral structures. While the major alkaline–alkaline earth elements (Na, K, Ca, Mg, Ba) occur structurally in the manganese oxide minerals birnessite, todorokite, psilomelane (see mineralogy section), a significant fraction of some of these elements also occurs in detrital and authigenic silicate phases (Manheim, 1965).

The organic-carbon content of rapidly accumulating freshwater and shallow-marine nodules is significantly higher than that of deep-sea nodules whose growth rates are much lower. The concentration of dissolved organic matter in solutions (bottom water, interstitial fluids) that nourish the nodules undoubtedly are much higher in freshwater and near-shore marine environments than in the deep ocean. The average inorganic carbon (carbonate) content of nodules from a spectrum of freshwater and marine environments (Table II) varies little with the exception of material from Loch Fyne, Scotland. There, ferromanganese oxides are intimately mixed with manganous carbonate that forms diagenetically within the recent sediments (Calvert and Price, 1970). Surficial sediments from Green Bay, Lake Michigan, are composed of significant quantities of detrital calcite and dolomite (Rossmann, 1973) which become part of the nodules' detrital component as they interact with particulate matter during growth.

On examination of Table II, there appears to be no general relationship between the phosphorous and iron contents. However, when the phosphorous and iron contents of nodules from a specific environment are compared, a relatively good correlation exists. The Fe/P correlation for Loch Fyne nodules is particularly good (Calvert and Price, 1970). High levels are found in iron-rich nodules and oxidate crusts from the English

TABLE II

Elemental composition of freshwater and marine ferromanganese nodules

Element	Lake Michigan	Lake Ontario	Lake Oneida	English lakes	Swedish lakes	Baltic Sea	Loch Fyne	Atlantic Ocean	Ocean average
As (ppm)	475	50	—	0.8–8.0	—	—	245	—	—
Ba (%)	0.96	1.20	0.30	—	0.10	0.25	0.31	0.17	0.25
Inorganic C (%)	0.40	—	—	—	0.08	0.20	3.2	—	0.17
Organic C (%)	0.83	—	—	—	1.4	2.5	—	—	0.1
Ca (%)	1.34	3.07	1.02	—	1.3	1.3	5.5	2.7	1.56
Cd (ppm)	3	—	—	—	10	10	—	—	10
Ce (ppm)	145	47	—	—	—	—	—	—	1460
Co (ppm)	134	650	70	40	80	160	120	3100	3500
Cr (ppm)	25	45	75	32	10	10	—	20	10
Cu (ppm)	32	360	80	10	40	48	17	2000	4300
Fe (%)	19.8	20.5	23.0	22.5	35.6	22.5	3.9	17.5	20.5
Ga (ppm)	1	—	10	13	10	20	—	—	10
K (%)	0.15	0.24	—	1.7	0.17	0.76	1.03	0.7	0.68
La (ppm)	35	78	200	30	—	—	—	—	175
Mg (%)	0.28	2.13	0.14	—	0.45	0.57	1.84	1.7	1.38
Mn (%)	8.9	17.1	14.4	7.2	4.7	13.9	30.2	16.3	23.0
Mo (ppm)	33	0.06	32	5	30	130	55	350	380
Na (%)	0.04	—	0.38	0.6	0.08	0.35	—	2.3	2.07
Ni (ppm)	358	2410	40	25	40	750	77	4200	5800
P (%)	0.4	0.21	0.17	0.36	0.30	0.70	0.36	—	0.19
Pb (ppm)	70	1890	140	500	27	38	42	1200	1000
Sb (ppm)	2	—	—	—	—	—	—	—	30
Sc (ppm)	0.6	27	—	—	—	—	—	20	11
Sm (ppm)	9	12	—	—	—	—	—	—	55
Sr (ppm)	162	160	—	62	300	—	770	900	850
Th (ppm)	0.5	—	—	—	—	—	—	—	3–150
U (ppm)	0.9	—	—	—	10	10	—	—	6–10
V (ppm)	—	127	127	80	10	150	—	550	440
Zn (ppm)	405	2020	2020	1000	50	80	60	—	400–4000

Sources of data: Lake Michigan—Rossmann (1973), Edgington and Callender (1970), Rossmann and Callender (1969); Lake Ontario—Cronan and Thomas (1972); Lake Oneida—Dean (1970); English lakes—Gorham and Swaine (1965); Swedish lakes—Manheim (1965); Baltic Sea—Manheim (1965); Loch Fyne—Calvert and Price (1970); Atlantic Ocean—Manheim (1965); Ocean average—Manheim (1965).

Lake District (Gorham and Swaine, 1965), the Baltic Sea (Manheim, 1965; Winterhalter, 1968), and the Black Sea (Sevastyanov and Volkov, 1966). Phosphorous is probably associated with the iron either as an amorphous ferric phosphate (Nriagu, 1972) or adsorbed by hydrous ferric oxides (Berner, 1971; Winterhalter and Siivola, 1967). Electron-microprobe analyses of ferromanganese nodules from Green Bay show a good correlation between Fe and P in the iron-rich phase identified as goethite (Bowser et al., 1970; Rossmann et al., 1972).

Minor-element chemistry

Generally, the minor element chemical content of freshwater and shallow-marine ferromanganese nodules is significantly lower than that of deep-sea nodules (Manheim, 1965; Price, 1967; Table II). This is thought to be due to the faster rates of accretion and thus less time for "scavenging" of trace elements by lacustrine and shallow-marine nodules (Goldberg, 1954). While this observation may be generally true, it is not necessarily true when different nodule localities are examined in detail. The minor element content of ferromanganese oxides is probably a function of several factors including growth rate, chemistry of source material(s), trace-element complexation, and diagenetic fractionation.

The Co/Mn and Ni/Mn ratios in ferromanganese nodules from the Great Lakes (Table IV) are significantly higher than for other freshwater environments listed in Table IV. However, when other freshwater localities from North America are considered (Table III), Lake George and Lake Champlain also have high values of Co and Ni relative to Mn. Cobalt and nickel are well correlated with Mn in nodules from Lake Michigan (Rossmann et al., 1972) and Lake Ontario (Cronan and Thomas, 1972), but are poorly correlated in nodules from several Canadian Shield lakes (Harriss and Troup, 1970) and the English Lake District (Gorham and Swaine, 1965). It seems probable that the accretion rate of ferromanganese nodules in the Great Lakes is significantly lower than the rate for concretions from Canadian Shield Lakes. Undoubtedly the metal flux rates are much lower in the Great Lakes.

The Cu/Mn ratio varies considerably between the several freshwater localities (Table IV). This variability may reflect the trace-element composition and the organic chemistry of waters that nourish the ferromanganese nodules. The copper content of Lake George nodules (Table III and IV) appears to be anomalously high relative to all other lakes in North America and Europe. The copper content of Lake Ontario ferromanganese oxide coatings is also relatively high (Table I). The geochemical affinity of copper for dissolved organic matter may explain some of the variability since the types and amount of organic matter in overlying and interstitial water may vary considerably from locality to locality.

The Zn/Mn ratio also varies greatly between nodule localities. Again, the geochemical nature of the source fluids and the rate of accretion strongly influence the minor-element chemistry of these deposits. It is interesting to note that the ferromanganese oxide

TABLE III

Comparison of chemical composition of freshwater ferromanganese nodules

Locality	Fe (%)	Mn (%)	Co (ppm)	Cu (ppm)	Ni (ppm)	Zn (ppm)
Green Bay[1]	28.6	12.5	159	40	432	444
Lake Michigan[1]	20.6	13.9	366	96	1670	1490
Lake Ontario[2]	20.0	20.5	305	90	725	460
Lake Ontario coatings[2]	20.6	17.0	643	363	2385	1996
Lake Superior crusts[3]	8.8	2.46	–	93	21	180
Lake Oneida[4]	23.5	14.4	70	80	40	150
Lake George[5]	33.5	3.6	220	1310	700	1180
Lake Champlain[6]	29.5	5.4	230	60	–	240
Grand Lake[7]	16.6	33.0	196	14	296	1665
Ship Harbour Lake[7]	16.7	26.6	221	7	112	475
English lakes[8]	15.2	11.1	10	40	20	11000
Swedish lakes[9]	34.1	10.8	40	155	40	50

[1] Rossmann (1973); [2] Cronan and Thomas (1970); [3] Nussmann (1965); [4] Dean (1970); [5] Schoettle and Friedman (1971); [6] Johnson (1969); [7] Harriss and Troup (1970); [8] Gorham and Swaine (1965); [9] Ljunggren (1955a,b), Manheim (1965).

coatings from Lake Ontario (Table IV) contain significantly greater concentrations of Pb relative to Mn than do oceanic nodules.

TABLE IV

Elemental ratios for ferromanganese nodules from several freshwater and marine localities.

Locality	Fe/Mn	Cu/Mn*	Co/Mn*	Ni/Mn*	Zn/Mn*	Pb/Mn*
N. Lake Michigan[1]	1.5	6.9	26	120	107	–
Green Bay[1]	2.1	3.2	13	34	35	–
Lake Ontario[2]	1.0	4.4	15	35	22	110
Lake Oneida (N.Y.)[3]	1.6	5.6	5	3	10	10
Lake George (N.Y.)[4]	9.3	364	55	194	328	–
Lake Champlain (N.Y.)[5]	5.5	11.1	42	–	44	–
Grand Lake (N.S., Can.)[6]	0.5	0.4	6	9	50	0.8
Ship Harbour Lake (N.S., Can.)[6]	0.6	0.3	8	4	18	1
English lakes[7]	3.1	1.4	6	4	139	71
Swedish lakes[8]	7.6	8.5	17	8	11	6
Loch Fyne (Scotland)[9]	0.13	0.6	4	3	2	1
Baltic Sea[8]	1.6	3.5	12	54	6	3
Ocean (ave.)[8]	0.9	187	152	252	87	43

* Ratio values are multiplied by 10^4. [1] Rossmann (1973); [2] Cronan and Thomas (1972); [3] Dean (1970); [4] Schoettle and Friedman (1971); [5] Johnson (1969); [6] Hariss and Troup (1969); [7] Gorman and Swaine (1965); [8] Manheim (1965); [9] Calvert and Price (1970).

Regional variability in nodule composition

There have been very few comprehensive studies of the variation in chemical composition of nodules from freshwater localities. Rossmann et al. (1972) and Rossmann (1973) analyzed an extensive suite of nodules from Green Bay, and Cronan and Thomas (1972) conducted analyses for iron and manganese on ferromanganese-oxide coated sands from north-central Lake Ontario.

Figure 4 shows the location of three intensive survey areas in Green Bay. Table V gives the average transition-metal content and the metal/Mn ratios for each area plus those from nodules collected in northern Lake Michigan. While nodules from northern Lake Michigan do not have the lowest Fe/Mn ratio, they do contain the highest proportion of associated minor elements, such as Cu, Co, Ni, and Zn. There appears to be substantial fractionation of iron and manganese in nodules from Green Bay. Nodules from survey area III (Fig. 4) are adjacent to the Menominee River whose mass of iron is quantitatively precipitated in near-shore sands adjacent to the nodule-bearing sands (Rossmann, 1973). Survey area II is located adjacent to dark gray, organic-rich muds and survey area I is located at the mouth of the channel of the Escanaba River (Fig. 4). Proximity to the source of metals for nodule growth appears to be the dominant factor in determining the chemical composition of ferromanganese oxides in Green Bay, Lake Michigan (Rossmann, 1973).

Cronan and Thomas (1972) have noted a persistant regional variation in the ferromanganese-oxide geochemistry of the Lake Ontario deposits. They present regional maps of ferromanganese oxide chemistry (Fe, Mn) that show the Fe/Mn ratio varying from 0.40 in the northern part to 11 in the southern part of the deposit. They further point out that the concentrations of Co, Ni, and Zn largely follow those of manganese. Nickel and zinc are most abundant in the northern part of the deposit, while Co reaches a maximum in the center of the deposit (Cronan and Thomas, 1972). Considering the distribution of the redox potential in Lake Ontario sediments, iron is likely to be selectively precipitated in the south and manganese in the north of the ferromanganese-oxide deposit (Cronan and Thomas, 1972).

MINERALOGY

There are many iron- and manganese-oxide phases that precipitate in a low-temperature aqueous environment (Bricker, 1965; Stumm and Morgan, 1970). At present, there appears to be no clear agreement concerning mineralogic nomenclature and the proper means for distinguishing one phase from another. The confusion over characterization of these oxyhydroxide phases is due to several factors: (1) the inherent fine-grained nature of the phases which results in broad X-ray diffraction lines; (2) the poorly crystalline to amorphous structure of the phases which results in diffuse X-ray patterns; (3) the admix-

TABLE V

Average acid-soluble transition-metal chemistry and elemental ratios of ferromanganese nodules from northern Lake Michigan and three survey areas in Green Bay, Lake Michigan (after Rossmann, 1973)

Location	Fe (wt.%)	Mn (wt.%)	Cu (ppm)	Co (ppm)	Ni (ppm)	Zn (ppm)	Fe/Mn	Cu/Mn	Co/Mn	Ni/Mn	Zn/Mn
N. Lake Michigan	20.6	13.9	96	366	1670	1490	1.5	7	26	120	107
Survey area I (south of Escanoba R.)	40.0	6.8	26	136	123	354	5.9	4	20	18	52
Survey area II (Chambers Is.)	20.0	12.2	26	168	291	371	1.6	2	14	24	30
Survey area III (east of Menominee R.)	15.0	21.9	56	138	295	585	0.7	3	6	13	27

ture of several phases on the micron scale making it difficult to distinguish single phases by X-ray or microscopic techniques; and (4) the probable precipitation of these phases under metastable conditions where kinetic conditions, such as precipitation rate, temperature, partial pressure of oxygen, and adsorbed trace metals, play an important role in determining the crystallinity and phase composition. There is evidence (Brown, 1972; Greenslate, 1974b) that the structure of iron/manganese oxyhydroxide phases can be altered by sampling, storage (dehydration), and preparative (grinding) procedures. The fine-grained nature and the admixture of phases make it very difficult to obtain reliable chemical compositional data using electron-microprobe and scanning electron-microscopic characteristics of artifically synthesized iron/manganese oxides and naturally occurring phases exhibiting similar diffraction patterns. The situation is further complicated by the effect of other trace metals (Cu, Co, Ni, Ba) on unit cell dimensions and the stabilization of different crystalline structures. Presently, the characterization of these oxyhydroxide phases is being improved with the use of transmission electron-microscopy and other solid-state techniques. However, it is important to evaluate the effect of sample handling in relation to mineralogical characterization of these phases. Final elucidation of the mineralogy of this complex system of iron/manganese oxyhydroxides must await further systematic synthesis of these minerals under carefully controlled conditions of temperature, hydrostatic pressure, oxygen partial pressure, solution composition (trace metals), and precipitation/growth rate. Such synthesis must be accompanied by definitive X-ray and electron-diffraction studies to characterize the synthesized phases.

Because of the present nomenclature problems involved in accurate characterization of these phases (especially those of manganese), current identification of iron/manganese oxyhydroxide phases is partly operational. Part of the disagreement can be attributed to the problem of whether naturally occurring and synthetic phases are actually the same and if so what nomenclature should be used. For a more complete discussion of manganese oxyhydroxide mineralogy, the reader is referred to Glasby (1972 and Chapter 7, this volume), Sorem and Foster (1973), Cronan (1967), Bricker (1965), Manheim (1965), Buser and Grutter (1956), and Burns and Burns (in preparation).

The following manganese minerals have been observed by the authors in their study of freshwater ferromanganese deposits from the St. Lawrence Great Lakes area: birnessite (after Jones and Milne, 1956), todorokite (after Straczek et al., 1960), and psilomelane (after Wadsley, 1953). This nomenclature for manganese minerals will be used throughout the remainder of the discussion of ferromanganese mineralogy. Prior to about 1970 nearly all reported attempts to characterize the phases in freshwater ferromangenese deposits resulted in the observation that these contained "amorphous" compounds. Only Ljunggren (1955) reported the presence of crystalline manganese compounds from Swedish deposits (see Table VI). This lack of occurrence of crystalline compounds was probably due to the fact that goniometer-type diffractometers were used for these mineralogical studies and with this technique it is difficult to determine the poorly crystalline character of these oxyhydroxide phases. Although terminology differs from author to

TABLE VI

Summary of freshwater and marine ferromanganese nodule mineralogy

Date	Author	Mineral reported
Freshwater:		
1955	Ljunggren	goethite, δ-MnO_2, manganese manganite
1969	Harriss and Troup	X-ray amorphous
1970	Cronan and Thomas	X-ray amorphous
1970	Bowser et al.	goethite, birnessite, todorokite, psilomelane
1971	Schoettle and Friedman	goethite, δ-MnO_2 (birnessite)
1973	Callender et al.	rhodochrosite
1973	Callender	rhodochrosite
1974	Damiani et al.	goethite, rhodochrosite
Marine:		
1956	Buser and Grutter	10 Å- and 7 Å-manganite, δ-MnO_2
1964	Murata and Erd	psilomelane
1965	Manheim	todorokite, 7 Å-manganite, δ-MnO_2 10 Å-manganite, ramsdellite*
1966	Lynn and Bonatti	rhodochrosite
1973	Sorem and Foster	rancienite
1969	Andruschenko and Skornyakova	psilomelane, pyrolusite, woodruffite
1968	Cronan and Tooms	todorokite, δ-MnO_2 (birnessite)
1972	Glasby	10 Å-manganite, δ-MnO_2

* Interpreted by Sorem and Foster (1973) as nsutite.

author, numerous investigators have reported since 1970 the presence of crystalline iron and manganese compounds in freshwater nodules. These reported occurrences are listed in Table VI. A listing of reported occurrences from marine ferromanganese nodules is included for comparison.

Ferromanganese nodules from Green Bay, Lake Michigan, contain the greatest number of reported freshwater iron/manganese compounds which include goethite, birnessite, todorokite, psilomelane (Bowser et al., 1970; Rossmann, 1973) and rhodochrosite (Callender, 1973; Callender et al., 1973). Confirmatory studies involved X-ray powder diffractometry of micro-samples before and after treatment with 25% hydroxylamine hydrochloride. This treatment effectively solubilizes the manganese oxides, leaving the iron oxides and silicate materials intact (Arrhenius, 1963; D.S. Cronan, personal communication). Comparison of diffraction patterns taken before and after chemical treatment allows the identification of lines attributable to manganese oxide phases.

To date, too few systematic mineralogic studies of both freshwater and marine ferromanganese nodules are available in order to critically evaluate the important physical and chemical environmental parameters that result in discernible phase differences. In Green Bay, Lake Michigan, there is a tendency for psilomelane to be associated with nodules that exhibit a high iron content. However, the mineralogical data are too few to

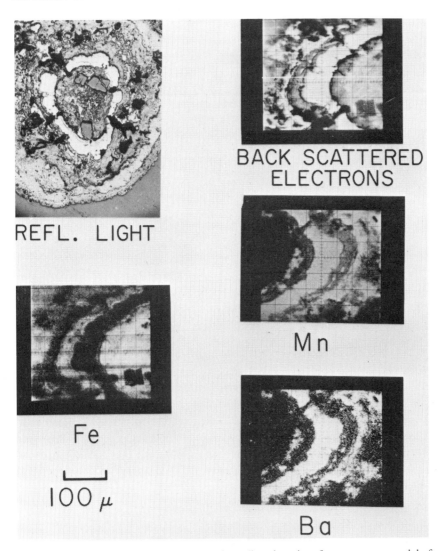

REFL. LIGHT

BACK SCATTERED
ELECTRONS

Mn

Fe

100 μ

Ba

Fig. 6. Electron-probe micro-chemical data for psilomelane in a ferromanganese nodule from Green Bay, Lake Michigan. The Fe X-ray map is reversed in orientation from the Mn and Ba maps.

be conclusive. Psilomelane is the one manganese-oxide mineral whose occurrence in fresh-water ferromanganese deposits was first reported by the authors (Bowser et al., 1970). It occurs as a discrete phase whose dimensions are large enough for electron-probe micro-analysis. Figure 3 is a reflected-light photomicrograph showing an area of highly reflective psilomelane. The highly reflective psilomelane in Fig. 6 surrounds a nucleus of admixed iron oxide and silicate material and in turn is surrounded by an iron-rich phase. X-ray scan maps (Fig. 6) of the nodule cross-section show a strong barium—manganese association. Chemical analyses of psilomelane from Green Bay and Tomahawk Lake (Wisconsin)

TABLE VII

Probe micro-chemical analyses of goethite and psilomelane from Green Bay, Lake Michigan

	Goethite	Psilomelane (1) (Sta. GB-69-20)	Psilomelane (2) (Sta. GB-Mi-48)	Psilomelanes (wc)*
Fe	50.30	0.66	1.20	1.01– 1.56
Mn	1.39	48.19	48.08	48.63–49.33
Ca	1.16	1.26	0.69	0.29–nd
Mg	nd	nd	nd	0.12–nd
Ba	nd	7.70	12.64	14.51–12.92
K	0.10	0.31	0.09	0.08–nd
Na	nd	nd	nd	nd–nd
Si	7.18	0.12	0.43	nd– 0.93
P	0.52	na	na	na–na
O as oxides	31.77	29.95	30.39	30.24–31.54
Total	92.42	88.19	93.82	94.88 96.28
"H$_2$O"	8.11	11.73	5.74	4.65 5.08

* Fleischer (1960), wet chemical analyses; nd = not detected; na = not analyzed.

are presented in Table VII along with comparative analyses reported by Fleischer (1960) and Levinson (1961).

Electron-probe analyses of goethite from Green Bay (Lake Michigan) are presented in Table VII. The silicon and phosphorous content of these iron-rich phases are interesting. To date, mineralogical investigations have failed to demonstrate whether the silicon and phosphorous are co-precipitated with the iron as crystalline phases or whether they are incorporated with the iron phase(s) by sorption. Recently, Müller and Forstner (1973) have reported on the association of nontronite and vivianite facies with limonite nodules in Lake Malawi (Africa). Obviously, other ligands (SiO_2, PO_4^{3-}) besides hydroxyl can buffer the iron content of waters adjacent to and within the sediment.

Rhodochrosite was first reported by Callender et al. (1973) and Callender (1973) as a diagenetic alteration product of ferromanganese nodules from Green Bay, Lake Michigan. An occurrence of rhodochrosite in Lake Ontario was reported recently by Damiani et al. (1973). The Green Bay rhodochrosite has been studied using X-ray diffraction, electron-probe, scanning electron microscopic, and wet chemical techniques. The data resulting from these analyses is summarized in Table VIII. Electron-probe analyses gave the most accurate compositional data, but corroborative chemical determinations were made by atomic-absorption analysis of hand-selected samples and by using X-ray derived unit-cell parameters (Table VIII). Atomic-absorption analytical data indicated that the rhodochrosite contained a small percentage of iron, but subsequent SEM analyses showed that the iron was an admixed oxide contaminant and consequently the calculation of mole-percent composition includes only manganese and calcium as cations.

TABLE VIII

Chemical composition of sedimentary manganese carbonates from Green Bay, Lake Michigan, and other recent environments

Locality	Composition	Source
Green Bay, Lake Michigan	$(Mn_{0.71}Ca_{0.29}) CO_3$ AAS	Callender (1973)
	$(Mn_{0.75}Ca_{0.25}) CO_3$ X-ray	Callender (1973)
	$(Mn_{0.73}Ca_{0.27}) CO_3$ probe	Emerson (1974)
Lake Pinnus-Yarvi	$(Mn_{0.51}Ca_{0.45}Fe_{0.04}) CO_3$ to $(Mn_{0.54}Ca_{0.09}Fe_{0.37}) CO_3$	Shterenberg et al. (1966)
Loch Fyne, Scotland	$(Mn_{0.48}Ca_{0.45}Mg_{0.07}) CO_3$	Calvert and Price (1970)
Baltic Sea	$(Mn_{0.70}Ca_{0.30}) CO_3$ to $(Mn_{0.60}Ca_{0.32}Mg_{0.08}) CO_3$	Manheim (1961)

COMPARISON BETWEEN MARINE AND FRESHWATER NODULES

Aside from the rather obvious differences in composition and ionic strength of waters in which marine and freshwater nodules grow, there are a number of similarities and dissimilarities between the nodules which help to focus on the nodule-forming processes common to both environments. While it may be somewhat premature to make definitive statements on the nature of the processes most important to nodule formation in both environments, a comparison of the physical and chemical aspects of freshwater and marine nodules is essential to the formulation of hypotheses to explain mechanisms in either environment. For example, any hypothesis concerning formation of some aspect of marine nodules that is dependent on volcanic or hydrothermal processes would certainly not apply to freshwater nodule environments discussed in this paper, where such activity is nonexistant. Yet if such marine nodule features were also found in their freshwater counterparts it should circumstantially help negate the volcanic/hydrothermal interpretation for the particular marine nodules, unless, of course, it could be shown that two or more different processes could form the same feature. Most of the specific descriptions of critical features/environments of freshwater and marine nodules are contained in either the body of this chapter or in that by Glasby and Read (Chapter 7, this volume) on marine nodules. However, the purpose of this section is to point out what we feel are critical differences and similarities between the two environments.

With regard to shape and internal form, the ranges of types of nodules found in both freshwater and marine nodules overlap considerably. Micro-nodules, crusts or pavements, and rounded to oblate, cobble- and pebble-sized nodules have been described from both environments. Typically the larger-sized freshwater nodules tend to be more flattened in shape, whereas marine nodules range from flattened to more spherical shapes. Thin oxide coatings on mineral grains and rocks are not uncommon in either environment. Marine micro-nodules tend to be dispersed in the pelagic muds, whereas similar freshwater nodules are found in much higher percentages, usually in sand rather than clay-sized sediments.

Internally, nodules from either environment generally demonstrate concentric laminae of the iron and manganese oxides. Microlaminations of the scale reported by Margolis (1973) for marine nodules have not been observed in non-marine nodules, but considering the differences in accretion rates of nodules from the two environments, perhaps it is not surprising. Generally, all marine nodules have some sort of recognizable internal layering, although weak in some localities. However, some of the millimeter-scale nodules from freshwater localities, particularly from Lake Michigan, show an absence of internal layering. Instead, the nodules are much richer in their percentage of included sand grains, suggesting they may have been formed by cementation of sands without any history of current rolling or sorting.

A characteristic of nodules from all environments is the presence of some sort of nucleus about which the iron and manganese oxides accrete. Nuclei are composed of locally available material and, hence, marine nodules are typically cored with volcanic fragments, fossil shell and bone debris, coralline fragments, glacially rafted pebbles, and even parts of nodules which, for some reason yet to be explained satisfactorily, have been broken during their growth history. Nuclei of freshwater nodules, on the other hand, are generally composed of glacial and stream fragments of Precambrian crystalline igneous and metamorphic rocks, sand-sized quartz and feldspar grains, and less commonly available materials such as wood fragments, clay chips and human artifacts (plastic and glass fragments). There appears to be no difference in the percentages of nuclei compositional types and their abundance in nearby nodule-free areas for both marine and freshwater environments, a fact that suggests little or no compositional "selectivity" for nodule nuclei. Presumably then, if given physical and chemical conditions that are favorable for the formation of nodules, but lacking suitable nuclei, the ferromanganese oxides would form as a "dispersed" phase much like Skornyakova (1964), Bostrom and Peterson (1969) and Sayles and Bischoff (1973) observed in the oceanic sediments.

Mineralogically, both marine and freshwater nodules have more similarities than dissimilarities. Most of the investigations on nodule mineralogy (and consequently most of the various discussions on mineralogic terminology, identification criteria, etc.) have been concerned with marine nodules; however, recent investigations on freshwater nodules (Ljunggren, 1955; Bowser et al., 1970; Rossmann, 1973; Schoettle and Friedman, 1973), have revealed a similar picture. In fact, the mineral birnessite was named for its occurrence in soils, an occurrence more similar to freshwater environs than to marine. Generally, however, freshwater nodules display a somewhat lower degree of crystallinity, an observation which helps, in part, to explain why early, preliminary investigations of freshwater nodules failed to recognize any crystallinity at all.

In part, however, the differences in crystallinity of nodules from the two environments may be related to the relative growth rates of nodules. The more rapidly accreting freshwater nodules presumably have had too little time to recrystallize since their initial precipitation as amorphous compounds. The effect of the minor elements such as copper, nickel, and cobalt in stabilizing the crystalline phases or perhaps promoting an increase in the rate of crystallization is not known at this time.

Quantitatively, the relative abundances of the ferromanganese minerals differ considerably from environment to environment. Goethite and amorphous ferric hydroxide are obviously more abundant in freshwater nodules owing to the relatively greater iron content of nodules from this environment, but relative variations in the todorokite and birnessite abundances in both marine and non-marine environments is, at present, poorly understood. Again it is possible that various nodule minor elements could stabilize one phase relative to the other or that differences may be solely due to variations in the oxygen content of waters in which they form.

In general, the nodules from freshwater and marine environments are chemically distinct from one another. Iron/manganese ratios in freshwater nodules and crusts are on the average distinctly higher than their marine counterparts. The oceanic mean Fe/Mn ratio is 0.47 (Horn et al., 1973) whereas the mean of all nodule analyses from northern Lake Michigan and Green Bay is 2.2, a difference of greater than four times (Rossmann, 1973). In contrast, however, nodules from both environments can be characterized by having a considerable range of compositions. Iron/manganese ratios for Green Bay nodules range from 111 to 0.21 and marine nodule ratios vary from 160 to 0.02.

Part of the variability of Fe/Mn ratios in nodules from all environments arises from the fact that the nodules are not chemically homogeneous. This is particularly true for freshwater and shallow-marine nodules where iron-rich rims on manganese-rich cores and vice-versa are common (Calvert and Price, 1970; Callender et al., 1973; Rossmann, 1973). Major compositional zoning is less apparent in data on marine nodules (see Glasby and Read, this volume, for further discussion).

Shallow-marine nodules have Fe/Mn ratios that are more typical of freshwater nodules (Manheim, 1965; Winterhalter, 1966). Exceptions to this are found in Loch Fyne, Scotland (Calvert and Price, 1970) and Jervis Inlet, British Columbia (Grill et al., 1968). The reasons for the *relative* concentration of manganese versus iron in marine nodules as compared to freshwater nodules is somewhat less well understood. As stated earlier, their respective average Fe/Mn ratios vary by a factor of greater than 4. Iron is, of course, relatively more abundant than manganese in the source rocks from which both freshwater and marine nodules ultimately owe their origin. However, the relative mobility of iron and manganese under varying Eh and pH conditions that exist in low-temperature environments leads to an initial relative decrease in Fe/Mn ratios during both marine and subaerial weathering (Krauskopf, 1957). Further decreases in Fe/Mn ratios in freshwater lakes appear to be related to selective precipitation and immobilization of iron relative to manganese from river waters that discharge into the lakes. This is particularly evident in Green Bay (Fig. 5) where Fe/Mn ratios range from well over 100 near the mouths of the

Fox and Escanaba Rivers to below 1 in the area of the bay most distal from river influences. Similar patterns have been noted in lakes of the Baltic Shield by Strakhov (1966).

Regional variations in iron/manganese ratios in marine nodules have been adequately noted (Mero, 1965; Price and Calvert, 1970; Glasby, 1973). Systematic variations were interpreted in terms of a diagenetic model where selective mobilization of elements and metal influx rates (sedimentation) play an important role. However, little has been noted of the contrast between marine and freshwater nodules. Two factors may be important in explaining the relative enrichment of manganese in marine nodules. First, iron is deposited in marine environments both as a "hydrous" oxide and as a sulfide (Berner, 1971). This immobilization of iron in a shallow fjord plus the high organic-carbon content of the sediment probably accounts for the fact that nodules reported by Calvert and Price (1970) are more manganese-rich than typical shallow-marine nodules of the Baltic and White Seas. The high sulfate content of seawater provides a source of sulfide ion in areas where the organic-carbon content of sediments supports bacterial sulfate reduction. Since no equivalent sulfide compound of manganese is stable under these conditions, the availability of iron for oxide precipitation is lessened. Freshwater environments, on the other hand, are generally noted for their lack of appreciable sulfate and, therefore, nearly all of the "mobile" iron (soluble, organically complexed, colloidal precipitates) is available for oxide deposition. Secondly, since organic-carbon contents of freshwater environments are generally higher, anoxic sediments and associated bottom waters are more common than in marine environments and therefore *both* iron and manganese are relatively mobile during the early stages of sediment diagenesis. Quantitatively, anoxic marine conditions, particularly in the open ocean, are virtually nonexistent. Bottom waters of nearly all of the oceans show oxygen saturations greater than 50%. Under these conditions, one would expect iron to be much less mobile than manganese. Pore-water iron and manganese contents of marine sediments generally support this observation. Manganese is more abundant in marine sediments than iron, whereas just the opposite is true for freshwater sediments. (High interstitial iron concentrations are found in some marine sediments, but generally below the low interstitial-iron zone of sulfide precipitation in cores.)

Trace and minor-metal concentrations from marine and freshwater nodules are distinctly different from one another. The most notable differences occur in the transition-metal contents (Table II; see also Fig. 7). Cobalt, copper, and nickel concentrations in marine nodules are between 20 and 100 times higher compared to freshwater ferromanganese nodules. The reason for this depletion in transition-mental content may be related to two factors: (1) mobilization of metals as metal-organic complexes in organic-rich sediment pore waters, and (2) reduced effective co-precipitation of minor elements with ferromanganese oxides as a result of higher nodule accretion rates. The amino acids and humic acids associated with soils and sediments are capable of complexing variable quantities of transition metals (see Chapter 5 by Saxby, Volume 2). The molecular weight of organic matter and the valency of the metals are important factors affecting the metal-

IRON AND ARSENIC IN GREEN BAY SEDIMENTS AND NODULES

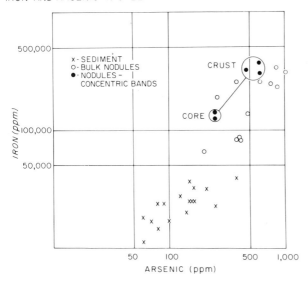

MANGANESE AND BARIUM IN GREEN BAY SEDIMENTS AND NODULES

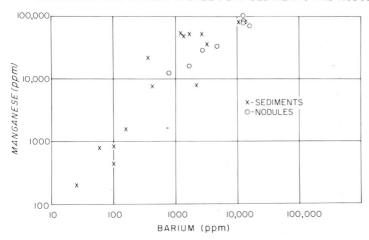

Fig. 7. Correlation between manganese and barium, and iron and arsenic in ferromanganese nodules and surficial sediment from Green Bay, Lake Michigan.

binding capacity (Rashid, 1971). Marginal marine and lacustrine sediments contain appreciable quantities of organic matter. Diagenesis of this sedimentary organic matter results in the release of various organic compounds to the pore water and the subsequent chelation/complexation of divalent and trivalent metal ions. The stability of various metal-organic chelates may follow the well-known Irving-Williams series (Irving and Williams, 1948); $Pb > Cu > Ni > Co > Zn > Cd > Fe > Mn > Mg$. This suggests that Pb and Cu may be chelated more strongly by dissolved natural organic matter than Zn and Cd. The concentrations of minor metals in lacustrine nodules (Table II) correlate relatively well with the stability order for organo-metallic chelates. In Green Bay, Lake Michigan, Cu shows the most striking depletion followed by Co and Ni. On the other hand, Zn shows relatively little depletion compared to marine nodules. Generally, the low molecular weight fractions of humic acids, the fulvic acids, are quantitatively more important in the chelation phenomenon. Fulvic acids have a higher number of functional groups than do humic acids (i.e., COOH, OH, C=O groups). Therefore, metal-organic complexes in sediments having higher concentrations of decaying organic matter will cause a general depletion in the specific minor-element content of nodules associated with rapidly accumulating sediment (marginal marine, lacustrine) compared to slowly accumulating sediment (deep-sea).

The significantly higher accretion rates of marginal marine and freshwater ferromanganese nodules compared with deep-sea nodules suggest a metal-uptake role in determining minor-element composition. The rate at which the Fe and Mn is attached to the nodule surface may ultimately determine the concentration of associated minor elements. If attachment is rapid, such as by coagulation or destabilization of a colloidal sol, then there may be less chance to retain adsorbed or co-precipitated metal ions. If attachment is slow, such as in the deep sea, then particle-by-particle accretion may result in a larger surface area which, when exposed to metal ions in solution, has sufficient time to concentrate these metals on an oxide substrate.

One notable exception to the minor-element depletion in freshwater relative to marine nodules is the alkaline-earth element Ba. In many North American lakes the Ba content is 4—10 times that of marine nodules (Table II). This freshwater Ba-enrichment is related to the relatively low sulfate content of freshwater lakes. In seawater, Ba is buffered by the mineral barite whose solubility is exceeded by the high sulfate concentration of ocean water (Cronan, 1974). In most freshwater environments, the solubility of barite is not even approached and thus barium is free to participate in other geochemical reactions, such as solid substitution in the manganese-oxide mineral psilomelane.

Generally, the inter-element associations are similar for freshwater and marine nodules. Goldberg (1954) and Cronan (1967), using bulk-chemical data from marine nodules, noted significant correlations between Mn—Ni—Cu, Fe—Ti—Co and Mn—Ni—Cu, Fe—Ti, Co—Pb, respectively. Using bulk-chemical data from Lake Michigan, Rossmann et al. (1972) showed that there was a significant correlation between Mn—Ba—Co—Cu—Ni—Sr—Zn and Fe—As (Rossmann, 1973). Using qualitative electron-microprobe analyses, Burns and Fuerstenau (1966) noted associations of Ni, Cu, Mg, Ba, Zn, K with Mn and Co, Ti, Ca, Si, with Fe. Similar work by Cronan and Tooms (1968) showed possible direct relationships between Mn and Co, Ni, Cu, K, Ca. Quantitative electron-probe analyses of several microcrystalline areas of psilomelane and goethite in nodules from Green Bay, Lake Michigan (Rossmann et al., 1972), showed significant positive correlations between Mn and Ba (psilomelane) and Fe—Si—P (goethite).

MOBILIZATION/PRECIPITATION OF IRON AND MANGANESE IN THE SEDIMENTARY ENVIRONMENT

Aqueous geochemistry of iron and manganese

The solution geochemistries of iron and manganese have some pronounced similarities and striking differences. Both elements experience oxidation/reduction under present environmental conditions of the earth's surface. Thus, both iron and manganese form insoluble oxy-hydroxides and carbonates/sulfides. However, the environmental conditions (e.g., geochemical variables) under which these occur are different, thus eventually leading to a relatively distinct separation in the sedimentary environment (Krauskopf, 1957).

Iron in aqueous solution is subject to hydrolysis with the species $Fe(OH)_2^+$ being the predominant form of ferric iron in most natural waters over a pH range of 6–8 (Hem and Cropper, 1959; Kester and Byrne, 1972). The concentration of soluble iron in equilibrium with $Fe(OH)_3$ under oxidizing, near-neutral pH conditions is substantially below 0.01 mg/l. Inorganic complexes (besides hydroxides) of iron in solution are generally insignificant compared with total "soluble" iron (Hem, 1972). Ferric fluoride complexes are significant at fluoride levels greater than 2 mg/l, sulfate complexes become significant at SO_4^{2-} concentrations exceeding 1000 mg/l, and chloride complexes are not important up to Cl^- concentrations approaching those of sea water (19,000 mg/l). Both ferrous (Fe^{2+}) and ferric (Fe^{3+}) iron form strong complexes with organic ligands (Hem, 1972). Many natural waters contain up to 10^{-4} mg/l "dissolved" organic matter (Semenov et al., 1967) which has a range of stability constants for ferrous/ferric-organic complexes between 10^4 and 10^8 (Hem, 1972; Kester and Byrne, 1972). The effect of organic complexing on iron solubility in natural waters is to increase substantially its solubility over that governed by ferric hydroxide under oxidizing conditions and ferrous compounds of carbonate–sulfide–phosphate under reducing conditions.

Manganese in aqueous solution is not hydrolyzed and exists as the Mn^{2+} ion over a wide pH range (0–10) in the system $Mn–H_2O$. The concentration of soluble manganese in equilibrium with several insoluble oxyhydroxides (MnO_2, Mn_2O_3, Mn_3O_4) under oxidizing, near-neutral pH conditions is between 1 and 100 mg/l (Hem, 1963). These concentrations are considerably higher than those for the $Fe–H_2O$ system. There are several important inorganic complexes of manganese including bicarbonate ($MnHCO_3^+$), sulfate ($MnSO_4^0$), and chloride ($MnCl^+$). At bicarbonate concentrations greater than 100 mg/l, 10% of the total soluble manganese exists as $MnHCO_3^+$; at sulfate concentrations greater than 50 mg/l, 10% or more of the total soluble manganese exists as $MnSO_4^0$ (Hem, 1963). In seawater with chloride concentrations near 19,000 mg/l, the manganese chloride complex ($MnCl^+$) accounts for approximately 50% of the total soluble manganese (Crerar and Barnes, 1974). Comparison between ferrous iron and manganese organic-complex stability constants shows (Stumm and Morgan, 1970) that iron (Fe^{2+}) is more strongly complexed by natural aqueous organic matter than manganese (Mn^{2+}).

A comparison of iron and manganese solubility and redox equilibria illustrates the geochemical pathways whereby iron is separated from manganese in the sedimentary environment. When Eh/pH stability diagrams for the two metal–water systems (Fe–Mn–H_2O) are superimposed (Fig. 8), dissolved-iron (Fe^{2+}) concentrations are limited by the oxyhydroxide solubility at pH 7.5/Eh 0 mV while dissolved manganese (Mn^{2+} concentrations are limited by the oxyhydroxide solubility at pH 7.5/Eh + 400 mV. Obviously, iron can be effectively separated from manganese by differential solubility and slow oxidation. Krauskopf (1957) has clearly demonstrated that iron oxides are uniformly less soluble than manganese oxides and that the ferrous ion (Fe^{2+}) is more readily oxidized than the manganous ion (Mn^{2+}).

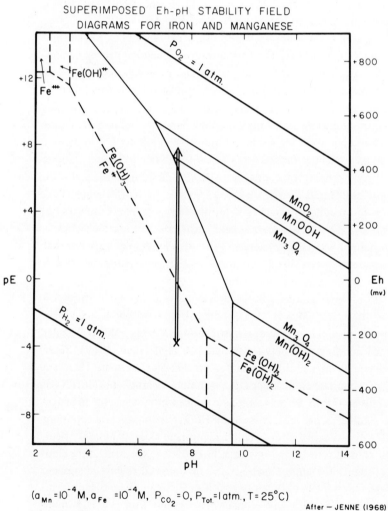

SUPERIMPOSED Eh-pH STABILITY FIELD DIAGRAMS FOR IRON AND MANGANESE

$(a_{Mn} = 10^{-4} M, a_{Fe} = 10^{-4} M, P_{CO_2} = 0, P_{Tot} = 1 atm., T = 25°C)$

After — JENNE (1968)

Fig. 8. Eh/pH stability diagram for ferromanganese oxides.

Oxidation is not the only mechanism for separation of iron from manganese. Ferrous sulfide (FeS_2) is much more insoluble than manganous sulfide (MnS) in low-temperature geochemical environments (Hem, 1972). In anoxic environments with moderate to high sulfate concentrations (marginal marine basins, ground water, some lacustrine environments), sulfate (SO_4^{2-}) is reduced to sulfide (S^{2-}) which reacts with ferrous iron (Fe^{2+}) to form insoluble sulfides (Berner, 1971). Buffering of soluble iron by insoluble sulfides tends to increase the soluble manganese content relative to iron.

Transport of iron and manganese

The source of "dissolved" iron and manganese in river water originates from soil weathering products. In temperate climates, iron- and manganese-bearing mineral phases are attacked by acid aqueous solutions containing dissolved gases and organic matter. These and other metals are leached into the soil water which eventually reaches streams. Considering the aqueous geochemistry of iron and manganese, these elements would exist predominantly as organic complexes of iron and bicarbonate/organic complexes of manganese. The predominant pH range for streams and rivers draining the glaciated northern temperate zone is between 5 and 7.5. Using an average pH of 6, the minimum iron concentration of aerated river water is 0.007 mg/l and the minimum manganese concentration is 100 mg/l. Chemical analyses of river water from the glaciated northern temperate zone (Lake Michigan Basin) show that "dissolved" iron ranges from 0.03 to 0.5 mg/l and manganese from 0.005 to 0.08 mg/l (Callender, unpublished data; Robbins et al., 1971). It is apparent that simple oxyhydroxide solubility does not control the concentrations of these metals in organic-rich, slightly acidic river water.

In the case of iron, a significant percentage of the "dissolved" metal may be complexed by dissolved organic matter which may resist oxidation. De Groot et al. (1968) have shown that iron is substantially mobilized by dissolved organic matter (organometallic complexes) produced as a decomposition product of degrading organic matter at the mouth of a salt-water estuary in the North Sea (Rhine River). The presence of organic matter and other oxygen-consuming compounds (pollution) in river water may lower the dissolved oxygen content to a level (1 mg/l) below which the redox potential decreases, thereby increasing the iron oxyhydroxide solubility. In the case of manganese, dissolved inorganic complexes with bicarbonate and sulfate anions will increase oxyhydroxide solubility (i.e., total dissolved manganese concentration in equilibrium with manganese oxyhydroxides) in the same way (but not magnitude) that a lower pH/Eh results in greater solubility.

The higher "apparent" solubilities of iron and manganese (as interpreted from chemical analyses) in river water from the glaciated northern temperate zone are the result of several experimental and geochemical factors: the ultra-fine grain size of iron-hydroxide colloidal suspensions; the pronounced organic complexing of iron, the significant inorganic complexing of manganese, the slow rate of oxidation of these complexes, and the lack of electroactive species that determine a representative redox potential. Commonly, water samples are filtered through a 0.45-mm pore-size membrane filter which does not retain some colloids. Metals, especially iron, in these filtrates are operationally defined as "soluble".

Interaction between source waters and lake waters

Eventually, river water with its dissolved organic matter and metals discharges into a lake or the ocean. At the point of river discharge there is a zone of mixing and the proportion of river water is reduced to a small fraction in a short distance. In the case of a river discharging into the ocean, colloidal and suspended particulate matter coagulate to form large aggregates which settle to the bottom. In addition, ion-exchange equilibria between the soluble and particulate phases shift at the freshwater—salt water interface so that certain transition metals are released to solution. Much of the iron in continental runoff is sedimented by this mechanism in coastal areas. Such is not the case for rivers discharging into lakes since there is no concentrated electrolyte to cause flocculation. Mixing with oxygenated lake water containing minor to trace amounts of transition metals and dissolved organic matter, the river water is diluted by an infinite volume of "fresh" water which causes a significant percentage of the inorganic and organic-metal complexes to break down and dissociate. The relatively free, uncomplexed soluble metals are more subject to solubility and redox equilibria controls characteristic of laboratory studies using "pure", dilute solutions. In addition, much of the suspended particulate load of streams and rivers is deposited at the mouth of rivers and, as a consequence, the adsorbed phase containing significant concentrations of transition metals is carried to the sediment. All of the above factors contribute to a lower analytical value for "dissolved" iron and manganese in lake water as well as to accelerating the rate of oxidation and thus equilibration between soluble iron and manganese and insoluble oxyhydroxide compounds.

The river water—lake water interface is thus important in decreasing the total "dissolved" manganese and iron. However, of even more importance to processes that selectively mobilize/immobilize iron and manganese is the sediment—water interface. In rapidly accumulating fine-grained sediments, diagenetic mobilization of iron, manganese, and other transition metals creates substantial concentration gradients from deeper sediment (lower redox potential/lower pH) to the sediment surface (higher redox potential/higher pH). Callender (1968) and Robbins and Callender (1973, 1975) have presented interstitial manganese data from Green Bay and southern Lake Michigan, while Cronan and Thomas (1972) have published transition-metal data for Lake Ontario interstitial water. Substantial interstitial manganese gradients exist in Green Bay and southern Lake Michigan sediments. These linear concentration gradients near the sediment—water interface suggest that manganese is diffusing into the bottom water. Robbins and Callender (1973,

1975) have presented a quantitative model for diagenesis of manganese in Lake Michigan sediments whereby sedimentary manganese is recycled between a surface (oxidized) zone and a lower reduced zone. Upward-diffusing soluble iron and manganese is either being oxidized at the sediment—water interface or enriches bottom water that is transported by currents into shallow areas where nuclei exist and oxidizing conditions persist. Like soil water, interstitial water from fine-grained, organic-rich sediments may contain appreciable concentrations of dissolved organic matter which complexes these transition metals and prevents their rapid oxidation/precipitation once the "dissolved" material reacts with more oxidizing, less acid lake water.

A similar situation may exist when iron- and manganese-rich ground water discharges into the near-shore region of a lake underlain by sand and gravel. Generally ferromanganese nodules, crusts, and coatings occur in shallow water at depths between 1 and 2 m where the lake is underlain by permeable gravel. It is suggested that ground water rich in dissolved iron and manganese enters the lake in these areas and that the more alkaline (pH 8), oxidizing conditions prevailing in the overlying lake water cause oxidation/precipitation of ferromanganese from this ground water inflow.

Deposition of iron and manganese oxyhydroxides

It is apparent from the previous discussion of aqueous iron and manganese geochemistry that deposition/precipitation of both these metals occur under several different geochemical conditions. Both iron (Fe^{2+}) and manganese (Mn^{2+}) are unstable in slightly alkaline, oxidizing aqueous environments. However, in the absence of significant organic complexes, ferrous iron (Fe^{2+}) oxidizes to ferric hydroxide more readily than manganese manganese (Mn^{2+}) oxidizes to manganese dioxide. That is to say, the stability field for Mn^{2+} is much greater than that for Fe^{2+} for the system $Fe-Mn-H_2O$ under the expected range of Eh/pH values (+400 to -200 mV, pH 6 to 9) in aqueous environments. In addition, the inorganic, uncatalyzed oxidation rates for iron and manganese oxides are strongly pH-dependent with measurable oxidation (with hours) occurring above pH 6 for iron and pH 8.5 for manganese (Stumm and Morgan, 1970). Even when other anions, such as bicarbonate (HCO_3^-) and sulfate (SO_4^{2-}) are added to the system, the stability field of "soluble" manganese is larger than that of "soluble" iron. If natural aqueous systems were purely mixtures of inorganic compounds, then the geochemical conditions under which iron and manganese in contact with their least soluble compounds could be predicted by classical solubility and redox equilibria. An example of this is the mechanism proposed by Krauskopf (1957) to separate iron from manganese in the sedimentary environment. The differential solubility of iron and manganese oxyhydroxides as ferrous and manganous ions encounter an oxidizing environment, results in the initial precipitation of ferric hydroxide with the solution phase becoming progressively enriched in dissolved manganese. This simple and straightforward hypothesis can be applied to many natural aqueous systems with at least qualitative success. An excellent example of this geochemical separation mechanism comes from northern Green Bay, Lake Michigan, where Callender (1973) has described a sequence of manganese-rich ferromanganese nodules overlying an iron crust. The mean Fe/Mn ratio of these nodules is 2.5 while that for the iron crusts is 22 (Fig. 9). Another example of Krauskopf's geochemical separation mechanism for iron and manganese can be found in the Lake Ontario ferromanganese-oxide deposit (Cronan and Thomas, 1972). The manganese content of oxide-coated sands is highest in the north-central part of the deposit where iron is lowest, and lowest in the southwest where iron is highest. Sediment redox potential increases from south to north across the deposit (Cronan and Thomas, 1972) so that iron may be selectively oxidized and precipitated in the south and manganese in the north. Both of these environments, north-central Green Bay (Lake Michigan) and north-central Lake Ontario are relatively oxidizing, slightly alkaline aquatic systems which contain relatively small amounts of dissolved organic matter. Thus, one expects that a simple inorganic mechanism may be useful in describing qualitatively the observed geochemical data.

Much of the geological/geochemical data from many ferromanganese nodule localities cannot be explained by the simple differential precipitation mechanism for inorganic systems proposed by Krauskopf (1957). In fact, most geochemical data for iron and manganese cannot be quantitatively described with this mechanism alone. The poorly-understood area of organo-metallic geochemistry must relate strongly to the form, concentration, and chemical reactivity of iron and manganese in aqueous systems. There are several important complexes of ferric iron (Fe^{3+}) with orthophosphate and many organic bases (Stumm and Morgan, 1970). The affinity of manganese (Mn^{4+}) for hydroxyl (OH^-) is so much larger than that of ferric iron (Fe^{3+}) that it is much more difficult, over the pH range of natural waters, for other potential organic or inorganic ligands to compete successfully with hydroxyl for manganese. The high concentrations of "soluble" iron in brown-colored natural waters are frequently associated with high levels of dissolved organic matter (Stumm and Morgan, 1970). Manganese does not appear to be strongly associated with most dissolved natural organic matter. It may be difficult to distinguish,

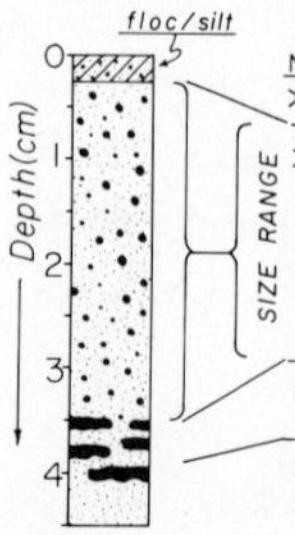

		Fe (%)	Mn(%)	Fe/Mn	Ba (%)
NODULES >1mm		17.1	19.7	0.87	2.4
>2 mm		18.7	19.9	0.94	2.5
1-2 mm		28.6	12.1	2.37	1.1
0.5-1.0mm		30.3	6.7	4.52	0.5
BROWN CRUST		22.4	3.6	6.22	0.6
RED CRUST		20.1	0.9	22.3	0.1

Fig. 9. Chemical composition of ferromanganese nodules and associated iron crusts from northern Green Bay, Lake Michigan.

by conventional analytical techniques, between soluble ferric complexes and dispersed colloidal sols of iron (Stumm and Morgan, 1970). The kinetics of iron and manganese oxidation may be strongly affected by the presence of other ions and dissolved compounds. The presence of anions, such as HPO_4^{2-}, increase significantly the ferrous iron oxidation rate (Stumm and Morgan, 1970). A variety of organic substances, especially those containing hydroxylic and/or carboxylic functional groups (e.g., phenols, gallic acid, tannic acid) can reduce both ferric iron and manganese dioxide (MnO_2) in synthetic solutions. In the case of iron, it is possible that the metal acts as a catalyst for the oxidation of organic matter by molecular oxygen (Stumm and Morgan, 1970). As long as organic matter is not completely oxidized in solution, a substantial concentration of ferrous iron (Fe^{2+}) can be maintained in the system since oxidation of ferrous iron may be slow relative to reduction of ferric iron by dissolved organic matter. Under this circumstance, dissolved organic matter retards the over-all oxidation of ferrous iron (Stumm and Morgan, 1970). The effect of natural dissolved organic matter on the oxidation/reduction and solubility of iron and manganese appears to be poorly understood.

Deposition as an oxide is not the only mode of precipitation of iron and manganese. In some instances (ground water, sediment pore-water) the activity of dissolved iron (Fe^{2+}), manganese (Mn^{2+}), and carbonate (CO_3^{2-}) is large enough to exceed the solubility of siderite ($FeCO_3$) and rhodochrosite ($MnCO_3$). In sediment pore-water environments such as Lake Michigan (Rossmann and Callender, 1969) and Lake Ontario (Cronan and Thomas, 1972) the pH/Eh of accumulating muds (pH 7.5/Eh + 100 mV) suggests that ferrous iron is in equilibrium with siderite and ferric hydroxide, while manganous manganese is saturated with respect to rhodochrosite (Stumm and Morgan, 1970). However, few occurrences of recent lacustrine siderite and rhodochrosite have been reported. Although these mineral phases may be present in amounts (1% by weight) sufficient to buffer dissolved iron and manganese, they may not be abundant enough (3% by weight) to detect by classical X-ray diffraction analysis of fine-grained material. Damiani et al. (1973) reported the occurrence of rhodochrosite in a ferromanganese nodule from the Bay of Quinte, northern Lake Ontario. Callender et al. (1973) described the occurrence of rhodochrosite, which cements ferromanganese nodules, in dark-gray silty sands that are located adjacent to organic-rich muds of southern Green Bay, Lake Michigan. Ferromanganese nodules occur in the gray silty sand to a depth of 15 cm, decreasing in abundance with depth. At about 3 cm, nodules are often cemented with manganese carbonate which occur as discontinuous masses throughout the sediment. The occurrence of manganese carbonate cement (identified as rhodochrosite) postdates the formation of the associated ferromanganese nodules and reflects the influx of finer sediment. Oxidation of organic matter and diagenetic mobilization of manganese from nodule oxyhydroxide phases results in a sedimentary environment conducive to precipitation of rhodochrosite. While the total sedimentary iron and manganese content remains constant with depth, the iron/ manganese ratio of the nodules increases with depth as manganese is selectively mobilized.

THEORIES OF ORIGIN

Historical development

Although the existence of freshwater ferromanganese deposits has been known since the late 1600's (see Introduction), systematic studies of these deposits has lagged behind marine investigations which more recently have been extensive due to the economic potential of this polymetallic resource. However, the first hypotheses of nodule formation emerged from the results of the "Challenger" expedition (Murray and Renard, 1891) when the nodules were just an intellectual curiosity. Those basic ideas concerning nodule formation are still considered to be viable working hypotheses. These hypotheses refer to the source of manganese and its subsequent precipitation as an oxide. The dissolved metal for precipitation as an oxide is derived from the subaqueous decomposition of volcanic material, from submarine springs (hydrothermal solutions), from sediment pore-water (diagenetic mobilization), and from overlying seawater. Since there is little if any volcanic activity associated with freshwater ferromanganese localities, the weathering of volcanic debris and hydrothermal activity hypotheses do not apply to freshwater nodules.

The early theories concerning formation of freshwater ferromanganese concretions emphasized the mechanisms for oxide precipitation (Zappfe, 1931; Kindle, 1932, 1935, 1936) given the source of iron and manganese in lake water overlying the sediment or ground water/springs percolating through the sediment. Zappfe (1931) noted the auto-catalytic effect of MnO_2 (pyrolusite) upon manganese oxidation and stated: "Once manganese oxides are formed they act quicker as precipitants than the bacteria and therefore do more work, but bacteria start the job." Kindle (1935, 1936), based upon his extensive studies of ferromanganese concretions in Canadian lakes, noted several facts that appear related to the occurrence of nodules, crusts, and coatings: (1) a pebble, nodule fragment, or a small boulder is always present as a nucleus; (2) growth of the ferromanganese oxide on cobbles or boulders is limited to the portion above the sand or gravel on which it rests; (3) saucer-shaped concretions are concave upward; and (4) ferromanganese-oxide deposits generally occur in shallow water subject to wave action. Kindle suggested that these facts appeared to warrant the conclusion that the presence of sunlight is a factor in the formation of some of the concretions. He further said that the availability of sunlight controls the presence of algal growth competent to precipitate iron and manganese.

Aarnio (1918) and Ljunggren (1953, 1955), after studying Swedish lake concretions, suggested that concretionary ferromanganese oxides formed as a result of oxidation of iron and manganese in ground water that discharges through porous lake sediments. Manheim (1965) discussed the effect of the source of dissolved iron and manganese (overlying water versus sediment interstitial water) on the morphology of oceanic and lacustrine concretions. He noted that disc-type (flattened) and girdle-shaped concretions (crusts), so common in near-shore marine and freshwater environments, indicate an interstitial source of metals. Such concretions have been commonly reported from many

North American lakes: Oneida Lake (Dean, 1970), Nova Scotia and Ontario lakes (Harriss and Troup, 1970), Lake George (Schoettle and Friedman, 1971), Lake Champlain (Johnson, 1969).

It might be well to recapitulate the information concerning the several modes of occurrence of freshwater ferromanganese concretions or nodules. Two major deposits, Green Bay, Lake Michigan, and northern Lake Ontario, consist of ferromanganese oxyhydroxide coatings about sand grain nuclei. In the case of Green Bay, these coatings become thick enough (1–5 mm) to form banded concretions, while in Lake Ontario the coatings are very thin. In smaller lakes across North America, the more usual occurrence of ferromanganese oxides is in the form of either flat concretions (2–10 cm in diameter) or girdle-shaped growths (crusts) around pebble or boulder nuclei. Obviously, the rate of accretion and the source of metals for nodule growth are different for these two types of deposits. In the case of the nodule-coated sands, growth may be relatively slow implying that oxidation of iron and manganese occurs in bottom water adjacent to the sands. These sands are at least a few centimeters thick and well oxidized throughout, so that interstitial iron and manganese concentrations are low. In the case of flat concretions or girdle-shaped growths (crusts) around nuclei, ferromanganese-oxide accretion has been relatively rapid suggesting that the source of iron and manganese is from interstitial water. The flux of dissolved metals to the sediment–water interface is accomplished either through a diffusion gradient set up by higher metal concentrations in the sediment pore-water or by metal-rich ground water migrating upward through porous sand and gravel. Whichever the mechanism for bringing reduced metals in contact with nuclei on the sediment surface, the sides of the nuclei adjacent to the sediment-water interface accumulate the thickest oxide layers, while the upper surfaces will accrete metal in proportion to the metal content of overlying bottom water. Nowhere is this more evident than in nodules found at Tomahawk Lake, Wisconsin (Bowser, personal communication). Taking into account the modes of occurrence of freshwater ferromanganese deposits, it appears that there are two major sources of iron and manganese; overlying bottom lake water, and underlying sediment pore-water. The absence of any sub-lacustrine volcanism, of course, precludes any volcanic or hydrothermal source.

Precipitation from overlying water

The occurrence of ferromanganese-coated sands in northern Lake Ontario (Cronan and Thomas, 1972), small spherical concretions in northern Green Bay and Lake Michigan (Rossmann and Callender, 1969; Callender, 1970) and isolated concretions lying on highly oxidized substrates in numerous small lakes strongly suggest precipitation of iron and manganese from bottom lake water. Such deposits are comparable to the marine hydrogenous iron-manganese deposits (Bonatti et al., 1972), whereby iron and manganese accumulate by slow precipitation from seawater in oxidized environments. Slow precipitation results in the formation of micro-nodules dispersed in oxidized sediments and nodules lying on oxidized sediments. Several sedimentologic and geochemical conditions must be satisfied in order that hydrogenous ferromanganese deposits form. The water in contact with nuclei and substrate must be oxidized (high redox potential); there must be an adequate supply of "dissolved" metals; the net sedimentation rate of associated sediment must be very low; and the supply of metals from underlying sediment pore-water must be small. These conditions are all met by the two large hydrogenous ferromanganese deposits in the Great Lakes (Green Bay, Lake Michigan, northern Lake Ontario). At both localities, bottom water of 90–100% saturation with dissolved oxygen is in contact with oxidized sands overlying stiff glacial till and glaciolacustrine clay (Callender, 1970; Cronan and Thomas, 1972). The oxidation potential (Eh) of these waters and sediments ranges between +300 and +500 mV. In both cases, the oxidized ferromanganese sands represent a lag deposit which is continually agitated by bottom currents; hence the spherical-shaped concretions. The "dissolved" metal concentrations in bottom water in contact with these deposits ranges between 10 and 25 ppb Fe and 0.5 and 2 ppb Mn, two or three orders of magnitude lower than pore waters extracted from more rapidly accumulating sediment (Rossmann and Callender, 1969). However, sediment pore-water may still represent a source or iron and manganese to these hydrogenous deposits. The ferromanganese oxide deposits in northern Green Bay and northern Lake Ontario are adjacent to more rapidly accumulating, organic-rich muds which contain levels of dissolved metals sufficiently greater than those of overlying bottom water to establish a diffusion gradient across the sediment–water interface (Rossmann and Callender, 1969; Cronan and Thomas, 1972; Rossmann, 1973). Thus bottom water, enriched in iron, manganese, and other transition metals, is transported by currents into areas underlain by oxidized sediments where the metals are precipitated as oxides on suitable nuclei, generally sand grains.

Further evidence that these Great Lakes hydrogenous ferromanganese deposits are formed by slow precipitation from bottom water overlying sediment comes from a comparison of their solid-phase chemistry with that of more rapidly accumulating oxide deposits such as flat concretions and crusts. A look at Table IV will show that ferromanganese oxides from northern Green Bay, northern Lake Michigan and northern Lake Ontario have Fe/Mn ratios close to unity, approximating the average (0.9) for marine nodules, while lacustrine nodules that reflect an interstitial metal source (southern Green Bay, Lake Oneida, Lake George, Lake Champlain) generally have much higher Fe/Mn ratios. Also, the more slowly accumulating oxide deposits have higher accessory transition-metal contents, e.g., northern Lake Michigan versus Green Bay (Table IV). The concentration of minor metals in hydrogenous ferromanganese oxides depends on the concentration of a particular metal in the lake water from which precipitation takes place, and on the amount of "scavenging" from lake water of minor metals by iron and manganese oxides (Goldberg, 1954).

Hydrous iron and manganese oxides are efficient "scavengers" of various cations and anions, that is they can adsorb and/or coprecipitate many dissolved species from aqueous solution. Hydrous oxides of iron and manganese carry a surface charge that varies in sign and intensity with the pH of the aqueous medium. At low pH the charge is positive and with increasing pH the charge decreases to zero and then becomes negative. The pH value at which the surface is uncharged is called the pH of zero point of charge (pH_{zpc}), or isoelectric point. Most naturally-occurring manganese-oxide phases appear to have iso-electric points that range from pH 2 to 4 (Healey et al., 1966) while hydrous ferric oxides range from pH 4.5 to 7 (Parks, 1965). Thus, in most lacustrine environments with an environmental pH range of 6–8, the manganese oxide component of precipitated ferro-manganese oxides is assumed to be strongly negative, while the ferric-oxide component may carry a weak positive charge. On at least a qualitative basis, the sign of these charges is substantiated by solid-phase chemistry data where aqueous cations such as Na^+, K^+, Ba^{2+}, Ca^{2+}, Co^{2+}, Ni^{2+}, Zn^{2+} are correlated (Rossmann et al., 1972; Callender, 1973; Rossmann, 1973) or associated (Bowser et al., 1970) with manganese in natural ferroman-ganese oxides. Conversely, arsenic (AsO_4^{3-}) and phosphorous (PO_4^{3-}) are correlated and associated with the ferric-oxide component of ferromanganese nodules from Green Bay, Lake Michigan (Edgington and Callender, 1970; Bowser et al., 1970; Rossmann et al., 1972; Callender, 1973). It appears that while the surface properties of hydrous iron and manganese oxides determine, in part, the minor-element content of ferromanganese de-posits, the accumulation or accretion rate of the deposit determines the amount or quantity of each element "scavenged" from solution. The lower the accretion rate, the longer the time for a ferromanganese-oxide surface to "scavenge" ions from solution, and the greater the amount of associated minor elements.

Diagenetic remobilization

Often pebbles and cobbles lying on sands are encrusted with ferromanganese oxide which forms a rim or "skirt" parallel to the sediment–water interface (Johnson, 1969; Bowser and Travis, 1970; Harriss and Troup, 1970; Dean, 1970; Rossmann, 1973). Man-heim (1965) suggested that an interstitial-water source of dissolved iron and manganese is responsible for the flattened shape of disc-type nodules whose nuclei resting in the sediment are normally free of any oxide coating. Another important occurrence of ferro-manganese in lakes is as a dispersed oxide phase that concentrates in the upper, oxidized layer of fine sediment (mud and clay). The surficial oxidized layer generally shows a significant increase in manganese concentration (Callender, 1968; Li et al., 1969; Bonatti et al., 1972; Robbins and Callender, 1975). The thickness of such a layer is dependent upon the several factors that affect the oxygen concentration in sediment pore-water and the establishment of reducing conditions that exist in underlying sediment layers.

The origin of high concentrations of dissolved transition metals in sediment pore-waters is related to either ground-water movement through porous media (sands) or sedimentary diagenesis. In either case, the flux of metals to the sediment surface is significantly higher than that from overlying bottom water, a situation that results in higher ferromanganese accretion rates. The contribution of ground water to ferromanganese oxide precipitation in lakes has been discussed in a previous section.

Postdepositional mobilization of iron and manganese occurs as a result of reducing conditions brought about by diagenesis of organic matter. Gradual oxidation of sedimentary organic matter results in the consumption of oxygen in pore water. The amount of organic matter in the sediment depends upon the rate of deposition of decomposable organic matter and inorganic sedimentary components (Lynn and Bonatti, 1965; Li et al., 1969; Price and Calvert, 1970; Bonatti et al., 1972; Robbins and Callender, 1975). If the deposition rate of organic matter is high, reducing conditions are established near the sediment—water interface, and the oxidized layer constitutes a "microzone" in contact with oxygenated bottom water (e.g., southern Green Bay, Lake Michigan; Callender, 1968; Rossmann, 1973; Callender, 1973). With a slower organic matter sedimentation rate, the thickness of the surface oxidized layer increases (Bonatti et al., 1972). In the former case, ferromanganese oxide is deposited but quickly redissolves as the base of the oxidized layer continually encounters less oxidizing or reducing conditions. In the latter situation, ferromanganese oxides are deposited in oxidizing sediment to a depth corresponding to the oxidizing—reducing interface. This process results in sediments displaying a surficial layer highly enriched in manganese (Lynn and Bonatti, 1965; Callender, 1968; Calvert and Price, 1970), especially since manganese is more geochemically mobile than iron (Krauskopf, 1957).

Diagenetic remobilization was first proposed by Murray and Irvine as a hypothesis to explain the manganese enrichment in surficial marine sediment (Murray and Irvine, 1895; Berzukov, 1960; Manheim, 1965; Lynn and Bonatti, 1965; Li et al., 1969; Bonatti et al., 1972). With this hypotheses excess manganese in surficial sediment results from diagenetic cycling of manganese within the sedimentary column. Upon burial, a layer of sediment may encounter local reducing conditions where dissolution of excess manganese can occur. Dissolved manganese (Mn^{2+}) can then migrate through sediment pore-water and reprecipitate as an oxyhydroxide in a relatively oxidizing environment near the sediment—water interface. Several recent studies (Presley et al., 1967; Li et al., 1969; Calvert and Price, 1972) of the distribution of dissolved manganese in marine pore-waters have supported this diagenetic remobilization mechanism. Calculations based on the pore-water manganese concentration gradient show that excess sedimentary manganese can be supplied by upward diffusion of Mn^{2+} toward the sediment—water interface (Li et al., 1969). While a diffusional source for excess manganese in surficial hemipelagic sediment appears probable, such is not the case for slowly accumulating pelagic sediment where diffusional gradients are too low to provide the needed flux of manganese toward the sediment surface (Bender, 1971).

Recently, Robbins and Callender (1975) have proposed a quantitative model to describe the vertical distribution of dissolved and sedimentary manganese in a core from southern Lake Michigan. The data suggest that a 30% enrichment in sedimentary manganese within the upper six centimeters may result from remobilization of the element after burial by local reducing conditions established by the diagenesis of organic matter. The distribution of Mn^{2+} in sediment pore-water is described by a steady-state solution of the one-dimensional diffusion equation with chemical reaction terms accounting for transfer of manganese from sediment solids (Robbins and Callender, 1975).

The chemical composition of diagenetic ferromanganese deposits in the ocean is characterized by high Mn/Fe and low minor metal/Mn ratios (Price and Calvert, 1970; Bonatti et al., 1972). The Mn/Fe ratio in Pacific sea-floor nodules is highest along the eastern margin (hemipelagic zone) and lowest in the southwest central region (Price and Calvert, 1970). The minor-metal/Mn ratios are lowest in the eastern Pacific. The enrichment of manganese relative to iron in marine sediments is a result of iron fixation by sulfides under local reducing conditions (Cheney and Vredenburgh, 1968) where Mn^{2+} may not be "buffered" by any solid phase. In freshwater deposits, the dissolved sulfide concentration of sediment pore water may be low (insufficient sulfate for bacterial reduction to sulfide) and thus Fe^{2+} is relatively free to migrate along a concentration gradient toward the more oxidizing sediment–water interface zone. Consequently, the Mn/Fe ratio of lacustrine ferromanganese deposits linked to a diagenetic source is substantially lower than similar marine deposits (Rossmann, 1973). Also, freshwater and marine diagenetic ferromanganese deposits contain small amounts of minor metals (Cu, Co, Ni) which are complexed by organic matter and resist stabilization as oxides in the oxidizing surficial layer (Price and Calvert, 1970; Rossmann, 1973). Table V presents metal/Mn ratios for ferromanganese deposits in Green Bay, Lake Michigan. Manganese nodules from Survey area III occur adjacent to rapidly accumulating, organic-rich muds, while Survey area II is far removed from this source of metals. Generally, trace transition-metals (Cu, Co, Ni, Zn) are lowest in the nodules that are apparently nourished by a diagenetic source of "soluble" metals. On the other hand, nodules whose source of metals comes from overlying water show a significant enrichment in trace transition-metals relative to manganese (northern Lake Michigan, Table V; Rossmann, 1973; Bonatti et al., 1972). It appears that the regional variability in ferromanganese nodule composition may be generally explained in terms of the rate of metal fluxes to the site of oxide deposition. If the flux is determined by mass transport of oxygenated bottom water, the flux is low, accretion rate is low, and accessory minor-element content is high. Conversely, if an interstitial water flux is important in determining nodule growth, accretion rate is high and accessory minor-element content is generally low. Naturally, the geochemical history of water in contact with precipitating ferromanganese oxides strongly influences the resultant chemical composition of ferromanganese nodules.

Ferromanganese oxide precipitation mechanism(s)

The mechanisms responsible for precipitation of iron and manganese oxides in natural waters can be separated into two major categories: inorganic versus organic. Is the oxidation of ferrous iron and manganous manganese accomplished by simple molecular oxygen in the presence of inorganic catalysts or is this oxidation accomplished by micro-organisms capable of converting these metal ions to their highest natural oxidation state?

Inorganic oxidation/precipitation. There have been several kinetic studies of manganese (Mn^{2+}) and iron (Fe^{2+}) oxidation by oxygen in aqueous solutions (Hem, 1963; Morgan, 1967; Stumm and Morgan, 1970; Elert and Brewer, 1973). The earlier oxidation studies were done using synthetic solutions not truly representative of natural waters (see Stumm and Morgan, 1970) while the oxidation study of Elert and Brewer (1973) used artificial seawater. In synthetic solutions buffered with carbonate—bicarbonate, the solubility product of metal carbonate may be exceeded causing the solutions to become super-saturated and thus accelerating the metal-removal rate thought to be caused by inorganic oxidation (Elert and Brewer, 1973). Oxidation of ferrous iron occurs at an appreciable rate above pH 6.5 with a one hundredfold increase in the reaction rate for a unit increase in pH (Stumm and Morgan, 1970). Thus, over the pH range of normal oxygenated lake water (pH 7–9), oxidation of ferrous iron to insoluble ferric hydroxide is expected to occur rapidly (in a matter of hours). The ferrous iron oxidation rate is retarded by some types of dissolved organic matter which complexes the ferrous iron (Hem, 1960). Conversely, oxidation and subsequent precipitation of iron is catalyzed by inorganic mineral grain surfaces (Collins and Buol, 1970).

The inorganic oxidation rate of manganous manganese (Mn^{2+}) is significantly slower than ferrous iron for a given pH. At pH 8, more than 5% of the original manganous manganese would remain in an oxidized aqueous solution that had been standing for 2 years (Hem, 1964), while at pH 7.2, less than 18% of the original ferrous iron would remain in an air-oxidized solution that had been standing for ten minutes (Stumm and Morgan, 1970). While the manganese oxidation rate in aerated water is very slow at near-neutral pH, the oxidation rate can be significantly increased by inorganic catalysis. The surfaces of quartzose and feldspathic sand grains (common nuclei for freshwater ferromanganese concretions) have cation-exchange sites that may strongly attract manganese ions (Hem, 1964). For instance, when sand grains are added to aerated solutions containing manganous ions, the rate of loss of dissolved manganese increases ten-fold over the rate for a similar solution with no solid surfaces (Hem, 1964). By contrast, manganese-oxide precipitation was essentially nil in supersaturated aqueous solutions containing no sand. Collins and Buol (1970) also showed that iron and manganese rapidly precipitated along Eh—pH gradients in quartz-sand columns and that uncatalyzed precipitation was slow.

Other substrates such as ferric oxyhydroxides, calcite, silica, freshly precipitated MnO_2, and ferromanganese nodules (Morgan and Stumm, 1964; Morgan, 1967; Michard, 1969; Jenkins, 1973) catalyze the oxidation/precipitation of Mn^{2+} from aqueous solutions. Kinetic oxidation rate data (Morgan, 1967) suggest an autocatalytic reaction mechanism. The reaction is autocatalytic with respect to MnO_2, first-order with respect to Mn^{2+} (Mn II) and dissolved oxygen (P_{O_2}), and is dependent on $(OH^-)^2$. Preliminary studies on

manganese (Mn II) oxidation rates in seawater (Elert and Brewer, 1973) suggest that the
rate may be described by:

$$\frac{d\,\mathrm{Mn(II)}}{dt} = K\,(\mathrm{Mn}^{2+})\,(\mathrm{MnO_2})\,(\mathrm{OH}^-)^2\,(\mathrm{O_2})$$

Elert and Brewer found that the rate constant, K, was equal to $1.2 \cdot 10^{11}\ \mathrm{l}^4/\mathrm{moles}^3/$
ml/min. Robbins and Callender (1974), using data from a southern Lake Michigan core
and the rate constant of Elert and Brewer, calculated a manganese removal rate of 5.8
$\mu g/cm^3/yr$, a value which compares favorably with the maximum manganese dissolution
rate (6 $\mu g/cm^3/yr$) computed by the mathematical model describing a steady-state solution of the one-dimensional diffusion equation with chemical reaction.

All inorganic mechanisms concerning ferromanganese-oxide precipitation have one
feature in common; they are concerned with the redox chemistry of manganese in natural
aqueous solutions and the oxidation of the ion Mn^{2+} to a manganese-oxide ("$\mathrm{MnO_2}$")
solid phase. If one is to apply equilibrium thermodynamic principles to this manganese
redox system, then the qualitative and quantitative evaluation of redox potential (Eh)
becomes a critical factor. The measurement and quantitative interpretation of redox
potentials in natural waters are subject to many practical and theoretical difficulties. Most
Eh measurements on natural waters represent mixed potentials that cannot be quantitatively interpreted in terms of specific redox equilibria (Morris and Stumm, 1967). Quantitative interpretation with respect to solution composition may frequently not be justified
because the required electro-chemical reversibility is usually not attained. With the excep-
tion of the $\mathrm{Fe}^{3+}-\mathrm{Fe}^{2+}$ couple at concentrations greater than 10^{-5} M and the $\mathrm{Mn}^{4+}-\mathrm{Mn}^{2+}$
couple at even higher concentrations, the over-all redox systems that are important in
natural waters are not electroactive (Morris and Stumm, 1967). The Eh of aerobic waters
(e.g., natural waters containing measurable concentrations of dissolved oxygen), as measured by the supposedly inert platinum electrode, does not agree with that predicted for
the reversible $\mathrm{O_2}-\mathrm{H_2O}$ half-cell at any given pH and the partial pressure of atmospheric
oxygen ($P_{\mathrm{O_2}}$ = 0.2 atm; Sillen, 1961; Berner, 1971). Recent experimental work on Eh
measurements using platinum electrodes (Whitfield, 1974) suggests that in well-mixed
aqueous environments thermodynamic considerations and empirical evidence indicate
that the platinum surface acts as an oxide electrode which responds to pH rather than to
oxygen partial pressure. Considering this fact, it may not be possible to use platinum
electrode measurements on aerobic natural waters even though they obey the empirical
equation (Eh = 0.84–0.059 pH) which is solely dependent on pH.

As a result of the difficulties in the measurement and interpretation of redox potentials in aerobic natural waters, it has been difficult also to interpret manganese redox
equilibria in terms of the aquatic chemistry of manganese and the stability of manganese
oxide phases found in the natural environment. For aerobic aquatic environments, dissolved oxygen–dissolved manganese redox potential data seldom indicate equilibrium
between the aqueous phase and the solid oxide phase. This discrepancy may be due in

part to the lack of good thermodynamic data for iron- and manganese-oxide phases actually found in nature, but also to the redox potential problem mentioned above and to the measurement of "dissolved" Mn^{2+} in natural waters. Crerar and Barnes (1974), in developing their model for nodule growth, postulated that MnO_2 precipitation requires a catalytic process favoring equilibrium with the available oxygen in water. They suggested that catalysis may be provided by adsorbing substrates, such as a detrital nucleus during early stages of nodule growth and the continually accreting ferromanganese-oxide surface during later stages of nodule growth. The free energy of adsorption contributes substantially to the overall free energy change (ΔG_r) of the oxidation reaction:

$$Mn^{2+} + 1/2\ O_2 + 2OH^- = MnO_2 + H_2O.$$

Crerar and Barnes (1974) calculated that catalyzing surfaces lower the activation energy of this oxidation reaction by an amount (-11.5 k cal/mole) equal to the free energy of adsorption at the catalyzing surface. They conclude that catalysis effectively elevates the local Eh at the nodule surface to a level where the abundant oxygen of aerobic natural waters can precipitate highly oxidized phases. Crerar and Barnes cite the feldspathic sand manganese oxidation studies of Hem (1963b; 1964) as experimental evidence supporting their adsorption model. As an alternative to this model, Glasby and Read (1974) postulate that the partial pressure of dissolved oxygen in the bulk solution in contact with a ferromanganese-oxide surface may not be the same as that on the nodule surface. They suggest that a film of manganese oxide containing Mn(III) coats MnO_2, thereby reducing the partial pressure of oxygen from an atmospheric value of 0.2 atm to a value four orders of magnitude lower. Glasby and Read suggest that aerobic natural waters may not be far removed from equilibrium between Mn^{2+} and δ-MnO_2 (birnessite), and that the phase in contact with δ-MnO_2 may be Mn_2O_3.

Biologic precipitation. For as long as ferromanganese nodules have been known to exist in lakes and seas, there has been speculation concerning the biological origin of these oxide precipitates. Early observations (Ehrenberg, 1836) on iron bacteria led to the suggestion that bog iron ore was formed as a result of biologic precipitation. Either the bacteria catalyze the precipitation of iron and manganese oxides (Zappfe, 1931), or algae and diatoms exhibit a capability to separate these metals from water and deposit them as oxides within their cellular structure (Ehrenberg, 1836; Kindle, 1935). The literature appears to be full of contradictory evidence regarding the role of microbiota in ferromanganese-oxide precipitation. The subject is reviewed extensively by Perfilér et al. (1965), Harder (1919), and Silverman and Ehrlich (1964). For a general treatment on bacterial processes, see Chapter 6 by Trudinger, Volume 2.

The role of freshwater algae in precipitation of freshwater ferromanganese oxides was suggested strongly by Kindle (1932, 1935) and Gorham (personal communication in Harriss and Troup, 1970). Gorham suggests that the oxidizing potential (Eh) of the water overlying beds of aquatic macrophytes (epilimnion) will be higher (more positive) during times (spring, summer) when the vegetation is actively photosynthesizing, while the potential will be less positive during times (winter) when the vegetation is inactive. While it is true that a more positive Eh at high pH levels promotes the inorganic oxidation of manganese, it is questionable whether the dissolved oxygen content of the water has any relationship to the measured oxidation potential. It is well known that a large change in dissolved oxygen concentration produces a small change in the calculated Eh, and Baas Becking et al. (1960) have shown that the measured oxidation potential in sea water varies little for a great range in percent oxygen saturation (3–24%). In addition, there are many known occurrences of freshwater ferromanganese nodules (Green Bay, Lake Michigan; eastern Lake Superior; Lake Ontario) where the water depth is below the photic zone of active photosynthesis. Johnson (1969) suggests that the rooted green plant (alga) *Chadophora* sp., attached to the larger nodules in Lake Champlain, functions as an iron/manganese concentrator which upon death contributes metals to solution which are immediately oxidized/precipitated onto the nodule surface. While the presence of epiphytic and macrophytic algae on ferromanganese nodule surfaces may influence the physico-chemical environment adjacent to the nodule or oxide coating, their presence is probably a result of substrate choice and may have little relationship to the mechanism of ferromanganese oxide precipitation and nodule growth. However, once freshwater ferromanganese nodules have been examined more closely by electron-microscopic and microchemical techniques, this view that microscopic and macroscopic flora exert little influence upon ferromanganese-oxide accretion may change.

Recent studies (Greenslate, 1974a,b) concerning the presence and role of biotic structures associated with deep-sea manganese nodules have demonstrated that a number of micro-organisms contribute to nodule growth by building a variety of shelter structures on the surface. The building material is partly ferromanganese oxide, partly detrital silicate grains, and organic membrane material (Greenslate, 1974a,b). Benthic foraminifera of the genus *Saccorhiza* actually attach ferromanganese micro-nodules to the surfaces of macro-nodules as part of their tube-building activities (Greenslate, 1974a). The nodule framework which is formed by these biotic structures can be followed into the interior of the nodule. Even the center of many of these deep-sea nodules contain fossilized remnants of these biotic structures. In addition, Greenslate (1974b) found that incipient manganese concretions (1–30 μm in diameter) occur in microcavities of planktonic skeletal debris (especially diatom frustules) in Pacific deep-sea sediments. These embryonic concretions contain more than 50% manganese and minor amounts of iron. Greenslate (1974b) speculates that the biogeochemical process responsible for concentrating manganese oxide in the microcavities of planktonic skeletal debris may also be responsible for manganese infilling of biotic structures that occur on the surface of macro-nodules.

This process may be mediated by manganese-precipitating bacteria which have been shown to occur on the surface of deep-sea manganese nodules (Ehrlich, 1972). Ehrlich found that manganese nodules collected from the tropical eastern and central Pacific Ocean as well as the Blake Plateau in the northwestern Atlantic Ocean contained significant numbers of microbial flora consisting of Mn(II) oxidizers and MnO_2 reducers. These bacteria may be found at or near the nodule surface and in some cases throughout the nodule structure. In the laboratory (Ehrlich, 1966), these bacteria are capable of enzymatically catalyzing the removal of Mn(II) from solution and possibly its oxidation. Ehrlich (1972) proposed a two-step model for the accretion of manganese; the sorption of Mn(II) onto an oxidized Mn(IV) species followed by the biological oxidation of adsorbed Mn(II) by manganese oxidizing bacteria. The nonbiological adsorption of Mn(II) proceeds rapidly while the biological oxidation (enzymatic catalysis) is the rate-limiting reaction. However, these studies were conducted using pure laboratory bacterial cultures and it is difficult to generalize to in situ field conditions.

Perfilér et al. (1965) have studied extensively the role of micro-organisms in the formation of iron–manganese deposits. They conclude from laboratory and field studies of Karelian lake muds that bacteria (principally *Metallogenium* and *Siderococcus*) bring about the oxidation and deposition of iron and manganese oxides in these sediments. Concretionary oxides were not formed under the laboratory conditions used. In both the case of Ehrlich (1972) and Perfilér et al. (1965), the resultant oxidation of iron and manganese could not be explained solely by biological processes. It is difficult to assess the role of bacteria for systems (iron and manganese) where a purely physico-chemical mechanism readily applies. However, it cannot be denied that bacteria create a microenvironment which may be conducive to oxidation of iron and manganese through elevated pH and Eh, decreased activation energies, and catalysis of oxidation reactions.

The fact that the surface of marine ferromanganese nodules contain an active faunal and microfloral community suggest that the biological precipitation of iron and manganese is an important process in the growth of nodules. Several of the organisms described by Greenslate (1974a,b) are only found in marine environments. Once the surfaces and interiors of freshwater nodules have been examined for ultrafine structure, it may become apparent that the growth of these ferromanganese-oxide concretions is aided by the activity of a diverse community of freshwater micro-organisms such as algae, diatoms, and bacteria.

SUMMARY AND CONCLUSIONS

Freshwater ferromanganese deposits occur in lakes and streams that occupy local and regional depressions in glaciated terrains. Morphologically, ferromanganese oxides occur as coatings and crusts and distinct concretions surrounding a variety of geologic nuclei. The Fe/Mn ratio of these deposits varies widely, but most analyses fall within the range of 10–0.6. The generally low minor-element content of freshwater ferromanganese oxides is a result of rapid nodule accretion rates and metal-organic complexation/diagenetic fractionation of transition metals in the lacustrine environment. The mineralogy of freshwater ferromanganese nodules is similar to marine nodules with birnessite, todorokite, and goethite the most common minerals found. Psilomelane, a Ba-rich manganese dioxide, appears to be abundant in the Lake Michigan ferromanganese deposits.

Two major sources of dissolved metals appear important in the development of fresh-water ferromanganese concretions: lake and river water overlying the nodule substrate, and interstitial water/ground water percolating through the substrate. Once aqueous solutions containing iron, manganese, and other less abundant transition metals encounter suitable nuclei in an oxidizing environment, ferromanganese oxides of varying Fe/Mn ratios and minor-metal contents precipitate. The geochemical state and history of the metal sources are very important in determining the final chemical composition of the ferromanganese oxides.

REFERENCES

Aarnio, B., 1918. Om sjomalmerna i nagra sjoari pusula, pyhyjarui, loppis, somerniemi och tammela socknar. *Geol. Komm. Finl. Geotekn. Medd.*, 4: 20.

Arrhenius, G., 1963. Pelagic sediments. In: M.N. Hill (Editor), *The Sea, 3*. Wiley, New York, N.Y., pp. 665–727.

Baas Becking, L.G.M., Kaplan, I.R. and Moore, D., 1960. Limits of the natural environment in terms of pH and oxidation–reduction potentials. *J. Geol.*, 68: 243–284.

Bartlett, J.H., 1893. The manufacture of iron in Canada. *Trans. Am. Inst. Min. Metall. Pet. Eng.*, 14: 508–542.

Beals, H.L., 1966. Manganese–iron concretions in Nova Scotia lakes. *Marit. Sediments*, 2: 70–72.

Bender, M.L., 1971. Does upward diffusion supply the excess manganese in pelagic sediments? *J. Geophys. Res.*, 76: 4212–4215.

Berner, R.A., 1971. *Principles of Chemical Sedimentology*. McGraw-Hill, New York, N.Y., 240 pp.

Berner, R.A., 1973. Phosphate removal from seawater by adsorption on volcanogenic ferric oxides. *Earth Planet. Sci. Lett.*, 18: 77–86.

Bezrukov, P.L., 1960. Sedimentation in the northwestern part of the Pacific Ocean. *Proc. Int. Geol. Congr.*, 21: 39–49.

Bonatti, E., Kraemer, T. and Rydell, H., 1972. Classification and genesis of submarine iron–manganese deposits. In: D.R. Horn (Editor), *Ferromanganese Deposits on the Ocean Floor*. Nat. Sci. Found., Washington, D.C., pp. 149–166.

Bostrom, K. and Peterson, M.N.A., 1969. The origin of aluminium-poor ferromanganoan sediments in areas of high heat flow on the East Pacific Rise. *Mar. Geol.*, 7: 427–447.

Bowser, C.J. and Travis, P.A., 1970. Electron-probe and X-ray analysis of ferromanganese nodules from Lake Tomahawk. *Int. Assoc. Great Lakes Res.* (abstr.)

Bowser, C.J., Callender, E. and Rossmann, R., 1970. Electron-probe and X-ray studies of freshwater ferromanganese nodules from Wisconsin and Michigan. *Geol. Soc. Am. Bull.*, 2 (7): 500–501 (abstr.).

Bricker, O.P., 1965. Some stability relations in the system $Mn-O_2-H_2O$ at 25° and one atmosphere total pressure. *Am. Miner.*, 50: 1296–1354.

Brown, B.A., 1972. A low-temperature crushing technique applied to manganese nodules. *Am. Miner.*, 57: 284–287.

Buchanan, J.Y., 1878. Manganese nodules in Loch Fyne. *Nature*, 18: 628.

Burns, R.G. and Burns, in preparation. Mineralogy of ferromanganese nodules. In: G.P. Glasby (Editor), *Marine Manganese Deposits*. Elsevier, Amsterdam.

Buser, W. and Grutter, A., 1956. Über die Natur der Manganknollen. *Schweiz. Mineral. Petrogr. Mitt.*, 36: 49–62.

Callender, E., 1969. Geochemical characteristics of Lakes Michigan and Superior sediments. *Proc. Conf. Great Lakes Res.*, 12: 124–160.

Callender, E., 1970. The economic potential of ferromanganese nodules in the Great Lakes. *Proc. 6th Forum Geol. Ind. Miner.*, Misc-1: 56–65.

Callender, E., 1973. Geochemistry of ferromanganese crusts, manganese carbonate crusts, and associated ferromanganese nodules from Green Bay, Lake Michigan. *Inter-Univ. Progr. Ferromanganese Res.*, Phase I Rep.: 105–120.

Callender, E., Bowser, C.J. and Rossmann, R., 1973. Geochemistry of ferromanganese and manganese carbonate crusts from Green Bay, Lake Michigan. *Trans. Am. Geophys. Union*, 54: p. 340 (abstr.).

Calvert, S.E. and Price, N.B., 1970. Composition of manganese nodules and manganese carbonates from Loch Fyne, Scotland. *Contrib. Miner. Petrol.*, 29: 215–233.

Chalmers, R., 1884. Report on the surface geology of western New Brunswick. *Geol. Surv. Can. Rep.*, 46: 47 pp.

Cheney, E.S. and Vredenburgh, L.D., 1968. The role of iron sulfides in the diagenetic formation of iron-poor manganese nodules. *J. Sed. Pet.*, 38: 1363–1365.

Collins, J.F. and Buol, S.W., 1970. Patterns of iron and manganese precipitation under specified Eh–pH conditions. *Soil Sci.*, 110: 157–162.

Crerar, D.A. and Barnes, H.L., 1974. Deposition of deep-sea manganese nodules. *Geochim. Cosmochim. Acta*, 38 (2): 279–300.

Cronan, D.S., 1967. *The Geochemistry of Some Manganese Nodules and Associated Pelagic Sediments.* Thesis, Univ. London, 342 pp. (unpublished).

Cronan, D.S., 1974. Authigenic minerals in deep-sea sediments. In: E.D. Goldberg (Editor), *The Sea, 5,* Interscience, New York, N.Y., pp. 491–525.

Cronan, D.S. and Thomas, R.L., 1970. Ferromanganese concretions in Lake Ontario. *Can. J. Earth Sci.*, 7: 1346–1349.

Cronan, D.S. and Thomas, R.L., 1972. Geochemistry of ferromanganese oxide concentrations and associated deposits in Lake Ontario. *Geol. Soc. Am. Bull.*, 83: 1493–1502.

Cronan, D.S. and Tooms, J.S., 1968. A microscopic and electron probe investigation of manganese nodules from the northwest Indian Ocean. *Deep-Sea Res.*, 15: 215–223.

Damiani, V., Morton, T.W. and Thomas, R.L., 1973. Freshwater ferromanganese nodules from the Big Bay section of Quinte, northern lake, Ontario. *Proc. Conf. Great Lakes Res.*, 16: 397–403.

Dean, W.E., 1970. Fe–Mn oxidate crusts in Oneida Lake, New York. *Proc. Conf. Great Lakes Res.*, 13: 217–226.

De Groot, A.J., Zschuppe, K.H., De Bruin, M., Houtman, J.P.W. and Amin Singgih, P., 1968. Activation analysis applied to sediments from various river deltas. *Proc. Int. Conf. Modern Trends Activ. Anal., 1968*, pp. 62–71.

Edgington, D. and Callender, E., 1970. Minor-element geochemistry of Lake Michigan ferromanganese nodules. *Earth Planet. Sci. Lett.*, 8: 97–100.

Ehrenberg, C.G., 1836. Vorläufige Mitteilung über das wirkliche Vorkommen fossiler Infusorien und ihre grosse Verbreitung. *Ann. Phys.*, 38: 213–227.

Ehrlich, H.L., 1966. Reactions with manganese by bacteria from marine ferromanganese nodules. *Dev. Ind. Microbiol.*, 7: 279–286.

Ehrlich, H.L., 1972. The role of microbes in manganese nodule genesis and degradation. In: D.R. Horn (Editor), *Ferromanganese Deposits on the Ocean Floor.* Nat. Sci. Found., Washington, D.C., pp. 63–70.

Elert, M.L. and Brewer, P.G., 1973. The kinetics of manganese oxidation in sea water (unpublished manuscript).

Fleischer, M., 1960. Studies of the manganese oxide minerals, 3. Psilomelane. *Am. Miner.*, 45: 176–187.

Gillette, N.J., 1961. Oneida Lake Pancakes. *N.Y. State Conserv.*, 18: 41.

Glasby, G.P., 1972. The mineralogy of manganese nodules from a range of marine environments. *Mar. Geol.*, 13: 57–72.

Glasby, G.P., 1973. Mechanisms of enrichment of the rarer elements in marine manganese nodules. *Mar. Chem.*, 1: 105–125.

Goldberg, E.D., 1954. Marine geochemistry, 1. Chemical scavengers of the sea. *J. Geol.*, 62: 249–265.

Gorham, E. and Swaine, D.J., 1965. The influence of oxidising and reducing conditions upon the distribution of some elements in lake sediments. *Limnol. Oceanogr.*, 10: 268–279.

Greenslate, J., 1974a. Microorganisms participate in the construction of manganese nodules. *Nature*, 249: 181–183.

Greenslate, J., 1974b. Manganese and biotic debris associations in some deep-sea sediments. *Science*, 186: 529–531.

Griffin, P.H., 1893. The manufacture of charcoal-iron from the bog and lake ores of the Three Rivers district, Province of Quebec, Canada. *Trans. Am. Inst. Min. Metall. Pet. Eng.*, 21: 974–992.

Grill, E.V., Murray, J.W. and MacDonald, R.D., 1968. Manganese nodules from Jervis Inlet, a British Columbia fjord. *Svesis*, 1: 57–63.

Hall, A., 1969. *The Sedimentation of Green Bay*. Thesis, Univ. Wisconsin, 117 pp., unpublished.

Harder, E.C., 1919. Iron-depositing bacteria and their geological relations. *U.S. Geol. Surv. Prof. Pap.*, 113: 1–87.

Harriss, R.C. and Troup, A.G., 1969. Freshwater ferromanganese concretions: chemistry and internal structure. *Science*, 166: 604–606.

Harriss, R.C. and Troup, A.G., 1970. Chemistry and origin of freshwater ferromanganese concretions. *Limnol. Oceanogr.*, 15: 702–712.

Healey, T.W., Herring, A.P. and Fuersterran, D.W., 1966. The effect of crystal structure on the surface properties of a series of manganese dioxides. *J. Colloid Interface Sci.*, 21: 435–444.

Hem, J.D., 1960. Complexes of ferrous iron with tannic acid. *U.S. Geol. Surv. Water-Supply Pap.*, 1459 (D): 75–94.

Hem, J.D., 1963a. Chemical equilibria and rates of manganese oxidation. *U.S. Geol. Surv. Water-Supply Pap.*, 1667 (A): 1–64.

Hem, J.D., 1963b. Increased oxidation rate of manganese ions in contact with feldspar grains. *U.S. Geol. Surv. Prof. Pap.*, 475 (C): 216–217.

Hem, J.D., 1964. Deposition and solution of manganese oxides. *U.S. Geol. Surv. Water-Supply Pap.*, 1667 (B): 1–42.

Hem, J.D., 1972. Chemical factors that influence the availability of iron and manganese in aqueous systems. *Geol. Soc. Am. Spec. Pap.*, 140: 17–24.

Hem, J.D. and Cropper, W.H., 1959. A survey of chemical equilibria and redox potentials. *U.S. Geol. Surv. Water-Supply Pap.*, 1459 (A): 1–31.

Horn, D.R., Delach, M.N. and Horn, B.M., 1973. Metal content of ferromanganese deposits of the oceans. *NSF-IDOE Tech. Rep.*, 3: 51 pp.

Inostrantsev, A.A., 1877. Geologicheskii ocherk' Povenetskago Olonetskoi Gubernii. In: *Materialy dlja Geologii Rossii*. Izd. Imper. S. Petersb. Miner. Obshch., 7: 1–728.

Irving, H. and Williams, R.J.P., 1948. Order of stability of metal complexes. *Nature*, 162: 746–747.

Jenkins, S.R., 1973. Effect of selective cation concentration on coagulation and adhesion to silica surfaces of δ-MnO_2. *Environ. Sci. Technol.*, 7: 43–47.

Johnson, D.G., 1969. *Ferromanganese Concretions in Lake Champlain*. Thesis, Univ. Vermont, Burlington, Ve., 96 pp. (unpublished).

Jones, L.H.P. and Milne, A.A., 1956. Birnessite, a new manganese oxide mineral form Aberdeenshire, Scotland. *Miner. Mag.*, 31: 283–288.

Kester, D.R. and Byrne Jr., R.H., 1972. Chemical forms of iron in seawater. In: D.R. Horn (Editor), *Ferromanganese Deposits on the Ocean Floor*. Nat. Sci. Found., Washington, D.C., pp. 107–116.

Kindle, E.M., 1932. Lacustrine concretions of manganese. *Am. J. Sci.*, 224: 496–504.

Kindle, E.M., 1935. Manganese concretions in Nova Scotia lakes. *Trans. R. Soc. Can.*, 29: 163–180.

Kindle, E.M., 1936. The occurrence of lake bottom manganiferous deposits in Canadian lakes. *Econ. Geol.*, 31: 755–760.

Klenova, M.J. and Paknomova, A.S., 1940. Manganese in the sediments of the Bolar seas. *C. R. Acad. Sci. U.R.S.S.*, 28 (1): 87–89.

Krauskopf, K.B., 1957. Separation of manganese from iron in sedimentary processes. *Geochim. Cosmochim. Acta*, 12: 61–84.

Kurbatov, L.M., 1936. Age of ferromanganese concretions. *Nature*, 137: 949–950.

Kurbatov, L.M., 1937. On the radioactivity of bottom sediments, 1. Some determinations of the radioactivity of ferromanganese formations in seas and lakes of U.S.S.R. *Am. J. Sci.*, 33: 147–153.

Landergren, S., 1948. On the geochemistry of swedish iron ores and associated rocks. *Sver. Geol. Unders. Ser. C*, 496: 1–179.

Levinson, A.A., 1961. A poorly crystallized, low-barium, psilomelane-type mineral. *Am. Miner.*, 46: 355.

Li, Y-H., Bischoff, J. and Mathieu, G., 1969. The migration of manganese in the Arctic Basin sediment. *Earth Planet. Sci. Lett.*, 7: 265–270.

Ljunggren, P., 1953. Some data concerning the formation of manganiferous and ferriferous bog ores. *Geol. For. Stockh. Forh.*, 75: 277–297.

Ljunggren, P., 1955a. Geochemistry and radioactivity of some Mn and Fe bog ores. *Geol. For. Stockh. Forh.*, 77: 33–44.

Ljunggren, P., 1955b. Differential thermal analysis and X-ray examination of Fe and Mn in bog ores. *Geol. For. Stockh. Forh.*, 77: 135–147.

Lynn, D.C. and Bonatti, E., 1966. Mobility of manganese in diagenesis of deep-sea sediments. *Mar. Geol.*, 3: 457–474.

Manheim, F.T., 1965. Manganese-iron accumulations in the shallow-marine environment. In: *Symposium on Marine Geochemistry—Occ. Publ. Univ. Rhode Island*, 3: 217–276.

Margolis, S.V., 1973. Manganese deposits encountered during Deep-Sea Drilling Project Leg 29 in sub-antarctic waters. In: M. Morgenstein (Editor), *The Origin and Distribution of Manganese Nodules in the Pacific and Prospects for Exploration*. A symposium organised by the Valdivia Manganese Explor. Group and the Hawaii Inst. Geophys., Honolulu, Hawaii, pp. 109–113.

Mero, J.L., 1965. *The Mineral Resources of the Sea*. Elsevier, Amsterdam, 312 pp.

Michard, G., 1969. Kinetics of manganese oxidation on the sea floor. *Trans. Am. Geophys. Union*, 50: 349.

Moore, E.J., 1909. Bog iron on the English River. *18th Annual Rep., Ont. Bur. Mines*, pp. 180–195.

Moore, J.R. and Meyer, R.P., 1969. Progress report on the geological-geophysical survey of Green Bay, 1968. *Univ. Wisc. Sea Grant Progr., Tech. Rep.*, 1: 16 pp.

Morgan, J.J., 1967. Chemical equilibria and kinetic properties of manganese in natural waters. In: S.D. Faust and J.V. Hunter (Editors), *Principles and Applications of Water Chemistry*. Wiley, New York, N.Y., pp. 561–624.

Morgan, J.J. and Stumm, W., 1964. Colloid-chemical properties of manganese dioxide. *J. Colloid. Sci.*, 19: 347–359.

Morris, J.C. and Stumm, W., 1967. Redox equilibria and measurements of potentials in the aquatic environment. In: R.F. Gould (Editor), *Equilibrium Concepts in Natural Water Systems*, 67: 270–285.

Mothersill, J.S. and Shegelski, R.J., 1973. The formation of iron- and manganese-rich layers in the Holocene sediments of Thunder Bay, Lake Superior. *Can. J. Earth Sci.*, 10: 571–576.

Müller, G. and Forstner, U., 1973. Recent iron ore formation in Lake Malawi, Africa. *Mineralium Deposita*, 8: 278–290.

Murray, J. and Irvine, R., 1894. On the manganese oxides and manganese nodules in marine deposits. *Trans R. Soc. Edinb.*, 37: 721–742.

Murray, J. and Renard, A.F., 1891. Report on deep-sea deposits. In: *Rep. Sci. Res. Voyage H.M.S. Challenger – Deep-Sea Deposits*, pp. 1–525.

Naumann, E., 1922. Sodra och mellersta sveriges sjo-och myrmalmer. *Sver. Geol. Unders., Ser. C.*, 297: 1–194.

Nriagu, J.P., 1972. Stability of vivianite and ion-pair formation in the system $Fe_3(PO_4)_2-H_3PO_4-H_2O$. *Geochim. Cosmochim. Acta*, 36: 459–470.

Nussmann, D.G., 1965. *Trace Elements in the Sediments of Lake Superior*. Thesis, Univ. Michigan, 243 pp. (unpublished).

Parks, G.A., 1967. Aqueous surface chemistry of oxides and complex oxide minerals. In: R.F. Gould (Editor), *Equilibrium Concepts in Natural Water Systems*, 67: 121–160.

Perfilér, B.V., Gabe, D.R., Galpernia, A.M., Rabinovich, V.A., Sapotnitskii, A.A., Sherman, E.E. and Troshanov, E.P., 1965. *Applied Capillary Microscopy*. Consultants Bureau, New York, N.Y., 122 pp.

Presley, B.J., Brooks, R.R. and Kaplan, I.R., 1967. Manganese and related elements in the interstitial water of marine sediments. *Science*, 158: 906–910.

Price, N.B., 1967. Some geochemical observations on manganese-iron oxide nodules from different depth environments. *Mar. Geol.*, 5: 511–538.

Price, N.B. and Calvert, S.E., 1970. Compositional variation in Pacific Ocean ferromanganese nodules and its relationship to sediment accumulation rates. *Mar. Geol.*, 9: 145–171.

Rashid, M.A., 1971. Role of hurnic acids of marine origin and their different molecular weight fractions in complexing di- and tri-valent metals. *Soil Sci.*, 111: 298–306.

Robbins, J.A. and Callender, E., 1973. Manganese distribution in rapidly accumulating sediments from southern Lake Michigan. *Trans. Am. Geophys. Union*, 54: 340 (abstr.).

Robbins, J.A. and Callender, E., 1975. Diagenesis of manganese in Lake Michigan sediments. *Am. J. Sci.*, 275 (in press).

Robbins, J.A., Landstrom, E. and Wahlgren, M., 1972. Tributary inputs of soluble trace metals to Lake Michigan. *Proc. Conf. Great Lakes Res.*, 15: 270–290.

Rossmann, R., 1973. *Lake Michigan Ferromanganese Nodules*. Thesis, Univ. Michigan, 151 pp. (unpublished).

Rossmann, R. and Callender, E., 1968. Manganese nodules in Lake Michigan. *Science*, 162: 1123–1124.

Rossmann, R. and Callender, E., 1969. Geochemistry of Lake Michigan manganese nodules. *Proc. Conf. Great Lakes Res.*, 12: 306–316.

Rossmann, R., Callender, E. and Bowser, C.J., 1972. Inter-element geochemistry of Lake Michigan ferromanganese nodules. *Proc. 24th Int. Geol. Congr., Sect. 10*: 336–341.

Schoettle, M. and Friedman, G.M., 1971. Freshwater ironmanganese nodules in Lake George, New York. *Bull. Geol. Soc. Am.*, 82: 101–110.

Semenov, A.D., Pashanova, A.P., Kishkinova, T.S. and Nemetseva, L.I., 1967. Content of individual groups of organic substances in the waters of some Soviet rivers. *Sov. Hydrol. Select. Pap.*, 5: 549–554.

Semenovitch, N.I., 1958. Limnological conditions of accumulation of iron-bearing sediments in lakes. *Tr. Lab. Ozeroved. Akad. Sci. U.S.S.R.*, 6.

Sevastyanov, V.F. and Volkov, I.I., 1966. Chemical composition of iron-manganese concretions of the Black Sea. *Dokl. Akad. Sci. S.S.S.R.*, 166: 701–704.

Shterenberg, L.Y., Bazilevskaya, Y.S. and Chigireva, T.A., 1966. Manganese and iron carbonates in bottom deposits of Lake Pinnus-Yarvi. *Dokl. Akad. Nauk. S.S.S.R.*, 170: 205–209.

Sillen, L.G., 1961. The physical chemistry of sea water. In: M. Sears (Editor), *Oceanography--Am. Assoc. Adv. Sci.*, 67: 549–581.

Silverman, M.P., and Ehrlich, H.L., 1964. Microbial formation and degradation of minerals. *Adv. Appl. Microbiol.*, 6: 153–206.

Skornyakova, N.S., 1965. Dispersed iron and manganese in Pacific Ocean sediments. *Int. Geol. Rev.*, 7: 2161–2174.

Sorem, R.K. and Foster, A.R., 1973. Mineralogical, chemical, and optical properties and standards for study of growth features and economic potential of manganese nodules. *Inter-Univ. Progr. Ferromanganese Res.*, Phase I Rep., pp. 23–38.

Straczek, J.A., Horen, A., Ross, M. and Warshaw, C.M., 1960. Studies of the manganese oxides, 4. Todorokite. *Am. Miner.*, 45: 1174–1184.

Strakhov, H.M., 1966. Types of manganese accumulation in present-day basins: their significance in understanding of manganese mineralization. *Int. Geol. Rev.*, 8: 1172–1196.

Stumm, W. and Morgan, J.J., 1970. *Aquatic Chemistry*. Wiley, New York, N.Y., 583 pp.

Terasmae, J., 1971. Notes on lacustrine manganese-iron concretions. *Geol. Surv. Can., Pap.*, 70-69: 1–13.

Twenhofel, W.H., McKelvey, V.E., Nelson, H.F. and Feray, D.E., 1945. Sediments of Trout Lake, Wisconsin. *Geol. Soc. Am. Bull.*, 56: 1099–1142.

Vaasjoki, O., 1956. On the natural occurrence of manganese in Finland. *Symposium Sobre Yacimiento de Manganeso–20th Int. Geol. Congr., Mexico*, 5: 51–62.

Varentsov, I.M., 1972. On the main aspects of formation of ferromanganese ores in recent basins. *Int. Geol. Congr., Sect. 1*: 395–403.

Vogt, J.H.L., 1915. Om manganrik sjomalm: storsjoen, nedre odalen. *Norg. Geol. Unders.*, 75 (4): 1–43.

Wadsley, A.D., 1953. The crystal structure of psilomelane, $(Ba, H_2O)_2Mn_5O_{10}$. *Acta Crystal.*, 6: 433–438.

Whitfield, M., 1974. Thermodynamic limitations on the use of the platinum electrode in Eh measurements. *Limnol. Oceanogr.*, 19: 857–865.

Winterhalter, B., 1968. Iron-manganese concretions from the Gulf of Finland. *Geotekn. Julkaisuja N.*, 69: 1–77.

Winterhalter, B. and Siivola, J., 1967. An electron-microprobe study of the distribution of iron, manganese, and phosphorous in concretions from the Gulf of Bothnia, northern Baltic Sea. *C. R. Soc. Geol. Finl.*, 39: 161–172.

Zappfe, C., 1931. Deposition of manganese. *Econ. Geol.*, 26: 799–832.

Chapter 9

ANCIENT MANGANESE DEPOSITS

SUPRIYA ROY

INTRODUCTION

Sedimentary manganese deposits and their metamorphosed equivalents occur in different ages from the Early Precambrian to the Recent, and account for a major part of the world's manganese-ore resources. The discussions in this Chapter will be restricted to the ancient manganese deposits only.

A broad division of these deposits into nonvolcanogenic and volcanogenic-sedimentary[1] types, according to the source of manganese being from the weathering crust or from direct volcanism, is widely accepted. Lithologic association, sedimentary environment and tectonic framework may form a basis for further subdivisions (Roy, 1969; Rakhmanov and Tchaikovsky, 1972). These two parameters are somewhat interdependent and they also afford some guide to the source of the manganese sediments, though no unique interrelationship can be established. For example, manganese orebodies associated with carbonate sediments or iron-formation may be derived from both volcanic and terrigenous sources and may be deposited either in geosynclines or on platforms. Thus, both lithologic association and tectonic framework are only of limited value as the basis of further subdivision.

The distribution of the manganese deposits in different geological ages shows that the Precambrian deposits, save for a few exceptions, are geosynclinal and contain considerable amounts of ores in the traditionally well-known (India, Brazil, Ghana) and recently explored (Kalahari belt, South Africa) deposits. Large nonvolcanogenic deposits of Paleozoic age occur in carbonate formations in the U.S.S.R., in orthoquartzite-siliceous shale-carbonate formations in China and in iron-formations in Brazil. Varentsov (1964) estimated that about 60–70% of Paleozoic deposits are geosynclinal. About 20% of the total ore reserve in the Precambrian is volcanogenic. Varentsov showed that the Mesozoic was very poor in manganese deposits, but recent large finds in Molango, Mexico and Groote Eyelandt, Australia, have changed the position considerably. A large part of the Mesozoic deposits are of platform type. The deposits of Cenozoic age are mostly of platform type

---

[1] $\equiv$ Volcanic-sedimentary or exhalative-sedimentary.

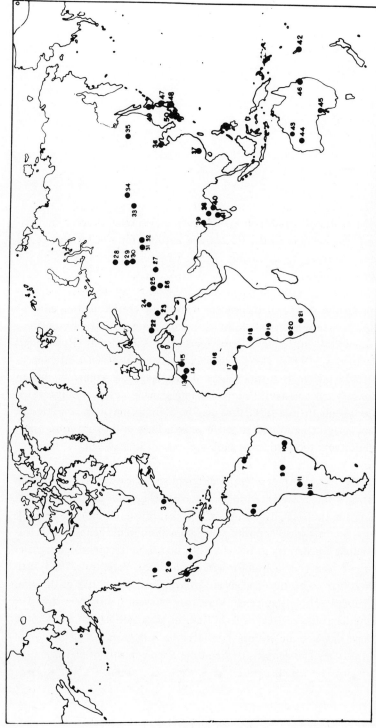

Fig. 1. World map showing important manganese deposits. *1* = Three Kids; *2* = Artillery Peak; *3* = Elkton and Crimora; *4* = Telamantes; *5* = Lucifer; *6* = Charco Redondo; *7* = Serra do Navio; *8* = Pasaje; *9* = Morro do Urucum; *10* = Morro da Mina; *11* = Faralion Negro; *12* = Ovalle and La Serena; *13* = Imini; *14* = Guettara; *15* = Bou Arfa; *16* = Ansongo; *17* = Nsuta; *18* = Moanda; *19* = E Coquendo Angola; *20* = Otjosondu; *21* = Postmasburg and Kalahari; *22* = Urkut; *23* = Varna; *24* = Nikopol and Bol'shoi Tokmak; *25* = Laba; *26* = Chiatura; *27* = Mangyshlak; *28* = Polunochnoe; *29* = Ulu-Telyak; *30* = Kusa; *31* = Dzhezda; *32* = Karadzhal; *33* = Usinsk; *34* = East Sayan; *35* = Khirgansk; *36* = Wafantsu; *37* = Wu Hsuan; *38* = Madhya Pradesh - Maharashtra belt; *39* = Panch Mahals; *40* = Srikakulam; *41* = Sandur; *42* = Raymond (New Caledonia); *43* = Woody-Woody; *44* = Peak Hill; *45* = Iron Baron; *46* = Gladstone; *47* = Noda Tamagawa; *48* = Kaso; *49* = Kokko, Pirika, Kinjo; *50* = Kiuragi.

and these account for the major share of the world reserve, represented mainly by the nonvolcanogenic Oligocene deposits in the U.S.S.R. The manganese deposits, therefore, show an increasing shift from geosynclinal to platform areas with passage of time.

All large and superlarge sedimentary manganese deposits, those containing 100 million to a few billion tons of ore, are of nonvolcanogenic type. Volcanogenic deposits are generally small and rarely contain more than one million tons of ore. In Fig. 1 the more important manganese deposits are shown on a world map. In Table I a number of deposits have been listed according to their geological age with brief indications as to their lithologic setting, source and mineralogy. Some of these deposits will be described in this Chapter. The nonvolcanogenic and volcanogenic deposits will be discussed separately under subdivisions based on lithologic associations. Classification based on mineralogical facies (e.g., oxide, carbonate, silicate, etc.) has been avoided as sedimentary deposits may not retain their pristine mineralogy after diagenesis. In the case of volcanogenic-sedimentary deposits, the variation in mineralogy of the ore types during sedimentation has been related to compositional changes in ore-bearing solutions (Sokolova, 1970). These may also be further modified during diagenesis.

NONVOLCANOGENIC-SEDIMENTARY MANGANESE DEPOSITS

The manganese deposits of this type were deposited from material transported from the weathering zone on the continents. The average manganese and iron contents of the crust are 0.1% and 5%, respectively (Mn/Fe = 1 : 50). With reference to iron, manganese may be preferentially leached due to its larger ionic size, lower ionic potential and enzymatic microbial reduction in the source area.

The average manganese content of river water is 0.1 p.p.m., but the gross contribution of this metal by rivers to the marine basins is considerable; for example, about 210,000 tons of manganese is supplied annually by rivers to the Black Sea and the Sea of Azov (Sapozhnikov, 1970). Manganese may occur both in solutions and in suspensions and their relative importance is debatable. Both Sapozhnikov (1970) and Strakhov (1969) assumed that the dissolved manganese is the main source for the ore deposits. Manganese may migrate in the form of humates. It is transported as bicarbonate complexes in anaerobic groundwater and perhaps also in slightly acidic surface water and as sol of $Mn(OH)_3$ stabilized by adsorbed organic substances. Manganese may be separated from iron during transportation due to its higher mobility (Strakhov, 1969).

The average manganese content of sea water is 0.002 p.p.m., but in the presence of H_2S, a large quantity may be retained in the dissolved state (e.g., Baltic Sea, Black Sea). About 100 million tons of manganese is reported to be present in solution in the Black Sea.

The separation of iron and manganese during deposition is mostly controlled by Eh and pH. In a reducing medium, $Fe(OH)_2$ is separated at a pH of 5.5 while $Mn(OH)_2$ is

TABLE I

Distribution of sedimentary manganese deposits in different geological ages

Age	Country	Deposits	Significant lithology and possible source of manganese	Mineralogy of ores
Pleistocene	Chile	Tarapaca Province	rhyolite, ignimbrite, conglomerate, sandstone (V)	cryptomelane, hollandite, psilomelane
	U.S.A.	Golconda, Nev.	clay, travertine (V)	psilomelane, cryptomelane
Pliocene	U.S.A.	Artillery Peak, Ariz.	tuffs, flows, sandstone (V)	psilomelane
		Lake Mead, Nev.	sandstone, siltstone, gypsum, tuff, lava (V)	cryptomelane, hollandite, coronadite
	Mexico	Lucifer area	conglomerate, tuff (V)	cryptomelane, pyrolusite
	Italy	Viterbo, Fontanelle	marl, shale, (U.D.)	pyrolusite
Miocene	Italy	Matessa	marl, shale (U.D.)	manganese oxides
	Japan	Kokko, Pirika, Kinjo (Hokkaido)	tuff, tuffaceous shale, lava (V)	pyrolusite, cryptomelane, manganite, groutite
	U.S.A.	Little Florida mine, N. Mex.	tuff, lava flows, breccia (V)	psilomelane, pyrolusite, manganite
Oligocene	U.S.S.R.	Laba, Nikopol, Bol'shoi Tokmak, Chiatura, Mangyshlak, Polunochnoe	*discussed in text* (N.V.)	*discussed in text*
	Bulgaria	Varna	diatomite, clay (N.V.)	pyrolusite and other manganese oxides
	Czechoslovakia	Kisovce	sandstone, limestone, shale (N.V.)	rhodochrosite, Mn-calcite, pyrolusite, manganite
	Italy	Gambatessa	shale, chert, marl, basic lava (V)	braunite, pyrolusite, rhodochrosite, tinzenite, parsettensite
Eocene	Cuba	Oriente Province	*discussed in text* (V)	*discussed in text*
	U.S.A.	Olympic Peninsula	*discussed in text* (V)	*discussed in text*
	Iran	Assad	lava, tuff, jasper (V)	manganese oxides
	France	La Valmasque	sandstone, clay (U.D.)	cryptomelane, todorokite, pyrolusite, braunite, hollandite

TABLE 1 (continued)

Age	Country	Deposits	Significant lithology and possible source of manganese	Mineralogy of ores
Cretaceous	Indonesia	Timor	*discussed in text* (N.V.)	*discussed in text;* fossil nodules
	Morocco	Imini, Tasdremt	*discussed in text* (N.V.)	*discussed in text*
	Bulgaria	Sredna Gora	*discussed in text* (V)	*discussed in text*
	U.S.S.R.	Armenia	*discussed in text* (V)	*discussed in text*
	Turkey	Eregli, Ordu	flows, tuffs, marls, (V)	hausmannite, pyrolusite
	Chile	Coquimbo	*discussed in text* (V)	*discussed in text*
	Australia	Groote Eyelandt	sand, clay (N.V.)	higher oxides of manganese
Late Jurassic to Early Cretaceous	U.S.A.	Franciscan Formation, Calif.	*discussed in text* (V)	*discussed in text*
	Japan	Tokoro Dt., Kokuriki, Shibayama, Nikura mines	*discussed in text* (V)	*discussed in text*
	Rumania	Pirnesti, Soimus-Buceava	diabase, jasper (V)	pyrolusite, psilomelane
Jurassic	Switzerland	Parsetten and Faletta	*discussed in text* (V)	*discussed in text*
	U.S.A.	Amador group, Sierra Nevada, Calif.	*discussed in text* (V)	*discussed in text*
	Germany	Eastern Alps	marl, black shale and tuff (V)	Mn carbonate, braunite
	Hungary	Urkut	radiolarian chert, clay and marl (U.D.)	rhodochrosite, manganite, pyrolusite, cryptomelane
	Morocco	Bou Arfa, M'Koussa, Tiaratine.	*discussed in text* (N.V.)	*discussed in text*
	Mexico	Molango	carbonaceous limestone, limey shale, (N.V.)	kutnahorite, rhodochrosite
	U.S.A.	S.E. Utah	*discussed in text* (N.V.)	*discussed in text,* fossil nodules
	Sicily and Austria	Northern Limestone Alps	*discussed in text* (U.D.)	*discussed in text,* fossil nodules
Permo-Triassic	Morocco	Narguechoum	*discussed in text* (N.V.)	*discussed in text*

TABLE I (continued)

Age	Country	Deposits	Significant lithology and possible source of manganese	Mineralogy of ores
Permo-Triassic (continued)	France	Montels, Ariège	ferruginous sandstone (U.D.)	Mn oxides including ranceite
Late Paleozoic	U.S.A.	Galaverous formation, Sierra Nevada, Calif.	*discussed in text* (V)	*discussed in text*
Permian	U.S.A.	Dillon, Mont.	*discussed in text* (N.V.)	*discussed in text,* fossil nodules
	U.S.S.R.	Ulu Telyak, W. Urals	*discussed in text* (N.V.)	*discussed in text*
Permo-Carboniferous	Japan	Noda Tamagawa, Iwate Prefecture.	*discussed in text* (V)	*discussed in text*
	Japan	Kaso, Tochigi Prefecture	*discussed in text* (V)	*discussed in text*
Carboniferous	China	Lohua-Lop'in, Chiangshi Province	orthoquartzite, siliceous shale, carbonate (N.V.)	–
	Morocco	Glib en Nam	*discussed in text* (V)	*discussed in text*
	France	Hautes Pyrénées	"Griotte" marble, microquartzite (U.D.)	cryptomelane, groutite, braunite, rhodonite, tephroite, spessartite friedelite, dialogite, alabandite
	Spain	Huelva Province	*discussed in text* (V)	*discussed in text*
	Germany	Kellerwald and Harz	*discussed in text* (V)	*discussed in text*
	Egypt	Um Bogma	dolomite, marl, shale, silt (N.V.)	pyrochroite, hausmannite, manganite, psilomelane, pyrolusite
Late Devonian to Early Carboniferous	U.S.S.R.	Atasu Region, Central Kazakhstan	*discussed in text* (V)	*discussed in text*
Devonian	France	Las Cabesses, Casalas, Brachy (Ariège)	"Griotte" marble, keratophyre(?) (U.D.)	manganite, cryptomelane, pyrolusite, todorokite
	U.S.S.R.	Magnitogorsk	*discussed in text* (V)	*discussed in text*

TABLE I (continued)

Age	Country	Deposits	Significant lithology and possible source of manganese	Mineralogy of ores
Silurian	U.S.A and Canada	Aroostook County, Maine and Woodstock, N.B.	graywacke, slate, siltstone, volcanic ash (V)	ferroan rhodochrosite, braunite, bementite, spessartite, manganoan cummingtonite
	U.S.S.R.	Dautash, Zeravshan Range	quartz-sericite schist, quartz-porphyry, limestone (V)	Mn-carbonate, rare Mn-oxide
		Takhta Karacha, Zeravshan Range	quartz-porphyry and albitophyry, siliceous limestone (V)	Mn-carbonate, Mn-garnet, braunite, hausmannite
Ordovician	Israel	Timna dome	sandstone, shale (N.V.)	pyrolusite, psilomelane, ramsdellite(?), hollandite(?)
	Great Britain	Caenarvonshire	spilitic lava, mudstone, keratophyric tuff (V)	rhodochrosite, spessartite, pennantite, rhodonite, tephroite, alleghanyite, jacobsite, pyrochroite, psilomelane
Canbrian–Ordovician	Brazil	Morro do Urucum, Mato Grosso	*discussed in text* (N.V.)	*discussed in text*
Cambrian	U.S.S.R.	Mazul'skii, Durnovso	*discussed in text* (V)	*discussed in text*
		Usinsk, S. Khingan	*discussed in text* (N.V.)	*discussed in text*
	Great Britain	Harlech Dome, Wales	shale, mudstone, graywacke (U.D.)	rhodochrosite, spessartite, rhodonite
Early Paleozoic	Australia	Mary Valley, Queensland	andesite, jasper, shale, quartzite (V)	hausmannite, braunite, cryptomelane, pyrolusite, nsutite, rhodonite, piemontite
Precambrian	U.S.S.R.	Ikat-Gargisk, Tala-Usoysk Watershed, Transbaikal geosyncline	ferruginous jasper, siliceous-carbonate rocks, rhyolitic lava, diabase, carbonate-terrigenous rocks (U.D.)	braunite, hausmannite, manganite, Mn-calcite, rhodochrosite

TABLE I (continued)

Age	Country	Deposits	Significant lithology and possible source of manganese	Mineralogy of ores
Precambrian (continued)		Eastern Sayan	red arkosic sandstone, dolomite, silt, argillite (N.V.)	braunite, haussmannite
	Rumania	Globu Rau, Cosna, Sebes Mt., Delinesti	crystalline schists (N.V.)	rhodonite, pyroxmanganite, knebelite, dannemorite, spessartite
	Union of S. Africa	Postmasburg-Aucampsrust	discussed in text (N.V.)	discussed in text
		Kalahari field, Kuruman Dt.	discussed in text (N.V.)	discussed in text
	China	Hsiangt'an, Tsunhsi	orthoquartzite, carbonaceous slate, bituminous limestone, dolomite (N.V.)	
	S.W. Africa	Otjosondu	discussed in text (N.V.)	discussed in text
	Gabon	Moanda	discussed in text (V)	discussed in text
	Ghana	Nsuta	discussed in text (V)	discussed in text
	Ivory Coast	Grand Lahou, Korhogo	discussed in text (V)	discussed in text
	Upper Volta	Tiéré	discussed in text (V)	discussed in text
	Mali	Tikanasité Hill	discussed in text (V)	discussed in text
	Zaire	Kisenge	discussed in text (U.D.)	discussed in text
	Madagascar	Ampanihy and Bekily Dts.	crystalline schists (U.D.)	spessartite, rhodonite, tephroite
	Tanzania	Mwhana	marble, calc-silicate, quartzite, micaschist (N.V.)	spessartite, piemontite, viridine, Mn-phlogopite
	Morocco	Tiouine, Idikel, Migouden	discussed in text (V)	discussed in text
	Algeria	Guettara	rhyolite flows, tuff, sandstone, argillite (V)	braunite, haussmannite, manganite, pyrolusite, psilomelane, rhodonite, spessartite, piemontite, winchite
	South America	Guiana Shield	discussed in text (N.V.)	discussed in text

TABLE I (continued)

Age	Country	Deposits	Significant litho-logy and possible source of manganese	Mineralogy of ores
Precambrian (continued)	Brazil	Minas Gerais, Bahia, Amapa	*discussed in text* (N.V.)	*discussed in text*
	U.S.A.	Big Indian Deposit, Sierra Nevada, Calif.	greenschist, quartz-ite (V)	rhodochrosite, tephroite, rhodon-ite, bementite
	Sweden	Långban, Harstigen etc.	*discussed in text* (V)	*discussed in text*
	Norway	Mount Brandnuten	arkosic quartzite (N.V.)	braunite, jacobsite, hausmannite, spes-sartite, rhodonite
	Czechoslovakia	Chvaltice	pyrite-bearing graphitic shales, basic lava, tuff (V).	ferrian rhodochro-site
	India	Madhya Pradesh (Sausar and Ara-valli Groups), Maharashtra (Sausar Group), Gujarat (Cham-paner Group), Orissa (Gangpur Group), Andhra Pradesh (Khon-dalite Group)	*discussed in text* (N.V)	*discussed in text*
		Bihar and Orissa (Iron Ore Group)	shale, chert, basic lava, iron forma-tion (U.D.)	braunite, pyrolu-site, cryptomelane, manganite
		Mysore, Sandur	phyllite, ferrugin-ous quartzite, basic igneous rocks (U.D.)	pyrolusite, crypto-melane, ramsdellite, braunite(?), jacobsite(?)

V = volcanogenic-sedimentary deposits; N.V. = nonvolcanogenic-sedimentary deposits; U.D. = deposits of undetermined source.

Note: In mineral assemblages only manganese minerals are quoted; supergene manganese minerals have been excluded.

precipitated at a pH of 8.5 (Marchandise, 1956). A part of the Mn^{2+} in solution may, however, be adsorbed by and precipitated with $Fe(OH)_2$ (Collins and Buol, 1970). The $Mn(OH)_2$ is rapidly oxidized to MnO_2. During gradual oxidation, iron precipitates at a much lower Eh compared to manganese. The rate of oxidation and precipitation of manganese from an aerated solution is increased by rising pH and decreased by the presence of HCO_3^- and SO_4^{2-} (Hem, 1963).

In the manganese-water system, at room temperature and pressure (Fig. 2), studied by

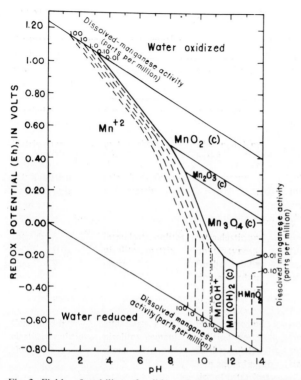

Fig. 2. Fields of stability of solids and solutes and solubility of manganese as functions of pH and redox potential at 25°C and one atm. in the system Mn–H_2). (After Hem, 1972; *Bull. Geol. Soc. Am.,* 83, p. 448.)

Hem (1963, 1972), areas for stability for solids and the solubility of manganese and also the dominant solute forms are shown. The oxides shown in Fig. 2 include MnO_2, Mn_2O_3 and Mn_3O_4. $Mn(OH)_2$ is also stable at low Eh. Solute complexes considered in this figure are $MnOH^+$ and $HMnO_2^-$. If other anions are introduced into the manganese-water system, new solids and solute complexes are added. With bicarbonate species activity equivalent to 2000 mg/1 HCO_3^- ($10^{-1.48}$ mol/l), a large field of stability for $MnCO_3$ is introduced together with the solute complex $MnHCO_3^+$, whose effect is important (Fig. 3; Hem, 1963, 1972). The complexing effect results in a bulging of the stability boundary of MnO_2. In Fig. 4 (Hem, 1963, 1972) a sulfate complex is introduced where the system has the equivalent of 2000 mg/l activity of SO_4($10^{-1.68}$ mol/l). Hem (1972) considered that the solute complexes influence the behaviour of iron more than that of manganese.

Manganese is considerably more soluble than iron in the Eh-pH range of the studied systems. In Fig. 5 (Hem, 1972) a general comparison of the solubilities of manganese and iron is represented. The solubility of iron is indicated by the dashed line. For almost any Eh and pH within the water stability-field, more manganese will be in solution than iron will be in equilibrium.

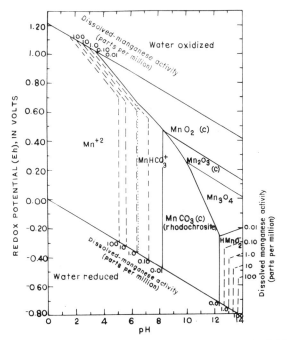

Fig. 3. Fields of stability of solids and solutes and solubility of manganese as functions of pH and redox potential at 25°C and one atm. in the system $Mn-CO_2-H_2O$. Bicarbonate species activity 2000 mg/l as HCO_3^-. (After Hem, 1972; *Bull. Geol. Soc. Am.*, 83, p. 448.)

Borchert (1970) stated that as a rule manganese passes from HCO_3 compounds in ionic solution to colloidal solution after iron, from which precipitation occurs in marine basins almost immediately by the effect of oppositely charged saline ions. In an electro-lyte-poor milieu, the oppositely charged iron and manganese hydroxides can discharge each other and form mixed assemblages. The precipitation of iron and manganese as carbonate occurs in weakly reducing environments and may overlap. The carbonate stability-field for manganese is much wider than that for iron (Fig. 6), but the manganese-sulfide domain is effectively greatly restricted as compared to the iron-sulfide stability-field and it partly covers that of $MnCO_3$. Michard (1968) suggested that in reducing conditions manganese associates with calcium in preference to iron in the formation of carbonate. Stashchuk (1972) recognized theoretically the possible formation of alaban-dite in a strongly alkaline environment which, however, is much beyond the pH values in natural processes. He concluded, therefore, that the MnS-type sulfide cannot form in normal sedimentary rocks. Consequently, manganese sulfide has not been reported from sedimentary ore deposits. Low-temperature manganese silicates occur only in volcano-genic-sedimentary deposits.

Biological agencies may selectively oxidize and precipitate manganese from solution,

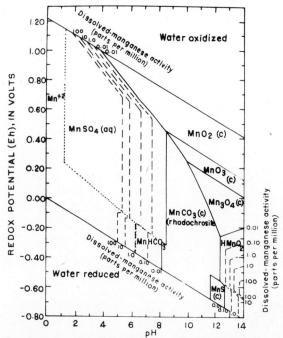

Fig. 4. Fields of stability of solids and solutes and solubility of manganese as functions of pH and redox potential at 25°C and one atm. in the system $Mn-S-CO_2-H_2O$. Total CO_2 species activity 2000 mg/l as HCO_3^-, total sulfur species activity 2000 mg/l as SO_4^{2-}. (After Hem, 1972; *Bull. Geol. Soc. Am.,* 83, p. 448.)

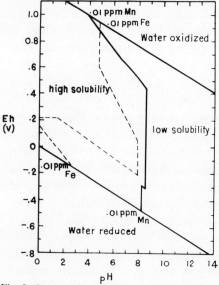

Fig. 5. Comparative solubility of manganese and iron in the system $H_2O-Mn-Fe-CO_2-S-H_2O$ at 25°C and one atm. Total CO_2 species activity 2000 mg/l as HCO_3^-, total sulfur species activity 2000 mg/l as SO_4^{2-}. (After Hem, 1972; *Bull. Geol. Soc. Am.,* 83, p. 449.)

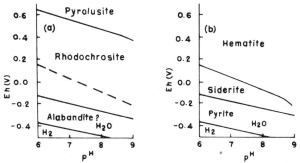

Fig. 6. Eh–pH diagram for the system (a) pyrolusite–rhodochrosite–alabandite (after Marchandise, 1956) compared with the system (b) hematite–siderite–pyrite (after Krumbein and Garrels, 1952). The dashed line in (a) indicates the inferred but not determined $MnCO_3$-MnO_2 boundary by Krumbein and Garrels.

e.g., *Crenothrix polyspora* and *Leptothrix ochracea* (Zapffe, 1931), and *Metallogenium, Kusnezovia* and *Caulococcus* (Perfilér and Gabe, 1965; Gabe et al., 1965).

Manganese ores tend to be deposited mainly in stable areas under humid-temperate and humid-tropical conditions. In the absence of tectonism, chemical differentiation of the Al–Fe–Mn triad is carried to completion and with enhanced mobility under humid condition, manganese tends to migrate farther from continental areas (Strakhov, 1969). Due to higher contents of CO_2 in the atmosphere and lower pH in surface water, the preference of manganese to be deposited in the pelagic areas was more marked in the Precambrian than in later periods. Mobility of the Al–Fe–Mn triad was markedly reduced in the Phanerozoic eon due to decline in CO_2 in the atmosphere and consequently the sites of deposition of the members of the triad showed a shoreward shift. Deposits of the Al–Fe–Mn triad are not known to intergrade along depositional strike and manganese tends to be concentrated in the finer terrigenous fraction (Strakhov, 1969).

In sedimentary manganese deposits, pyrolusite, cryptomelane, psilomelane, birnessite, todorokite, coronadite, manganite and rhodochrosite (or manganoan calcite) are generally present. Jacobsite (low in manganese) and hollandite are rarely encountered. Braunite, bementite and neotocite have rarely been reported and then only from volcanogenic-sedimentary deposits.

During diagenesis, the manganese sediments (of both terrigenous and volcanic derivation) are generally modified and separation of manganese from iron and transformation of manganese oxide to manganese carbonate may take place (Zen, 1959; Manheim, 1961; Hartman, 1964; Lynn and Bonatti, 1965; Shterenberg et al., 1966; Calvert and Price, 1970; Logvineko et al., 1972; Logvineko, 1973; Rozhanov et al., 1973; and others). Boström (1967) suggested that the transformation of manganese oxides to carbonates during diagenesis may take place according to the reaction $x\ CaCO_3 + y\ Mn^{2+} = (Ca_{x-y} \cdot Mn_y)CO_3 + yCa^{2+}$. Many of these deposits, particularly those of Precambrian age have also been modified by thermal or regional metamorphism or both. In all such cases, the effect of metamorphism is limited to reconstitution of the mineralogy and texture of the pre-existing orebodies and no particular improvement of tenor is known to have taken place by this process. Rather, in many cases, metamorphism has destroyed the economic potentiality of low-grade sedimentary ores (simple admixture of manganese oxides with chert, mudstone or shale) which were originally easily amenable to beneficiation. These have been recrystallized to commercially useless complex manganese silicates (cf. gondite). In this sense, meta-sedimentary manganese-ore deposits are of "metamorphosed" and not of "metamorphic" type. These deposits, therefore, will not be taken up separately and will be discussed under the sedimentary types to which they originally belonged.

Roy (1966, 1968, 1972, 1973), Huebner (1967), Peters et al. (1973), and others used petrographic and phase-equilibrium data to show that the original bulk composition of the sediments, the reactions during metamorphism at variable temperature and fugacities of oxygen, CO_2 etc., generally control the mineralogy of the metamorphosed manganese

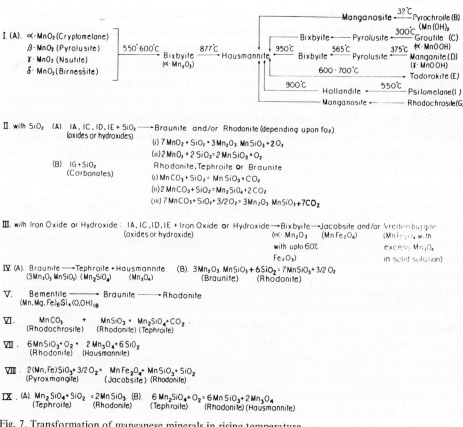

Fig. 7. Transformation of manganese minerals in rising temperature.

formations. In cases of thermal metamorphism, however, metasomatism may often be an important contributor to new mineral phases.

The formation and transformation of different mineral phases in rising temperature during metamorphism are explained in Fig. 7. The data presented in this figure have been taken mainly from laboratory phase-equilibrium studies carried out by a number of workers.

In Fig. 7, in reactions IA to IE, it is shown that all higher oxides and hydroxides of manganese occurring without admixture in sedimentary manganese orebodies are transformed to hausmannite, often through bixbyite (iron-free or negligible iron). Psilomelane (IF) with essential barium, converts first to hollandite and finally to hausmannite in rising temperature. Manganese carbonate (rhodochrosite, IG) is dissociated in high temperature to form manganosite (MnO) which is converted to hausmannite. In reactions under IIA it is shown that the oxide and hydroxide phases under IA, IC, ID and IE, when admixed with silica in the sediments, react with the latter in rising temperature giving rise to either braunite or rhodonite. Braunite is formed in favour of rhodonite in higher oxygen fugacity. In IIB the reactions of manganese carbonate (rhodochrosite) with admixed silica, in rising temperature, giving rise to rhodonite, tephroite or braunite are shown. Braunite is, however, extremely rare in metamorphosed manganese-carbonate deposits. When iron oxide or hydroxide is admixed with higher oxides or hydroxides of manganese, reaction in rising temperature gives rise to bixbyite (with up to 60% Fe_2O_3 but generally restricted to 30% Fe_2O_3 in the temperature regime of metamorphosed deposits), jacobsite and/or vredenburgite. The phase relations in the $Fe_3O_4-Mn_3O_4$ and $Fe_2O_3-Mn_2O_3$ systems in rising temperatures have been studied in detail by Van Hook and Keith (1958) and Muan and Somiya (1962). Reactions shown in IVA and IVB, suggested by Huebner (1967), are of doubtful significance in natural metamorphosed manganese deposits as no unequivocal evidence of derivation of tephroite and hausmannite or rhodonite from braunite has so far been found from them. Similarly, reactions V, VII and IX have, so far, not been verified from natural deposits. Reactions VI and VIII have been verified from metamorphosed manganese formations of Brazil (Morro da Mina) and India (Sausar Group), respectively.

The distribution of common manganese minerals in sedimentary, metamorphosed and supergene deposits is given in Table II.

The principal deposits of nonvolcanogenic-sedimentary manganese ores will now be described under three broad types, e.g., terrigenous formation, carbonate formation and iron-formation, classified according to the specific lithological association of ores.

Manganese deposits associated with terrigenous formations

The unmetamorphosed deposits of the U.S.S.R., Israel and Australia (Nikopol type) and the metamorphosed deposits of Brazil, Guiana Shield, Zaire and India will be discussed here.

TABLE II

Distribution of manganese minerals in different types of deposits

	Minerals formed in sedimentary condition	Minerals formed due to metamorphism	Minerals formed by supergene process
Oxides and hydroxides			
Pyrolusite	very common	x	very common
Cryptomelane	very common	x	very common
Psilomelane	common	x	rather rare
Nsutite	x	x	fairly common in carbonate host
Birnessite	present in deep-sea nodules	x	minor but fairly distributed in carbonate host
Todorokite	present in sediments and in deep-sea nodules	x	rare
Coronadite	rarely present	x	x
Pyrochroite	x	very rare	x
Manganite	fairly common	present	fairly common
Bixbyite	x	common in low to high grades	x
Braunite	present only in volcanogenic deposits	very common in all grades	x
Hollandite	present but uncommon	very common in all grades	sometimes present
Hausmannite	x	very common in higher grades	rare, only after rhodochrosite
Jacobsite	rarely present as colloform bodies	common in higher grades	x
Vredenburgite[1]	x	common in higher grades	x
Carbonate			
Rhodochrosite	very common	very common in carbonate deposits	x
Silicate			
Neotocite	present only in volcanogenic deposts	x	x
Bementite	present only in volcanogenic deposits	x	x
Rhodonite[2]	x	very common in silicate deposits	x
Spessartite	x	very common in silicate deposits	x
Tephroite	x	common in silicate-carbonate deposits only	x
Mn-pyroxene[3]	x	mon	x
Mn-amphibole[4]	x	fairly common	x
Mn-mica	x	fairly common	x

[1] Includes hausmannite-jacobsite, hetaerolite-franklinite and hausmannite-galaxite intergrowths; [2] includes bustamite and pyroxmangite; [3] includes blanfordite, manganoan diopside, brown manganese pyroxene, etc.; [4] includes tirodite, winchite, juddite, etc.

U.S.S.R. The vast deposits of unmetamorphosed platform-type sedimentary manganese ores of Oligocene age, developed in terrigenous formations in the U.S.S.R., may be grouped under the Nikopol type. The important deposits at Nikopol, Bol'shoi Tokmak (Ukraine), Chiatura (southern Caucasus), Laba (northern Caucasus) and Mangyshlak in the south of the U.S.S.R., and Polunochnoe, Marsyatskoe, Novo Berezovskoye, etc., in the northern Ural belong to this type. Outside the U.S.S.R., the manganese deposits of Timna Dome, Israel (Upper Ordovician) and Groote Eyelandt, Australia (Lower Cretaceous) may also be included under the Nikopol type.

Deposits of the Nikopol type occur as beds of manganese oxides and carbonates near the base of the marine ore-bearing sequence, and are all of Early Oligocene age excepting that of Laba (Late Oligocene). The deposits at Nikopol and Bol'shoi Tokmak rest on the southern edge of the Ukrainian Shield. The Chiatura deposit occurs on the slopes of the Dzirul crystalline massif which forms the stable median part of a geosyncline. The Laba and the Ural deposits rest on a dislocated epi-Hercynian basement.

Nikopol and Bol'shoi Tokmak occur as twin deposits, on the western and eastern banks of the Dneiper in southern Ukraine. The ore-bearing formation at Nikopol rests transgressively on the crystalline basement and the Buchaksk and Kiev Stages. The lower part of this formation consists of beds of orthoquartzite and glauconitic clays. The beds of manganese ores, represented by the oxidic (pyrolusite, psilomelane), mixed (psilomelane, manganite, manganoan calcite, rhodochrosite) and carbonate (calcian rhodochrosite and manganoan calcite) assemblages, occur transgressively at different stratigraphic horizons in the lower part of the section. The manganese oxides occur nearest to the shore of the basin, giving way to mixed ores and finally to manganese carbonates towards the deeper parts (Fig. 8). The orebodies, generally of a concretionary nature, form a continuous horizon for more than 150 miles with an average thickness of 4–8 ft. Shallow-water gastropods, crabs, shark-teeth, balanas, stenohaline lamellibranchs, sea-urchins and solitary corals have been detected in the ore horizon. Pyrolusite, crypto-

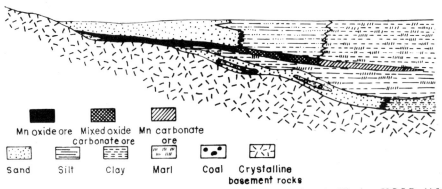

Fig. 8. Diagrammatic cross-section of the Nikopol manganese deposit, Ukraine, U.S.S.R. (After Varentsov, 1964.)

melane, psilomelane, todorokite and birnessite have been formed by supergene oxidation of carbonate ores. Plastic greenish clay overlies the ore-beds. At Bol'shoi Tokmak, the carbonate ores are much more extensively developed than the oxide and mixed ores. Otherwise, this deposit is geologically similar to Nikopol.

Around the Chiatura deposit in the southern Caucasus, Georgia, a series of older rocks (Precambrian Dzirul granitoids, Paleozoic crystalline schists, Mesozoic quartz-porphyry volcanic series and limestone) occur below the ore-bearing formation. At Chiatura the ore-bearing formation rests discordantly on Upper Cretaceous limestones and the ore horizon is up to 45 ft. thick (average 13 ft.) in which the individual orebands (<0.5 inch to 1.5 ft., rarely 3 ft. thick) are inter-laminated with glauconitic clay and sandy shale. There are about twenty-five orebands in all, of which three to eighteen occur in different parts of the exploitable areas as flat lenses elongated towards the northeast. They merge horizontally or vertically, finally aggregated to one massive ore horizon. The average tenor of the ore-beds is 35% Mn. Oolitic and fine pisolitic varieties of ore are fairly common. The thickness of the barren rock intercalations generally increases towards the northeast, concomitant with a decrease in their grain size. The higher-oxide ores pass over to pure manganese-carbonate ore from the southwest to the northeast direction through a zone of mixed oxide-carbonate ores with manganite oolites in calcic rhodochrosite and manganoan calcite. The higher-oxide and carbonate ore facies are interlayered with coarse-grained (poorest in C_{org}) and very fine-grained clastic rocks (richest in C_{org}), respectively. The thickness of the ore-beds is maximum towards the southwest, declining gradually towards the northeast. The shoreline of the Paleogene basin in which this ore-bearing formation was deposited was, therefore, situated towards the southwest. Abundant remains of sponges, mollusks, fishes and aquatic mammals have been found in the basin.

At Mangyshlak, the ore-bearing formation is composed of silt-clay and fine-grained argillaceous rocks, containing the orebodies in the upper part as continuous NNW–SSE trending lenses and beds. The total thickness of the ore-member (with two to ten beds) varies between 4 and 7 ft. These orebodies also exhibit a zonal distribution, with the manganese oxides and hydroxides (pyrolusite, manganite, cryptomelane, todorokite) in the northern part passing southwards into mixed oxide-carbonate and finally carbonate (rhodochrosite, manganoan calcite) ores. The average manganese ore is low-grade (about 20% Mn).

The Nikopol-type deposit at Laba (Strakhov et al., 1970; Kalinenko et al., 1970), is perhaps the only major deltaic occurrence of manganese in the world. The manganese ores occur mainly in the well-washed and sorted sands and also in sands containing gravel. The ore horizon (60 ft. thick) occurs approximately at the middle of the subaqueous facies, underlain by argillaceous silty sand beds and overlain by argillaceous silts, all forming a single genetic unit. Thin lenses of manganese carbonate (calcian rhodochrosite, manganoan calcite, oligonite) constitute the ore horizon and in the gravel sands near the strand, the ores are oolitic. The average manganese content of the ores is 25%.

The deposits at Polunochnoe, Marsyatskoe, Berezovskoye and Novo Berezovskoye, northern Ural, occur in a N–S trending belt running for about 100 miles. Andrushenko (1954; cited by Varentsov, 1964) described the Polunochnoe deposit where oxidic ores (pyrolusite and psilomelane) occur in the western and northern part of the area, passing into carbonate ores towards the southeast. Here, the ore-bearing horizon overlies Paleozoic porphyrites, tuffs and tuffaceous shales and is constituted of argillaceous clays, carbonate ores, diatomites and fine-bedded oxide ores. It is overlain by diatomites and diatomaceous clays (Ampilogov, 1970). Ampilogov studied intensively a section in the Yuzhnaya mine in which an ore horizon, about 11 ft. thick, is constituted of very fine rhythmic interlayers of manganese oxide and fine-grained quartz and opal, occasionally interrupted by slightly thicker manganite interlayers. From this section he calculated the rate of sedimentation and estimated that this ore horizon formed in about 1800 years.

Almost all workers on the Nikopol-type deposits agree that these sedimentary ores were formed by materials derived from weathering of older rocks. Only Dzotsenidze (1966) advocated a volcanogenic source for the manganese in the Chiatura deposit, but his arguments have been convincingly contradicted by Strakhov and Shterenberg (1966). The ore formations were deposited in the littoral zone in a shallow-water marine basin as indicated by the disposition of the beds, their granulometric composition and the faunal assemblage (shallow-water mollusks, crabs and balanas). Sokolova (1964) thought that the water of the Chiatura basin was of low salinity but Gryaznov (1970) concluded that normal salinity prevailed in the Nikopol basin because typical stenohaline lamellibranchs, sea urchins and solitary corals are found in the ore horizon. Selin (1964; cited by Gryaznov, 1970) concluded from paleoecological analysis of mollusks in the ore-bearing horizons of Nikopol that the temperature regime of the Oligocene basin was comparable to that of present-day sub-tropical seas. The same conclusion was drawn by Sokolova (1964) about the Chiatura basin. The deposition of the manganese ores at Nikopol and Chiatura took place in humid conditions. The Mangyshlak deposit was formed at the boundary of humid and arid zones whereas the Timna deposit (Israel) was in an arid zone. The manganese ores of the northern Ural were formed in a temperate, probably even cold climate (Varentsov, 1964).

Betekhtin (1937) and Sokolova (1964) explained the zonal disposition of the oxidic, mixed and carbonate manganese ores at Chiatura as due to facies change during deposition. Identical zonation of manganese minerals is exhibited in most deposits of the Nikopol type. Strakhov and Shterenberg (1966), however, cited the abundance of sponges, mollusks, fishes and aquatic mammals on the sea bottom at the site of ore deposition as evidence of well-aerated water throughout the depth of the basin. This precludes the possibility of a euxinic depositional environment and the formation of manganese carbonates as a primary sediment. Therefore, Strakhov and Shterenberg, and others concluded that the manganese carbonates were formed by diagenesis of the oxidic ores, and thus that the ·Nikopol-type deposits (in the U.S.S.R.) are sedimentary— diagenetic. Similar diagenetic transformation of manganese oxides to carbonates has been widely reported from Recent oceanic nodules (Lynn and Bonatti, 1965; Shterenberg et al., 1966; Calvert and Price, 1970; Logvineko, 1973; Logvineko et al., 1972).

The manganese-carbonate orebodies of the Laba deposit were formed in deltaic sediments entirely by diagenetic enrichment (Strakhov et al., 1970; Kalinenko et al., 1970). The absence of continuous ore horizons, the small dimensions of individual orebodies with an irregular vertical distribution and the association of the ores only with sands and thoroughly washed sediments support the above conclusion.

The iron-poor character of the Nikopol-type manganese ores led Hewett (1966) to doubt the terrigenous source of the metal and he suggested their derivation from hypogene solution. This suggestion, however, is not substantiated by evidence. The alternative suggestion of Strakhov et al. (1970), that almost total separation of manganese from iron took place in the weathering zone at the source, sounds more convincing. The selectively leached manganese (with only minor iron) was then deposited in marine basins. This separation of manganese from iron was further continued during diagenesis, assisted by the relatively higher mobility of manganese (cf. Lynn and Bonatti, 1965; Strakhov, 1969).

Betekhtin (1937) and Sokolova (1964) concluded that the Dzirul granitoid massif was the source of manganese for the Chiatura deposit. Strakhov and Shterenberg (1966), Strakhov et al. (1970) and Gryaznov (1970), however, contended that the Middle Jurassic prophyrites and metabasites with much higher manganese content (0.2–0.5%), acted as the source. For the Laba Deposit, the adjacent detrital facies is considered to be the source of the manganese carbonate ores (Strakhov et al., 1970).

Sapozhnikov (1970) suggested that the water of the Paleogene Maikop basin (Nikopol, Bol'shoi Tokmak, U.S.S.R.; Varna, Bulgaria) or in areas adjoining the islands situated within this basin (Chiatura, Laba, Mangyshlak, etc.) could have been contaminated by H_2S, similar to the water of the Recent Black Sea (Strakhov, 1971), but for a much longer period. In that case, the deeper parts of the ancient Maikop basin might have acted as a great reservoir of manganese. Upwelling of manganese-rich waters resulted in precipitation of manganese oxides near the shore. When the water was partly contaminated by H_2S, compounds with Mn^{2+}, such as $CaMn(CO_3)_2$ and $MnCO_3$ might have formed, corresponding to the carbonate ores of the Oligocene deposits. Another part of the manganese might precipitate as Mn-hydrates at intermediate depth and under a reducing atmosphere to form the primary stage of the manganite facies. Manganese sulfide could not form at any stage because of its very high solubility (cf. Strakhov et al., 1971; Black Sea). Sapozhnikov (1970), however, did not preclude the possibility that manganese oxides might also have been initially precipitated to the bottom and were later reduced during diagenesis to form the manganese carbonates.

Brazil. The Precambrian eugeosynclinal Rio das Velhas Series (>2700 m.y.) containing manganese carbonate and silicate-carbonate protore associated with graphitic phyllite, mica schist, quartzite, meta-conglomerate and amphibolite, occur in a 150 miles long belt striking northeast from São João del Rei, Minas Gerais, Brazil. Multiple thin iron-formations of carbonate and oxide facies are also present but are separated from the manganese formation in space and time. Free carbon is ubiquitous in the manganese silicate-carbonate protore and in enclosing phyllites and schists.

The manganese silicate-carbonate protore (Dorr et al., 1956; Ebert, 1963) consists of rhodochrosite and manganoan calcite (most common), spessartite, rhodonite, manganoan cummingtonite, graphite, quartz, tephroite, pyrophanite, thulite, neotocite, bementite, pyroxmangite and apatite. Alabandite and other iron and copper sulfides and sulfarsenides are sometimes present. The manganese carbonate protore is rich in rhodochrosite with only minor manganese silicates.

Most workers (Dorr et al., 1956; Ebert, 1963; Dorr, 1973) suggested a meta-sedimentary origin of the manganese protores with the metal derived from terrigenous source. There is also general agreement that the original sediments were carbonates, formed in a reducing condition. The mineralogy of the protore (rich in rhodochrosite and totally devoid of metamorphic oxides) and the presence of graphite and pyrite in the sediments corroborate this idea. The primary manganiferous sediments were probably a variable mixture of manganese carbonate, chert and mudstone. The pure and admixed manganese-carbonate sediments were later metamorphosed to form the manganese-carbonate and silicate-carbonate protores, respectively. The nature of the metamorphism, contact or regional, has been debated by many workers (see Dorr et al., 1956). Dorr et al. concluded that the rocks were regionally metamorphosed to greenschist facies. Ebert (1963) suggested that regional metamorphism to amphibolite facies was attained. Both Ebert and Horen (in Dorr et al., 1956) contended that the regionally metamorphosed rocks were further modified by contact metamorphism.

The manganese silicate-carbonate protore was originally named queluzite by Derby (1901). Most of the later workers, however, equated this protore to the manganese-silicate rocks of the Sausar Group of India and called it gondite. The fundamental difference in the nature of the primary manganiferous sediments in the two cases as reflected in the mineral composition of the respective protores has been pointed out by Roy (1965, 1966) and by Roy and Purkait (1968). It is, therefore, important that either the names queluzite and gondite be used to denote specific types of metamorphosed manganese protores or that both the names be dropped and the rocks be designated only by their composition, viz., manganese silicate-carbonate protore and manganese silicate-oxide protore.

Supergene enrichment of the manganese carbonate and silicate-carbonate protore gave rise to ore-grade deposits (viz., Morro da Mina) of manganese oxide (cryptomelane, pyrolusite). Dorr et al. (1956) estimated a reserve of approximately 7 million tons of manganese oxide ores (plus 40% Mn). Until recently only the oxidized enrichment zone was being exploited, but now mining and concentration of rhodochrosite-rich protore has also been started (J.V.N. Dorr, personal communication, 1974).

The extensive manganese deposits in the Amapa Series, Serra do Navio area, Brazil, form part of the Guianan Shield. The Amapa Series (>1700 m.y) consists of the Lower

Jornal group (amphibolite, schist and quartzite) and the Upper Serra do Navio group. This latter group exhibits at least three rhythmic cycles, each consisting of quartzose (base), biotitic and graphitic facies (Scarpelli, 1973). The manganese protores occur as lenses only in the upper part of the graphitic facies in each cycle.

Scarpelli described two distinct types of manganese protores: carbonate and silicate. The more important carbonate protore occurs as lenses of variable thickness (30–90 ft.) and length (up to 0.5 mile), consisting principally of rhodochrosite, with minor spessartite, tephroite and rhodonite. Graphite, sphalerite, niccolite and gersdorfite occur as rare accessories. Nagell (1962) reported alabandite from the carbonate protore. The silicate protore (<6 ft. thick), generally confined to the contact of carbonate protore and the schists, is composed essentially of spessartite with minor graphite, quartz and manganese amphibole.

Nagell (1962, p. 426) suggested that the sediments in the ore horizon were syngenetically deposited in an euxinic environment, as indicated by the highly carbonaceous character of the enclosing rocks. Scarpelli (1973) contended that the sediments were laid down on a subsiding neritic environment, and that the upper part of every cycle is a pelitic zone which was later enriched in organic matter. The manganese carbonates were deposited in an unstable shelf or lagoonal environment.

The manganese carbonate-rich sediments were later metamorphosed. Nagell estimated that the grade of regional metamorphism reached amphibolite facies. Scarpelli concluded that the sediments were metamorphosed three times: an older regional metamorphism of amphibolite facies, followed by thermal metamorphism of hornblende-hornfels facies, finally superimposed by regional metamorphism of amphibolite facies.

The meta-sedimentary manganese protores were later oxidized during weathering to higher oxides (cryptomelane and pyrolusite), which are now exploited as commercial deposits. The reserve of ores in Amapa has been estimated to be more than 30 million tons (Dorr et al., 1973).

The Guiana Shield (South America). The manganese deposits of the Guiana Shield (consisting of several political territories such as Venezuelan Guiana, Guyana, Surinam and French Guiana) have been described by Holtrop (1965) and Choubert (1973). The Brazilian territory of Amapa, already discussed, is also a part of the Guiana Shield.

The lowermost formation of the geosynclinal sequence of the Guiana Shield (>1700 m.y.) consists of thick beds of phyllite, mica schists, black carbonaceous rocks, manganese-silicate protore (gondite) and banded iron-formation. This formation is represented by the Yuruari Series in Venezuela, the Barame Series in Guiana and the Lower Paramaca Series in French Guiana and Surinam. Volcanic rocks (ophiolites) and schists overlie this formation.

In the Saut Ampouman-Mt. Richard area, French Guiana, and at Maripa, Surinam, beds of gondite (spessartite-quartz rock) occur in carbonaceous schist and quartzite. The carbonaceous schists occur mainly at the base of the gondites. Spessartite, braunite, rhodonite, lithiophorite and groutite have been reported from gondite. In the Matthews Ridge—Arakaka area of northwest Guiana, rhodonite-bearing gondite beds are intercalated with quartzite, and quartz-sericite schists with carbonaceous horizons in the Barama Series (≡ Lower Paramaca of French Guiana). Beds of braunite (up to 5 ft. thick) are intercalated with metamorphosed chert. At Matthews Ridge, the manganiferous zone is about 500 ft. thick, running east-west. In all, the manganiferous band is about 20 miles long in this area.

Choubert (1973) concluded that everywhere in the Guiana Shield manganese was deposited as carbonates in a reducing environment (invariably associated with carbonaceous rocks), which, on metamorphism gave rise to the gondites. He considered the ultrabasic rocks, emplaced along deep fractures in pre-geosynclinal basement, to be the source of manganese.

This conclusion on the nature of the primary manganese sediment, however, leaves an element of doubt. Though the abundance of carbonaceous matter testifies to a reducing environment, manganese carbonate is absent in the gondites. Even if all the manganese carbonates in the sediments were used up in the formation of manganese silicates during metamorphism, the existence of braunite bands interstratified with metamorphosed chert cannot be explained. It is very unlikely that braunite would form by metamorphism of manganese carbonate, in preference to rhodonite and tephroite. Therefore, it is difficult to equate these gondites to the metamorphosed manganese-carbonate protores of Serra do Navio, Amapa (Brazil) and Upata (Venezuela). Rather, these rocks are very similar to the gondites of the type area (Sausar Group, India) which formed by the metamorphism of manganese oxide sediments admixed with clay and silica.

The gondites have often been oxidized during weathering, producing ore deposits consisting of pyrolusite, cryptomelane, lithiophorite, groutite, manganite and chalcophanite.

Zaire. The most important ore-bearing horizon in Zaire runs for about 2.5 miles, with an ENE—WSW trend, from Kisenge to Kamata and Kapolo and is part of the regionally metamorphosed rocks of the Lukoshi Complex in the Upper Lulua basin. The Lukoshi Complex (>1845 m.y.) is made up of sericite schist, graphitic schist, quartzite and spessartite-rich rock. At Kisenge, the spessartite-rich rock occurs as lenses interstratified with sericitic and graphitic schists and these are often enriched to oxidic manganese ores by the supergene process. At Kamata, a well-stratified and almost pure manganese-carbonate bed occurs at depth. This bed is made up mostly of rhodochrosite accompanied by organic carbon and garnets. Inclusions of manganese oxides and hydroxides (braunite, bixbyite, manganite) and small flakes of nickel and cobalt oxides sometimes occur in manganese carbonates (Doyen, 1973).

The apparent lithological succession in the Kisenge-Kamata area shows an oxidized ore zone at the top followed downwards by manganese-carbonate formations containing stromatolites (*Collenia*) at different levels, interstratified spessartite-bearing and graphitic schists, manganese-carbonate rock richer in garnets with depth, interlaminated spessartite-bearing and graphitic schists and nearly pure graphite formations (Doyen, 1973).

The ore deposits of this area, but for the supergene concentrations, were formed as sediments and were modified by later metamorphism. Doyen visualized metasomatic (not hydrothermal) transformation of biogenic limestone to form manganese carbonates comparable to the process of dolomitization.

The ores formed by supergene concentrations consist of cryptomelane, pyrolusite and lithiophorite (?) and constitute high-grade commercial deposits (Mn 50%, Fe 4–5%, SiO_2 + Al_2O_3 9–10%, P < 0.18%).

India. Syngenetic nonvolcanogenic manganese deposits associated with terrigenous rocks occur in India in the Precambrian Sausar, Aravalli (≡ Champaner), Gangpur and Khondalite Groups. These deposits have been later metamorphosed to different grades. The distribution of the manganese ore deposits of India is shown in Fig. 9.

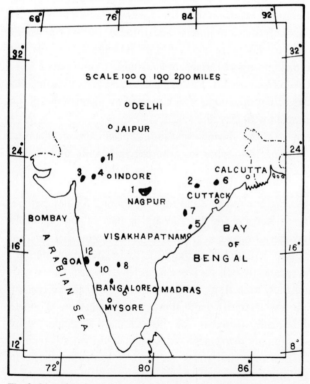

Fig. 9. Map showing manganese ore deposits of India. *1* = Madhya Pradesh - Maharashtra ore belt; *2* = Gangpur-Bamra deposits; *3* = Panch Mahals Dt. deposits; *4* = Jhabua Dt. deposits; *5* = Srikakulam Dt. deposits; *6* = Keonjhar-Bonai Dt. deposits; *7* = Kalahandi-Koraput-Patna deposits; *8* = Sandur deposits; *9* = Shimoga Dt. deposits; *10* = North Kanara deposits; *11* = Banswara deposits; *12* = Goa deposits.

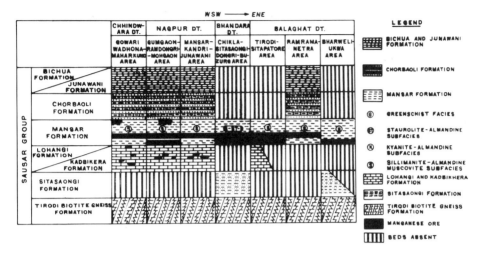

Fig. 10. Diagrammatic representation of the stratigraphic positions of the manganese ore horizons in the Sausar Group of Madhya Pradesh and Maharashtra. (Thickness and lateral extent not to scale.)

The manganese formations of the Sausar Group were first studied by Fermor (1909), followed by others including Straczek et al. (1956), Narayanswami et al. (1963) and Roy (1966). The Sausar Group of rocks occur in Madhya Pradesh and Maharashtra as an arcuate belt, trending NE–SW, E–W, and NW–SE from the eastern to the western part for 130 miles. The stratigraphic succession has been shown in Fig. 10. The lithology suggests that the original sediments represented by orthoquartzite-carbonate formation of platform to miogeosynclinal type, deposited in a marginal basin (Narayanaswami et al., 1963). Interbanded oxide ore and manganese-silicate rock (gondite[1]) are conformably enclosed in and co-folded with pelitic, and psammitic rocks, and were regionally metamorphosed to greenschist and amphibolite facies. The stratigraphically controlled manganese formations occur at the bottom, middle and top of the Mansar Formation, designated as Lohangi zone, Mansar zone and Chorbaoli zone, respectively. Minor occurrences of syngenetic manganese-oxide beds and lenses are found in the calcitic marble and calc-silicate rocks of the Lohangi Formation.

The mineralogy of the manganese orebodies and interbanded gondites of the Mansar Formation is shown in Table III. The ore deposits consist entirely of high-temperature lower oxides and the gondites contain manganese-silicate minerals and some lower oxides.

---

[1] The name gondite was first introduced and defined by Fermor (1909) and later elaborated by Roy and Mitra (1964) and Roy (1966). It is a regionally metamorphosed manganiferous, noncalcareous, pelitic to psammopelitic sediment with spessartite and quartz as essential minerals. Other manganese silicate minerals such as rhodonite, Mn-pyroxenes, Mn-amphiboles, etc., and also lower oxides may be present, but tephroite and manganese carbonates are conspicuously absent. Thus the manganese silicate-carbonate protores, described from many areas including Morro da Mina, Brazil, cannot strictly be equated to gondite.

TABLE III

Mineralogy of some important syngenetic manganese deposits of India

Deposits	Grade of metamorphism	Oxide minerals[1]	Silicate minerals[2]
Shivrajpur, Gujarat (Champaner Group)	greenschist facies	braunite	none
Kajlidongri, Madhya Pradesh (Aravalli Group)	greenschist facies	braunite, bixbyite, hollandite, jacobsite	spessartite, rhodonite, blanfordite, juddite, winchite, manganophyllite, alurgite, quartz
Bharweli-Ukwa, Madhya Pradesh (Sausar Group, Mansar Formation)	greenschist facies	braunite, bixbyite, hollandite	
Chikla-Sitasaongi, Maharashtra (Sausar Group, Mansar Formation)	amphibolite facies	braunite, bixbyite, hollandite, jacobsite, vredenburgite	spessartite, rhodonite, tirodite, alurgite, manganophyllite, apatite, quartz
Ghoriajor, Orissa (Gangpur Group)	amphibolite facies	braunite, bixbyite, hollandite, jacobsite, hausmannite, vredenburgite	spessartite, rhodonite, blanfordite, tirodite, winchite, manganophyllite, apatite, quartz
Tirodi-Sitapatore, Madhya Pradesh (Sausar Group, Mansar Formation)	amphibolite facies	braunite, bixbyite, hollandite, jacobsite, hausmannite, vredenburgite	spessartite, rhodonite, blanfordite, brown manganiferous pyroxene, winchite, juddite, tirodite, alurgite, manganophyllite, piemontite, apatite, quartz
Mohgaon, Maharashtra (Sausar Group, Lohangi Formation)	amphibolite facies	braunite, bixbyite, hollandite	piemontite
Junawani-Junapani, Maharashtra (Sausar Group, Lohangi Formation)	amphibolite facies	braunite, hollandite	piemontite
Kodur-Garbham, Andhra Pradesh (Khondalite Group)	granulite facies	braunite, bixbyite, hollandite, jacobsite, hausmannite, vredenburgite	spessartite, rhodonite, apatite, quartz

TABLE III (continued)

Deposits	Grade of metamorphism	Oxide minerals[1]	Silicate minerals[2]
Jothvad, Gujarat (Champaner Group)	pyroxene-hornfels facies	braunite, bixbyite, hollandite, hausmannite	spessartite-andradite garnet, rhodonite, blanfordite, brown manganiferous pyroxene, winchite, alurgite, manganophyllite, potash felspar, apatite, quartz

[1] These constitute the orebands. Supergene oxides such as pyrolusite and cryptomelane are often detected but not shown here.

[2] These constitute gondite and kodurite (only in the case of the Jothvad deposit). Lower oxides of manganese found in the orebands are also present in minor amounts but not shown here. Brown manganiferous pyroxene and blanfordite are equivalent to manganoan aegirine-augite with varying quanta of aegirine; juddite is equivalent to manganoan magnesio-riebeckite; tirodite is equivalent to manganoan magnesio-richterite and winchite is equivalent to manganoan richterite.

Manganese carbonate is totally absent. Relict banding, both on a macro- and micro-scale, is commonly exhibited by the mineral constituents of the ore and the gondite. Deformation of ore minerals is a common feature in low-grade metamorphism and in the higher grades granoblastic texture is common. A detailed description of the mineralogy and the textural features of the metamorphosed ores and gondites of the Mansar Formation has been given by Mitra (1965), Roy (1966, 1973), Roy and Mitra (1964) and Roy and Purkait (1968). It has been established that the manganese ores and gondites were originally deposited in shallow-water oxygenated conditions as syngenetic pure and admixed (with clay and silica) manganese-oxide sediments, respectively, from a nonvolcanogenic source.

Manganese-oxide orebodies and interbanded gondites are conformably enclosed in pelitic schists of the Ghoriajor Formation of the Precambrian Gangpur Group. The pelitic schists have been regionally metamorphosed to amphibolite facies. The mineralogy of the manganese-oxide ores and the gondite is given in Table III. As in the Sausar Group, the orebodies and the gondite are separate entities originally deposited as pure and admixed manganese-oxide sediments, respectively, in shallow water oxidized conditions, and were later regionally metamorphosed. The mode of occurrence of the manganese formation and the accompanying lithology of the Gangpur Group point to its striking similarity with the Sausar Group and both belong to the Satpura orogenic belt.

Syngenetic manganese formations occur interbedded with terrigenous sediments in the Precambrain Aravalli Group (Jhabua, Madhya Pradesh) and its equivalent, the Champaner Group (Panch Mahals, Gujarat). These manganese formations and the interbedded rocks have later been regionally metamorphosed. Fermor (1909) first described the manganese deposits around Kajlidongri Dt., Jhabua, Madhya Pradesh. Manganese-oxide ores and gondite are interbedded with quartzite and enclosed conformably in phyllite, regionally meta-morphosed to greenschist facies. The mineralogy of the ores and the gondite, studied by Roy (1966), Nayak (1966, 1968) and Lahiri (1971), is stated in Table III. Relict collo-form texture is exhibited by braunite and bixbyite indicating that the minerals have formed by transformation of low-temperature oxides originally deposited as sediments from colloidal gel (Roy, 1966). The nature of the manganese formations and lithological association suggest that these deposits were formed in similar geological conditions as those for the Sausar Group. In fact, Fermor (1950) suggested that these formations might represent the western extension of the rocks of the Sausar Group. Sarkar (1968) also correlated the Aravalli, Sausar and Gangpur Groups in his generalized Precambrian succes-sion of the orogenic-metamorphic cycles of India.

In the Panch Mahals Dt., Gujarat, manganese-oxide orebodies are interbedded and co-folded with quartzite and phyllite (regionally metamorphosed to greenschist facies) of the Champaner (≡ Aravalli) Group in the Shivarajpur–Bamankua area. Braunite is the only metamorphic mineral formed in the ore, and gondite is absent (Table III). A few miles to the east, manganese formations are enclosed in pelitic rocks and calc-granulites in a small deposit near Jothvad. This deposit has been thermally metamorphosed to pyrox-ene-hornfels facies by intrusive porphyritic biotite-granite (Roy, 1966; S.K. Roy, 1967). The mineralogy of the oxidic ores and the interbanded manganese silicate rocks has been given in Table III. Fermor (1909) described kodurite (spessartite-andradite garnet, potash felspar and apatite) form Kodur (Khondalite Group), which he considered to be a hybrid rock formed by the contact-metasomatic effect of a later granitic pluton on manganese formation. The contact-metamorphic manganese-silicate rock of Jothvad strongly resembles Fermor's kodurite.

The meta-sedimentary sequence of the Precambrian Khondalite Group in the Eastern Ghats region of Andhra Pradesh and Orissa, India, contains syngenetic manganese-oxide orebodies and minor manganese-silicate rocks (Roy, 1960, 1966). These rocks have been regionally metamorphosed to granulite facies (garnet–sillimanite–graphite granulite, calc-granulite, garnetiferous quartzite, charnockite). Manganese formations occur in two stratigraphic horizons: one at the contact of calc-granulite and garnet–sillimanite–graphite granulite and sometimes within calc-granulite (deposits of Kodur, Garividi, Duvaam, Sadanandapuram in a belt trending NNW–SSE) and the other within garneti-ferous quartzite (Garbham deposit with E–W trend). Graphite is ubiquitous in the pelitic rocks and has also been reported from ore horizons. The mineralogy of the ores and manganese silicate rocks is shown in Table III.

Manganese deposits associated with carbonate formation

Under this type, the manganese deposits associated with the red carbonate-terrigenous formation and the limestone-dolomite formation of Morocco and the U.S.S.R. will be discussed.

Morocco. In Morocco, bedded manganese-oxide deposits of Mesozoic age occur in the middle of a transgressive sequence of red carbonate-terrigenous sediments and limestone-dolomite formations lying on the stable platform-type basement of different ages. These deposits occur in the close proximity of Precambrian vein-type and volcanogenic-sedimentary orebodies (Fig. 11). The positions of these orebodies in the stratigraphic succession are shown in Table IV.

The red carbonate-terrigenous formation developed at Narguechoum (Permo-Triassic) consists of two or three ore-beds (1–2 ft. thick), separated by red clays and clayey sandstones (Fig. 12). Braunite is the major constituent of the upper bed and it is also disseminated in red sandstone. The lower ore-bed consists of pyrolusite. Barium and lead are consistently high in the ores.

The limestone-dolomite formation of a transgressive sequence at Imini, Tasdremt (Upper Cretaceous), Bou Arfa, Tiaratine and M'Koussa (Lias) contain two or three persistent beds of manganese oxide at the contact of sandstone and dolomite horizons, and also within the dolomites (Fig. 13). Varentsov (1964), following Bouladon and Jouravsky (1952), concluded that the coarsely clastic continental-type red beds were deposited towards the shore, passing into a thicker sequence of dolomites towards the deeper parts of the basin. No evidence of volcanism has been found in the ore-bearing sequence.

The orebodies in the Imini area extend for about 16 miles and merge towards the

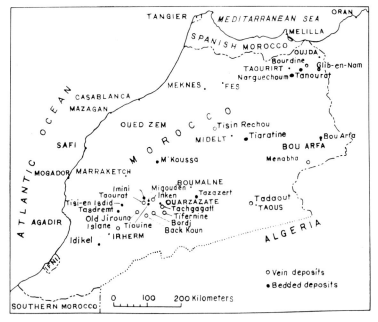

Fig. 11. Map showing the important manganese deposits in Morocco. (After Hewett, 1966; reproduced from *Econ. Geol.,* 61: 438. With permission of *Economic Geology.*)

TABLE IV

Stratigraphic positions of Mesozoic manganese deposits of Morocco (after Bouladon and Jouravsky, 1952; Varentsov, 1964; Pouit, 1964)

		Narguechoum deposit	Imini deposit	Tasdremt deposit	Bou Arfa deposit	M'Koussa deposit	Tiaratine deposit
Upper Cretaceous	Senonian		red sandstones, red gypsiferous clays with bands of argillaceous limestones				
Upper Cretaceous	Cenom.-Turonian		white and pink dolomites; fine-grained, thick-bedded *manganese ore bands* (mostly pyrolusite) occur in sandstone-dolomite contact zone; cherty bands and detrital dolomites are present in the upper part of the series; arkosic sandstones with rhyolite and quartzite pebbles	red arkosic sandstones, conglomerates and more rarely red clays; the rubble contains dolomite and ore; sedimentary breccia with fragments of dolomite and manganese ore; fine-grained dolomites with *manganese ore-beds* and thin streaks of white marl			
Lower Cretaceous	Infra-Cenomanian			red conglomeratic sandstones and clays (thickness increases to the east and decreases to the west); coarse pebbly conglomerate with dolomite fragments			
Upper Jurassic							

Upper Lias	massive sandy dolomite		gray marl with black limestone intercalations; gray marl
Middle Lias	upper detrital series of red clays with gypsum, arkosic sandstones and conglomerates containing granite, pegmatite and mica schist pebbles; to west and east this detrital series becomes thinner and passes into a series of dolomites and limestones	red sandstones, conglomerates and clays	gray and rose limestone with intercalated gray-green marl
Lower Lias	limestone-dolomite rocks and *manganese oxide ore-beds* are associated with calcareous dolomites and red clays; thickness in the west (Hamaraouet) 90 ft and in the east (Ain Beida) up to 750 ft; red clays with lenses of brown dolomitic limestones and arkosic sandstones; conglomerate with granite, pegmatite, schist, andesite and rhyolite pebbles	black limestones; light massive dolomites, red clays; *lenticular ore-bed* (up to 6 ft. thick) consisting of psilomelane and pyrolusite, sandy dolomites stained with iron and manganese oxides; red clays with layers of sandy dolomite	gray and black limestone with siliceous intercalations, organic debris with calcarenite oolites and sedimentary breccia; sedimentary breccia with oolitic cement, *manganese ore deposits of Tiaratine and Youdi*; limestone massif, partly siliceous with organic debris saccharoidal gray and black dolomites

Lower Jurassic

TABLE IV (continued)

	Narguechoum deposit	Imini deposit	Tasdremt deposit	Bou Arfa deposit	M'Koussa deposit	Tiaratine deposit
Permo-Triassic	red and green clays; basalt; red clay; red arkosic sandstone; red clay, clayey sandstone with 2–3 beds of *manganese-oxide ores*; red pebbly arkosic sandstones with fragments of basement rocks	red conglomeratic, arkosic sandstones, with fragments of rhyolite and quartzite			basement rock composed of basalts	basement rocks composed of red clay and basalts
Paleozoic	basement rocks composed of dacites and granodiorites with vein-type manganese segregations		basement rocks composed of slates and dolomites	basement rocks composed of schists and altered igneous rocks		
Precambrian		basement rocks composed of rhyolites, dacites and green slates				

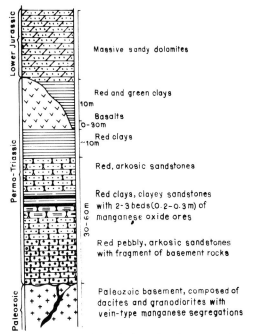

Fig. 12. Section through the red carbonate-terrigenous formation at the Narguechoum deposit, northeast Morocco. (After Varentsov, 1964.)

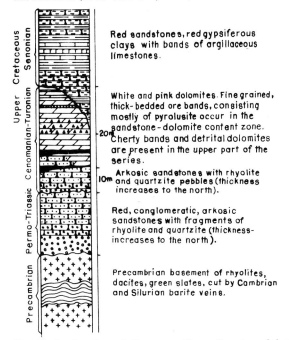

Fig. 13. Section through the manganiferous limestone-dolomite formation (sensu stricto) of the Imini-Tasdremt type of the Imini deposit, Morocco. (After Varentsov, 1964.)

west-southwest with the Tasdremt deposit. There are three ore-beds (pyrolusite, holland-ite, cryptomelane, corondite) at Imini of which the lower two often coalesce into one. The lower ore-beds are separated by a sandy layer to the west and by a dolomite layer towards the east. The ore horizon is invariably underlain by dolomite and is usually overlain by red sandy clay. The deposits of Bou Arfa and M'Koussa are similar to those of the Imini–Tasdremt area but for the more conspicuous continental features in the latter (Varentsov, 1964). The orebodies at both Bou Arfa and M'Koussa are interbedded with dolomites and red clays and consist of pyrolusite and psilomelane. Stratigraphically controlled thick beds and lenses of ores with an E–W trend at Tiaratine (Vincienne, 1956; Pouit, 1964) consist of hausmannite, jacobsite (concretionary), magnetite, hematite, pyrolusite, psilomelane and todorokite. A vertical and horizontal zoning of minerals is characteristic. In vertical section, hematite and magnetite form a bed at the base followed upwards by a hausmannite zone consisting of several layers (<3 ft. thick). A red-clay formation follows the hausmannite zone. The syngenetic horizontal zonation is shown by beds of jacobsite that on one side pass into magnetite and on the other into hausmannite. The hausmannite bed also merges into manganiferous chocolate limestone (3% Mn) (Pouit, 1964). The manganese-ore horizon is confined between beds of limestone.

The manganese in the bedded orebodies was evidently derived by continental erosion during the Liassic and Cretaceous marine transgression and was deposited in an arid zone. The volcanogenic-sedimentary and vein-type manganese deposits of Precambrian (Tiouine, Idikel) and Carboniferous (Glib en Nam) age occurring in the near proximity (Fig. 11), apparently served as the principal source for manganese. Vincienne (1956) suggested that the ore-bearing sequence was probably deposited in small basins and lagoons in the coastal parts at shallow depth, with oscillation of the sea level and movement of the sea floor.

The presence of braunite in the unmetamorphosed nonvolcanogenic-sedimentary ore deposits and red sandstones of Narguechoum and those of hausmannite and jacobsite in Tiaratine, cannot be explained by precipitation from surface water (Roy, 1968). It may be possible that a part of the manganese ores was deposited as clastic sediments derived from ore deposits of an earlier age as hinted by Pouit (1964).

U.S.S.R. The Ulu-Telyak deposit in the western Urals, U.S.S.R., has been equated to the Moroccan-type deposits associated with limestone-dolomite formations by Varentsov (1964) in view of its occurrence on a platform-type basement, its lithological association and the arid condition of formation. This Upper Permian ore horizon (Ufimian Stage) is represented by almost horizontal manganiferous limestone beds (thickness averaging 15 ft.) overlying sandstones and clay horizons, which in their turn, lie on the stable basement of limestones and gypsiferous rocks. The primary carbonates have been oxidized and enriched to higher-oxide ores.

The manganiferous formation of the Lower Cambrian Usinsk suite, at Kuznetsk Altau, U.S.S.R., occurs in a eugeosynclinal limestone-dolomite sequence with volcanic rocks (andesite, tuff) and differs from the Moroccan deposits which are platform-type. Red tuffaceous sandstones occur at the base of the suite at places. The ore-member (manganese carbonate) lies conformably on dolomitic limestone and consists of three lenticular deposits trending NNW—SSE for about 3 miles. The northern deposit gradually thins out towards the south. In the central zone manganese carbonate ores and black manganiferous slates are interlayered; further south they give way to manganiferous limestone and pyritiferous black shale. The southern orebody consists of oolitic ferroan rhodochrosite and manganoan calcite lenses, alternating with dark manganiferous limestone and sericitic slates (Varentsov, 1964). Carbonaceous matter, converted to anthracite-graphite, is present in these ores, associated with pyrite and pyrrhotite.

Varentsov concluded that in spite of the association of andesitic lava and tuff in an eugeosynclinal sequence, the manganese orebodies themselves formed as nonvolcanogenic sediments because they are separated from the volcanic rocks by a limestone-dolomite formation barren of manganese. The carbonate ore formation, associated with carbonaceous sediments and iron sulfides, apparently formed in a reducing environment. Sokolova (1970), however, states that the source of manganese for the Usinsk deposit has not been unequivocally established and thinks that the deposit may be volcanogenic.

Manganese deposits associated with iron-formation[1]

Several major nonvolcanogenic manganese deposits are intimately associated with iron-formation in both platform areas and in geosynclines. Such deposits in Brazil, the Union of South Africa, Southwest Africa and the U.S.S.R. will be discussed here.

Brazil. Stratigraphically-controlled beds and lenses of manganese-oxide ores (<10 ft. thick and several hundred feet in length) are included in the metamorphosed iron-formation—dolomite sequence of the miogeosynclinal or platform-type Minas Series (2200—1350 m.y) in Minas Gerais. In places, the manganese-oxide beds are intercalated with the iron-formation in the total absence of dolomite (e.g., Natividade deposit). Beds and lenses of manganese ore also occur conformably at the contact of the iron-formation and dolomite where these are interfingered, indicating a change of chemical environment (e.g., Miguel Burnier). A reserve of about 5 million tons of ore (30—48% Mn) has been estimated (Dorr, 1973).

Manganese-ore beds associated with iron-formation occur as lenses in meta-sedimentary rocks in the Urandi Dt., Bahia; these have been tentatively correlated with the Minas Series. According to Dorr no contemporary volcanic activity has been found in this region and the sedimentary sequence is probably of miogeosynclinal or platform type. Rebeiro

---

[1] The term "iron-formation" represents here the rock composed of intimately banded iron minerals and silica as developed in Lake Superior iron deposits.

(1973) reported bixbyite, jacobsite, hausmannite, manganite, cryptomelane, todorokite and pyrolusite from the Barnabé mine and mangano-dolomite, spessartite, rhodonite, hollandite, cryptomelane, pyrolusite, todorokite and ramsdellite from the Barreiro dos Campos mine of the Urandi Dt.

Dorr et al. (1956) concluded that in the Minas Series, the transitional sedimentary environment between deposition of iron-formation and dolomite was particularly favourable for the deposition of manganese, either as manganoan dolomite or calcite or "more commonly as primary manganese oxide mixed with iron oxide". Dorr (1973) also concluded that the manganese orebodies of the Minas Series are supergene, derived by weathering of either manganoan dolomite or manganese-bearing iron-formation. He suggested that the iron and manganese in the sediments were probably derived from the deposits in the older Rio das Velhas Series.

While widespread weathering in the rocks of the Minas Series is characteristic, it is difficult to overlook the strong evidence of stratigraphic control of the manganese orebodies and to favour a supergene origin of the ores. The manganese content of dolomites varies between only 0.5–4% Mn and the iron-formations contain much less. Therefore, the supergene concentration of manganese from these rocks to form sizeable manganese oxide beds, would have destroyed the bedded character of the iron-formations and dolomites substantially, with a considerable change in volume in the latter case. The conformable bedded nature of the iron and manganese formations, therefore, does not apparently support a supergene derivation of the manganese ores, and points to syngenetic deposition.

The interbedded nature of manganese ores with iron-formation is best demonstrated in the platform-type Jacadigo Series (Cambrian–Ordovician) in Mato Grosso, Brazil (Dorr, 1973). This series is unmetamorphosed and relatively unweathered. At the base, coarse arkosic sandstone and conglomerate occur, overlain by massive bedded jasper. The jasper beds are overlain by the Band'–Alta Formation, composed of banded hematite-jasper containing conformable lenses and beds of manganese oxide which are invariably associated with detrital rocks (sandstone and conglomerate). Two main beds of manganese oxide (cryptomelane) occur at Morro do Urucum, the principal deposit in the Jacadigo Series, in the lower parts of the Band'–Alta Formation (Dorr, 1973). The lower bed is most widespread with an average thickness of about 6 ft. The upper bed is about half as thick on the average. The manganese-oxide ores contain 39.4–50.7% Mn and 8–16% Fe. Similar manganese orebodies are also found at Serra do Rebicho and other areas.

Dorr (1973) concluded from stratigraphic evidence that the manganese-oxide beds were deposited as chemical sediments from a terrigenous source and their deposition with clastic rocks within the iron-formation suggests an abrupt change in sedimentary environment. The very high state of oxidation in the manganese ores ($MnO_2/MnO = 23.7$) indicates a strongly oxidizing depositional condition. Dorr believed that the iron-formation was deposited in an estuarine or lacustrine basin in an arid climate in the absence of detritals. Sharp but temporary climatic changes might have induced local incursions of detritals and change in the chemical environment, facilitating deposition of manganese oxides.

Union of South Africa. The manganese deposits of the Postmasburg-Kalahari field, forming a N–S trending, 180 miles long belt, occur in the north-central part of the Union of South Africa. This field lies near the eastern edge of a mobile belt, extending from the Orange River northwards into the Kalahari field. In the latest stratigraphic succession the oldest Transvaal System (Precambrian) has been divided into a Lower Dolomite Series and an Upper Pretoria Series (P.R. de Villiers, 1970). In the Dolomite Series, the Lower Dolomite Stage (dolomite, chert, breccia) is overlain by the Banded Ironstone Stage (iron-formation and jasper). The Timeball Hill Stage (quartzite, shale, conglomerate, breccia) forms the base of the Pretoria Series, and is overlain by the Daspoort Stage consisting of tillite, shale, quartzite and limestone in its lower part and Ongeluk andesitic lava, tuff, chert, quartzite, shale, limestone and iron-formation in the upper part. The Daspoort Stage is overlain by the Smelterskop or Hartley Hill Stage within the Pretoria Series. The Pretoria Series is overlain by the Waterberg System, followed by the Karroo System and Tertiary to Recent deposits. During the Carboniferous the whole area was glaciated.

The manganese orebodies are confined to four stratigraphic horizons in the Transvaal System, viz., the Dolomite Stage and the Timeball Hill Stage (Postmasburg–Aucampsrust area), in the shaly facies of the lower part of the Daspoort Stage and interlayered with iron-formation of the Upper Daspoort Stage (Black Rock area, Kalahari field). The manganese ore deposits of the Kalahari field (Kuruman Dt.) and the Postmasburg–Aucampsrust areas are particularly important. P.R. de Villiers (1970) estimated a total original reserve of 9,000 million tons of manganese ores in the Kalahari field of which about half has been eroded away.

The deposits of the Kalahari field are subdivided into eastern, central and western belts, the important aspects of which have been summarized in Table V. Earlier workers (John de Villiers, 1956, 1960; Boardman, 1961, etc.) recognized that the manganese ore-beds are conformable to the enclosing iron-formation but, at the same time, concluded that these were formed by replacement of the host rock by circulating manganiferous ground water. P.R. de Villiers (1970), however, advocated a sedimentary origin for the manganese orebodies from a nonvolcanogenic source, and his views were later confirmed by Beukes (1973). The latter pointed out that a complete separation of iron and manganese took place during the deposition of the orebodies at Hotazel, and that a facies change of both manganese and iron ores is evident in this area (Fig. 14).

The mineralogical composition of the orebodies cannot, however, be explained by either supergene deposition from circulating meteoric water or simply by a syngenetic sedimentary origin. Braunite, which is the chief component of the ore, and bixbyite do not form by precipitation from surface water (Roy, 1968). The Fe_2O_3 content of bixbyite (25.6%, Black Rock deposit) suggests its formation within the pressure-temperature

TABLE V

Mode of occurrence and mineralogy of the manganese orebodies of the Kalahari field

---

Eastern Belt (Hotazel, Langdon and Devon mines)

Mode of occurrence

Hotazel mine: manganese orebodies confined within iron-formation of Daspoort Stage; three orebodies occur in different levels interlayered conformably with iron-formation; a transition rock composed of ferruginous, manganiferous and siliceous material occurs at the base of the lower and middle
orebodies

Devon mine: an extension of the lower orebody is present and the same orebody continues in the
Langdon mine to the east

Mineralogy of manganese ores

Hotazel mine: braunite, bixbyite, hausmannite, cryptomelane, pyrolusite, todorokite, chalcophanite,
lithiophorite, manganite, nsutite, goethite and hematite

Devon and Langdon mines: braunite, hausmannite, jacobsite (46.41% Fe_2O_3), cryptomelane, pyrolusite, todorokite, goethite and hematite; no carbonates reported from this belt

---

Central Belt (Mamatwan, Adams and Smartt mines)

Mode of occurrence

Mamatwan mine: manganese ore horizons present in a basin; only one orebody present in the mine
overlying the iron-formation of the Daspoort Stage; the same orebody (40–50 ft. thick) continues
westward in Adams mine overlain by Kalahari limestones. Manganese orebody in the Smartt mine
(40–50 ft. thick) confined within iron-formation with conformable attitudes.

Mineralogy of manganese ores

Mamatwan, Adams and Smartt mines: ores are mainly braunite-rich though most of the minerals found
in Hotazel mine are present in minor proportion; this belt contains many carbonates as oolites, len-
ticles and veins

Western Belt (Black Rock Mine)

Mode of occurrence

Black rock: three persistent beds of manganese ore confined within iron-formation of Daspoort Stage;
the lower and middle orebodies are both 20 ft. thick; the upper orebody is lenticular and impersis-
tent; it clearly transgresses across the lamination of iron-formation; towards east of Black Rock, four
persistent bands of manganese ore and a conformable sheet of felsitic igneous rock confined to different levels of a 350-ft. sequence of iron-formation of the Daspoort Stage; the topmost manganese ore-
bed (No.1) is about 20 ft. thick with 40–80% Mn and 10–20% Fe; No.2 ore-bed (4 ft. thick) has
equal proportions of Mn and Fe; No.3 ore-bed varies on thickness from 45 to 90 ft. (Mn– 40%, Fe–
15–20%); lowermost orebody (No.4), variable in thickness and highly ferruginous, occurs near the
base of the iron-formation succession

Mineralogy of manganese ores

Black Rock mine: mainly braunite-rich; two kinds of braunite, one the ordinary braunite, the other
(braunite II), a ferrain, low-silica braunite (Fe_2O_3 – 16.3%, SiO_2 – 4.4%); bixbyite (Fe_2O_3 – 25.6%),
hausmannite, andradite, cryptomelane, pyrolusite, lithophorite, goethite and hematite

---

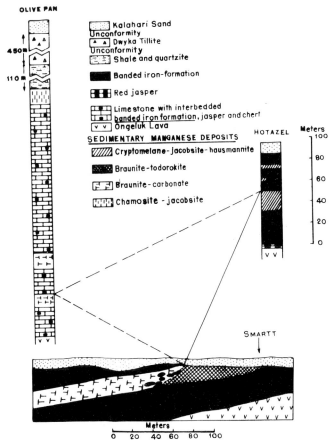

OLIVE PAN

Kalahari Sand
Unconformity
Dwyka Tillite
Unconformity
Shale and quartzite

Banded iron-formation

Red jasper

Limestone with interbedded
banded iron formation, jasper and chert
Ongeluk Lava

SEDIMENTARY MANGANESE DEPOSITS

Cryptomelane-jacobsite-hausmannite

Braunite-todorokite

Braunite-carbonate

Chamosite - jacobsite

HOTAZEL

SMARTT

Meters
0   20   40   60   80   100

Fig. 14. Stratigraphy of the Hotazel Formation in the Kalahari manganese field, South Africa. Note facies change from Hotazel towards Olive Pan. Compiled from De Villiers, 1971. (After Beukes, 1973; reproduced from *Econ. Geol.*, 68: 994. With permission of *Econ. Geol.*)

regime of a metamorphic environment (Mason, 1944). The presence of hausmannite, jacobsite (46.41% Fe_2O_3) and andradite also indicates an elevated temperature of formation.

It is, therefore, evident that a syngenetic sedimentary origin of the manganese orebodies once affirmed, carries a corrolary that the ores were also subjected to metamorphism. Regional metamorphism in the Daspoort Stage has been ruled out by earlier workers. P.R. de Villiers (1970) advocated thermal metamorphism by magmatic rocks hidden at depth, though the evidence is scanty.

The manganese deposits of the Postmasburg–Aucampsrust area, though forming part of the Postmasburg–Kalahari belt, show a different geologic setting. In the eastern belt, in the Klipfontein Hills, commercially best-quality manganese ores are associated with siliceous breccia in direct contact with the underlying dolomites. The larger orebodies occur in favourable cul-de-sac structures (paleokarst) in dolomite. In the western belt, the orebodies occur in central Gamagararand in the ferruginous shales of the Timeball Hill Stage, again in contact with the underlying dolomites. Karst topography in the dolomite, later filled up by manganese ore, is also characteristic. At Japies Rust, however, the orebody is located in the middle of the shale succession with conformable attitudes.

Thus, the deposits in the Postmasburg—Aucampsrust area are associated with different rocks (dolomite, silicified breccia, shale) and are not directly related to iron-formation. But in view of their controversial origin and varying mode of occurrence, they also cannot be related to any other unique lithological association. They are only tentatively included here as part of a belt where manganese ore is clearly associated with iron-formation (Kalahari area). The following minerals are present in these ores: braunite, bixbyite (Fe_2O_3 19.3—21.9%), hausmannite, jacobsite, pyrolusite, psilomelane, chalcophanite, lithiophorite, manganite, hematite, barite, diaspore, ephesite, amosite, acmite, albite, apatite, gamagarite, quartz, chalcedony, kaolinite.

The genesis of these deposits remains a problem. Most workers believe that circulating manganiferous ground water, which dissolved manganese from the underlying dolomites (MnO up to 3.03%), deposited the ore by replacement. Borchert (1970) equated these deposits to the Lindener Mark ore type and considered that manganese went into solution in a reducing condition in an upper ground-water body rich in organic matter, only to be precipitated as Mn^{4+} compound by an oxygenated lower ground-water body in a milieu of karst hydrography. But the above concept, unless the ores were later modified, is in conflict with the mineral constituents (braunite, bixbyite, jacobsite, hausmannite) which represent a high-temperature suite. A hydrothermal source for the orebodies (J.E. de Villiers, 1944) explains the presence of these minerals and of Li, Na, F and B, but this was not accepted by other workers. The suggestion of Schneiderhöhn (1931) that the ores were sedimentary-metamorphic also did not find support in the absence of other evidences of metamorphism.

John de Villiers (1960) visualized that a part of the manganese ores, formed by weathering, was subjected to "prolonged load metamorphism during the deep burial of the area under the Karroo rocks". These ores were thus recrystallized to braunite, bixbyite, jacobsite and hausmannite. Ores composed of psilomelane and pyrolusite were formed by weathering in post-Karroo times. P.R. de Villiers (1970) contended that the manganese ore were formed first by replacement and were later modified by thermal metamorphism. But the inadequacy of evidence of metamorphism was pointed out by different workers including John de Villiers (1960) himself to repudiate the sedimentary-metamorphic origin advocated much earlier by Schneiderhöhn (1931). Thus, the origin and subsequent modifications of the manganese-ore deposits of the Postmasburg—Aucampsrust area, have not yet been unequivocally established.

Southwest Africa. The manganese-ore deposits of Otjosondu occur at the junction of the three districts of Okahandja, Otjiwarongo and Gobabis in Southwest Africa. Bedded and lenticular manganese orebodies occur conformably at the bottom, middle and top of metamorphosed iron-formation (Itabirite schist zone: quartz-biotite-specularite and hornblende-specularite schists) of the Precambrian Damara System ($\equiv$ Transvaal System, Union of South Africa; Roper, 1956). A porphyritic biotite-granite (Salem Granite) of post-Damara age has invaded the manganese orebodies at several places. The ore-beds and lenses range in thickness from 6 to 22 ft. with an average of 15 ft.

J.E. de Villiers (1951) described the following minerals from the Otjosondu deposit: braunite (ferrian; Fe_2O_3 23.59%), jacobsite, hausmannite, vredenburgite, bixbyite, hollandite, pyrolusite, psilomelane, hematite, garnet, rhodonite, diopside-acmite, celsian, hyalophane, barite and quartz. The texture of the ore is generally granoblastic.

Roper (1956) concluded that the manganese orebodies of Otjosondu were deposited as syngenetic sediments. The ore minerals were formed by thermal metamorphism of originally layered sediments and a minimum temperature of $500°C$ was attained during metamorphism (J.E. de Villiers, 1951). The absence ,of any volcanic rock in the Damara System rules out any possibility of a volcanogenic source of the manganese.

U.S.S.R. Manganese deposits associated with iron-formation in a miogeosynclinal environment have been described from Maliy Khingan in the U.S.S.R. In south Khingan a bed of manganese ore (about 25 ft. thick) conformably underlies the iron-formation (60–75 ft. thick) in the middle part of the Lower Cambrian ore-bearing series. Different mineralogical facies are encountered in the manganese-ore bed, e.g. oxide-facies (braunite, hausmannite-braunite, braunite-hematite), oxide-carbonate facies (hausmannite-rhodochrosite) and carbonate facies (siliceous rhodochrosite). Manganese silicates such as rhodonite, bustamite and tephroite are also found. A layer of braunite-hematite ore is present as a transition stage between manganese and iron ores. The transition of the various manganese-ore types is gradual. Carbonaceous limestone and dolomite and argillaceous rocks overlie the ore-bearing series. All these sedimentary formations were later intruded by biotite-granite and were subjected to regional and contact metamorphism.

Chebotarev (1960) concluded that the manganese ores and iron-formation are of nonvolcanogenic-sedimentary origin; they formed near the coast in shallow-water closed bays, as indicated by the littoral nature of the enclosing rocks, the presence of intraformational breccia and evidence of temporary dessication (mud cracks in ore horizon). The ore minerals indicate recrystallization of the sedimentary manganese oxides, hydroxides and carbonates during subsequent metamorphism. The Maliy Khingan area has a total reserve of 13 million tons of manganese ores.

Fossil manganese and iron-manganese nodules

Fossil manganese and iron-manganese nodules similar to those of Recent origin found in deep-sea, shallow-marine and lake deposits, have been described from ancient rocks of different ages. The first reference to fossil nodules, from Tertiary Barbados Earth, was made by Jukes-Browne and Harrison (1892); this was followed closely by Sokolow (1901) describing Tertiary deposits of the U.S.S.R. Jenkyns (1975) classified fossil Mn and Fe-Mn nodules into those occurring in rocks deposited in deep-sea, continental-margin seamount, and littoral environments.

The fossil nodules of deep-sea environment have been described from Timor, Indonesia and other areas. Molengraaf (1916, 1922) and Audley-Charles (1965, 1972) described fossil Fe-Mn nodules embedded in Cretaceous red clay with shark's teeth and fish remains in western Timor, and found that their chemistry, physical characters and lithologic associations suggest deposition on a deep-sea floor. These nodules, containing clay, chalcedonic silica and complex manganese and iron minerals, have a Mn/Fe ratio of slightly less than 1 and are rich in nickel and cobalt. In eastern Timor, both Mn-rich (pyrolusite; Mn/Fe = 745) and Fe-rich (goethite, pyrolusite, cryptomelane; Mn/Fe = 0.4) nodules occur in certain horizons of the Wai Bua Formation, consisting of radiolarian cherts interbedded with ferromanganese shales. The nodules are considered to be nonvolcanogenic-sedimentary in origin and modified by diagenesis (Audley-Charles, 1965). The manganese nodules of eastern Timor have a composition intermediate between those of modern deep-sea and shallow-marine nodules and a neritopelagic or bathypelagic environment of deposition has been suggested. The pelagic limestones of the Seical Formation (Middle Eocene, eastern Timor), containing discrete laminations of pyrolusite and ferric oxide and without any evidence of volcanogenic derivation, resemble calcareous and manganiferous mud described from the Eastern Pacific Rise (Audley-Charles, 1965).

Jenkyns (1975) described deep-sea fossil Fe—Mn nodules from other localities such as the Numidian flysch of north-central Sicily (Oligocene—Miocene) and northern Borneo (Paleocene—Eocene). He also included the Eocene manganese deposits of the Olympic Peninsula, Washington State, U.S.A. (see later in this chapter) following the observations of Sorem and Gunn (1967) and R.E. Garrison (1973, cited by Jenkyns, 1975). The latter considered that a part of the Eocene sequence of the Olympic Peninsula perhaps represents oceanic crust with the sediment cover that has been pushed on the continental margin.

Jenkyns (1975) subdivided fossil deep-sea nodules into two types: (a) those accumulated on the ocean floor, and (b) those found on the continental margin. The ocean-floor fossil nodules (western Timor) show a Mn/Fe ratio of slightly less than unity, with a high content of silica and alumina and relatively abundant trace elements. These are comparable with the composition of some Recent nodules from red and brown clays in the Atlantic, Pacific and Indian oceans. The continental-margin fossil nodules are generally iron-poor, though those described from the Cretaceous of eastern Timor and the Oligocene—Miocene from north-central Sicily range in composition from Mn-rich to Fe-rich. Such nodules are usually not enriched in trace elements (Cretaceous Wai Bua nodules, eastern Timor).

Fossil manganese nodules of continental-margin seamount environment (Jenkyns, 1975), have been described from the Jurassic of the Alps, Sicily, the Carpatho-Balkan

Fig. 15. Discrete, concentrically laminated fossil ferromanganese nodules concentrated in one main horizon of Jurassic pelagic limestone. Vertical section. Rocca Argentina, western Sicily. Length of hammer handle = 36 cm. (After Jenkyns, 1973; *Eclogae Geol. Helv.*, 63, p. 745.)

chain, the Pyrénées (Devonian), the Montagne Noire in southern France and the Rhein-isches Schiefergebirge, West Germany (Upper Devonian).

The Middle-Jurassic condensed pelagic limestones of western Sicily contain fossil ferro-manganese nodules (Fig. 15), pancakes (Fig. 16), crusts and pavements (Jenkyns, 1967, 1970). Distinct populations of nodules, with particular size ranges, are noted from each of the ferromanganese horizons which are generally separated by barren sediments, simi-lar to the Recent nodule deposits of Blake Plateau (Mero, 1965; Pratt and McFarlin, 1966). Though most of the nodules have grown either around limestone intraclasts or ammonite shells, some of them do not have any nucleus. The nodules are constituted of goethite, hematite and todorokite. Hematite is a diagenetic product. The internal struc-ture of the nodules shows ferromanganese segregations set in a calcite matrix in contrast to the aluminosilicate matrix described from some Recent nodules (Cronan and Tooms, 1968). The chemical composition of these fossil nodules varies widely. The Fe/Mn ratio is extremely variable and Fe- and Mn-rich nodules and crusts are often juxtaposed similar to the Recent deposits of the East Pacific Rise (Bonatti and Joensuu, 1968). Nodules with very high iron or manganese contents contain relatively smaller amounts of minor ele-ments. The common, but not universal, inter-element relationships are Co, Ni and Ba with Mn and Ti with Fe. Submarine volcanism has been considered by Jenkyns (1970) to be

Fig. 16. Close-up view of fused fossil pancakes of ferromanganese from the Jurassic Monto Kumeta crust, western Sicily. (After Jenkyns, 1973; *Eclogae Geol. Helv.*, 63, p. 747.)

the principal source of manganese, iron and other elements in these fossil nodules together with contributions from continental run-off.

Deposits similar to those found in western Sicily are characteristic of the whole Tethyan region. The Tethyan ferromanganese crusts and nodules were possibly formed on ancient nonvolcanic limestone seamounts probably reaching within about 300 ft. of the surface (photic zone) as indicated by the association of algal stromatolites (Jenkyns, 1970).

Heim (1924) described fossil nodules in the Alps (Tethyan region) from the Lower Jurassic limestones of Gosau, Austria, and compared them with Recent deep-sea nodules. Garrison and Fischer (1969) described such nodules and crusts from a Jurassic sequence in the Adnet Beds in Austria in the Northern Limestone Alps. The Adnet Beds are characterized by red limestones that partly correspond to the present-day "hard grounds" (cf. near Barbados; Fischer and Garrison, 1967). The uppermost part of the Adnet Beds consists of manganiferous, coccolith-rich limestones comparable to present-day globigerinid ooze. It is overlain by Ruhpolding radiolarites (similar to present-day radiolarian ooze), which are also locally capped by red manganiferous coccolith-rich limestones.

The manganese oxides occur as concentrically laminated nodules and crusts on bedding planes and fossils in hard, dark red-brown limestone. The rocks show a skeletal-micritic composition, with fragments of echinoderms, pelecypods, ostracods and ammonite aptychi (but no ammonite shells) and abundant coccoliths (*Thoracosphaera*) in the micritic matrix.

Garrison and Fischer (1969) believed that most of the Adnet Beds were probably laid down in the bathyal zone with a very slow rate of sedimentation. The radiolarites were derived from sediments resembling modern radiolarian deep-sea oozes and their origin could not be related to volcanism as ophiolites were not known from the Northern Limestone Alps.

Jurgan (1969) compared Recent ferromanganese concretions from the Baltic, Atlantic and Pacific with those from the Jurassic of the Berchtesgadener Alps, Germany, and considered that the latter were deposited in an oxidizing condition with a low sedimentation rate. Fabricius (1968) has described fossil manganese nodules from the Sonnwend Mountains, Tirol, Austria and compared some of the structural features of these nodules with those of modern concretions.

Germann (1971, 1972, 1973) described fossil manganese nodules and crusts from the condensed red limestones, marls, radiolarian cherts and shales (manganese shales) from the Jurassic Northern Limestone Alps. The nodules and crusts contain abundant calcite and lesser amounts of goethite, hematite and pyrolusite, and, therefore, differ from most of the Recent deep-sea deposits which have a low carbonate content. The abundance of Fe, Mn, Ni, Co, Cu, Cr, Zn, and Pb in these nodules, though relatively similar, is about half as high compared to Recent deposits. The nodules were formed in shallow water accompanied by minimal clastic sedimentation, comparable to the manganese-paved Blake Plateau or some Pacific seamounts.

Strata-bound manganese ores occur in thinly laminated Upper Liassic marls and shales (manganese shales) dispersed over 150 miles from the Allgäu and Lechtal Alps to the Berchtesgaden and Salzburg region in the Northern Limestone Alps (Germann, 1973). These ores contain calcian rhodochrosite (and oligonite) and braunite as primary precipitate, together with sedimentary iron carbonate, silicate (chamosite) and pyrite. Pyrolusite and todorokite are present as supergene minerals. These ores are considered to be volcanogenic (Germann, 1973) as opposed to the common belief of absence of volcanism in the Northern Limestone Alps.

Fossil manganese nodules of a littoral evironment have been described by Gulbrandsen and Reeser (1969) from Permian argillaceous sandstones (Park City Formation) underlying phosphatic shale beds of Montana, U.S.A. The nodules, composed of chalcophanite and todorokite, have a very high Mn/Fe ratio (34 and 15 in two samples), and a high content of Ni, Co and Zn. Such Mn-rich and Fe-poor Recent nodules have been described from Loch Fyne and the Jervis Inlet (British Columbia). The sediments of the Park City Formation and the associated fauna (brachiopods, bryozoans, crinoids, bivalves and gastropods) were possibly deposited at a depth of less than 50 m.

The sedimentary nodular manganese-oxide deposits of Nikopol, U.S.S.R. (Oligocene; already described in this text), Timna Dome, Israel (Silurian) and Botswana (Precambrian) have been considered to be fossil nodules (Sokolow, 1901; Litherland and Malan, 1973; Jenkyns, 1975). The extensive manganese-oxide deposits of Groote Eyelandt, Australia (Lower Cretaceous; Dorr, 1968) may also be considered as fossil nodules. These are all shallow-water deposits.

Manganese deposits (pyrolusite, psilomelane, manganite) of southeastern Utah occur as nodules in clay beds of the Morrison and Summerville Formations of Jurassic age. Baker et al. (1952) considered these nodules as ancient analogues of the Recent deposits in fresh-water lakes.

Sedimentary manganese ores and stromatolites

Sedimentary manganese deposits are associated with stromatolites in a few areas. Doyen (1973) described stromatolites (*Collenia*) from a manganese carbonate ore sequence at different stratigraphic levels at Kamata in the Precambrian (>1845 m.y.) Kisenge-Kamata manganese belt of Zaire. In Maton and Bargaon, near Udaipur, Rajasthan, India, manganese oxides are related to Precambrian phosphorite beds associated intimately with stromatolites (A.B. Roy, personal communication). Jenkyns (1970) reported the association of fossil Mn- and Fe—Mn nodules with algal stromatolites in Jurassic red limestones of the Tethyan region.

A few other workers have described stromatolitic features in both ancient and Recent manganese ores. Aumento et al. (1968) described the Recent ferromanganese pavement from the San Pablo seamount in the western Atlantic from a depth of 1800 m in which Hofmann (1969) referred to the stratiform, turbinate and branching columnar forms as resembling those of stromatolites. He also mentioned the bathymetric problem involved. Litherland and Malan (1973) described manganese ores with stromatolitic structures from ore stock piles of the Kgwakwe Hill manganese mine in southeastern Botswana, South Africa. The manganese deposits are of Precambrian age (ca. 2000 m.y.), but the ore types described here have not been detected in situ. The ores exhibiting stromatolitic structures (columnar growth of subparallel tubes with digitations and ramifications and also branched, cabbage-shaped isolated forms) contain 70–95% MnO_2. Litherland and Malan called these structures manganiferous stromatolites that might have either been formed directly or as replacement of carbonates.

Monty (1973) considered the Recent manganese nodules to be oceanic stromatolites. He described nodules from Blake Plateau (depth 500–1100 m) which exhibit very fine and regular lamellar structure showing characteristic stromatolitic undulations and which have developed turbinate or columnar structures. He concluded that these structures have been formed by filament-type bacteria concentrating Fe- and Mn-oxides. Monty also concluded that different types of bacteria give rise to nodules of variable composition. He also stressed that in most cases the distinction between bacterial stromatolite and cyanophytic stromatolite is difficult and stromatolitic structures are not always related to the photic zones. Walter et al. (1972) described Recent siliceous stromatolites formed by bacteria.

Jenkyns (1975) referred to the encrusting foraminifers (*Nubecularia* and *Tolypammina*), boring algae, fungi, bryozoa and serpulids that occur in shallow-seamount Mn- and Fe—Mn fossil nodules. He also quoted Krumbein (1971) who showed that the precipitation of manganese in concentric rings may be induced by fungi.

VOLCANOGENIC-SEDIMENTARY MANGANESE DEPOSITS

Volcanogenic-sedimentary manganese deposits occur in different geological ages (Table I). In high temperature, acidic magmatic gases dissolved in sea water leach out manganese and iron from the extruding hyaloclastites. The acidified sea water with manganese and iron in solution, on being constantly mixed with fresh sea water, is gradually made alkaline again and the supply of dissolved oxygen induces precipitation of iron at a lower Eh and pH in preference to manganese which is deposited at a higher Eh and pH. If the rate of basification and oxidation of the solution is fast, manganese and iron may precipitate together. During the entire process silica is leached from hot lava in considerable quantity. The resultant deposits may form at the site of volcanism or close to it (Krauskopf, 1956; Bonatti, 1967).

The active Banu-Wuhu submarine volcano in Indonesia (Zelenov, 1965) and the Mendeleev volcano, Kunashir Island, U.S.S.R. (Zotov, 1968) show concentrations of manganese oxides. Manganese compounds as exhalative products have also been reported from Vesuvius and Etna, from the Valley of Ten Thousand Smokes in Alaska and from volcanoes in Japan.

The general features of volcanogenic-sedimentary manganese deposits as described by different workers, including Strakhov (1967), Suslov (1970), Sapozhnikov (1970) and Sokolova (1970), are summarized on next page.

(1) The extrusion of volcanic rocks giving rise to these ore deposits generally took place in geosynclines during the initial stages of their development.

(2) These deposits are generally associated with submarine volcanism of both acidic and basic types. Shatskiy (1954) accordingly subdivided the deposits into a greenstone-siliceous group (associated with spilite, diabase, etc.) and a porphyry-siliceous group (associated with quartz-porphyry, rhyolite, dacite, andesite, etc.). The ore deposits may occur within lavas and tuffs or in jaspers, siliceous-shale and siliceous-carbonate rocks associated with the volcanic series. All these associations may grade into each other. Accordingly, Shatskiy classified the greenstone-siliceous group into greenstone formation, jasperoid formation, siliceous-shaly formation and remote siliceous formation, and the porphyry-siliceous group into porphyritic formation, siliceous-shaly formation and remote siliceous formation. The remote siliceous formation, supposed to represent volcano-genic deposits in sedimentary rocks far removed from the volcanic foci, more than often without any characteristic feature confirming such derivation, is of doubtful standing (Strakhov and Shterenberg, 1966; Roy, 1969; Suslov, 1970). Sokolova (1970) divided volcanogenic-sedimentary manganese deposits into volcanogenic-carbonate and volcano-genic-terrigenous formations, depending upon the areas of carbonate or terrigenous deposition where the volcanism occurred.

(3) These deposits may form at various distances from the volcanic foci. Conditions for formation of rich ore deposits are more suitable in depositional sites away from active volcanism or at a time after the main period of volcanic activity, as dilution by pyro-clastics is thereby minimal. Fumeroles related to volcanic systems are particularly respon-sible for ore deposition. Hydrothermal mineralization is often associated with these deposits (Suslov, 1970) and the clearly stratified and vein-type deposits often grade into each other in the field.

(4) In a volcanogenic-sedimentary sequence, iron and manganese ores are found in mixed or well-differentiated assemblages. Manganese may be present as oxides, carbon-ates, hydrosilicates and rarely sulfides (associated with hydrothermal mineralization). During volcanism a well-defined reducing environment persists which favours precipita-tion of manganese carbonates and silicates. If H_2S is present in the gases, sulfides of Fe, Pb, Zn and other elements precipitate. Such sulfide minerals are sometimes present in manganese deposits. Beyond the locally reducing zone, manganese and iron may precipi-tate as hydroxides. Manganese deposits form at a greater distance from the volcanic center than those of iron due to higher mobility (Strakhov, 1967).

(5) The trend of volcanogenic-sedimentary manganese deposits, controlled by the volcanic foci following the general trend of the geosynclinal zones, may cut across those of the climatic belts at all angles or may coincide only accidentally.

(6) Even in regions of intense volcanic activity, the total amount of manganese (and iron) deposited in basins is rather small (cf. Valley of Ten Thousand Smokes, Alaska; Zeis, 1929) compared to very large nonvolcanogenic-sedimentary deposits (cf. Kalahari field, South Africa). Further, the volcanic activities are generally of relatively short dura-

tion and of irregular nature (Suslov, 1970), and even in case of major volcanic piles such as those in the Olympic Peninsula (Wash., U.S.A.) and eastern Cuba, the concentration of manganese was not a continued process but was rather sporadic.

Important volcanogenic-sedimentary manganese deposits will now be briefly described. They have been classified into different types, taking into account the deposits representing the different subdivisions in the classification proposed by Shatskiy (1954). Thus, the greenstone-siliceous group has been subdivided into an Olympic Peninsula type (greenstone formation), a Noda Tamagawa type (jasperoid formation) and a West African type (siliceous-shaly formation), and the porphyry-siliceous group into a Långban type (porphyritic formation) and a Karadzhal type (siliceous-shaly formation).

Deposits of Olympic Peninsula type

The Early–Middle Eocene geosynclinal sequence of the Olympic Peninsula, Wash., (U.S.A.), is composed of spilites, diabases, graywackes, red limestones and argillites and jaspers (Park, 1946). The spilites are very often interbedded and interfingered with argillites, graywackes and siliceous red limestones. Manganese-ore deposits occur as beds, lenses, veins and pockets in the spilites and are intimately associated with red limestones, argillites and jaspers. The individual ore deposits are small but the co-distribution of spilites, red limestones, argillites and manganese deposits extends for over 150 miles. Shatskiy (1954) considered these deposits as one of the best examples of greenstone formation in his classification. Park (1946) concluded that the manganese was a normal constituent in basalt which was leached along with silica during spilitization at the time of subaqueous extrusion of the lavas.

The manganese deposits exhibit a diverse mineralogy (Park, 1946; Sorem and Gunn, 1967): *oxides*: braunite, hausmannite, jacobsite, crednerite, hematite, cuprite; *silicates*: bementite, neotocite, alleghanyite, inesite, johannsenite, rhodonite, tephroite; *carbonates*: rhodochrosite, manganoan calcite; *sulfide*: alabandite; *native metal*: copper. Supergene oxides and hydroxides reported from this area are nsutite, birnessite, todorokite and ranceite.

Manganese deposits of Devonian age in the Magnitogorsk synclinorium, southern Ural (U.S.S.R.), occur in the volcanic Karamalytash (fissure eruption: diabase, spilite, jasper) and the pyroclastic Irendyk and Ulutau (andesite, basalt) formations and are included in the Olympic Peninsula type due to their close association with basic volcanic rocks. The ore deposits are preferentially related to fissure eruption rather than to explosive volcanism (Sokolova, 1970) as opposed to the generalized observation of Bonatti (1967). In the Karamalytash Formation, the manganese ores and jaspers, though intimately related to the basic lavas, formed during a period of relative quiescence (Sokolova, 1970). The ores occurring in jaspers usually consist of braunite while carbonate-siliceous manganese ores occur in tuffites and siliceous shales. The occurrence of manganese oxides and siliceous carbonates in separate lenses has been explained by Sokolova as being due to compositional changes of the solution derived from volcanism. A reserve of 5.3 million tons of low-grade (20% Mn) siliceous ores has been estimated.

At Mazul'skii, Arga Range, western Siberia (U.S.S.R.), lenticular manganese orebodies occur in the lower part of the Lower Cambrian geosynclinal formation which consists of diabase-porphyrite greenschists with alternate layers of tuff, tuffites, siliceous-aluminous schists and jaspers (Suslov, 1970). The volcanic activity was periodic and the orebodies, as thin and small lenses, are irregularly distributed in stratigraphic horizons, often separated by barren layers of microquartzite and diabase porphyrite (Suslov, 1970, fig. 3, p. 68). The ores are composed of rhodochrosite, manganoan calcite, manganite, neotocite, hisingerite and sometimes siderite. Hydrothermal mineralization is superimposed on the orebodies. The deposit contains 6 million tons of ore with an average of 20% Mn and 11% Fe.

Manganese deposits occur in a 70 mile long belt across the Oriente Province, Cuba (Simons and Straczek, 1958). Manganese-oxide beds occur in the Ponopo and Sabamilla districts, in different stratigraphic levels in the upper part of the Cobre volcanics (Late Cretaceous to Middle Eocene) composed largely of basic lava, layered tuff, agglomerate and jasper. The Cobre volcanics are overlain by the Charco Redondo limestone (Middle Eocene) which also contains important beds of manganese oxide interlayered with tuff. Todorokite is the most abundant mineral in most of the deposits with occasional manganite, cryptomelane and pyrolusite.

Manganiferous iron deposits (maximum 15% Mn) are concentrated on the Pacific side of the Japanese islands in geosynclinal sediments and volcanic rocks of the Paleozoic Chichibu complex and the Mesozoic Shimanto terrain, in Tokoro, Hokkaido and Abukama, Fukushima Prefecture, and in Kunimiyama, Kochi Prefecture. These volcanogenic-sedimentary ores, with considerable lateral extension, are associated with spilitic lava flows or bedded basic tuffs as conformable beds or lenses, overlain by radiolarian or ferruginous chert beds (Takabatake, 1956). The ores are composed of hematite, magnetite, opal, chalcedony, bementite, penwithite and epidote. Earlier workers believed that the manganese occurs mainly in hematite, but Shimazaki (1970) showed that in the Kunimiyama mine, Shikoku, and the Kokuriki mine, Hokkaido, manganese is contained almost entirely in bementite and penwithite.

Besides the above deposits, iron-poor manganese-ore deposits associated with spilitic rocks occur in the Paleozoic geosynclinal formations at the Shiromaru mine, Tokyo, and the Muramatsu mine, Nagashaki Prefecture (Watanabe et al., 1970a). At Shiromaru mine, the orebodies (braunite, rhodonite) have been regionally metamorphosed under low-temperature and high-pressure conditions. At the Muramatsu mine, bedded orebodies have been regionally metamorphosed to amphibolite facies and contain braunite, piemontite, spessartite and rhodonite.

Deposits of Noda Tamagawa type

Syngenetic volcanogenic-sedimentary manganese orebodies, restricted to definite stratigraphic horizons, occur interbedded with the dominant chert member and are associated with slate, graywacke and rare basic tuff and limestone of the Permo-Carboniferous Chichibu geosyncline in the Ashio Mountainland (Fig. 17), the Kitakami Mountainland and the Tamba Highland, Japan. Deposits of this type, of which the one in Noda Tamagawa, Iwate Prefecture, is an important representative, have been considered by Watanabe et al. (1970a) to belong to the jasperoid formation of the greenstone-siliceous group of Shatskiy (1954) and will be referred to here as the Noda Tamagawa type. Late Cretaceous granitic intrusives (Kobugahara, Sori and Nagusa, Ashio Mountainland; Tanohata, Kitakami Mountainland) have thermally metamorphosed these orebodies and the associated rocks to different grades. Effects of metasomatism are also prominent in certain deposits.

Ore deposits of the Noda Tamagawa type occur profusely in Japan and include those of Noda Tamagawa, Kitakami Mountainland, Iwate Prefecture (Watanabe et al., 1970b), the Kaso mine, Kanoiri, and the Yokoneyama mines and Manako and Ohkaki mines, Ashio Mountainland, Tochigi Prefecture. Excepting those at the Manako and Ohkaki mines, all the above deposits have been thermally metamorphosed to different grades (Watanabe et al., 1970a). The regionally metamorphosed manganese-ore deposits of the Tomisato and Kusami mines, Yamanashi Prefecture, and the Kiuragi mine, Saga Prefecture, though associated with basic tuff and amphibolite, have been included under the jasperoid formation (Noda Tamagawa type) by Watanabe et al. (1970a). The geological features and mineralogy of all the above-mentioned deposits have been summarized in Table VI.

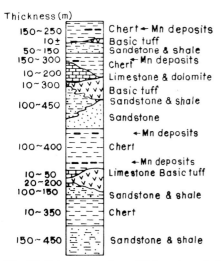

Fig. 17. Columnar section of Paleozoic rocks in the Ashio Mountainland, showing the position of the manganese deposits. (After Watanabe et al., 1970a. With permission of Tokyo Univ. Press.)

TABLE VI

Characteristic features of the volcanogenic-sedimentary Noda Tamagawa-type manganese ore deposits of Japan associated dominantly with chert (jasperoid formation of greenstone-siliceous group of Shatskiy, 1954)

Deposits	Geological aspects	Mineralogy
Unmetamorphosed		
Manako mines, Tochigi Prefecture, Ashio Mountainland	conformable beds of manganese ore enclosed in thin-bedded and massive chert; passes over to ore deposits of greenstone formation nearby	rhodochrosite, hausmannite, manganosite, bementite
Contact-metamorphosed		
Noda-Tamagawa mine, Iwate Prefecture, Kitakami Mountainland	roof pendant rocks of Akkagawa formation (≡ Chichibu geosynclinal formation) on Cretaceous Tanohata granodiorite, consists of slate, graywacke and chert, thermally metamorphosed to medium grade; lenticular manganese orebodies are exclusively confined to the massive and thin bedded cherts with which the ores are conformably interbedded and cofolded; three ore zones, viz., Shinmorida, Misago and Kamishiro are known of which the Misago ore zone is most important	pyrochroite, hausmannite, alabandite, feitknechtite, manganosite, braunite, jacobsite, vredenburgite, pyrophanite, rhodochrosite, manganoan calcite, rhodonite, pyroxmangite, bustamite, tephroite, spessartite, galaxite, alleghanyite, bementite, neotocite, parsettensite, penwithite, yoshimuraite, dannemorite, manganophyllite, etc., together with different non-manganiferous silicates, magnetite, hematite, barite, sulfides of Fe, Cu, As, Co, Pb, Ni, Mo and uraninite in thermally metamorphosed orebodies, hornfels, skarns and hydrothermal veins; supergene manganese oxides such as pyrolusite, psilomelane and ramsdellite are present
Kaso Mine, Tochigi Prefecture, Ashio Mountainland	layered manganese deposits of carbonate-silicate type conformable with meta-cherts; thermally metamorphosed; grade of metamorphism lower than that at Noda Tamagawa mine; a cryptobatholithic body on the northwest side of the mine responsible for thermal metamorphism	about 40 different minerals described; the following manganese minerals are important: rhodochrosite, rhodonite, pyroxmangite, tephroite, knebelite, spessartite, dannemorite, alleghanyite, sonolite, penwithite, alabandite, galaxite, braunite, jacobsite, manganosite, pyrochroite, huebnerite, pyrophanite; products of boron metasomatism: jimboite, wiserite
Kanoiri and Yokoneyama mines, Tochigi Prefecture, Ashio Mountainland	layered manganese carbonate-silicate deposits in meta-chert sequence; thermally metamorphosed to very high grade with	no original rhodochrosite left after thermal metamorphism; minerals present are: spessartite, rhodonite, bustamite, tephroite, pyroxmang-

TABLE VI (continued)

Deposits	Geological aspects	Mineralogy
	development of orthophyroxene-cordierite-biotite hornfels by Kobugahara granite	ite, Mn-Ca pyroxene, Mn-amphibole; pyrrhotite, pentlandite and other sulfides present in minor amounts
Regionally metamorphosed		
Tomisato and Kusama mines, Yamanashi Prefecture	layered deposits of manganese in Miocene clastic rocks, chert and basic tuff; metamorphosed to zeolite facies; the manganese ore beds are cut by later rhodochrosite veinlets	braunite, hausmannite, rhodonite, tephroite
Kiuragi mine, Saga Prefecture	layered manganese orebodies present in biotite-quartz schist and amphibolite; metamorphosed to amphibolite facies	rhodochrosite, spessartite, rhodonite, tephroite, jacobsite, galaxite.

Manganese deposits of the Noda Tamagawa type occur in the Graubünden Kanton, Swiss Alps, in the deposits of Parsetten and Faletta where thin layers and lenses of manganese oxides and carbonates are conformably interbedded with Upper Jurassic radiolarian jaspers that overlie thick, barren ophiolitic formations of diabase and spilitic lava.

The manganese deposits occurring over a distance of 30 miles in the Davos—Oberhalbstein—Maleneo area in the Swiss Alps, contain tephroite, pyroxmangite, rhodochrosite and quartz in different metamorphic grades from zeolite to amphibolite facies (Peters et al., 1973). Similar deposits of manganese ores are found in radiolarian chert in Italy (Rapolano, Toscana, Gambatesa, etc.). Syngenetic braunitic orebodies occur as lenses and thin beds conformably interlaminated with Jurassic radiolarian jasper at Chevlyanovich, Yugoslavia.

In the central part of the Huelva Province, Spain, manganese-ore deposits occur in close geological association with such important cupriferous pyrite deposits as those of Rio Tinto and Tharsis. The orebodies are clearly related to submarine basic and acid lava flows (spilite, quartz-keratophyre) preceding the Hercynian folding, together with thick layers of volcanic tuff and banded hematite-jasper formations. The pyrite and the manganese orebodies (oxides and carbonates) occurring as conformable beds and lenses, are exclusively confined to acid tuffs and hematite-jaspers, respectively (Fig. 18). Déprez and Soler (1971) consider that manganese was retained in solution when pyrite was formed and was deposited later as carbonates and oxides in a condition of sharp change in Eh-pH, giving rise to beds of banded hematite-jasper and manganese orebodies. Shatskiy (1954) placed these manganese deposits in the siliceous-shaly formation of his green-

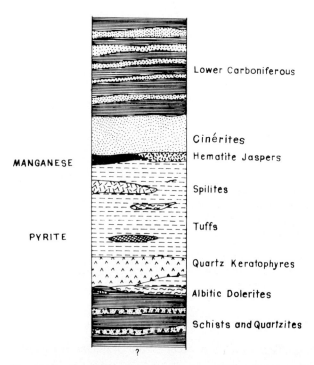

Fig. 18. Stratigraphic section showing the position of the manganese deposits of the Huelva Province, Spain. (After Déprez and Soler, 1971; *Bull. B.R.G.M.*, No.6, p. 9.)

stone-siliceous group, but from the recent observations of Déprez and Soler (1971) it seems that these orebodies are more closely related to the jasperoid formation (Noda Tamagawa type).

A very important analogue of the Noda Tamagawa type deposits is developed in the Franciscan Formation of the Coast Ranges (Upper Jurassic to Upper Cretaceous) and the Calaverous Formation (Paleozoic) and the Amador Group (Jurassic) of the Sierra Nevada in California. The eugeosynclinal Franciscan Formation consists predominantly of gray-wacke with basic volcanic rocks, radiolarian chert, shale and limestone. Basic volcanic rocks (spilite, diabase) altered by reaction with sea water, represent about a tenth of the lithology. The manganese orebodies occur as lenses (thickness 1—35 ft.) from a few feet to several hundred feet long, enclosed conformably in the chert member, particularly within white cherts, throughout the Coast Ranges from Humboldt County in the north, to Santa Barbara County in the south. Rhodochrosite, bementite, braunite, hausmannite, rhodonite, spessartite and neotocite have been described from the ores (Trask and co-workers, 1950). Huebner (1967) recorded 7-Å layered silicates from the ores and contended that the bementite described by earlier workers yields X-ray patterns of mangan-pyrosmalite, friedelite, antigorite and septechlorite.

All workers are unanimous on the volcanogenic source of the manganese orebodies and the enclosing chert (Taliaferro and Hudson, 1943; Trask and co-workers, 1950; Hewett et al., 1956; Bailey et al., 1964; Huebner, 1967). Manganese and silica were either leached by the hot-lava—seawater reaction and then precipitated following the mechanism suggested by Krauskopf (1956), or they were precipitated from submarine thermal springs connected with volcanism.

Bedded manganese deposits, conformably enclosed in radiolarian chert and associated with spilitic lava, occur in the Calaverous Formation (Paleozoic) and the Amador Group (Jurassic) in the Californian Sierra Nevada. These ore-bearing sequences have been metamorphosed to low and high grades (Trask and co-workers, 1950; Hewett et al., 1956, 1961). The original manganiferous sediments possibly contained beds of nearly pure manganese carbonate and oxide, hydrous manganese silicates and admixed (with silica) manganese oxides and carbonates (Hewett et al., 1961). On metamorphism to different grades, these gave rise to tephroite, rhodonite, spessartite, rhodochrosite, bementite, alleghanyite, piemontite and hausmannite. The manganiferous sediments, along with the enclosing cherts were possibly deposited in the same manner as in the Franciscan Formation.

Deposits of West African type

Under this type the volcanogenic-sedimentary manganese deposits that developed in siliceous-shales associated with basic volcanic rocks of the greenstone-siliceous group (Shatskiy, 1954) will be discussed.

The Precambrian Guinean Shield of West Africa, extending from Conakry (Guinea) to Accara (Ghana) for a distance of about 900 miles, is constituted of the geosynclinal Birrimian System (2400–2200 m.y.), unconformably overlain by the Tarkwaian System (Precambrian). The Birrimian rocks, with gondite and manganese ores, occur in the adjoining states of Ghana, Ivory Coast, Upper Volta and Eastern Liberia with a generally NNE–SSW trend. The NW–SE trending Precambrian Ansongo Series in Mali contains gondites similar to those of the Birrimian System.

In Ghana, the Upper Birrimian System is composed of basic to intermediate lavas and tuff metamorphosed to greenschists, interbedded with phyllitic rocks generally trending NNE–SSW. The phyllitic zone, enclosed in volcanic rocks and tuff (Service, 1943, p. 25 and plate III), is composed of interbedded sericitic and graphitic phyllites, tuff, graywacke and gondite (spessartite-quartz rock, occasionally with rhodonite). Such a zone, 375–400 ft. thick, at Nsuta (the most important mine in Ghana), with tuffaceous horizons, contains the most important orebodies. The unaltered phyllites contain 0.6–6.6% of free carbon and less than 1% of manganese. Supergene manganese oxides form good deposits by surface enrichment, consisting of cryptomelane, pyrolusite, manganite, lithiophorite, nsutite and goethite (Sorem and Cameron, 1960). Service (1943) discounted any possibility of the existence of manganese carbonates in the sediments. Most workers concluded that the manganese-oxide ores formed by supergene enrichment of the gondites. Dorr (1968), however, noted a persistent bed of rhodochrosite (about 60 ft. thick) below the oxidation zone at Nsuta, into which supergene oxide ores merge. The lower part of the supergene ore zone also contains remnants of rhodochrosite. He concluded, therefore, that the supergene oxides were formed by weathering of the rhodochrosite bed which originally contained 28–32% Mn. The high nsutite content of the supergene ore also supports derivation from a manganese carbonate protore (Roy, 1968). That the manganese in the original sediments resulted from volcanism has been suggested by most of the earlier workers, and Shatskiy (1954) corroborated this view.

Occurrences of manganese ores in the Birrimian System are known from many localities in the Republic of Ivory Coast. In the Boundoukou district, manganese orebodies occur in NNE–trending Birrimian rocks at Naniango, containing manganite and hausmannite and partially altered to pyrolusite and chalcophanite (Servant, 1956). The Grand Lahou deposit is the principal producer; gondite and manganiferous quartzite are interstratified with graphitic schists and metamorphosed basic volcanic rocks extending for about 5 miles with a NNE–SSW trend. The gondite contains 22% MnO, whereas the enriched supergene oxidic ores contain 48–50% Mn. In the Korhogo area, the manganiferous horizon extends for 90 miles, trending NNE–SSW. At Dassoumble, 18 miles west-southwest of Korhogo, beds of gondite, with manganese-oxide enrichment (pyrolusite, psilomelane) form the ore horizon (reserve 3.3 million tons). The deposits at M'Bouessou and Ziemougoula are also important.

In Upper Volta, a manganiferous zone extends from Tiéré to Bouere (Hounde). At Tiéré, a thick tuffaceous and siliceous phyllite bed contains an interstratified, 1600 ft. long lens of gondite. Two other lenses of gondite, 120 ft. and 80 ft. long, are also present. The manganese-oxide orebodies, formed by superficial enrichment of manganiferous phyllites and gondite, consist of pyrolusite, cryptomelane and manganite. Servant (1956) suggested a probable reserve of 900,000 tons of 46–48% Mn and 11–13% SiO_2 at Tiéré.

Gondites are interbedded with quartzites at the base of the Precambrian Ansongo Series in Mali. The lenses of the manganiferous rocks extend for about 20 miles, parallel to the NW–SE trend of the Ansongo Series. The oxidic manganese deposits (psilomelane and pyrolusite) were formed by supergene enrichment of gondite (Servant, 1956). The major ore deposit is located at Tikanasité Hill, near Ansongo, with a reserve of 7 million tons. Two other deposits, 15 miles to the south of Ansongo, at Agaoula and Tondibi Hill, contain 5 million and 3 million tons of reserves, respectively (De Kun, 1965).

Servant (1956), Shatskiy (1954) and others suggested that the manganese in the Birrimian sequence was derived during widespread volcanism and was deposited along with argillaceous sediments in shallow-water basins. Thus the original deposits were classed by Shatskiy as siliceous-shaly formation of the greenstone-siliceous group. The gondites were formed by low-grade regional metamorphism of sediments composed of manganese oxide, clay or mudstone and quartz. Service (1943, p. 25) discounted any possibility of the presence of manganese carbonates in the original sediments. Apart from the observation of Dorr (1968) on the presence of a thick rhodochrosite bed at Nsuta, manganese carbonate has not been reported from any other Birrimian deposit. The manganese-oxide deposits were formed by supergene enrichment in all cases.

The manganese-ore deposits in the Republic of Gabon, West Africa, occur mainly in the Upper Precambrian Franceville Series (1740 ± 20 m.y.) consisting of unmetamorphosed sediments. The sediments were deposited on both sides of a median northwest–southeastern ridge, which originally corresponded to a submarine rise, separating the two paleogeographic domains, viz., (a) the northeastern "Okondja deep" with a very thick series of argillaceous and sandy sediments and lava flows (in part spilitic); and (b) a southwestern epi-continental domain with a thinner sequence of sandstone, pelite (with organic remains) and dolomite. The known deposits of Moanda lie in one of the several basins in the epi-continental domain (Weber, 1973).

Among the manganese deposits around Moanda, those of the Bangombé, Okouma and Bafoula plateaus are the most important. At Bangombé and Okouma, a 40 ft. thick pelite (with organic remains) formation is enriched by pisolitic higher oxides of manganese. In the Okouma and Bafoula plateaus, at the periphery of the ore zone, the manganese ore overlies a 30 ft. thick iron-formation with the sulfide facies at the base passing upwards to carbonate and silicate facies. A phosphate bed is sometimes found at the top of the iron-silicate beds. A deep borehole, sunk at the centre of the Bangombé plateau, passed through sandstone, and pelitic rocks and reached the basal sandstone. The upper part of the pelitic formation in this borehole is constituted of a 225 ft. thick, low-grade (13% Mn) manganiferous carbonate (manganoan dolomite and calcian rhodochrosite) formation, with intercalated pelites (with organic remains) sandstone and dolomite. Iron is present here as pyrite.

Weber (1973) calculated that for the formation of the deposits of the Franceville Series, an amount of manganese much larger than that dissolved in the oceans of today would have been necessary. He related this supply of manganese to the spilitic volcanism of Okondja, where the hyaloclastites (up to 0.8%; average 0.35% Mn) were extruded at the same time as the deposition of the manganese beds. Thus, the manganese deposits are volcanogenic-sedimentary in nature. The manganiferous formations of both the Bangombé (borehole section) and Okouma-Bafoula areas were preceded by deposition of iron.

According to Weber the deposition of manganese in the Franceville Series took place in a coastal basin, which was barred from the source of spilitic volcanism by the submarine rise. The reducing environment allowed the manganese to remain in solution and to migrate over long distances. The concentration of manganese in the ore deposits around Moanda took place in three stages: (a) supply of manganese by spilitic volcanism of Okondja; (b) sedimentary deposition and diagenetic concentration of manganese as carbonates; and (c) supergene enrichment of sedimentary-diagenetic ores to manganese oxides (pyrolusite, cryptomelane, manganite, lithophorite, nsutite). The reserve of supergene manganese-oxide ores alone is about 200 million tons.

Shatskiy (1954) included the manganese deposits of Kellerwald, Germany, and the Molucca Peninsula in the siliceous-shaly formation (West African type). At Kellerwald, manganese-ore beds occur in siliceous shales in a Lower Carboniferous sequence of gray-wacke, siliceous limestones, siliceous shales and radiolarian cherts underlain by diabase and basic tuff. At Machang, Satakhun and Trenggen in the Molucca Peninsula, manganese ores are interbedded with a Triassic siliceous-shaly formation composed of shale and chert with tuffaceous intercalations. This siliceous-shaly formation is spatially related to the Pakhang volcanic series consisting of diabase, tuff and agglomerates.

Deposits of Långban type

The Långban deposit ("Långbanshyttan" or "Långban's smelter") in central Sweden, is the most well-known among those related to acid volcanism of porphyritic formation of the porphyry-siliceous group of Shatskiy (1954). In this text, other similar deposits of manganese will also be described under the Långban type.

In the Varmland Province, central Sweden, the Långban and other smaller deposits at Harstigen, Pajsberg, Sjö, Jakobsberg, Brattfors (Moore, 1971) and Slöjdartorp (Koark, 1970a,b) occur associated with the Precambrian Leptite Formation, represented by acid volcanic rocks and tuffs of extremely sodic (quartz-keratophyric) to extremely potassic (rhyolitic) composition. Bedded manganese and iron-oxide deposits are separated from each other and both are enclosed in dolomites. These were originally precipitated as hydroxides from solutions derived from acid volcanism, the iron preceding manganese in deposition in oxidizing conditions. In typical Långban-type deposits in Sweden, the Mn/Fe ratio in manganese ores is very high (13 : 1) with the exception of the Slöjdartorp deposit, where mixed ores (Mn/Fe = 1 : 1) occur. These volcanogenic-sedimentary manganese-oxide ores were subjected to more than one episode of thermal metamorphism during which the acid volcanic rocks were also metamorphosed to sodic and potassic leptites and hälleflintas. The manganese minerals in the sediments were themselves re-crystallized to lower oxides and their reaction with silica and carbonates (from dolomite) produced a host of skarn minerals. The maximum temperature attained during thermal metamorphism was at least 650°C (Moore, 1971). A large number of manganese-bearing minerals of diverse composition formed in fissures and hydrothermal veins at much lower temperature. Such diversity of manganese minerals is due to the different valence states and coordination numbers in which manganese occurs and the unusual association of Mn^{2+}, Mn^{3+}, Sb^{5+}, As^{3+}, Pb^{2+}, Ba^{2+}, Be^{2+}, etc., either originally present in the volcanogenic sediments or later introduced by granitic intrusives. The manganese-bearing minerals have been placed into four periods of formation by Magnusson (1930; quoted by Moore, 1971) as follows: Period A — the meta-sedimentary ores and the earliest skarns; Period B — the bulk of the skarns; Period C — minerals formed in Sköl (rocks intermediate to skarns and leptites in composition formed by metasomatic exchange of major elements) and local invasion of some sulfides; and Period D — the formation of low-temperature fissure-filling or hydrothermal minerals. The manganese-bearing minerals of the Långban and similar deposits in Sweden are listed in Table VII. For a detailed list of all minerals occurring in Långban-type deposits of Sweden, the reader is referred to the excellent account by Moore (1971).

The Late Precambrian platform-type manganese deposits of Tiouine, Migouden, Oufront and Idikel in Morocco, may be referred to the Långban type. At the Idikel deposit, which is older than the others, the orebodies are interlayered with red pelites and sandstone with volcanic debris. The main ore bed (4.5—6 ft. thick; Mn 37—51%, SiO_2 1—13%, BaO 5—10%, Pb 0.02—1.3%) consist of braunite and psilomelane with minor hausmannite, pyrolusite, rhodonite and dialogite. The bedded deposits of Tiouine, Migouden and Oufront occur in the Tiouine Series, consisting of conglomerate, sandstone, shale and limestone (intercalated with red tuffaceous shales) and isolated bodies of trachyte and andesite. At Tiouine five to fourteen beds of manganese ores (thickness 2—3 ft., locally 10 ft.) occur in red tuffaceous horizons. Vein deposits of manganese in rhyolite and ignimbrite occur near the Tiouine deposit. At the Tiouine, Migouden and Oufront deposits, braunite, hausmannite, coronadite, hollandite, cryptomelane and psilomelane are present. The average composition of the ore at Tiouine is: Mn 42—48%, SiO_2 6—21%, BaO 2—9.5%, Pb 0.2—2.1%.

Intense volcanism is characteristic of the Late Precambrian formations of Morocco. Andesitic volcanism is followed by extrusions of rhyolitic composition (ignimbrite, lava, tuff) with some andesite, latite and trachyte and finally by rhyolite and porphyritic andesite flows associated with detrital continental sediments (Choubert and Faure-Muret, 1973). Veins of manganese ore (braunite, hausmannite, hollandite, psilomelane, cryptomelane, pyrolusite, todorokite) in ignimbrite, rhyolite and andesite, are intimately associated with stratified deposits, suggesting a close genetic link between the vein deposits, stratified deposits and acid volcanism.

Bouladon and Jouravsky (1955) considered the Tiouine and related stratified deposits to be volcanogenic-sedimentary of the prophyry-siliceous group (cf. Shatskiy, 1954) whereas Choubert and Faure-Muret (1973) concluded that both the vein and stratified deposits are hydrothermal-epigenetic in origin. However, as the volcanogenic-sedimentary and hydrothermal deposits are, more often than not, intimately associated in space and time (Suslov, 1970), the clearly stratified deposits of Idikel, Tiouine, Migouden and Oufront are considered to be syngenetic and are included under the Långban type.

In the Lower Carboniferous deposit at Glib en Nam, Morocco, stratified manganese ores are conformably interbedded with tuff, red jasper and siliceous-schists in a syngenetic sequence (Vincienne, 1956). Braunite, hausmannite, cryptomelane, pyrolusite, piemontite, rhodonite, parsettensite and manganoan calcite constitute the ores. Vincienne concluded that the ore-beds (Mn 35—40%, Fe 3%, Pb 0.05%, BaO 0.3%) were syngenetically deposited in shallow water at the same time with the enclosing tuff. Manganese was directly precipitated from fumaroles connected with volcanism.

The major manganese deposits of Chile occur in the Coquimbo Province in the Arque-

TABLE VII

Manganese-bearing minerals from Långban-type ore deposits, Sweden

Minerals	Formula	Location	Paragenesis	Comment
Manganosite	MnO	B,L	A	common at B
Bixbyite	$(Mn,Fe)_2O_3$	L,U	B	metamorphic product
Pyrochroite	$Mn(OH)_2$	L,B,S,P,H,J	D	open-fissure mineral
Feitknechtite	β-$MnOOH$	L,B,S,P,H,J	D	oxidation product of pyrochroite
Manganite	γ-$MnOOH$	L,H,S	D	rare
Galaxite	Al_2MnO_4	B	B	
Jacobsite	$MnFe_2O_4$	J.L	A	common at J
Hausmannite	Mn_3O_4	L,B,J,H,P,S	A,B,C,D	major ore of Mn
α-vredenburgite	$(Mn,Fe)_3O_4$	L	B	
Pyrophanite	$MnTiO_3$	L,J,H	C	in sköl rocks
Melanostibite	Mn_2SbFeO_6	S	B	very rare
Crednerite	$CuMn_2O_4$	L	D	very rare
Braunite	$Mn^{2+}(Mn^{4+}Si^{4+})O_3$	L,S,H,P,B,Sl,U	A,B	major ore of Mn
Manganostibite	Mn_7SbAsO_{12}	B	B	very rare
Catoptrite	$Mn_{13}Al_4Sb_2Si_2O_{28}$	B,S,L	B	
Parwelite	$Mn_5Sb(Si,As)_2O_{10}$	L	C	
Langbanite	$Mn_4Mn_9SbSi_2O_{24}$	L,S	B	
Quenselite	$Pb(OH)MnO_2$	L	D	rare
Wickmanite	$MnSn(OH)_6$	L	D	rare
Pyrobelonite	$PbMn(OH)[VO_4]$	L	D	very rare
Manganberzellite	$(Ca,Na)_3(Mn,Mg)_2[AsO_4]_3$	L,S	B,C	common
Caryinite	$(Ca,Na,Pb)_2(Mn,Mg)_3[AsO_4]_3$	L,S	B	
Sarkinite	$Mn_2(OH)[AsO_4]$	L,H,B,S	C,D	
Eveite	$Mn_2(OH)[AsO_4]$	L	D	very rare
Arsenoclasite	$Mn_5(OH)_4[AsO_4]_2$	L	C	rare
Allactite	$Mn_7(OH)_8[AsO_4]_2$	L,B,S,H	D	
Brandtite	$Ca_2Mn(H_2O)_2[AsO_4]_2$	H,L	D	
Akrochordite	$Mn_4Mg(OH)_4(H_2O)_2[AsO_4]_2$	L	D	very rare
Flinkite	$MnMn_2(OH)_4[AsO_4]$	H	D	very rare
Retzian	γ-$Mn_2(OH)_4[AsO_4]$	B	D	very rare
Manganhornesite	$Mn_3(H_2O)_8[AsO_4]_2$	L	D	rare
Magnussonite	$Mn_5(OH)[AsO_3]_3$	L,B	C,D	
Trigonite	$Pb_3Mn[AsO_3]_2[AsO_2(OH)]$	L	D	
Armangite	$Mn_3[AsO_3]_2$	L	D	very rare
Synadelphite	$Mn_9(OH)_9[AsO_4]_2[AsO_3]$	B,L	D	
Dixenite	$Mn_6(OH)_2SiO_4[AsO_3]_2$	L	C	
Hematolite	$Mn_4Al(OH)_2[AsO_4][AsO_3]_2$	B,L	D	
Pinakiolite	$(Mg,Mn)_2MnO_2[BO_3]$	L	C	uncommon
Tephroite	Mn_2SiO_4	L,H,S,J,P,B	B,C	
Leucophoenicite	$Mn_7[SiO_4][SiO_4(OH)_2]$	P	C	
Sonolite	$Mn_9(OH)_2[SiO_4]_4$	L,B	B,C	
Manganohumite	$Mn_7(OH)_2[SiO_4]_3$	B	C	
Welinite	$MnMn_3O_3[SiO_4]$	L	C	

TABLE VII (continued)

Minerals	Formula	Location	Paragenesis	Comment
Spessartite	$Mn_3Al_2Si_3O_{12}$	L,H,J,Sl,S,P,B,U	B,C	minor, in skarn
Piemontite	$Ca_2(Al,Mn)Al_2O(OH)$ $[Si_2O_7][SiO_4]$	J.S,L,U	C	
Harstigite	$MnCa_6(Be_2OOH)_2[Si_3O_{10}]_2$	H	D	
Kentrolite	$Pb_2(MnO_2)_2Si_2O_7$	L,P,H,J	B	
Barysilite	$Pb_8Mn[Si_2O_7]_3$	L,H,P,J	C	
Ericssonite	$Ba_2MnFeO(OH)[Si_2O_7]$	L	B	
Margarosanite	$Pb(Ca,Mn)_2[Si_3O_9]$	L	C	uncommon
Schefferite	$Ca(Mn,Mg,Fe)[Si_2O_6]$	L,H,J,S,P	B,C	
Rhodonite	$MnSiO_3$	L,H,S,Sl,P,J,B	B,C	
Bustamite	$(Ca,Mn)_2[Si_2O_6]$	L,H,S	B	
Inesite	$Ca_2Mn_7(OH)_2(H_2O)_6$ $[Si_{10}O_{28}]$	L,H,J.S	C,D	
Richterite	$(Na,Cl)Ca_2(Mg,Mn)_5$ $(OH)_2(Si,Al)_8O_{22}$	L,H,P,J,S	B,C	
Bementite	$Mn_{14}(OH)_{14}[Si_2O_5]_7$	L	C,D	
Ganophyllite	$NaMn_3(OH)_4[(Si,Al)_4O_{10}]$	H,S	C	
Neotocite	Hydrated manganese silicate	L,H,J,P,S	D	
Trimerite	$CaMn_2[BeSiO_4]_3$	L,J,H	C	rare

Localities: Långban (L); Harstigen (H); Pajsberg (P); Sjö (S); Jakobsberg (J); Brattfors (B); Slöjdartorp (Sl); Ultevis (U).
Paragenesis: meta-sedimentary ores and early skarns (A); major period of skarn formation (B); formation of sköl (C); formation of low-temperature fissure-filling or hydrothermal minerals (D).

ros and Quebrada Marquesa Formations of Early Cretaceous age (Aguirre and Mehec, 1964). The lower unit, the Arqueros Formation, is marine and consists of porphyritic andesite flows, ferruginous chert, sandstones with volcanic constituents and limestone. Three beds of manganese oxide (several inches to 7 ft. thick) occur near the top of this formation, intercaled with sandstone containing andesitic and trachytic lava casts. Braunite, manganite, pyrolusite and psilomelane constitute the ore, which has a persistent copper content of 1–3%. The overlying Quebrada Marquesa Formation consists of limestone and quartzite, closely associated with andesite porphyrites, and contains two thin zones of manganese-oxide beds in the middle part. Braunite (colloform), manganite and minor pyrolusite occur in these ores. The ore deposits in both the Arqueros and Quebrada Marquesa Formations have been derived from andesitic volcanism.

The manganese-iron ore deposits at Pozharevo, Bulgaria, in the Upper Cretaceous Sredna Gora geosyncline, occur either within andesite and andesitic breccia or in overlying red marl, marly tuff and calcareous marl (Fig. 19). The orebodies (rich ores: Mn 17–48%, Fe 0.3–9.6%, SiO_2 11–55%, S 0.003–0.005%, Al_2O_3 up to 6.8%, P 0.02–0.06%; Fe-Mn ores: Mn up to 30%, Fe 24%, SiO_2 30.5%) extend laterally for about 500 ft., with thickness varying from 5–15 ft. and the reserve of low-grade ore is only 100,000 tons. Small ore lenses are restricted to definite stratigraphic horizons. Pyrolusite, psilomelane and braunite, intergrown with opal and chalcedony constitute the orebodies.

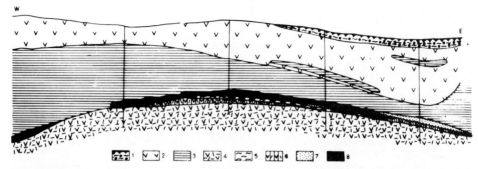

Fig. 19. Schematic geological section of the Pozharevo deposit. *1* = Deluvium; *2* = andesites; *3* = tuffs, tuffites and marls; *4* = andesitic breccia; *5* = red marly clay; *6* = mineralized andesitic breccia; *7* = silicified sediments with manganese oxides; *8* = manganese ores. (After Suslov, 1970.)

According to Suslov (1970), the submarine volcanogenic-sedimentary series, with genetically related manganese and iron orebodies, developed during the early stages of the Sredna Gora geosyncline.

Manganese deposits of Late Cretaceous age related to acid volcanic rocks (plagioclase-porphyries, quartz-porphyries, albitophyres, keratophyres, dacites) and their tuffs and alternating sequences of limestone and sandstone, occur in the Kafan and Alaverdi tectonic zones of Armenia, U.S.S.R. Sheet-like conformable orebodies, located at the contact of the volcanic and sedimentary rocks and also within volcanic rocks and jaspers, are composed of braunite, rhodochrosite, hausmannite, pyrolusite, psilomelane and rare pyrite, chalcopyrite, molybdenite, galena and sphalerite. Gulyan (1970) suggested that the manganese ores were formed during the middle stage of development of the Upper Cretaceous–Eocene geosyncline and the ore deposits are genetically related to the extrusion of intermediate to acid lavas.

The Durnovso deposit, located on the Salair Ridge, western Siberia, U.S.S.R., has been described by Suslov (1970) and classified under the porphyry-siliceous group by Rakhmanov and Tchaikovsky (1972). Sheet-like manganese-iron and pure manganese orebodies occur conformably in a volcano-sedimentary sequence of quartz-keratophyre, tuff, tuffites, limestone and jasper (Fig. 20) of the upper horizons of the Gavrilovskoe Formation and lower parts of the Pecherkina Formation (Lower Cambrian). Nine orebodies have been traced. The largest orebodies are 600–700 ft. long with an average thickness of about 12 ft. Carbonate ores (manganoan calcite) are subordinate to braunitic oxide ores. A reserve of 850,000 tons of ore, with Mn 9–19%, Cu 0.003%, Zn 0.1–0.3% and Co 0.01%, has been estimated.

Deposits of Karadzhal type

Manganese and iron deposits of Late Devonian to Early Carboniferous age occur in the Atasu region in Central Kazakhstan, U.S.S.R. The major deposits at Karadzhal, Ktai,

SW

NE

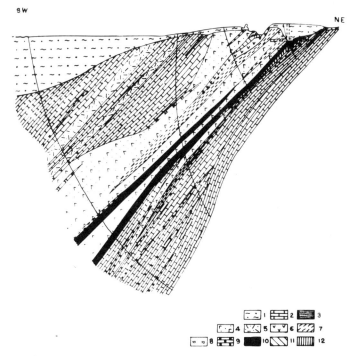

Fig. 20. Geological section across the Durnovso deposit. *1* = Clays and gravel; *2* = limestones; *3* = sericite schists; *4* = quartz keratophyres; *5* = tuffs and tuffites; *6* = diabases; *7* = jaspers; *8* = quartz veins; *9* = carbonate ores; *10* = braunite ores; *11* = hematite ores; *12* = psilomelane ores. (After Suslov, 1970).

Dzhumart, Dzhairem, Kamys, Ushkatyn, etc., occurring in the Dzhail'min trough, show an individuality in the association of manganese and iron oxides, carbonates, silicates and polymetallic sulfides as syngenetic beds and epigenetic veins and have earlier been referred to as "Karadzhal-type" or "Atasu-type". Shatskiy (1954) referred this type to the siliceous-shaly formation of the porphyry-siliceous group while Sokolova (1970) placed it under the volcanogenic-carbonate formation. Carbonate formations are definitely much more abundant in these deposits as compared to terrigenous rocks. In this Chapter these deposits will be classed under the Karadzhal type.

The characteristic features of these deposits are as follows:

(1) The ore-bearing area extends as a narrow band for more than 11 miles along the northern flank of the E—W trending Dzhail'min trough. Stratigraphically-controlled, lenticular and sheet-like manganese and iron orebodies occur in red siliceous-carbonate sequence with sharp contact and conformable attitudes.

(2) The ore-bearing horizon can be stratigraphically divided into two groups separated by a thick horizon of barren limestone. The lower group (90—300 ft. thick) consists of

the deposits at Kamys, Dzhumart, Dzhairem, etc., and the upper group (250–300 ft. thick) contains Karadzhal, Ktai, Klich and other deposits (Novokhatskiy, 1970).

(3) The ore-bearing sequence is finely bedded and composed of numerous horizons with beds of argillaceous rocks, silts, sandstones, jaspers and considerable carbonaceous matter. Red limestone beds occur above and below the orebodies at Karadzhal.

(4) Kavun (1970) delineated the following zones from north to south in the ore-bearing horizon of the Karadzhal deposit: (i) siliceous-carbonate rocks, argillites and silts; (ii) red ferruginous-siliceous-carbonate rocks; (iii) jaspers, sometimes baritised; (iv) mainly magnetite ores; (v) hematite ores; (vi) manganese-oxide ores; (vii) mixed manganese oxide-silicate-carbonate ores; (viii) red manganiferous and siliceous-carbonate rocks; (ix) greenish-gray siliceous-carbonate rocks.

(5) Lenticular or sheet-like polymetallic sulfide bodies (Pb-Zn and minor Fe, Cu) occur below the red limestone of the ore-bearing sequence at Karadzhal. In the western part of the Dzhail'min trough (Dzhumart, Dzhairem, Ushkatyn, Kamys), Pb-Zn orebodies with melnikovite-pyrite are conformably interbedded and co-folded with manganese ore beds (Rozhnov, 1970). Discordant Pb-Zn orebodies with barite are also present.

(6) Kavun (1970) contended that the ore-bearing horizons contain interlayers of tuff and tuffite but no volcanic rock, and the spilites and porphyrites described from the far west and north Dzhairem areas are later than the ore-bearing horizon. Novokhatshiy (1960, 1970) and Sokolova (1958, 1970), on the other hand, confirmed the presence of basic and acidic volcanic rocks (basalt, spilite, dacite, albitophyre, etc.) associated with tuffs as contemporaneous concordant bodies of considerable size in the ore-bearing horizon.

(7) The manganese and iron ores are both widespread and well separated, the former being associated with carbonate and the latter with siliceous (jasper) rocks. They sometimes occur in alternate beds, or the iron ores give way to manganese ores along both dip and strike. Manganese ores are more abundant in the eastern Karadzhal deposit, whereas in western Karadzhal iron ores predominate.

(8) Manganese ores are mainly oxidic in nature though subordinate carbonate ores are also found.

(9) Manganese ores show strong evidence of diagenesis, regional and thermal metamorphism, hydrothermal metasomatism and supergene alteration.

Diagenetic features are mainly demonstrated by manganese carbonate ores with oolitic manganoan calcite following or cutting across the lamination. Such microstructures are also found in hematite and jacobsite (Kalinin, 1965). The ores have been metamorphosed both regionally and thermally. The regional metamorphism was weak in nature, resulting in dehydration and recrystallization of manganese hydroxides and carbonates without tangible redistribution of material. Braunite and a part of the hausmannite and jacobsite formed by recrystallization of manganese hydroxides. Contact metamorphism produced hausmannite, jacobsite, rhodonite, tephroite, etc. Hydrothermal activity, shown by veins of manganoan calcite, friedelite, fluorite, barite, siderite, galena, sphalerite and different

TABLE VIII

Important minerals in the Karadzhal deposit (after Kalinin, 1965)

Minerals formed during sedimentation and diagenesis	Minerals formed during metamorphism	Minerals connected with hydrothermal activities	Minerals in the zones of oxidation
Manganocalcite	braunite	friedelite	psilomelane
Calcite	hausmannite	manganocalcite	vernadite (?)
Rhodochrosite	jacobsite	barite	pyrolusite
Opal	manganite	hematite	martite
Chalcedony	rhodochrosite	pyrite	hydrogoethite
Mn-hydroxides	rhodonite	marcasite	maghemite
Fe-hydroxides	epidote	arsenopyrite	gypsum
Leptochlorites	garnet	tourmaline	opal
Fe-disulfides	cummingtonite	quartz	
	hematite	calcite	
	magnetite	fluorite	
	siderite	galena	
	chlorite	sphalerite	
	pyrite	chalcopyrite	
		bornite	
		pyrrhotite	

iron and copper sulfides, is prominent. The ore horizon was subjected to supergene alteration, giving rise to higher oxides of manganese, at a later date. The mineralogy of the manganese and iron ores at the Karadzhal deposit is shown in Table VIII.

The mode of origin of the Karadzhal-type deposits is controversial. The earlier workers (Nikolaev, 1931, Rusakov and Satpayev, 1935, both cited by Kavun, 1970) consider these deposits to be of hydrothermal-metasomatic origin. Shtreys (1938, cited by Shatskiy, 1954) and Konev and Kheruvimova (1941, cited by Kavun, 1970) proposed a sedimentary origin related to submarine volcanic activity for the deposits. Betekhtin (1944) and Kavun (1970) concluded that these deposits are of nonvolcanogenic-sedimentary type that have been subsequently metamorphosed. Maksimov (1960) and Kalinin (1970) accepted the sedimentary origin of the deposits, but were uncertain about the source. Novokhatskiy (1960, 1970), Sokolova (1958, 1970), Sapozhnikov (1963) and Kayupova (1970) confirmed the volcanogenic-sedimentary origin of the Karadzhal-type deposits.

The following observations have been cited in support of a volcanogenic source of the manganese and iron deposits of Karadzhal type:

(1) Occurrence of volcanic rocks and layers of tuff in the same stratigraphic horizon as that of the ores (Sokolova, 1958; Novokhatskiy, 1960, 1970).

(2) Manganese and iron were precipitated almost simultaneously in the marine basin. Sapozhnikov (1963) concluded that due to intense tectonic movement during the Devonian period, weathering zones in surrounding rocks were not developed and so paleogeographic conditions did not permit terrigenous contribution of the metals. Therefore, the

source of these elements was volcanogenic.

(3) Sokolova (1970) cited the close association and sometimes interbedded nature of orebodies of different compositions (Fe-rich, Mn-rich, polymetallic sulfides) and the presence of varying amounts of jasper (with radiolarites) as indications of a volcanogenic origin. She concluded that this variation of composition cannot be explained by assuming terrigenous source, particularly in the absence of rapid changes of paleogeographic environment during ore formation. Different volcanic foci related to deep faults supplied solutions of different composition and the composition of ore-bearing solutions, derived from a particular source, also changed with time and distance.

(4) Rozhnov (1970) showed that manganese and some Pb–Zn orebodies with melnikovite-pyrite are conformably interbedded and co-folded while other Pb–Zn orebodies associated with barite exhibit discordant relations and distinct wall rock alterations in the western part of the Dzhail'min trough (Dzhumart, Dzhairem, Ushkatyn, and Kamys). He concluded that both the concordant and discordant polymetallic sulfide orebodies and the manganese and iron ores belong to a single genetic unit connected to ore-bearing thermal solutions of volcanic source injected into sea water close to deep-seated fault zones. Rozhnov further mentioned the discovery of feeder veins of iron (at Yuzhnyi Klych and southern Akkuduk) and manganese ore (in the Akashi area) from the Dzhail'min trough, with composition similar to those of bedded deposits.

The manganese ores of Karadzhal-type deposits are low-grade. Kavun (1970) gave the following average compositions of the ores (in percent): western Karadzhal: Mn 21.15, Fe 6.04, SiO_2 18.04, S 0.31, P 0.018; eastern Karadzhal: Mn 27.2, Fe 4.6, SiO_2 16.2, S 0.16, P. 0.032; Ktai: Mn 23.31, Fe 12.38, SiO_2 17.87, S 0.1, P 0.08; Dzhumart: Mn 24.0, Fe 5.5, SiO_2 14.0, S 0.25, P. 0.03; Kamys: Mn 24.3, Fe 3.0; Ushkatyn III: Mn 29.0, Fe 2.1. Kavun estimated the total reserve of manganese and iron-manganese ores of these areas at 150–175 and 250–275 million tons, respectively.

SUMMARY AND CONCLUSION

Manganese deposits of different geological ages are distributed throughout the world and most of them are formed as chemical sediments in varying tectonic (eugeosynclinal to platform) and physico-chemical environments. It has been shown that while the geosynclinal deposits are more common in the Precambrian, they gradually give way to those of platform type and the latter became most prevalent towards the later part of the Phanerozoic. The sources of these manganese-rich sediments were either the weathering zone on the continents or direct (mainly submarine) volcanism of both basic and acidic type. The actual mode of formation of sedimentary manganese deposits from nonvolcanogenic or volcanogenic source and the possible mode of separation of manganese from iron, have been briefly outlined in this text. The deposits that were formed from a nonvolcanogenic source may either be geosynclinal or platform-type and are characteristically associated with terrigenous formations (argillaceous rocks), carbonate formations (limestone-

dolomite) and iron-formations. The volcanogenic-sedimentary manganese deposits are mainly geosynclinal and rarely of platform type and belong to greenstone-siliceous (with basic volcanic and subvolcanic rocks) and porphyry-siliceous (with acid volcanic and subvolcanic rocks) groups in which the manganese deposits are either associated directly with the basic or acidic volcanic or subvolcanic rocks or with chert, jasper and siliceous shales or carbonates, directly related to volcanic activity. It has been shown that while lithologic association and tectonic framework are somewhat interdependent and afford some guide for the source of manganese sediments, no unique interrelationship between them can be established. A detailed discussion on the tectonic and lithologic set-up, characteristic depositional pattern, mineralogy, effects of diagenesis and metamorphism and other characteristic features of the important nonvolcanogenic and volcanogenic manganese ore deposits in different rock associations, has been offered in the text. In Table IX an attempt has been made to summarize the information on the sequence of events leading to the formation of sedimentary manganese deposits from volcanogenic and nonvolcanogenic sources.

The mineralogy of the unmetamorphosed sedimentary manganese deposits indicates their environment of deposition and/or effect of diagenesis. This has been adequately emphasized in the text. Many of these deposits have later been modified by thermal or regional metamorphism or both and these have been extensively discussed. In all cases, the effect of metamorphism is limited to reconstitution of mineralogy and texture of the pre-existing orebodies and no particular improvement of tenor took place by this process. Thus, such ore deposits have been considered to be "metamorphosed" and not "metamorphic". The original bulk composition of the sediments, the reactions during metamorphism at variable temperature and fugacities of oxygen, CO_2, etc., generally control the mineralogy of the metamorphosed manganese formations. In cases of thermal metamorphism, however, metasomatism is an important factor in many cases, and gives rise to a number of unusual mineral phases (e.g., the deposits of Långban, Noda Tamagawa, Karadzhal, and others). The mineralogy of the primary manganese sediments and its modification by diagenesis and metamorphism, as shown by important manganese deposits, have been summarized in Table X.

ACKNOWLEDGEMENTS

The co-operation of the authors, editors and publishers of different papers, journals and books, who permitted the writer to use published material, including figures, for this chapter, is gratefully acknowledged. The writer is indebted to Dr. Hugh Jenkyns of Durham University who very generously offered the use of his unpublished material. The writer also wishes to record his thanks to Dr. S.K. Chanda for critically reading the manuscript and to Dr. S.K. Ghosh and Dr. S.C. Sarkar for translating some important papers. The suggestions offered by Dr. K.H. Wolf, on whose invitation this chapter was writen, are gratefully acknowledged.

REFERENCES

Aguirre, L. and Mehech, S., 1964. Stratigraphy and mineralogy of the manganese sedimentary deposits of Coquimbo Province, Chile. *Econ. Geol.*, 59: 428–442.

Ampilogov, I.F., 1970. Facies study of the fine-bedded ores of the Polunochnoe deposits and certain considerations on the rate of sedimentation of the manganiferous sediments. In: D.G. Sapozhnikov (Editor), *Manganese Deposits of the Soviet Union*. Israel Program for Scientific Translations, Jerusalem, pp. 368–375.

Audley-Charles, M.G., 1965. A geochemical study of Cretaceous ferromanganiferous sedimentary rocks from Timor. *Geochim. Cosmochim. Acta.*, 29: 1153–1173.

Audley-Charles, M.G., 1972. Cretaceous deep-sea manganese nodules in Timor: Implications for tectonics and olistrome development. *Nature Phys. Sci.*, 240: 137–139.

Aumento, F., Lawrence, D.E. and Plant, A.G., 1968. The ferromanganese pavement on the San Pablo seamount. *Geol. Surv. Can., Pap.*, 68-32: 1–30.

Bailey, E.H., Irwin, W.P. and Jones, D.L., 1964. Franciscan and related rocks, and their significance in the geology of western California. *Bull. Calif. Div. Mines Geol.*, 183: 177 pp.

Baker, A.A., Duncan, D.C. and Hunt, C.B., 1952. Manganese deposits of southeastern Utah. *U.S. Geol. Surv. Bull.*, 979-B: 63–157.

Betekhtin, A.G., 1937. The genesis of the Chiatura manganese ore deposit. In: *Trudy Konferentsii po Genezisu rud Zheleza, Margantsa i Aluminiya*. Izd. Akad. Nauk S.S.S.R., Moscow-Leningrad (in Russian).

Betekhtin, A.G., 1944. Genetic types of manganese ore deposits. *Izv. Akad. Nauk S.S.S.R., Ser. Geol.*, 4 (in Russian).

Beukes, N.J., 1973. Precambrian iron-formations of southern Africa. *Econ. Geol.*, 68: 960–1004.

Boardman, L.G., 1961. Manganese in the Union of South Africa. *7th Commonw. Min. Metall. Congr., 1961, Johannesburg, Trans.*, 1: 201–216.

Bonatti, E., 1967. Mechanism of deep-sea volcanism in the South Pacific. In: P.H. Ableson (Editor), *Researches in Geochemistry, 2*. Wiley, New York, N.Y., pp. 453–491.

Bonatti, E. and Joensuu, O., 1966. Deep-sea iron deposit from the South Pacific. *Science*, 154: 634–645.

Borchert, H., 1970. On the ore deposition and geochemistry of manganese. *Miner. Deposita*, 5: 300–314.

Boström, K., 1967. The problem of excess manganese in pelagic sediments. In: P.H. Ableson (Editor), *Researches in Geochemistry, 2*. Wiley, New York, N.Y., pp. 420–452.

Bouladon, J. and Jouravsky, G., 1952. Manganèse. In: *Geologie des Gites minéraux Marocains–19th Int. Geol. Congr., Algiers–Monogr. Reg. Ser. Maroc.*, 1: 45–80.

Bouladon, J. and Jouravsky, G., 1955. Les gisements de manganèse volcanogenès de Tiouine (Infracambrien du Sud marocain). *Serv. Geol. Maroc., Notes Mém.*, 127: 1–180.

Calvert, S.E. and Price, N.B., 1970. Composition of Mn-nodules and Mn-carbonates from Loch Fyne, Scotland. *Contrib. Mineral. Pet.*, 29: 215–233.

Chebotarev, M.V., 1960. Geological structure of the south Khingan manganese deposit and the essential composition of its ores. *Int. Geol. Rev.*, 2: 851–866.

Choubert, B., 1973. Occurrence of manganese in the Guianas (South America) and their relation with fundamental structures. *Genesis of Precambrian Iron and Manganese Deposits–UNESCO, Earth Sci.*, 9: 143–152.

Choubert, G. and Faure-Muret, A., 1973. The Precambrian iron and manganese deposits of the Anti-Atlas. *Genesis of Precambrian Iron and Manganese Deposits-UNESCO, Earth Sci.*, 9: 115–124.

Collins, J.F. and Buol, S.W., 1970. Patterns of iron and manganese precipitation under specified Eh-pH conditions. *Soil Sci.*, 110: 157–162.

Cronan, D.S. and Tooms, J.S., 1968. A microscopic and electron-probe investigation of manganese nodules from the northwest Indian Ocean. *Deep-Sea Res.*, 15: 215–223.

De Kun, N., 1965. Manganese. In: *The Mineral Resources of Africa*. Elsevier, Amsterdam-London-New York, pp. 281–295.

Déprez, D. and Soler, E., 1971. Les mineralisations pyriteuses et manganésifères liées aux formations volcano-sédimentaires de la Province de Huelva, (S.W. de l'Espagne). *Bull. B.R.G.M., 2e Sér.*, 6: 5–16.

Derby, O.A., 1901. On the manganese ore deposits of the Queluz (Lafayette) District, Minas Gerais, Brazil. *Am. J. Sci.*, 12: 18–32.

De Villiers, J., 1956. The manganese deposits of the Union of South Africa. *Symp. Manganese–20th Int. Geol. Congr.*, 2: 61–63.

De Villiers, J., 1960. The manganese deposits of the Union of South Africa. *Union S. Africa Dept. Mines Geol. Surv., Handbook 2*: 271 pp.

De Villiers, J.E., 1944. The origin of iron and manganese deposits in the Postmasburg and Thabazimbi areas. *Trans. Geol. Soc. S. Afr.*, 47: 123–135.

De Villiers, J.E., 1951. The manganese ores of Otjosondu, South West Africa. *Trans. Geol. Soc. S. Afr.*, 54: 89–98.

De Villiers, P.R., 1970. The geology and mineralogy of the Kalahari manganese field north of Sishen-Postmasburg area. *Mem., Dept. Mines S. Afr.*, 59: 84 pp.

Dorr, J.V.N., 1968. Primary manganese ores. *Proc. 23rd Congr., Soc. Brasil. Geol.*, pp. 1–12.

Dorr, J.V.N., 1973. Iron-formation and associated manganese in Brazil. *Genesis of Precambrian Iron and Manganese Deposits–UNESCO, Earth Sci.*, 9: 105–114.

Dorr, J.V.N., Coelho, I.S. and Horen, A., 1956. The manganese deposits of Minas Gerais, Brazil. *Symp. Manganese–20th Int. Geol. Congr.*, 3: 277–346.

Dorr, J.V.N., Crittenden, M.D. and Worl, R.G., 1973. Manganese. In: D.A. Brobst and W.P. Pratt (Editors), *United States Mineral Resources–U.S. Geol. Surv. Prof. Pap.*, 820: 385–399.

Doyen, L., 1973. The manganese ore deposit of Kisenga-Kamata (western Katanga). Mineralogical and sedimentological aspects of the primary ores. In: G.C. Amstutz and A.J. Bernard (Editors), *Ores in Sediments*. Springer, Berlin, pp. 93–100.

Dzotsenidze, G.S., 1966. Genesis of Chiatura manganese deposits. *Int. Geol. Rev.*, 8: 559–569.

Ebert, H., 1963. The manganese-bearing Lafaiete-Formation as a guide-horizon in the Precambrian of Minas Gerais. *Acad. Brasil. Cienc.*, 35: 545–559.

Fabricius, F.H., 1968. Calcareous sea bottoms of the Raetian and Lower Jurassic sea from the west part of the northern Calcareous Alps. In G. Müller and G.M. Friedman (Editors), *Recent Developments in Carbonate Sedimentology in Central Europe*. Springer, Berlin, pp. 240–249.

Fermor, L.L., 1909. The manganese ore deposits of India. *Mem. Geol. Surv. India*, 37.

Fermor, L.L., 1950. Precambrian formations of India. Discussion. *Geol. Mag.*, 87: 140.

Fischer, A.G. and Garrison, R.E., 1967. Carbonate lithification on the sea floor. *J. Geol.*, 78: 488–496.

Gabe, D.R., Troshanov, E.P. and Sherman, E.E., 1965. The formation of manganese-iron layers in mud as a biogenic process. In: *Applied Capillary Microscopy: The Role of Microorganisms in the Formation of Iron-Manganese Deposits*. Consultants Bureau, New York, N.Y., pp. 88–105.

Garrison, R.E. and Fischer, A.G., 1969. Deep-water limestones and radiolarites of the Alpine Jurassic. In: G.M. Friedman (Editor), *Depositional Environments in Carbonate Rocks–Soc. Econ. Paleontol. Mineral., Spec. Publ.*, 14: 20–56.

Germann, K., 1971. Mangan-Eisen-führende Knollen und Krusten in Jurassischen Rotkalken der Nordlichen Kalkalpen. *Neues Jb. Geol. Paläontol. Monatsh.*, 3: 136–156.

Germann, K., 1972. Verbreitung und Entstehung Mangan-reicher Gesteine im Jura der Nördlichen Kalkalpen. *Mineral. Petrogr. Mitt.*, 17: 123–150.

Germann, K., 1973. Deposition of manganese and iron carbonates and silicates in Liassic marls of the Northern Limestone Alps (Kalkalpen). In: G.C. Amstutz and A.J. Bernard (Editors), *Ores in Sediments*. Springer, Berlin, pp. 129–138.

Gryaznov, V.I., 1970. Genesis of the manganese ores of the Nikopol basin and prediction of marine sedimentary and manganese deposits. In: D.G. Sapozhnikov (Editor), *Manganese Deposits of the Soviet Union*. Israel Program for Scientific Translations, Jerusalem, pp. 146–159.

Gulbrandsen, R.A. and Reeser, D.W., 1969. An occurrence of Permian manganese nodules near Dillon, Montana. *U.S. Geol. Surv., Prof. Pap.*, 650-C: 49–67.

Gulyan, E. KH., 1970. Mineralogical-geochemical features and environment of formation of manganese ores of the Armenian SSR. In: D.G. Sapozhnikov (Editor), *Manganese Deposits of the Soviet Union*. Israel Program for Scientific Translations, Jerusalem, pp. 263–266.

Hartman, M., 1964. Zur Geochemie von Mangan und Eisen in der Ostsee. *Meyniana*, 14: 3–20.

Heim, A., 1924. Über submarine Denudation und chemische Sedimente. *Geol. Rundsch.*, 15: 1–47.

Hem, J.D., 1963. Chemical equilibria and rates of manganese oxidation. *U.S. Geol. Surv. Water Suppl. Pap.*, 1667A (17): 64 pp.

Hem, J.D., 1972. Chemical factors that influence the availability of iron and manganese in aqueous systems. *Bull. Geol. Soc. Am.*, 83: 443–450.

Hewett, D.F., 1966. Stratified deposits of the oxides and carbonates of manganese. *Econ. Geol.*, 61: 431–461.

Hewett, D.F., Chesterman, C.W. and Troxel, B.W., 1961. Tephroite in California manganese deposits. *Econ. Geol.*, 56: 39–58.

Hewett, D.F., Crittenden, M.D., Pavlides, L. and De Huff, G.L., 1956. Manganese deposits in the United States. *Symp. Manganese–20th Int. Geol. Congr.*, 3: 169–230.

Hofmann, H.J., 1969. Attributes of stromatolites. *Geol. Surv. Can. Pap.*, 69-39: 58 pp.

Holtrop, J.F., 1965. The manganese deposits of the Guiana Shield. *Econ. Geol.*, 60: 1185–1212.

Huebner, J.S., 1967. *Stability Relations of Minerals in the System Mn–Si–C–O*. Thesis, The Johns Hopkins University, Baltimore, 279 pp.

Jenkyns, H.C., 1967. Fossil manganese nodules from Sicily. *Nature*, 216: 673–674.

Jenkyns, H.C., 1970. Fossil manganese nodules from the West Sicilian Jurassic. *Eclogae Geol. Helv.*, 63: 741–774.

Jenkyns, H.C., in preparation. Fossil nodules. In: G.P. Glasby (Editor), *Marine Manganese Deposits*. Elsevier, Amsterdam.

Jukes-Browne, A.J. and Harrison, J.B., 1892. The geology of Barbados, 2. The Oceanic Deposits. *Q.J. Geol. Soc. Lond.*, 48: 170–226.

Jurgan, H., 1969. Sedimentologie des Lias der Berchtesgadener Kalkalpen. *Geol. Rundsch.*, 58: 464–501.

Kalinenko, V.V., Shumikhina, I.V. and Gusareva, A.I., 1970. Manganiferous sediments and the distribution of V, Cr, Ni, Co and Cu in the Laba deposit. In: D.G. Sapozhnikov (Editor), *Manganese Deposits of the Soviet Union*. Israel Program for Scientific Translations, Jerusalem, pp. 267–283.

Kalinin, V.V., 1965. *Iron-Manganese Ores of the Karadzhal Deposit*. Nauka, Moscow, 124 pp. (in Russian.)

Kalinin, V.V., 1970. Structural and compositional features of the Karadzhal Fe-Mn Ore deposit. In: D.G. Sapozhnikov (Editor), *Manganese Deposits of the Soviet Union*. Israel Program for Scientific Translations, Jerusalem, pp. 335–340.

Kavun, V.I., 1970. Factors governing the occurrence of Mn-ores in the Karadzhal deposit. In: D.G. Sapozhnikov (Editor), *Manganese Deposits of the Soviet Union*. Israel Program for Scientific Translations, Jerusalem, pp. 323–334.

Kayupova, M.M., 1970. New mineralogical data on the Atasu Fe-Mn deposits (central Kazakhstan). In: D.G. Sapozhnikov (Editor), *Manganese Deposits of the Soviet Union*. Israel Program for Scientific Translations, Jerusalem, pp. 355–362.

Koark, H.J., 1970a. Sedimentary manganese ores in the Precambrian of Sweden. *Symp. Geology and Genesis of Precambrian Iron-Manganese Formations and Ore Deposits, 1970, Kiev* (preprint).

Koark, H.J., 1970b. Zur Geologie des neuentdeckten Jacobsit-Braunit-Hämatit-Mangansilikatlagers Slöjdartorp im Nybergelfelde in Zentralschweden. *Geol. Fören. Förhandl. Stockh.*, 92: 388–401.

Krauskopf, K.B., 1956. Separation of manganese from iron in the formation of manganese deposits in volcanic associations. *Symp. Manganese–20th Int. Geol. Congr.*, 1: 119–131.

Krauskopf, K.B., 1957. Separation of manganese from iron in sedimentary processes. *Geochim. Cosmochim. Acta*, 12: 61–84.

Krumbein, W.E., 1971. Manganese-oxidizing fungi. *Naturwissenschaften,* 58: 56–57.

Lahiri, D., 1971. Mineralogy and genesis of the manganese oxide and silicate rocks in Kajlidongri and surrounding areas, Jhabua Dt., Madhya Pradesh, India. *Econ. Geol.*, 66: 1176–1185.

Litherland, M. and Malan, S.P., 1973. Manganiferous stromatolites from the Precambrian of Botswana. *J. Geol. Soc. Lond.*, 129: 543–544.

Logvineko, N.V., 1973. Composition and origin of iron and manganese carbonates in sedimentary rocks. *Lithol. Mineral. Resour.*, 7: 328–337.

Logvineko, N.V., Volkov, I.I. and Sokolova, Ye.G., 1972. Rhodochrosite in deep-sea sediments of the Pacific Ocean. *Dokl. Acad. Sci., U.S.S.R., Earth Sci. Sect.*, 203: 178–181.

Lynn, D.C. and Bonatti, E., 1965. Mobility of manganese in diagenesis of deep-sea sediments. *Mar. Geol.*, 3: 457–474.

Maksimov, A.A., 1960. Types of manganese and iron-manganese deposits in central Kazakhstan. *Int. Geol. Rev.*, 2: 508.

Manheim, F.T., 1961. A geochemical profile of the Baltic Sea. *Geochim. Cosmochim. Acta*, 25: 52–71.

Manheim, F.T., 1965. Manganese iron accumulations in the shallow-marine environment. In: *Symp. Mar. Geochem.–Narragansett Mar. Lab. Occ. Publ.*, 3: 217–276.

Marchandise, H., 1956. Contribution à l'étude des gîsements de manganèse sédimentaires. *Symp. Manganese–20th Int. Geol. Congr.*, 1: 107–118.

Mason, B., 1944. The system $Fe_2O_3-Mn_2O_3$: some comments on the names bixbyite, sitaparite and partridgeite. *Am. Mineralogist*, 29: 66–69.

Mero, J.L., 1965. *The Mineral Resources of the Sea*. Elsevier, Amsterdam-London-New York, 312 pp.

Michard, G., 1968. Coprécipitation de l'ion manganeux avec le carbonate de calcium. *Compt. Rend. Acad. Sci.*, 267: 1685–1688.

Mitra, F.N., 1965. Genesis and mineralogenetic trend of manganese orebodies at Chickla, Sitasaongi; and Dongri Buzurg, Bhandare Dt., Maharashtra, India. *Econ. Geol.*, 60: 299–316.

Molengraaf, G.A.F., 1916. On the occurrence of nodules of manganese in Mesozoic deep-sea deposits from Borneo, Timor and Rotti; their significance and mode of formation. *Proc. Acad. Sci. Amst.*, 18: 415–430.

Molengraaf, G.A.F., 1922. On manganese nodules in Mesozoic deep-sea deposits of Dutch Timor. *Proc. Acad. Sci. Amst.*, 23: 997–1012.

Monty, C., 1973. Les nodules de manganèse sont des stromatolithes océaniques. *Compt. Rend. Acad. Sci.*, 276: 3285–3288.

Moore, P.B., 1971. Mineralogy and chemistry of Långban-type deposits in Bergslagen, Sweden. *Mineral. Rec.*, Winter, 1971: 154–172.

Muan, A. and Somiya, S., 1962. The system iron oxide–manganese oxide in air. *Am. J. Sci.*, 260: 230–240.

Nagell, R.H., 1962. Geology of the Serra do Navio Districs, Brazil. *Econ. Geol.*, 57: 481–498.

Narayanswami, S., Chakravarty, S.C., Vemban, N.A., Shukla, K.D., Subramanyam, M.R., Venkatesh, V., Rao, G.V., Anandalwas, M.A. and Nagrajaiah, R.A., 1963. The geology and manganese ore deposits of the manganese belt in Madhya Pradesh and adjoining parts of Maharashtra, 1. General Introduction. *Bull. Geol. Surv. India, Ser. A, Econ. Geol.*, 22: 1–69.

Nayak, V.K., 1966. Mineralogy and genesis of the manganese ores of the Kajlidongri mine, District Jhabua, Madhya Pradesh, India. *Econ. Geol.*, 61: 1280–1282.

Nayak, V.K., 1968. Stability relations of manganese oxide minerals of the Kajlidongri mine, District Jhabua, Madhya Pradesh. *Bull. Geochem. Soc. India*, 3: 18–24.

Novokhatskiy, I.P., 1960. Ore genesis of the Atasu deposits. In: *Zhelezorudnye mestorozhdeniya Tsentral'nogo Kazakhstana i putti ikh ispol'zovaniya.* (In Russian.)

Novokhatskiy, I.P., 1970. Ferruginous-siliceous formations of Paleozoic age in Kazakhstan. *Symp. Geology and Genesis of Iron-Manganese Formations and Ore Deposits, 1970, Kiev* (preprint).

Park, C.F., 1946. The spilite and manganese problems of the Olympic Peninsula, Washington. *Am. J. Sci.*, 244: 305–323.

Perfilér, B.V. and Gabe, D.R., 1965. The use of the microbial-landscape method to investigate bacteria which concentrate manganese and iron in bottom deposits. In: *Applied Capillary Microscopy: The Role of Microorganisms in the Formation of Iron-Manganese Deposits.* Consultants Bureau, New York, N. Y., pp. 9–54.

Peters, T., Schwander, H. and Tromsdorff, H.V., 1973. Assemblages among tephroite, pyroxmangite, rhodochrosite, quartz: experimental data and occurrences in the Rhetic Alps. *Contrib. Mineral. Pet.*, 42: 325–332.

Pouit, G., 1964. Le manganèse dans la région de Tiaratine (Haut Atlas de Midlet, Maroc): origine syngènétíque et confrontation avec une théorie hydrothermale. *Compt. Rend. Acad. Sci.,* 258: 639–642.

Pratt, R.M. and McFarlin, P.F., 1966. Manganese pavements on the Blake Plateau. *Science*, 151: 1080–1082.

Rakhmanov, V.P. and Tchaikovsky, V.K., 1972. Genetic types of sedimentary manganese formations. *Acta Mineral. Petrogr.*, 20: 313–324.

Rebeiro, E., 1973. Jacobsites from the Urandi manganese district, Bahia (Brazil). *Genesis of Precambrian Iron and Manganese Deposits—UNESCO, Earth Sci.*, 9: 41–48.

Roper, H., 1956. The manganese deposits at Otjosondu, South West Africa. *Symp. Manganese—20th Int. Geol. Congr.*, 2: 115–122.

Roy, S.K., 1967. *Geology of the Area around Jothvad, Panch Mahals Dt., Gujarat, with Particular Reference to the Manganese Formations*. Thesis, Jadavpur Univ., Calcutta.

Roy, Supriya, 1960. Mineralogy and texture of the manganese ores of Kodur, Srikakulam Dt., Andhra Pradesh, India. *Can. Mineralogist*, 6: 491–503.

Roy, Supriya, 1965. Comparative study of the metamorphosed manganese protores of the world—the nomenclature of gondites and kodurites. *Econ. Geol.*, 60: 1238–1260.

Roy, Supriya, 1966. *Syngenetic Manganese Formations of India*. Jadavpur Univ., Calcutta, 219 pp.

Roy, Supriya, 1968. Mineralogy of the different genetic types of manganese deposits. *Econ. Geol.*, 63: 760–786.

Roy, Supriya, 1969. Classification of manganese deposits. *Acta Mineral. Petrogr.*, 19: 67–83.

Roy, Supriya, 1972. Metamorphism of sedimentary manganese deposits. *Acta Mineral. Petrogr.*, 20: 325–336.

Roy, Supriya, 1973. Genetic studies on the Precambrian manganese formations of India with particular reference to the effects of metamorphism. In: *Genesis of Precambrian Iron and Manganese Deposits—UNESCO, Earth Sci.*, 9: 229–242.

Roy, Supriya and Mitra, F.N., 1964. Mineralogy and genesis of the gondites associated with metamorphic manganese orebodies of Madhya Pradesh and Maharashtra, India. *Proc. Nat. Inst. Sci. India,* 30: 395–438.

Roy, Supriya and Purkait, P.K., 1968. Mineralogy and genesis of metamorphosed manganese silicate rocks (gondites) of Gowari Wadhona, Madhya Pradesh, India. *Contrib. Mineral. Petr.*, 20: 86–114.

Rozhanov, A.G., Sokolov, V.S. and Volkov, I.I., 1973. Forms of iron and manganese in sediments of the Northwest Pacific Ocean. *Lithol. Mineral. Resour.*, 7: 423–433.

Rozhnov, A.A., 1970. Geological-genetic features of Mn-mineralization and its significance among iron and polymetallic ore shows in the western part of the Dzhail'min trough. In: D.G. Sapozhnikov (Editor), *Manganese Deposits of the Soviet Union*. Israel Program for Scientific Translations, Jerusalem, pp. 341–354.

Sapozhnikov, D.G., 1963. The Karadzhal Fe-Mn ore deposit. *Tr. IGEM Akad. Nauk. S.S.S.R.*, 89. (in Russian.)

Sapozhnikov, D.G., 1970. Geological conditions for the formation of manganese deposits of the Soviet Union. In: D.G. Sapozhnikov (Editor), *Manganese Deposits of the Soviet Union*. Israel Program for Scientific Translations, Jerusalem, pp. 9–33.

Sarkar, S.N., 1968. *Precambrian Stratigraphy and Geochronology of Peninsular India*. Dhanbad Publishers, Dhanbad, 33 pp.

Scarpelli, W., 1973. The Serra do Navio manganese deposit (Brazil). *Genesis of Precambrian Iron and Manganese Deposits—UNESCO, Earth Sci.*, 9: 217–228.

Schneiderhöhn, H., 1931. Mineralbestand und Gefüge der Manganerze von Postmasburg, Griqualand-West, Südafrika. *Neues Jb. Geol. Paläontol.,* 64A: 701–726.

Servant, J., 1956. Les gîsements et indices de manganèse de l'Afrique occidentale Française. *Symp. Manganese—20th Int. Geol. Congr.*, 2: 89–114.

Service, H., 1943. The geology of the Nsuta manganese ore deposits. *Mem. Gold Coast Geol. Surv.*, 5: 32 pp.

Shatskiy, N.S., 1954. On manganiferous formations and metallogeny of manganese, 1. Volcanogenic-sedimentary manganiferous formations. (In Russian.) *Izv. Akad. Nauk. S.S.S.R., Ser. Geol.*, 4. (English translation in *Int. Geol. Rev.*, 6: 1030–1056.)

Shimazaki, Y., 1970. Mineralogy of the iron-manganese ores of the Kunimiyama mine, Shikoku, Japan. In: T. Tatsumi (Editor), *Volcanism and Ore Genesis*. Univ. Tokyo Press, Tokyo, pp. 303–308.

Shterenberg, L.Y., Bazilevskaya, Y.S. and Chigireva, T.A., 1966. Manganese and iron carbonates in bottom deposits of Lake Pinnus-Yarvi. *Dokl. Akad. Nauk. S.S.S.R.*, 170: 205–209.

Simons, F.S. and Straczek, J.A., 1958. Geology of the manganese deposits of Cuba. *Bull. U.S. Geol. Surv.*, 1057: 289 pp.

Sokolova, E.A., 1958. Conditions of formation of Upper Devonian and Lower Carboniferous sediments and related Fe-Mn Ores in the Dzhail'min trough. *Izv. Akad. Nauk. S.S.S.R., Ser. Geol.*, 5. (in Russian.)

Sokolova, E.A., 1970. Laws governing the distribution of ore concentrations in manganese-bearing volcanogenic-sedimentary formations. In: D.G. Sapozhnikov (Editor), *Manganese Deposits of the Soviet Union.* Israel Program for Scientific Translations, Jerusalem, pp. 76–100.

Sokolova, E.I., 1964. *Physico-Chemical Investigations of Sedimentary Iron and Manganese Ores and Associated Rocks*. Israel Program for Scientific Translations, Jerusalem, 220 pp.

Sokolow, N., 1901. Die Manganerzlager in den Tertiären Ablagerungen des Gouvernements Jekaterinislaw. *Mem. Com. Geol., St. Petersburg (Tr. Geol. Kom)*, 18: 61–82.

Sorem, R.K. and Cameron, E.N., 1960. Manganese oxides and associated minerals of the Nsuta manganese deposits, Ghana, West Africa. *Econ. Geol.*, 55: 278–310.

Sorem, R.K. and Gunn, D.W., 1967. Mineralogy of manganese deposits of Olympic Peninsula, Washington. *Econ. Geol.*, 62: 22–56.

Stashchuk, M.F., 1972. *The Oxidation-reduction Potential in Geology*. Consultants Bureau, New York-London, 121 pp.

Straczek, J.A., Narayanswami, S., Shukla, K.D., Vemban, N.A., Chakravarty, S.C., Subramanyam, M.R. and Venkatesh, V., 1956. Manganese ore deposits of Madhya Pradesh, India. *Symp. Manganese–20th Int. Geol. Congr.*, 4: 63–96.

Strakhov, N.M., 1967. *Principles of Lithogenesis, 1*. Consultants Bureau, New York–Oliver and Boyd, Edinburgh, 245 pp.

Strakhov, N.M., 1969. *Principles of Lithogenesis, 2*. Consultants Bureau, New York–Oliver and Boyd, Edinburgh, 609 pp.

Strakhov, N.M., 1971. Geochemical evolution of the Black Sea in the Holocene. *Lithol. Mineral. Resour.*, 6: 263–274.

Strakhov, N.M. and Shterenberg, L.E., 1966. Problems of the genetic type of the Chiatura deposit. *Int. Geol. Rev.*, 8: 549–558.

Strakhov, N.M., Belova, I.V., Glagoleva and Lubchenko, I.Yu., 1971. Distribution and forms of occurrence of elements in the surface layer of modern Black Sea deposits. *Lithol. Mineral. Resour.*, 6: 131–154.

Strakhov, N.M., Varentsov, I.M., Kalinenko, V.V., Tikhomirova, E.S. and Shterenberg, L.E., 1970. The mechanism of manganese ore-formation processes (Oligocene ores in the southern part of the U.S.S.R.). In: D.G. Sapozhnikov (Editor), *Manganese Deposits of the Soviet Union*. Israel Program for Scientific Translations, Jerusalem, pp. 33–57.

Suslov, A.T., 1970. Main features of volcanogenic sedimentary Fe-Mn deposits. In: D.G. Sapozhnikov (Editor), *Manganese Deposits of the Soviet Union*. Israel Program for Scientific Translations, Jerusalem, pp. 59–75.

Takabatake, A., 1956. Genesis of manganiferous iron deposits in Japan. *Symp. Manganese–20th Int. Geol. Congr.*, 4: 205–220.

Taliaferro, N.L. and Hudsón, F.S., 1943. Genesis of manganese deposits of the Coast Ranges of California. *Bull. Calif. Div. Mines*, 125: 271–275.

Trask, P.D. and co-workers, 1950. Geologic descriptions of the manganese deposits of California. *Bull. Calif. Div. Mines*, 152: 378 pp.

Van Hook, H.J. and Keith, M.L., 1958. The system $Fe_3O_4-Mn_3O_4$. *Am. Mineralogist*, 43: 69–83.

Varentsov, I.M., 1964. *Sedimentary Manganese Ores*. Elsevier, Amsterdam-London-New York, 119 pp.

Vincienne, H., 1956. Observations géologiques sur quelques gites marocains de manganèse syngénétique. *Symp. Manganese–20th Int. Geol. Congr.*, 2: 249–268.

Walter, M.R., Bauld, J. and Brock, T.D., 1972. Siliceous algal and bacterial stromatolites in hot spring and geyser effluents of Yellowstone National Park. *Science*, 178: 402–405.

Watanabe, T., Yui, S. and Kato, A., 1970a. Bedded manganese deposits in Japan. In: T. Tatsumi (Editor), *Volcanism and Ore Genesis*. Tokyo Univ. Press, Tokyo, pp. 119–142.

Watanabe, T., Yui, S. and Kato, A., 1970b. Metamorphosed bedded manganese deposits of the Noda-Tamagawa mine. In: T. Tatsumi (Editor), *Volcanism and Ore Genesis*. Tokyo Univ. Press, Tokyo, pp. 143–152.

Weber, F., 1973. Genesis and supergene evolution of the Precambrian sedimentary manganese deposits at Moanda (Gabon). *Genesis of Precambrian Iron and Manganese Deposits–UNESCO, Earth Sci.*, 9: 207–322.

Zapffe, C., 1931. Deposition of manganese. *Econ. Geol.*, 26: 779.

Zeis, E.G., 1929. The Valley of Ten Thousand Smokes. *Natl. Geol. Soc. Contrib., Tech. Pap.*, 1.

Zelenov, K.K., 1965. Iron and manganese in exhalations of the submarine Banu Wuhu volcano (Indonesia). *Dokl. Akad. Sci., U.S.S.R., Earth Sci. Sect.*, 155: 94–96.

Zen, E., 1959. Mineralogy and petrography of marine bottom sediment samples off the coast of Peru and Chile. *J. Sed. Pet.*, 29: 513–539.

Zotov, A.V., 1968. Recent formation of some manganese minerals on the Mendeleev volcano, Kunashir island. *Zap. Vses. Min. Obshch.*, 97: 273–281.

Chapter 10

THE STRATA-BOUND CINNABAR–STIBNITE–SCHEELITE DEPOSITS
(discussed with examples from the Mediterranean region)

ALBERT MAUCHER

INTRODUCTION

A cursory survey of the relevant passages in the classic text books on ore deposits shows that most, if not all, of the cinnabar and stibnite deposits are believed to be epigenetic vein deposits of epithermal (mostly volcanic) origin, whereas the scheelite deposits are interpreted as pegmatitic to mesothermal, mostly contact-metasomatic, formations related to the late stages following acidic intrusives. Thus, isogenetic hydrothermal occurrences of cinnabar and/or stibnite with scheelite seem to be incompatible. But, as shown by the author (Maucher, 1965) and his associates (Angermeier, 1964; Höll, 1966, 1971; Höll and Maucher, 1967; and Lahusen, 1969), the combination of stibnite with scheelite (sometimes even with cinnabar) is typical of the worldwide type of strata-bound deposits of the Sb–W–Hg formation. These deposits are mostly lithologically controlled, bound to metasedimentary–metalvolcanic rock series, and they show a distinct, time-bound maximum — especially the scheelite-bearing occurrences — in the Early Paleozoic era. Very similar deposits are also found in the metavolcanics of the Precambrian greenschist belts.

The Sb–W–Hg formation is represented not only by deposits containing all the three minerals (stibnite, scheelite and cinnabar) alternating in varying amounts, but also by those deposits containing just two of them, such as cinnabar–stibnite or stibnite–scheelite. But, the combination of cinnabar with scheelite alone has not been observed by the author up to the present. One of the three minerals may prevail to such an extent that the deposit is nearly monomineralic, with only small amounts of accessories. The monomineralic type is represented especially by scheelite in reaction skarns of primary volcanic-sedimentary origin.

Because mercury and (at a lower rate) also antimony easily become mobilized, nearly all strata-bound cinnabar and stibnite deposits show more or less epigenetic patterns caused by diagenetic or metamorphic influences. In many cases only small remnants of the primary fabrics are preserved and the superimposed structures become dominant in such a manner as to obliterate the primary genetic relationships completely.

It is known from many regions, and it has also been observed by the author (Maucher,

1965) and by Höll (1966) in Turkey, that stibnite and/or cinnabar often occur in ore-bodies of different types and ages in the same region and that they are found there even in recent hot-spring precipitates.

The spring solutions in areas of high temperature and in close physical association with volcanism, are mostly believed to originate from a volcanic source alone. The "hydrothermal" solutions may, however, also be formed by circulating meteoric or connate waters reacting with metal-bearing rocks in geothermal environments or they may be driven out from thermally affected sedimentary or metamorphic rocks. Isotope studies searching for proofs of possible origins of mineral water have often been discussed, for instance by White (1969). White et al. (1973) have studied the thermal waters of the northern Californian coast ranges because of their close association with mercury deposits and their unusually high contents of NH_3, B, CO_2, Cl, and H_2S. The results constitute strong evidence for large proportions of non-meteoric, deep waters of connate and metamorphic origin. These findings support the suggestion of Moiseyev (1971) that most of the mercury found in ore deposits could have been derived from sediments with heat as the only contribution of magmas. Nevertheless, this mercury must have been introduced into the sediments preliminarily and the question of the primary origin of mercury in the crust remains open.

The famous deposit of Idria (Yugoslavia) serves as an example of repeated deposition of mercury. As shown in Fig. 1, the cinnabar occurs in different clastic, pyroclastic and carbonate rocks of different ages. It has been found in all horizons of the Upper Paleozoic and the Lower and Middle Triassic. The Upper Triassic, Jurassic, Cretaceous and Tertiary rocks are barren. Mlakar and Drovenik, (1971, 1972) distinguish two phases of mineralization. The second phase coincides with the deposition of the "Skonca beds" and "Langobardian pyroclastics" of Ladinian age. In this phase, the Upper Paleozoic, Scythian and Anisian beds may also have received a second mineralization, but as the Langobardian conglomerate already contains mineralized pebbles of the Upper Scythian dolomite, a first mineralizing phase must have been active before the Middle Triassic tectonic, erosional unconformity. The ores of the older mineralization phase are controlled mainly by contacts between lithostratigraphic units and besides this, they show epigenetic patterns. The ore in the Langobardian Sandstone, Skonca beds and tuffites is characterized by many sedimentary fabrics. Mlakar and Drovenik (1971, 1972) describe graded bedding, cross-bedding, interformational unconformities and glide folds in the ore beds. A schematic sketch of the situation during the Ladinian stage, when the syngenetic stratabound orebodies were formed by submarine thermal springs in a subsiding basin, is given in Fig. 2. As the deposition of the ore-bearing layers coincided with tectonic and volcanic activity, causing turbidity currents and gliding of the unconsolidated sediments, mechanical transportation and redeposition of the ores took place before and during the diagenetic lithification.

The primary origin of the solutions and their mercury content still remains hypothetical, however. Even if we assume that the greatest part of the mercury, has been derived

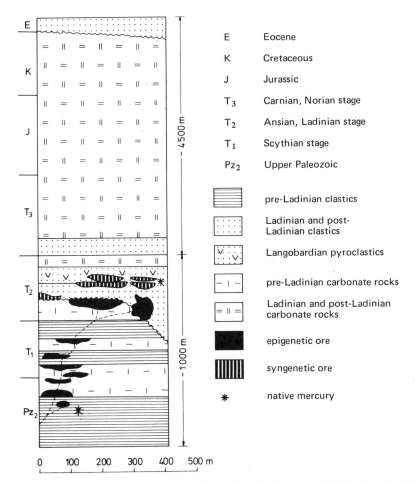

Fig. 1. Schematic stratigraphic sketch of the mineralized region of Idrija, Slovenia. (After Mlakar and Drovenik, 1972; courtesy of Drs. Drovenik and Mlakar.)

from the known Permian or Carboniferous mercury-bearing sediments, as a result of tectonic and/or volcanic pressure and heat, older source beds in Lower Paleozoic metavolcanics and metasediments cannot be excluded, particularly because strata-bound cinnabar deposits of this age are not uncommon in the Alps (compare Holl and Maucher, Chapter 1, Vol. 5).

Another example of cinnabar mobilization combined with stibnite has recently been studied by Neumann (1976) in Tuscany. Fig. 3 gives a schematic sketch of the ore-bearing horizons in Triassic, Jurassic, Cretaceous and Recent sediments. The Carboniferous Hg- and Sb-bearing beds of Jano are supposed to be the source beds. The volcanic heat is still active today and ore precipitation still takes place in favourable environments, especially where thermal and ground waters mix.

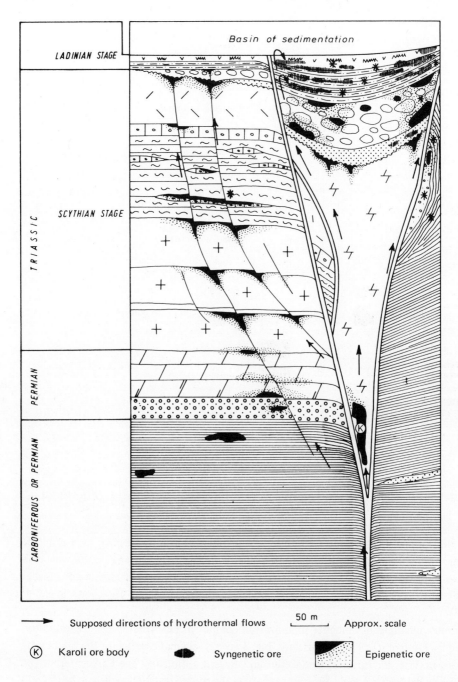

Fig. 2. Sketch showing the geologic structure of the mercury deposit of Idrija, Slovenia, during the time of the Middle Triassic ore precipitation. (After Mlakar and Drovenik, 1971; courtesy of Drs. Drovenik and Mlakar.)

As cinnabar and stibnite are found in many hot-spring deposits in alternating layers or even intermingled, the conditions of dissolution, transportation, migration and precipitation of mercury and antimony must be very similar and their mobility cannot differ very much. On the other hand, the mobilization of tungsten demands very different suppositions. Mobilization of scheelite is only observable in regions with intensive metamorphism.[1] It starts with the porphyroblastic growth of zonal scheelite and the filling of thin fissures with scheelite and quartz, sometimes grading into small veins. However, these fissures and veins are restricted to the ore-bearing beds themselves and to their very close neighbourhood. Only gneissification and beginning granitization result in the "sweating out" of pegmatoidic quartz–scheelite lenses and the formation of "hydrothermal" veins.

A compilation of the voluminous literature on the mobility and geochemistry of tungsten has been given by Wiendl (1968). He emphasizes the low-temperature solubility of tungsten in heteropolyacid compounds, as for instance:

$$H_8[Si(W_2O_7)_6]3H_2O, \quad H_3[P(W_3O_{10})_6] \cdot x\,H_2O \quad \text{or} \quad H_3[Sb(W_3O_{10})] \cdot x\,H_2O,$$

based on the research of Gundlach and Thormann (1960) who showed that scheelite is formed at $25°C$ by the titration of $H_8Si(W_2O_7)_6$ with NaOH and the presence of Ca-ions. The precipitation of scheelite started at pH 7.3. In an acidic environment tungsten heteropolyacids are stable up to temperatures of $250–300°C$. Gundlach and Thormann stress the presence of Si, P or Sb as nearly a precondition for the formation of the tungsten heteropolyacids. The formation of scheelite by neutralisation of these acids is accompanied by the formation of quartz, apatite and (if sulfur is present) by stibnite. This explains the high quartz and apatite and also the stibnite contents in the strata-bound scheelite deposits. Carpenter and Garret (1959) already assumed the existence of heteropoly tungsten ions in the Searls Lake brine. Besides the Searls Lake brine, the tungsten-bearing ferro-manganese sediments of the Ochotsk Sea (Issajeva, 1960) and the karstic filling with manganese ore containing up to 2.72% WO_3 in Liassic limestone near Aucillac, Lozère, France (Laboratoire Paris, 1973), are examples of supergene migration and sedimentation of tungsten, whereby manganiferous (colloidal) precipitates scavenge tungsten and other heavy metals. This gives a hint to the meteoric origin of the thermal springs of Golconda, Nevada, (Penrose, 1893) and Unica, Bolivia, (Lindgren, 1922) and explains the absence of cinnabar and stibnite in their tungsten-bearing manganese precipitates.

The gradual differences in the mobility of cinnabar, stibnite and scheelite lead to a differentiation by metamorphic mobilization with cinnabar at one end and scheelite at the opposite end of the sequence. Thus, an isogenetic migration and a coeval precipitation of scheelite with cinnabar or stibnite from metamorphic mobilized solutions is very improbable and one is compelled to conclude that the occurrences of the Sb–W–Hg formation, deposited contemporaneously with their embedding volcanic–sedimentary

---

[1] Editor's note: see Chapter 5 by Mookherjee, Vol. 4, on metamorphism of ores.

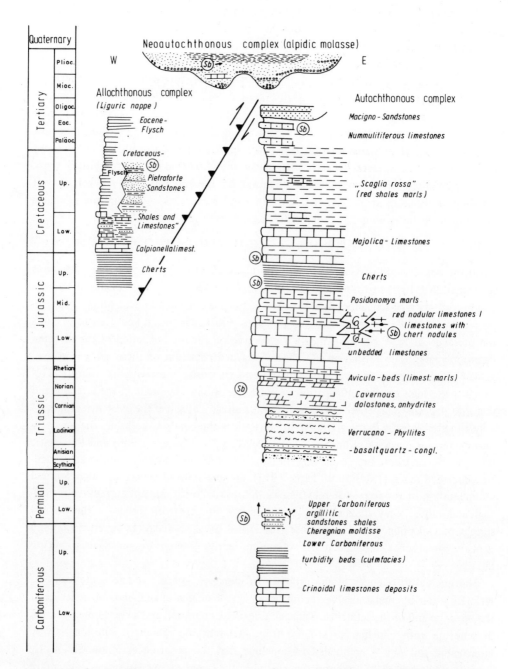

Fig. 3. Schematic geologic profile of the Tuscany region, Italy, with the different horizons with strata-bound Sb- (Hg-) mineralizations from Carboniferous to Recent precipitates. (After Neumann, 1976; courtesy of Mr. Neumann.)

host rocks, cannot be related to remobilized metamorphic solutions, but must originate from primary, deep-seated magmatic sources in connection with volcanic hydrothermal activity. This conclusion is not only forced upon us by the lack of scheelite in the cinnabar and stibnite deposits of post-Devonian age[1] and its predominant, time-bound, restriction to strata-bound deposits in metasediments and metavolcanics of Early Paleozoic units, but also by the significant dependence of the Sb–W–Hg formation upon geotectonic lineaments (Maucher, 1965), characterized by Benioff zones of Cordilleran type or of Islands arcs.

It would be impossible and go far beyond the aim of this paper to discuss in extenso all of the many deposits in question. Therefore, only a few representative ones, investigated by the author and his associates, are considered in detail on the following pages.

SARDINIA

The scheelite-bearing stibnite deposits of southeastern Sardinia occur in weakly metamorphosed rocks of Early Paleozoic age. Two types of stibnite mineralizations exist: concordant ore layers and lenses, and discordant veinlets. The concordant, strata-bound ore type is the much more important one with regard to its size, scheelite content and frequency. It consists of stibnite, scheelite and some framboidal pyrite, without any typical gangue, and is always bound to the same lithostratigraphic unit, the so-called "upper graphite schist", in the whole region of Ballao and Villasalto. The stratigraphic

TABLE I

Schematic stratigraphic column of the region of Ballao-Villasalto, province Gerrei, Sardinia, Italy (after Angermeier, 1964)

? Devonian	Clastic intercalations	
⎯⎯⎯⎯⎯⎯⎯	upper limestones and calcareous schists	500 m
Ludlow		
	upper graphite schists	Sb–W ores
		10 m upper porphyroids (5 m)
Wenlock	lower limestones and calcareous schists	80 m
⎯⎯⎯⎯⎯⎯⎯	lower graphite schists	30 m
Llandovery		
⎯⎯⎯⎯⎯⎯⎯	arenaceous shales and sandstones (partly con-	120 m
Ashgill	glomeratic)	lower porphyroids (up to 200 m)
Caradoc		
	- - - - - - -Unconformity- - - - - -	

[1] The only recent hot-spring discharges with high antimony, mercury and tungsten contents (up to 3%) known to the author have been reported from New Zealand by Weissberg (1969).

position is given according to Angermeier (1964) in Table I. The ore-bearing black shale is up to 10 m thick; in some places, intercalated thin stringers of grey limestone are found. The lower parts of the schists are locally represented by layers of porphyroids (foliated and sericitized quartz–porphyry and its tuff, produced by submarine volcanic activity). The ore-bearing horizons are also restricted to the lower parts of the schists. The preference of the ore for lithostratigraphic contacts, such as porphyroid–graphite schist or underlying limestone–graphite schist, is evident, whereby the bulk of the ores occurs near to or upon the porphyroids. The ore layers, though today tectonically deformed and sheared into lenses, still display primary patterns. Their original thickness changes within short distances, corresponding to the submarine morphology during deposition, and attains up to one meter and a half in basins and channels. The thick ore beds peter out or grade laterally into alternating thin layers of ore and black schist. The layers show macroscopically as well as microscopically rhythmic bedding of stibnite with graphite and calcite. Sometimes even cross-bedding, intraformational unconformities and glide-folds are still recognizable in the fine-grained stibnite ore, preserved in distinct niches protected against tectonic strain.

Regularities in the distribution of scheelite within the stibnite ore, especially in relation to limestone, have not been recognized; on the contrary, the scheelite-bearing stibnite beds do not show the fine-grained rhythmic repetitions. They consist mostly of alternating layers of massive ore with the scheelite bands in the lower parts.

The coeval sedimentation of the ores is not only proved by the sedimentary fabrics but also by the absolute lack of any tectonic control of the strata-bound ores. On the other hand, these ores have shared the same tectonic history as the porphyroids, graphite schists and limestones. The stibnite ores reacted, according to their plasticity, similarly to the black schist under plastic deformation, and they were foliated, sheared and folded, whereas the more brittle limestones, porphyroids and thicker scheelite layers were broken and pulled apart. The influences of several tectonic (mainly Variscan) phases may be observed in the strata-bound ores and the embedding rocks.

The second stibnite mineralization mentioned above was not deposited pre-tectonically but post-tectonically. It is bound to the fissures and faults extending from the upper graphite schist into the underlying limestone or porphyroids. The ore veins are narrow, short and of low grade. The stibnite crystals form a thin encrustation upon the walls of the fissures, which, besides stibnite, only contain calcite. Occasionally, some quartz may also be present. Scheelite has been found with the secondary ore just within or very near to the primary ore-beds, forming sparry aggregates. It does not reach far into the descending veins. Only in widely opened fractures, containing fragments of the brecciated rocks, was scheelite also found within the fragments a greater distance beneath the strata-bound ores. Besides their tectonic control, the ore-veinlets do not show any dependence upon the Variscan granites or upon any younger magmatic activity. They are bound to the primary ore layers themselves and to the rocks (porphyroids and limestones) just underneath; although not yet stratiform, they could be referred to as "strata-bound".

TURKEY

The very surprising results of the investigations of the Sardinian stibnite deposits – up to that time mostly described as typical epigenetic vein deposits of igneous-hydrothermal origin – led to intensive research on stibnite deposits in some other countries. Since the author was investigating copper deposits in Turkey for years and was acquainted with the Turkish Mining Research Institute (MTA-enstitüsü, Ankara, to which he is indebted for useful technical help in the field), this research was started there. The very close connection that stibnite often has with cinnabar in the same deposits in this country, of course led to including the cinnabar deposits in the investigations. A compilation of the results is given in Tables II and III. Details may be found in the thesis of Höll (1966).

Three epochs of cinnabar and stibnite deposition are discernible: the first one in the Early Paleozoic (*Gotlandian and ?* Ordovician), the second during the Permo-Triassic, and the third during the Tertiary (Oligocene to Miocene) stage.

The Early Paleozoic epoch is the most important one, not only regarding the stibnite but also the cinnabar production. The deposits (Table II) are bound to particular facies, lithostratigraphic contacts and mostly related to black shales. Connections with coeval submarine volcanic activity are observable at the mines of Keramos, Kalecik, Karareis and Alaşehir. They are probable also for other deposits where, by reason of the metamorphism, the tuffogeneous nature of the accompanying layers is not determinable with total accuracy.

The Early Paleozoic strata-bound deposits are not all of the same absolute age; they occur in Middle Godlandian as well as in Upper Gotlandian strata. Some occur above, the most below the pre-Upper Gotlandic unconformity. Possibly the scarcity of deposits of Upper Gotlandian age is due to the widespread erosion of the Upper Gotlandian strata in the eastern Aegeis and in western Turkey.

Similarly to the stibnite accumulations in Sardinia, some of the strata-bound stibnite deposits of Early Paleozoic age in Turkey also bear scheelite, whereas scheelite is absent in the other two epochs.

A remarkable exception is the vein deposit in the area of Gümüşler near Niğde in eastern Turkey. There, mostly quartz-bearing veins cross a rock unit of unknown age, consisting of alternating layers of paragneisses, micaschists, marbles and amphibolites. The comparison with Gotlandian to Devonian rock units in the neighbourhood leads to the conclusion that the rocks are of *Cambrian* to Ordovician age. The veins contain stibnite, stibiconite, chapmanite, cinnabar, scheelite, realgar, orpiment, arsenopyrite, pyrite, marcasite, enargite, chalcopyrite, covellite, malachite, azurite and chalcocite.

The genetic relationship and age of the vein deposit is still debatable, because the vein directions can be correlated with the oldest tectonic events as well as with the youngest ones. They do not show any clear relationship with the small occurrences of granitic rocks in the region, with which they perhaps could be correlated. Summarizing all the

Table II Strata-bound deposits of the Sb-W-Hg formation in Turkey and on the island of Chios/Greece.

	MUDARLI	KERAMOS (CHIOS)	KALECIK	KARAREIS	ALAŞEHIR	HALIKÖY	EMIRLI	ÇAMLICA	HABIBLER	DEMIRKAPI	SÜLÜKLÜ-EYMIR	DUDAŞ	TURHAL	ŞEYHŞABAN	SIZMA-LADIK-KURŞUNLU
PERMIAN	Lower Carboniferous	Permian	Permian	Permian					Marble (?Göktepe-formation)	Permian	Permian	"Permo-karbon"	discordant Stibnite veins ● EOCENE (TERTIARY)	Tertiary (?)	Permian to Mesozoic (?)
CARBONI-FEROUS		Upper Carboniferous, Upper Viséan	Upper Carboniferous, Upper Viséan	Upper Carboniferous						Upper Carboniferous	Upper Carboni-ferous (?)	Upper Carboni-ferous (?)	Cretaceous limestones (MESOZOIC)	Mesozoic (?)	marble-limestones series ●■
DEVONIAN	Devonian									Bänder-marmor von Da-naveli > 40 m					
UPPER GOTLAN-DIAN	Upper Gotlandian Limestones ca. 135 m	Limestone of Agre-lapos ■, Limestone of Melanios	Strata of Kalecik 80m, Limestone of Kalecik 80m	Limestone of Kalecik with chert and hornstone up to 120 m ■	● ■	■	●	(■●)	■ (●W)	● (■) epime-tamorphic schists 300 m exposed	● (■) epime-tamorphic schists several 100m exposed	●(W■) Schist and Marble 1000 m exposed	Permian limestones (PERMIAN)	Permian (?)	marble-limestones series ●■
MIDDLE GOTLAN-DIAN to ORDOVI-CIAN	Clastic Middle Gotlandian to Ordovician 4000 m (?) (total)	●(■W) Keramos strata Amani-strata Parparia-strata 3000 m (total)	strata of Denizgiren 2000 m	■	● ■	■	●	(■●)	■ (●W) middle complex of the Menderes - Massif some 1000 m				Turhal-series (?? Lower Paleozoic) (PRE-PERMIAN)	Schists and effusives (?? Devonian Lower to Permian) ■ (●) Schists and limestones	Paleozoic schists ■
CAMBRIAN	?	?	?	?	basis of the complex Menderes - Massif several 1000 m					?	?	?	?	?	?
PRE CAMBRIAN															

LEGEND:
- ● Cinnabar - occurrences
- ■ Stibnite - occurrences
- W Scheelite - occurrences
- ·( ) traces

TABLE III

Metallogenetic epochs of Sb—W—Hg mineralizations in Turkey

Lower Paleozoic		Permo-Triassic		Tertiary	
A. (Strata-bound)/		(Strata-bound)		(Veins, impregnations)	
Keramos	(Sb; Hg and W-traces)	Seyhşaban	(Hg, Sb)	Eğlence-Eskiköy	(Hg)
Karareis	(Hg)	Sizmy	(Hg, Sb)	Akkiz sivrisi tepe	(Hg)
Kalecik	(Hg)	Ladik-Kurşunlu	(Hg)	Baltali	(Hg)
Mudarly	(Hg)			Kestanlik tepe	(Hg)
Alaşehir	(Hg, Sb)			Karaağç	(Hg)
Habibler	(Hg; Sb- and W-traces)			Karacahisar	(Hg)
Haliköy	(Hg)			Çişekli tepe	(Hg)
Emirly	(Sb)			Çişekli kayasi tepe	(Hg)
Camliça	(Hg- and Sb-traces)			Göynük	(Sb; Hg-traces)
Demirkapi	(Sb; Hg-traces)			Cukurviran	(Sb)
Sülüklü-Eymir	(Sb; Hg-traces)			Oğulca	(Sb)
Dudaş	(Sb, W; Hg-traces)			Akhisar-Eynehan	(Sb)
Bilecik	(Sb, W; Hg-traces)			Dogiat	(Sb; Hg-traces)
Turhal	(Sb)			Yenice sağir	(Sb)
				Susuzyayla	(Sb)
B. Skarn deposit				Kinik	(Sb)
Uludağ-Bursa	(W; Bi-traces)			Akçal	(Sb)
C. Vein deposit				Korucu	(Sb)
?Gümüşler-Nigde (Sb—W—Hg)				Yenice kebir	(Sb)
				Taşdibi	(Sb)
				Turhal	(Sb)
				Sandiköy	(Sb)
				(strata-bound to limnic sediments)	

geological data available, the author assumes that the veins belong to the oldest mineralizations of the region and that they correlate to the strata-bound Sb—W—Hg mineralizations in western Turkey.

Finally, the scheelite occurrences in the Uludağ region near Bursa have to be mentioned (Van der Kaaden, 1958). As these "skarn" deposits occur near the Uludağ granite, they are normally described as contact-metasomatic mineralizations, but the host rocks are metasediments and metavolcanics (marbles and amphibolites) of Early Paleozoic age. The ore beds are not tectonically controlled, but they are strata-bound to folded reaction skarns. They are not restricted to or dependent upon the nearby granite, but are also found at a great distance from the granite contact. The scheelite content is pre-tectonic and pre-granitic. Directly at the contact with the younger granite, the scheelite has become partially transformed into wolframite. The scheelite deposit of the Uludağ corresponds to the strata- and time-bound scheelite deposits of the Alps and the Pyrenees.

The second, *the Permo-Triassic epoch* is characterized by only a few occurrences which are related to coeval submarine volcanic activity. They are mostly stratiform and strata-bound to the enclosing epimetamorphic sediments and volcanics.

The deposits of the third, *the Tertiary epoch* are, on the contrary, characterized by vein deposits and impregnations in silicified stockworks and quartz-veins within the andesitic to dacitic volcanites. A remarkable exception is the stibnite deposit of Sandiköy near Ismir: here, the ores (stibnite, pyrite, marcasite, realgar and orpiment) are strata-bound to a hornstone-bearing horizon intercalated between limnic limestones and conglomerates of Miocene age. The ores and the silicious (opalic) host rocks are believed to be hot-spring precipitates in a limnic environment. Recent hot-spring precipitates of stibnite have been observed by R. Höll and the author in a small pool, where hot springs are entering into a brook near the Thermae of Alaşekir. During their investigations the observers took all the stibnite-bearing mud from the pool, but during their next visit, one year later, new mud with stibnite-needles up to 4 cm long had been deposited.

Conclusions

The following conclusions are of general interest:

(1) The stibnite–cinnabar mineralizations are bound to three different epochs.

(2) The most important ones are strata-bound to metasediments and metavolcanics of Early Paleozoic age. They are partially scheelite-bearing and similar to the deposits in Sardinia as they are connected with black schists and metamorphic volcanics and very often lithostratigraphically controlled at the contact of different layers.

(3) The many, mostly not very important, veins and impregnations of Tertiary age are connected with the dacitic to andesitic volcanics of that time. They are free of scheelite and mostly monomineralic, with quartz as the typical gangue mineral.

(4) The partially important deposits of Permo-Triassic age are also mostly strata-bound and lithologically-controlled. They are free of scheelite and of special interest because cinnabar deposits of this age are also known in the Southern Alps, in Italy and in Spain.

(5) No clear evidence exists about the metal sources of the Permo-Triassic and Tertiary deposits. Whereas these deposits are clearly related to the coeval volcanics, their metal content may have been remobilized from the Early Paleozoic ore-bearing strata by the younger volcanic activities and redeposited by subsequent hydrothermal processes.

(6) The scheelite deposit at Uludağ near Bursa is strata-bound to reaction skarns primarily of Early Paleozoic age. Here, the scheelite content is older than the granitic intrusion, which locally transformed the scheelite-bearing reaction skarn into a contact-metamorphic skarn.

THE EASTERN ALPS

The investigations of the stibnite–scheelite–cinnabar deposits in the Eastern Alps lead to results very similar to those obtained in Sardinia and Turkey, as far as their fabrics and strata-bound character are concerned, but show differences in the relative proportions of the metals. Mercury (cinnabar) deposits in the Eastern Alps are not frequent and not of great economic value, whereas scheelite mineralizations are widespread and to some extent also economically promising. Even the first introductory visit to the abandoned stibnite mines in the Kreuzeckgruppe (Carinthia) resulted in the finding of scheelite in the dumps and galleries, which had absolutely not been noticed in these deposits until then (Höll and Maucher, 1967). Intensive research work executed by Lahusen (1969, 1972) proved that the deposits in the Kreuzeckgruppe, like those in Sardinia, show two types of mineralizations; concordant ore layers and lenses, and discordant veins, but both bound to the same stratigraphic unit.

The *concordant strata-bound ores* are much the more important ones. They can be followed over a distance of more than 7 km from west to east (Rabant, Eden, Goldbühel, Gloden, Gurser, Berl, Erler, Strieden) always in the same special unit of epizonal to mesozonal metamorphic rocks. The strata-bound cinnabar occurrence of Glatschach follows 10 km to the east near Dellach, and 20 km from there, the stibnite–scheelite deposits of Lessnig and Radlberg follow.

The ore-bearing unit lies in a series of phyllites, micaschists, gneisses and amphibolites of Early Paleozoic, probably Ordovician to Silurian age. It is characterized, over a thickness of up to 100 m, by layers of graphite schist, metadiabases, metatuffs and metatuffites embedded within phyllitic schists. Stibnite and scheelite mineralizations are bound to two, sometimes to three layers of graphite schist within a vertical distance of about 15 m. Metavolcanics lie below and above the graphitic beds with stratigraphic contacts. At some places metatuffites are embedded into the ore-bearing graphite schist. These metatuffites are also ore-bearing. The ores, for the most part banded, give evidence of primary sedimentary layers. In the fine-grained stibnite ore, even the primary rhythmic alternation with graphitic material is preserved. Besides the lithological and stratigraphical control, no other and especially no tectonic, control is recognizable in the strata-bound ores.

The *discordant ores*, on the contrary, are bound to fissures and brecciated faults cutting through the ore beds. Similarly to the Sardinian occurrences, these veins contain ore only within or very near to the strata-bound ore-bearing unit. On account of this spatial dependence, we must assume that the ore content of the veins has been derived by mobilization, from the primary concordant ores.

At Schlaining, Burgenland (Austria) rich stibnite ores, without any sign of scheelite, are mined. Concordant and discordant ores are also found there in a series of black schists and metavolcanics (Rechnitzer Schieferserie). The age of this series is still debatable (Maucher and Höll, 1968). Because Schönlaub (1973) has proved (paleontologically) a Cretaceous age for at least some limestones in the unit, an alpidic age of this part of the ore is out of the question. The existence of an older mineralization and older rocks in the series is still probable, however, especially because the strata-bound stibnite deposits of Pezinok–Pernek in the Male Karpaty Mountains (Czechoslovakia), which are supposed to be the continuation of the Sb–W–Hg belt of the Eastern Alps, are bound to rocks paleontologically proved to be of Early Paleozoic age. New findings of scheelite from this region have been reported recently by Kantor (1974).

In the ore-bearing units of Schlaining, as well as in those of the Kreuzeckgruppe, cinnabar contents are also known. Whereas cinnabar only occurs sporadically within the stibnite ore at Schlaining, it has formerly been mined from a small strata-bound occurrence at Glatschach near Dellach and from the small, abandoned cinnabar mine of Stockenboi in the Goldeckgruppe, from where Lahusen (1969, 1972) and Schulz (1968) describe three ore types:

(1) layers of cinnabar in sericitic quartzite with banded ores and synsedimentary fabrics;

(2) cinnabar impregnations in sericitic quartzite; and

(3) cinnabar, quartz and carbonates in stringers parallel to the bedding planes and in small discordant fissures.

Cinnabar is found in the intergranular interstices of the quartzite and also enclosed between the quartz grains and their diagenetically grown seams. It must, therefore, have been introduced into the arenaceous sediment before its diagenetic lithification (cf. Saupé, 1967). The age of the rock series (and the mineralization) near Stockenboi is only determinable by correlation with the cinnabar deposits near Turracher Höhe (Nock region, Austria). There, Höll (1970) found for the first time fossils which indicate the different time intervals of the Early Paleozoic. Höll could establish that not only the cinnabar deposits in various effusive rocks at "Hohes Kohr" and "Rottrasten" are strata-bound and time-bound to the Upper Ordovician deposition of the metasediments and metavolcanics, but also the small cinnabar occurrence in the metadiabase above Eisenkappel (Karawanken), the mercury traces in the effusive rocks of the Magdalensberg region and the cinnabar deposit of Stockenboi. Only the strata-bound cinnabar occurrence of Vellacher Kotschna is of Permian-Triassic (probably Ladinian) age and thus comparable to the above-mentioned cinnabar deposit of Idria, Yugoslavia (cf. p. 478 and Figs. 1, 2). The same three epochs of cinnabar and stibnite deposition as in Turkey (cf. p. 485) are discernable in the Eastern Alps: the first in the Early Paleozoic, the second during the Permo-Triassic and the third one during Cretaceous-Tertiary stages, whereby the stibnite deposits of Early Paleozoic age are locally scheelite-bearing, but scheelite is absent in the other two epochs.

Besides the scheelite recently detected within the strata-bound stibnite deposits, some other scheelite occurrences were already known from the Alps in quartz-rich veins and impregnations in the "central gneisses" of the Tauern Mountains and as layers underneath the magnesite deposits of Tux (Wenger, 1964). Because Wenger had also mentioned some stibnite content in the deposit of Tux, this deposit became of special interest in connection with the problems of the Sb–W–Hg formation. Investigations by Höll and Maucher (1967) confirmed the scheelite–magnesite deposit at Tux; it consists of an up to 3 m thick, scheelite-bearing, black-schist horizon and an overlying, dolomite-magnesite bed up to several tens of meters thick. The hanging wall and the footwall are built up of phyllitic rocks (Tuxer Phyllitserie). Intercalations of basic metavolcanics are locally present in the footwall. Three types of scheelite mineralization were described by Wenger (1964): banded scheelite (I), small scheelite veins (II) and small scheelite crystals in druses and fissures (III). All three types are bound to the black-schist layers only. The banded scheelite consists of alternating layers of scheelite and black schist. The primary sedimentary structure is still recognizable in rhythmic alternating layers of quartz and carbonates with scheelite and graphite. The graphite schists grade into the underlying phyllites by progressive decrease of graphitic material and quartz and the corresponding increase of sericite. A strong environmental control of the scheelite is shown by the corresponding cessation of the ore mineralization with the thinning out of the graphitic facies.

The metal supply of the synsedimentary ore is attributed to the hydrothermal aftermath of volcanic activity. The scheelite mineralizations of Wenger's (1964) type II and III are due to paradiagenetic and metamorphic recrystallization, especially in connection with saline brines. The age of the scheelite-bearing black schist and the first scheelite mineralization is not exactly determinable, but as the age of the overlying dolomite–magnesite bed is paleontologically limited to the period from the uppermost Ludlovian to Lower Ensian, an Early Paleozoic age is indicated.

Based upon knowledge of the numerous strata-bound deposits of the Sb–W–Hg formation of Early Paleozoic age, a systematic exploration for new deposits has been carried out in the metavolcanics and metasediments of probable Early Paleozoic age in the Alps (as for instance within the so-called Habachserie). The results substantiated the theory, and many unknown strata-bound scheelite occurrences have been discovered (Höll, 1970, 1971). They all show very intimate temporal, spatial and genetic relationships to the widespread basic volcanic activity of Early Paleozoic age. They are partly just varieties of the enclosing (host) rocks, with an increased scheelite content, but sometimes a special facies is developed with a WO_3 content of up to 10%.

One of the newly found deposits, namely that of "Kleinarltal", shows great similarities with the above-mentioned deposit at Tux. It lies within the "Radstätter Quarzphyllitserie" bound to a rock sequence composed of carbonate rocks, grey and black phyllites, quartzphyllites and quartzites, locally underlain by submarine, basic, volcanic rocks. The scheelite mineralizations within the coarse-grained dolomite are extremely pure, whereas those within the graphite-rich, finely laminated carbonate bands are accompanied by pyrite (partly framboidal) and pyrrhotite. The synsedimentary origin of these layered scheelite mineralizations is shown by their fabrics (Höll et al., 1972).

The most important new discovery is the "Felbertal" deposit, about 9 km to the south of the town of Mittersill. The up to 300 m thick scheelite-bearing series includes the lower part of the volcanic–sedimentary rock sequence in the Early Paleozoic "Habach-serie" within the "Tauernschieferhülle". Very characteristic, MgO-rich hornblendites and coarse-grained amphibolites are concentrated in two rock sequences, whereby the scheel-ite mineralizations are linked to the two hornblendite cycles. The ore and its surroundings are uniformly metamorphosed in the almandite–greenschist facies. The scheelite ores were deposited in separated basins, each basin with its own characteristic facies. There are three, strata-bound, scheelite generations: the first is stratiform, with excellent synsedi-mentary–syndiagenetic fabrics (Höll et al., 1972); the second is in the form of impregna-tions, with fairly coarse scheelite porphyroblasts, formed as a result of grain growth during the Alpidian orogeny, and the third is in discordant fissures, mobilized at the end of the regional metamorphism.

The formation of the primary ores was linked to submarine volcanic hydrothermal solutions coeval with the deposition of the enclosing rocks, such as tuffs, reworked volcanic material or even lava layers. The very rich, quartzitic ores presumably originate from submarine hot-spring precipitates (cf. Höll and Maucher, Chapter 1, Vol. 5).

It is genetically of great interest that the synsedimentary, strata-bound, scheelite mineralizations are accompanied by Bi-contents (native Bi, bismuthinite, galenobis-muthinite, cosalite, emplectite), locally in noteworthy amounts, and by sporadically dis-tributed Be-contents (beryl, bertrandite, helvite, phenacite) in the host rocks. These elements (especially bismuth) are also known from other strata-bound scheelite "skarns" normally thought to be of contact-metasomatic origin, such as, for instance, Sangdong, Korea (Bi) (So, 1968); Costabonne, France (Bi, Be) (Guitard and Laffitte, 1958); Salau, France (Bi) (Fonteilles and Machairas, 1968); Framont-Grandfontaine, France (Bi, Be) (Bouladon et al., 1964); White Pine County, Nev., U.S.A. (Be) (Kerr, 1946; Stager, 1960); Uludağ-Bursa, Turkey (Bi) (Van der Kaaden, 1958) or Seven Rila Lakes, Bulgaria (Bi, Be) (Zhelyaskova-Panajotova et al., 1972); The primary Bi- and Be-contents of the scheelite-bearing submarine volcanic sediments give strong evidence that these two elements or their minerals are not probative of a contact-metasomatic origin. However, they may be used, on the contrary, in connection with the strata-bound character of the mineraliza-tions in metavolcanic–metasedimentary host rocks, as an argument for the primary hy-drothermal–sedimentary nature of the ore. An augmented Au and Ag-content (up to 4 p.p.m.) of the scheelite-bearing hornblendites is typical, especially in horizons enriched in sulfides. This explains the Au- and Ag-content of the small scheelite–quartz veins in the partially granitized "central gneisses" and the famous gold–scheelite deposits of the "Schellgaden" type, with their high content of sulfides within quartzite layers. They too are considered to be synsedimentary–diagenetic in origin, but strongly metamorphosed.

Besides differences in the relative proportions of the metals and in details concerning the special tectonic evolution of the Alps, the stibnite, cinnabar and scheelite deposits of the Eastern Alps, as a whole, show the same lithological control, strata-bound character and time-bound dependencies (Early Paleozoic maximum) as the other Mediterranean deposits described above. As the author unfortunately has not had the opportunity to study the many other deposits in middle and southern Europe in the field, he is here only able to give some references. Hermann (1947) described the stibnite deposits of middle and southeastern Europe.

The greatest part of the Czechoslovakian stibnite deposits is (similarly to those near Schleiz and Greiz in Thuringia, G.D.R.) strata-bound to Early Paleozoic metasediments and metavolcanics (porphyroides and diabases and their tuffs), and some of them, such as those of Pernek and Pezinok (Kantor, 1974) are also scheelite-bearing.

The many stibnite occurrences in Yugoslavia are, according to the intersection of different tectonic lines and the still active tectonic mobility along the "Vardarzone", characterized by a combination of both tectonic and volcanic influences. Formerly, they have, on the whole, mostly been genetically attributed to the Cretaceous-Tertiary andesite volcanics. But recently Grafenauer (1964) has explained the genesis of the Slovanian stibnite deposits as being connected with the Middle Triassic volcanism, because at Lepa Nivja "the ore appears in lenses and in silicified cherts at the contact with the Middle Triassic limestones and dolomites". These strata-bound stibnite mineralizations are presumably the temporal equivalents of the strata-bound Triassic cinnabar mineralizations of Idria (cf. p. 481). Similarly to Idria, strata-bound impregnations and some lenticular orebodies occur in some Slovanian stibnite deposits (Trojane) along the layers in Carboniferous to Permian shales. There is a distinct dependence of the ore grade upon the amount of carbonaceous material. Therefore, there was also a stibnite mineralization of Carboniferous to Permian age, as a forerunner to that of the Triassic. From other Yugoslavian provinces and especially from the Drina region, Serbia, Jankovic (1960) also described typically strata-bound stibnite deposits in schists, sandstones and limestones of Triassic and of Carboniferous to Permian age, with the lithostratigraphic control at the contact between underlying limestones and overlying Permian schists. He also referred to deposits in higher metamorphic rocks as chlorite schists and amphibolites, and mentioned, incidentally, contents of bismuth and tungsten.

All the different authors described the strata-bound deposits as the richer, and the vein deposits as the less important ones, but modern systematic research paying special attention to the primary, synsedimentary mineralizations and their host rocks and age is still lacking. This research, not only with respect to stibnite and cinnabar, but also including scheelite (Bi, Be), would be of great local and general interest. The same would hold true for the deposits of the Sb−W−Hg formation in Bulgaria (e.g., the region of the Seven Rila Lakes) and in Roumania (e.g., the crystalline massif of Locva), especially in some regions with "skarn"-mineralizations in Early Paleozoic rock units.

SPAIN

The Iberian Peninsula is well known for its very old and rich mining industry. One of its most famous mines is the mercury mine of Almaden, situated in the Iberian Meseta between the Sierra Morena to the south and the mountains of Toledo to the north. The strata-bound character of the cinnabar mineralizations to three distinct horizons within the criadero–quartzite of Ordovician age, has always been an acknowledged fact. But, the origin of the ore has mostly been attributed to igneous hydrothermal solutions, produced from the Variscan granite intrusions, which for a long time have been supposed to be the main, if not the only, metal source of the peninsula.

Even before Saupé (1973) published his comprehensive monograph about the geology of the mercury deposit of Almaden, some special investigations pointed out that the cinnabar mineralizations are older than and independent of the granitic intrusions, because of the coincidence of cinnabar with the diagenetic growth of the quartz grains and the framboidal pyrites (Saupé, 1967; Maucher and Saupé, 1967; Arnold et al., 1971). According to Saupé (1973) the ore-bearing horizons are part of an up to 4000 m thick, very weakly metamorphosed rock series of epicontinental facies. Above the thick Armorican quartzite there follow siltstones, sandy-silty alternations and three quartzite horizons. Thin carbonate horizons are interstratified within the detrital sequence (Ashgill and Lower Devonian): "Among the three quartzite horizons, that of the Llandovery stage is remarkable as the only host of economic mercury mineralization (criadero–quartzite)."

Basic volcanic rocks are abundant during the Llandeilo, Llandovery-Wenlock and Middle Devonian. More or less contemporaneously with the intrusion of the granitic "Pedroches batholith" in the south, two granodioritic rocks intruded the series, accompanied along faults, by lamprophyric veins.

In the abstract of his monograph, Saupé (1973, p. 13) described the situation as follows:

"The Almaden mine, five smaller, exhausted and presently inaccessible mines, as well as several prospects are all located within the criadero–quartzite, which is the only horizon bearing pay ore. The mineralization is thus typically strata-bound. The criadero–quartzite is subdivided in two quartzite units, separated and bordered by siltstones. The ortho-quartzitic material was deposited, almost contemporaneously with the beginning of the basic volcanism of the Lower Silurian. The latter began by a lava-flow at the footwall of the quartzite and by a few interlayers of lava within the quartzite seam. A series of alternating volcanic and sedimentary units accumulated to a thickness of 450 m on top of the quartzite. A pyroclastic facies (frailesca) overlies the quartzite at the place where the latter is mineralized. The cinnabar impregnations have a lenticular shape, the three lenses being stratigraphically superposable. The sulphide occurs mainly in the intergranular interstices of quartz grains, or in small fractures, depending upon the lens. The faulting was clearly post-mineralization, because the faults cut the lenses and are barren of ore. Dykes of ? lamprophyres (301 ± 5 m.y.) resulted also post-mineralization, since they cut and roasted the ore. Introduction of mercury occurred before lithification because: (1) sedimentary features were observed in massive ore; and (2) inclusions of cinnabar were observed between the nuclei and their diagenetic coronae, both for the detrital quartz of the quartzites, as well as for the pyrite.

The source of the metal cannot be definitely identified: the volcanic rocks have a similar Hg content to the Paleozoic siltstones, which is distinctly higher than in the other rocks of the Almadén district. Both could therefore be the source rock. The correlation of mineralization and maximum thickness of volcanism, in the Chillón syncline, the occasional occurrence of cinnabar in volcanic rocks, and the large amount of tardi-magmatic[1] alteration of these, asserting the former presence of abundant fluids, strongly suggest a direct genetic relationship of the mineralization to the volcanism. However, the full nature of the genetic relationship remains partly hypothetical."

Neither the strata-bound character nor the synsedimentary–prediagenetic emplacement of the cinnabar mineralizations into the Early Paleozoic clastic sediments are hypothetical, but the source of the metal and the origin and nature of the transporting solutions are both debatable. In spite of the evidence that the age of the mineralizations and their close relationship to volcanism is congruent to the other cinnabar mineralizations of Early Paleozoic age within the Mediterranean Sb–W–Hg belt, Saupé (1973) does not believe in the volcanics as the source of the ore or in the time-bound nature of the Sb–W–Hg formation proposed by the present author (1965). Before discussing his objections, a short abstract of his genetic model ("un modèle cyclique ou mobiliste") may be given as follows:

"A first concentration of mercury took place by adsorption in pelitic sediments rich in carbonaceous material during the Ordovician stage. As a result of Taconic tectonic movements, the pelitic sedimentation was followed by an arenaceous sedimentation within a relatively fast-subsiding basin. The center of this basin, and therefore the region of the greatest thickness of the sandstones, coincides with the center of a thermic dome created by the volcanic activity reviving parallel to the subsidence of the basin. The heat flow of the thermic dome above the reviving volcanic center set the convection of fluids in motion, which transported the mercury from the pelitic source beds into the clastic sediments. The cinnabar became partially precipitated at the reduction–oxydation border within the sands and partially in massive ores with sedimentary fabrics upon the sea floor. A renewal of rapid clastic sedimentation led to a new sandy layer with another ore layer upon it. Thus three cycles of clastic sedimentation and ore precipitation resulted in the three ore horizons within the criadero sandstone. After this, the volcanic activity became effusive and gave rise to the overlying basaltic lavas and the pyroclastic layers (frailisca)."

Saupé (1973) thinks that this model (of a hypothetical preconcentration with a thermal remobilization and reconcentration) is necessary because the precipitation of the ores in the clastic basin predates the main basaltic lava flows and pyroclastics. He neglects, however, the basaltic lava underlying the criadero sandstone, which separates the criadero from the pelitic "source beds", as well as the small sporadic volcanic intercalations within the criadero. Volcanism started before the clastic sedimentation and came to an end after it! The ore-bearing solutions may have been the result of the first volcanic phase and it is

---

[1] The term "tardi-magmatic" refers to the late-magmatic gas- and fluid-rich stage.

not necessary that the fluids entered the basin near its center. They could also have carried the mercury to the margins of the basin from whence it was transported to the central parts. This situation may also explain two observations, namely, first, the presence of clastic cinnabar grains within the sediments which were formed as a result of sedimentary reworking of syngenetic–diagenetic cinnabar, thus forming intraclastic grains that were retransported and redeposited. Secondly, the volcanic solutions may also have supplied the occasional large amount of the chemically precipitated silica present in the quartzite. But, even if the mercury content was preconcentrated in and remobilized from an Ordovician pelitic sediment, this preconcentration would have been strata-bound and time-bound to Early Paleozoic events.

Some other differences between the deposits around Almaden and those of the other Early Paleozoic cinnabar mineralizations in the Mediterranean region are worth considering:

(1) the cinnabar lenses are strata-bound to sandstones and not to either shales, schists nor pyroclastics;

(2) the regional metamorphism is very weak;

(3) the stibnite and scheelite (tungsten) deposits are not "solidary" with the cinnabar deposits, because the stibnite mineralizations are not stratiform even if strata-bound and the scheelite occurrences are controlled by granites; and

(4) the paragenesis of scheelite with stibnite is alleged to be missing not only in the region of Almaden, but on the whole Iberian Peninsula.

Points 1 and 2, as well as the absence of spilitic phenomena, are explained by the fact that the region has not been involved in a deep "geosynclinal" development, but was situated at the margin of a more or less stable plate near the subduction zone in the north and related transcurrent faults.

The answer to points 3 and 4 must remain incomplete, as the investigations of the abandoned mines are inadequate. Only vein deposits of stibnite are reported, but the veins occur preferably in the criadero and in Ordovician schists. The occurrences, especially those of the De Porto province, are bound to particular strata of the same Early Paleozoic stage as the cinnabar of Almaden. From the Porto province, scheelite and stibnite mineralizations, strata-bound within metasediments, are also reported.

The scheelite occurrences of the Almaden region are partially connected with granites, but no systematic search for strata-bound mineralizations has been made. The close relationship to the bismuth occurrences and the deficiency of tin is typical. It is still an open question whether the stibnite, scheelite and bismuth mineralizations are really controlled by the granite, or whether, on the other hand, the deposits are only the contact-metamorphic products of the primary ore-bearing Ordovician and Silurian source beds. After comparison with the stibnite in scheelite occurrences in the northern provinces of Spain, the author must assume that this is the case.

Though the most important cinnabar mineralizations in Spain are bound to the criadero quartzite of Silurian age, there are some deposits in northern Spain, which are strata-bound to Carboniferous rocks. Different types of ores exist. Near to Mieres (Asturias), cinnabar and pyrite (sometimes accompanied by arsenopyrite) are found as impregnations and small fissures within clastic rocks (sandstones and conglomerates), forming parallel lenses; near Pola de Lena (Asturias) the ores (cinnabar, realgar, orpiment and arsenopyrite) are bound to mantos (flattish pipes) within Carboniferous limestones. Anger et al. (1968) explain the ores as hydrothermal deposits, formed during the Variscan orogenesis by mobilization of the mercury from older rocks. The cinnabar ores near Riaño (León) and Pedroso del Rey (León) are bound to the Carboniferous "Caliza de montaña", cementing karst fillings together with fluorite. Cinnabar has even been found within the coal seams near Oviedo, and some other occurrences exist which are not known in detail, within the Upper Carboniferous. The Carboniferous cinnabar ores in Spain may be compared with those of Carboniferous to Permian age in Turkey, Yugoslavia and Italy. It is interesting that these ores are almost free of stibnite which is found, on the other hand, in the Silurian deposits. This may be explained by the different reaction to the mobilizing agents and the greater mobility of mercury.

The absence of stibnite within the cinnabar deposits of Carboniferous age is especially surprising because stibnite and other antimony-bearing deposits of Early Paleozoic age are well known in the Asturian province. Guillou (1971) emphasizes the connection of antimony mineralizations with three episodes of carbonate sedimentation. The antimony contents are thereby always restricted to the uppermost parts of the carbonate sequence and are paleogeographically and lithologically controlled. The oldest mineralization consists of poor stratiform impregnations localized at the contact of the Gandana limestones (Lower Cambrian) with the overlying shales. The ore minerals are either galena, with lead—antimony sulfosalts, or chalcopyrite with silver-bearing tetrahedrite. They are partially bound to a lagoonal facies and are of synsedimentary to syndiagenetic origin. The second antimony mineralizations occur either in lagoonal facies or within thin sandy layers or lenses related to channel structures of the Vegado limestones and dolomites (Middle Cambrian). Also in these mineralizations, the ore does not consist of stibnite, but of complex sulfides and sulfosalts such as galena, sphalerite, pyrite, chalcopyrite, bournonite, tetrahedrite, schwatzite, boulangerite and jamesonite. In some cases, a synsedimentary zoning is reported with lead and zinc in the inner and copper in the marginal parts of the layers. These kinds of mineralization are not typical for the Sb—W—Hg formation but for the worldwide strata-bound sulfide mineralizations, especially of lead and zinc, within carbonate rocks. They are not typical for a special time, but began to form with the Cambrian (after Assynthian) and are still forming today. Unlike the two antimony mineralizations mentioned above, the third one which is bound to the limestones of the Ashgillian stage, consists of stibnite ores and must be considered in connection with the other stibnite mineralizations, bound to the Ordovician-Silurian transition in the Asturian basin (Guillou, 1969). The first stibnite mineralizations were formed within the black schists and volcanic rocks of the Upper Ordovician stage (Llandeilo). These mineralizations are mostly found only in traces, but at Biobra a stibnite deposit of probable exhalative–synsedimentary origin has been mined. The other stibnite deposits of the Ordovician-Silurian stage have been formed after the Taconic tectonic movements, which led to a partial erosion of Ordovician rocks. They are bound to marine sediments above the erosional surface, especially to the shales intercalated between the underlying limestones (Ashgill) and the overlying sandstones of Lower Silurian age (Valentian). Presumably, these sandstones correspond to the "criadero" of Almaden. In the mining region of Villarbacu, Guillou (1969) has shown that the stibnite deposits of the Ashgillian stage cannot be genetically explained by the action of hydrothermal solutions only, but that supergene, pedological events in the soils and sediments must also have played an important role in the concentration of the Ashgillian stibnite deposits. Finally, stibnite mobilizations are observed in reaction to the Hercynic tectonic events. But, it is very typical that these mineralizations are also restricted in space to their original stratigraphic environment.

Neither in the ores of the Llandeilo nor in those of the Ashgill stage, in the Sierra de Chaurel, is any scheelite content reported. This is in-so-far surprising as scheelite is not unknown in northern Spain (Ypma, 1966, and personal communication). In this respect, the late findings of scheelite in the axial zone of the Pyrenees near the Pic de Costabonne, France, are very interesting. The scheelite mineralizations are strata-bound there to skarn horizons in a probably Cambrian unit of dolomites, metaschists and metavolcanics. For the simple reason that a granite of Variscan age (granite of Costabonne) is in some places in contact with the ore-bearing unit, a contact-metasomatic origin of the scheelite is assumed (Guitard and Laffitte, 1960).

The scheelite-bearing skarns are not restricted to the contact of the granite with the dolomite alone, but occur also at great distances from any granite. This is especially the case with the southern skarns, which extend across the Spanish-French border to the Spanish mining region of Turun and Fra Joan. The skarns are interstratified with the dolomite and are mostly controlled by the lithological contact between the underlying dolomite and the overlying mica-schist with intercalations of metavolcanics (keratophyres and albitic tuffs). There are no differences between the skarn mineralizations at the contact or far from the granite. The granitic contact is marked by small, not very abundantly mineralized seams of 10–30 cm only. The skarns are typically banded parallel to the sedimentary layers, the different bands being characterized by their different contents of carbonate, garnet, pyroxene, diopside, mica, and quartz. The skarn layers can be followed on the French side over an extent of more than 1000 m. They are normally 10 m thick, but can reach up to 25 m or be restricted to a thickness of 1 m only. The scheelite occurs in a different manner; it forms very fine-grained impregnations, greater prophyroblasts (sometimes with inclusions of apatite) or even small veins with quartz. The highest scheelite contents have been found in the pyroxenitic layers, especially those rich in quartz and sulfides. Here also, beryllium minerals (helvite), native bismuth and bismuthite are typical. The strata-bound character, the independence of the mineralization from the granitic contact, the lithological control, the accessory minerals, the restriction of the veins to the ore-bearing beds, the volcanic—sedimentary origin of the host rocks and the premetamorphic nature of the scheelite, are so greatly similar to the synsedimentary—syndiagenetic scheelite deposits in the Alps, that the present author cannot agree to the contact-metasomatic replacement origin supposingly being the result of Variscan granitic intrusions (Guitard and Laffitte, 1960). Rather they must postulate a pre-granitic synsedimentary origin coeval with sedimentation of the (? Cambrian) Early Paleozoic host rocks and only locally influenced by the younger granite. This applies also for the deposit of Salau (Ariège) described by Fonteilles et al. (1968).

The continuation of the scheelite-bearing skarn unit is known on the Spanish side over an extent of some kilometers. It has not yet been intensively investigated, but from the abandoned mine of Turun, stibnite mineralizations are also mentioned. These stibnite occurrences have formerly been mined in this part of the Spanish Pyrenees, especially in the schists of the Ribas valley and from there in continuations towards the northeast (Borchert, 1942, p. 113). The stibnite ore occurred in small quartz veins and massive stibnite ore bodies, grading into impregnations in the accompanying schist layer. Also, the veins were strictly confined to the ore-bearing layer of about 1 m thickness. The coincidence of scheelite and stibnite in the metasediments and metavolcanics is further support of the primary sedimentary nature of these ores and of their belonging to the Sb—W—Hg formation of Early Paleozoic age. In spite of the special development of the different stibnite, cinnabar and scheelite deposits on the Iberian Peninsula, according to their special tectonic and magmatic development after the Early Paleozoic, their spatial temporal and genetic connection between Early Paleozoic submarine basic volcanism and the intercalated or overlying mineralized (volcanic—) sedimentary series, is evident. Also evident are the metamorphic influences and the younger metamorphic mobilizations and redepositions of Carboniferous and post-Carboniferous age.

CONCLUSIONS

(1) The fundamental metal supply into the South European Mediterranean cinnabar—stibnite—scheelite province took place during the Early Paleozoic period, genetically connected with basic volcanism and its (partially alkali-rich) acidic differentiates.

(2) The strata-bound cinnabar, stibnite and scheelite mineralizations deposited during this early stage took regionally different courses in their later geologic development, according to the particular geotectonic positions of the distinct subprovinces during the Caledonian, Variscan and Alpidian (Laramic) orogenies, respectively. They partially gave rise to the formation of younger deposits.

(3) The peculiarities of the younger deposits are not only due to the differences in the magmatic and metamorphic events causing the transformation, mobilization and redeposition of the primary ore content into new deposits, but also to the dissimilar reactivities and mobilities of the different ore minerals.

Scheelite, because of its low metamorphic mobility, remained spatially connected with the primary strata-bound and stratiform mineralizations of the Sb–W–Hg formation. It is therefore missing in the "younger" deposits. Its first reaction to regional metamorphism was the formation of reaction skarns; then followed a porphyroblastic growth and the migration into small quartzose fissures within the primary ore-bearing layers. Only in the case of granitization of the scheelite-bearing source beds or of the intrusion of magmatic melts into the ore-layers did the scheelite become involved in magmatic differentiation.

Stibnite, primarily mostly bound to lithostratigraphic contacts and controlled by carbonaceous shales and submarine volcanics, reacted mechanically similarly to a micaceous rock-forming mineral. It became plastically deformed and was also involved in the deformations of the surrounding schists. Additionally, it was mobilized into fissures and cracks within and in the neighbourhood of the ore-bearing layers. According to its solubility it was partly dissolved by magmatic or metamorphic hydrothermal solutions and reconcentrated in younger deposits in favourable environments. These deposits do not contain scheelite.

Cinnabar, having a higher grade of mobility, especially in its reaction to volcanic heat, has locally been driven out from the primary strata-bound complex mineralizations even before the stibnite. Thus, on one hand the primary ore horizons became poorer in cinnabar, whereas on the other the younger redepositions of cinnabar became mostly poor in stibnite. According to the mobility of cinnabar, its mobilization and redeposition may even have taken place at the end of the Early Paleozoic stage, thus forming "younger" mineralizations and deposits already coeval with the concluding stage of the Early Paleozoic volcanism.

(4) Mercury deposits are not only of Mesozoic-Cenozoic age and formed during the late stages in the formation of mobile zones in the earth's crust, but are also in many cases primarily connected with ancient provinces reactivated during the later geotectonic development.

(5) The first Sb–W–Hg supply was due to volcanic activity from deep-reaching Benioff zones along Cordilleran-type subduction zones. The oldest mineralizations and deposits of this kind are known from Precambrian greenschist belts (e.g., the scheelite-bearing stibnite deposits of Gravelotte, Murchison Range, Transvaal: Boese, 1964). Therefore, it can be assumed that the time-bound nature of the Early Paleozoic Sb–W–Hg formation is due to a specific geotectonic development along plate margins similar to those of ancient greenschist belts, the metals (Sb, Hg, W, Be, Bi, Au and Ag) being derived from the mantle and raised to the crust by volcanism of deep-seated origin. This also explains the fact that the cinnabar, stibnite and scheelite deposits of the time-bound Early Paleozoic Sb–W–Hg formation are bound to belts along ancient geotectonic lineaments (Andino-type margins of continents: Maucher, 1965). The mercury belt in Central Asia (Kuznetsov, 1974, a,b), with its mercury–antimony–tungsten (bismuth) mineralizations, fits very well into these characteristics.

(6) The time- and strata-bound character of many stibnite and scheelite deposits with-

in metasediments and metavolcanics of Early Paleozoic age around the Pacific Ocean constitute evidence that there also exists a circum–Pacific belt of the Sb–W–Hg formation. Research work undertaken by So (1968) has already proved the congruency between the famous scheelite deposit of Sangdong and the Felbertal deposit in the Eastern Alps. Burchard (1972) showed that the scheelite deposit of King Island, Tasmania, consists of an older Early Paleozoic strata-bound scheelite mineralization contact-metamorphically superimposed by a later granite intrusion. The stibnite belt in Bolivia is bound to Early Paleozoic strata with Mesozoic-Cenozoic discordant mobilizations. Ahlfeld (1974) describes the monomineralic antimony deposits as being independent from the Hercynian and Andinian orogenesis and not spatially or genetically related to the magmatic activities of these orogenies. Many other examples could be given from the U.S.A. and Canada.

⌣ (7) It is the aim of this paper to stimulate research onto time- and strata-bound cinnabar, stibnite and scheelite deposits within distinct Early Paleozoic strata and to give some useful data for prospecting and exploration work.

REFERENCES

Ahlfeld, F., 1974. Neue Beobachtungen über die Tektonik und die Antimonlagerstätten Boliviens. *Mineralium Deposita*, 9: 125–131.

Angermeier, H.O., 1964. *Die Antimonit–Scheelit-Lagerstätten des Gerrei (Südostsardinien, Italien) und ihr geologischer Rahmen.* Thesis, Univ. Munich, 62 pp.

Anger, G., Borchert, H., Gies, H., Lehmann, F. and Rieck, K., 1968. Die Quecksilber-Vererzung von Soterrana-Mieres, Asturien (Spanien). *Freib. Forsch. H.,* C230: 311–371.

Arnold, M., Maucher, A. and Saupé, F., 1973. Syngenetic pyrite and associated sulphides at the Almadén mercury mine (Spain). In: G.C. Amstutz and A.J. Bernard (Editors), *Ores and Sediments.* Springer, Heidelberg, pp. 7–19.

Boese, R., 1964. *Die Antimonglanzgänge von Gravelotte.* Thesis, Univ. Hamburg, 85 pp.

Borchert, H., 1942. Antimon. Irdisches Vorkommen. In: *Gmelins Handbuch der anorganischen Chemie.* (System Nummer 18, Teil A–Lieferung 1.) Verlag Chemie, Berlin, pp. 54–226.

Bouladon, J., Burnol, L., Picot, P. and Sainfeld, P., 1964. Les skarns métallifères de Framont-Grandfontaine (Bas-Rhin), leur minéralisation en fer et en tungstène. *Bull. B.R.G.M.,* 4: 55–109.

Burchard, U., 1972. *Geologische Untersuchungen zur Genese der Scheelitlagerstätte King Island, Tasmanien.* Thesis, Univ. München, 123 pp.

Carpenter, G. and Garrett, D.E., 1959. Tungsten in Searls Lake. *Min. Eng.,* 11: 301–303.

Fonteilles, M. and Machaires, G., 1968. Description pétrographique et métallogénique du gisement de scheelite de Salau (Ariège). *Bull. B.R.G.M., 2me Sér. Sect. II,* 3: 63–85.

Grafenauer, S., 1964. Deposits of stibnite in Slovenia. *Rudarsko Metall. Zb.,* 3: 257–269.

Guillou, J.J., 1969. Contribution à l'étude des minéralisations ordoviciennes en antimoine de la Sierra de Caurel (Provinces de Lugo et d'Orense, Espagne). *Sci. Terre,* 14 (1): 5–26.

Guillou, J.J., 1971. Quelques régularités dans la distribution de minéralisations sulfurées (en particulier en antimoine) dans les niveaux carbonates du Paléozoïque inférieur du géosynclinale Asturien. *Ann. Soc. Geol. Belg.,* 94: 21–37.

Guitard, G. and Laffitte, P., 1960. Les calcaires métamorphiques et les skarns du Pic de Costabonne (Pyrénées-Orientales). *Sci. Terre,* 6: 57–137.

Gundlach, H. and Thormann, W., 1960. Versuch einer Deutung der Entstehung von Wolfram- und Zinnlagerstätten. *Z. Dtsch. Geol. Ges.,* 112 (1): 1–35.

Hermann, F., 1947. Die Antimonerzvorkommen Mittel- und Südosteuropas, ihre lagerstättenkundliche Stellung und wirtschaftliche Bedeutung. *Verh. Geol., Bundesanst. Wien*, 1947: 57–83.

Höll, R., 1966. Genese and Altersstellung von Vorkommen der Sb–W–Hg-Formation in der Türkei und auf Chios, Griechenland. *Bayer. Akad. Wiss. Math. Naturwiss. Kl., Abh., N.F.*, 127: 118 pp.

Höll, R., 1970. Die Zinnober-Vorkommen im Gebiet der Turracher Höhe (Nock-Gebiet, Österreich) und das Alter der Eisenhut-Schieferserie. *N. Jb. Geol. Paläontol. Mh.*, 4: 201–224.

Höll, R., 1970. Scheelitprospektion und Scheelitvorkommen im Bundesland Salzburg, Österreich. *Chem. Erde*, 28: 185–203.

Höll, R., 1971. Scheelitvorkommen in Österreich. *Erzmetall*, 24: 273–282.

Höll, R. and Maucher, A., 1967. Genese und Alter der Scheelit–Magnesit-Lagerstätte Tux. *Bayer. Akad. Wiss. Math. Naturwiss. Kl., Sitzungber.*, 1967: 1–11.

Höll, R., Maucher, A. and Westenberger, H., 1972. Synsedimentary–diagenetic ore fabrics in the strata- and time-bound scheelite deposits of Kleinarltal and Felbertal in the Eastern Alps. *Mineralium Deposita*, 7: 217–226.

Issajeva, A.B., 1960. Tungsten in the deposits at the bottom of the Okhotsk Sea. *Dokl. Akad. Nauk, S.S.S.R.*, 131: 416–419.

Jankovic, Sl., 1960. Allgemeine Charakteristika der Antimon-Erzlagerstätten Jugoslaviens. *N. Jb. Mineral. Abh.* (Festband Ramdohr) 94: 506–538.

Kantor, J., 1974. Scheelite in the Malé Karpaty Mts. crystalline and its genetic relationship to basic volcanism. *Geol. Zb. Geol. Carp.*, 25: 1–208.

Kerr, P.F., 1946 (1958). Tungsten mineralization in the United States. *Geol. Soc. Am. Mem.*, 15: 241 pp.

Kuznetsov, V.A., 1974a. The mercury provinces of the U.S.S.R. *Econ. Geol.*, 69: 715–716.

Kuznetsov, V.A., 1974b. Mercury mineralization belt in Central Asia. *Abstr. 1st Int. Mercury Congr., Barcelona*, 2 (15): 30.

Laboratoire de Géologie Appliquée, Paris, 1973. Some major concepts of metallogeny (consanguinity, heritage, province). *Mineralium Deposita*, 8: 237–258.

Lahusen, L., 1969. *Die schicht- und zeitgebundenen Antimonit–Scheelit-Vorkommen und Zinnober-vererzungen der Kreuzeck- und Goldeckgruppe in Kärten und Osttirol, Österreich.* Thesis, Univ. München, 139 pp.

Lahusen, L., 1972. Schicht- und zeitgebundene Antimonit–Scheelit-Vorkommen und Zinnober-Vererzungen in Kärnten und Osttirol, Österreich. *Mineralium Deposita*, 7: 31–60.

Lindgren, W., 1922. A recent deposit of a thermal spring in Bolivia. *Econ. Geol.*, 17: 201–206.

Maucher, A., 1965. Die Antimon–Wolfram–Quecksilber-Formation und ihre Beziehungen zu Magmatismus und Geotektonik. *Freib. Forsch. H.*, C.186: 173–187.

Maucher, A. and Höll, R., 1968. Die Bedeutung geochemisch-stratigraphischer Bezugshorizonte für die Altersstellung der Antimonitlagerstätten von Schlaining im Burgenland, Österreich. *Mineralium Deposita*, 3: 272–285.

Maucher, A. and Saupé, F., 1967. Sedimentärer Pyrit aus der Zinnober-Lagerstätte Almadén (Provinz Ciudad Réal, Spanien). *Mineralium Deposita*, 2: 312–317.

Mlakar, I. and Drovenik, M., 1971. Structural and genetic particularities of the Idrija mercury ore deposit. *Geol. Razpr. Poročila, Ljubljana*, 14: 67–126.

Mlakar, I. and Drovenik, M., 1972. Geologie und Vererzung der Quecksilberlagerstätte Idrija. Proceedings of the Second International Symposium on the mineral deposits of the Alps, Bled, 1971. *Geol. Razpr. Poroçila, Ljubljana*, 15: 47–62.

Moiseyev, A.N., 1971. A non-magmatic source for mercury ore deposits. *Econ. Geol.*, 66: 581–601.

Neumann, N., 1976. *Geologische und geochemische Parameter der Hg- und Sb- Lagerstätten in der Toskana, Italien.* Thesis. Univ. München (In press).

Penrose, R.A.F., Jr., 1893. A Pleistocene manganese deposit near Golconda, Nevada. *J. Geol.*, 1: 275–282.

Saupé, F., 1967. Note préliminaire concernant la genèse du gisement de mercure d'Almadén. *Mineralium Deposita*, 2: 26–33.

Saupé, F., 1973. La géologie du gisement de mercure d'Almadén (Province de Ciudad Real, Espagne). *Sci. Terre, Mem.*, 29: 342 pp.

Schönlaub, H.P., 1973. Schwamm-Spiculae aus dem Rechnitzer Schiefergebirge und ihr stratigraphischer Wert. *Jb. Geol., Bundesanst. Wien*, 116: 35–49.

Schulz, O., 1968. Schicht- und zeitgebundene paläozoische Zinnober-Vererzung in Stockenboi (Kärnten). *Sitzungsber. Bayer. Akad. Wiss. Math. Naturwiss. Kl.*, 1968: 113–139.

So, Ch.S., 1968. *Die Scheelit-Lagerstätte Sangdong.* Thesis Univ. München, 71 pp.

Stager, H.K., 1960. A new beryllium deposit at the Mount Wheeler mine, White Pine County, Nevada. *U.S. Geol. Surv., Prof. Pap.*, 400B: 70–71.

Van der Kaaden, G., 1958. On the genesis and mineralization of the tungsten deposit Uludağ. *Bull. Mineral. Res. Explor. Inst. Turkey*, Foreign ed., 50: 33–42.

Weissberg, B.G., 1969. Gold–silver ore-grade precipitates from the New Zealand thermal waters. *Econ. Geol.*, 64: 95–107.

Wenger, H., 1964. Die Scheelitlagerstätte Tux. *Radex-Rdsch.*, 1964: 109–131.

White, D.E., 1969. Thermal and mineral waters of the United States–brief review of possible origin. *Proc. 23rd Int. Geol. Congr., Prague, 1968*, 19: 269–286.

White, D.E., Barnes, J. and O'Neil, J.R., 1973. Thermal and mineral waters of non-meteoric origin, California coast ranges. *Geol. Soc. Am. Bull.*, 84: 547–600.

Wiendl, U., 1968. *Zur Geochemie und Lagerstättenkunde des Wolframs.* Thesis. Tech, Univ. Clausthal, 295 pp.

Ypma, P.J.M., 1966. Sumario de la mineralización metalifera y su genesis en Galicia Occidental (España). *Leidse Geol. Mededel.*, 36: 279–291.

Zhelyaskova-Panajotova, M. Petrussenko, Sv. and Iliev, Z., 1972. Tungsten and bismuth-bearing skarns of the Sangdong type from the region of the Seven Rila Lakes in Bulgaria. *Proc. 24th. Int. Geol. Congr., 1972, Montreal, Sect. 4*, pp. 519–522.

Chapter 11

SEDIMENTARY PHOSPHATE DEPOSITS

PETER J. COOK*

INTRODUCTION

   Phosphate ore comes from three main sources: igneous apatite accumulations such as those associated with the nephelene syenites and carbonatites of southern Africa and the Kola Peninsula (Fiveg, 1937; Deans, 1966, 1968); guano-derived deposits such as those of Nauru and Christmas Island (White and Warin, 1964); and marine sedimentary phosphate deposits. Only the sedimentary deposits will be considered here. They are known to occur on every continent except Antarctica (Fig. 1), and range in age from Precambrian to Recent.

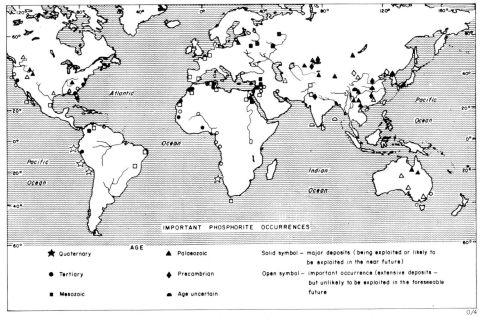

Fig. 1. Distribution of major sedimentary phosphate deposits.

* Published with the permission of the Director of the Bureau of Mineral Resources, Canberra.

Because of their economic importance (they contribute more than 80% of the world's production of phosphate rock) they have been the subject of numerous studies, and an extensive literature has developed on them. In this brief review article only the more important aspects of the geology of marine sedimentary phosphate deposits are mentioned and the major references cited. Outstanding publications to which the reader's attention is particularly directed include that on the Asian deposits by Bushinski (1969a), the papers on phosphate ores in the United Nations volume *Mineral Resources Development Series, No. 32,* the series of United States Geological Survey Professional Papers (313A-F) on the Western Phosphate Field, and the *World Survey of Phosphate Deposits* by the British Sulphur Corporation (1971).

The general term "phosphate" is used to describe phosphate-rich sedimentary rocks. Most phosphorites are of marine origin or result from the weathering of marine deposits. A few deposits such as those of the Green River Formation of the western United States (Love, 1964) are of lacustrine origin. Such non-marine occurrences are not, however, of economic interest, and consequently this discussion will be directed primarily towards marine phosphorites.

The phosphate content of a rock is generally expressed as percentage P_2O_5 and this practice is followed exclusively in this paper. Alternative units which are commonly used by mining companies are BPL (bone phosphate of lime or tricalcium phosphate) where

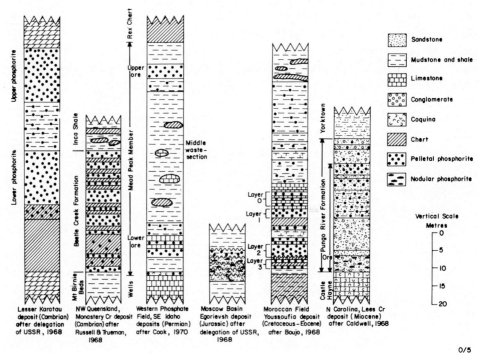

Fig. 2. Stratigraphic columns for some major phosphate deposits.

BPL = $2.185 \times \% P_2O_5$, and elemental phosphorus where $P = 0.436 \times P_2O_5$. The grade of phosphate rock which may be economically mined depends on mining, transportation, and beneficiation costs. In some areas such as the Western Phosphate Field in the United States, it is possible to selectively mine beds with a P_2O_5 content in excess of 30%. Elsewhere, such as at the Lee Creek mine of North Carolina, the ore averages less than 15% P_2O_5. The thickness of minable units is also highly variable depending on location and the mining methods used. In some deposits it is necessary to selectively mine units a metre or less thick; in others the minable unit is 10 m or more thick.

Stratigraphic columns through some of the world's major phosphate deposits are given in Fig. 2, and from this a wide range of ore thicknesses is evident. Some of the phosphatic beds are lenticular over distances of a few metres; others are extremely uniform in lithology and thickness over hundreds of square kilometres.

The phosphate ore is generally pelletal or nodular, though in a few deposits the ore is clay-size material. Individual deposits may range in area from a few to hundreds of square kilometres. Reserves similarly vary from small deposits containing a few million tonnes of ore which are worked, sometimes by fairly primitive methods, for local consumption, to others which contain reserves of several billion tonnes.

The "dilutents" (non-phosphatic matrix and thin interbeds) and associated sediments are also rather variable. They include mudstone and shale (e.g., southeast Idaho), chert (e.g., northeast Utah; Karatau), limestone and dolomite (e.g., northwest Queensland), and sand and sandstone (e.g., central Florida). The occurrence of some of these sediments is illustrated in Fig. 2. Regional stratigraphic studies have revealed that the phosphatic sequences grade into synchronous non-phosphatic sediments. The phosphorites of northwest Queensland grade into limestone and massive dolomite. The phosphorites of the Western Phosphate Field grade into carbonates then red beds and evaporites (Fig. 3). The Karatau deposits grade into massive chert sequences.

It is clear from this brief introduction that phosphorites are a highly variable group of sediments which are difficult to deal with adequately in a short paper. In the subsequent discussion the writer will consider the distribution of phosphate deposits (in space and time), the types of deposits, their petrology and geochemistry, and the various theories for their origin.

DISTRIBUTION OF PHOSPHATE DEPOSITS

Attempts have been made to show that there is a worldwide cyclicity in the deposition of phosphate. Strakhov (1969) has suggested that worldwide phosphate maxima occur in the Late Cretaceous—Early Tertiary, the Permian, and the Early Cambrian. Maxima have also been suggested for the Sinian (Riphean) and the Proterozoic. However, the Sinian and the Proterozoic are each periods of about 1000 m.y. — considerably in excess of the Phanerozoic. Consequently, to assert that there is a phosphate maximum in the Sinian

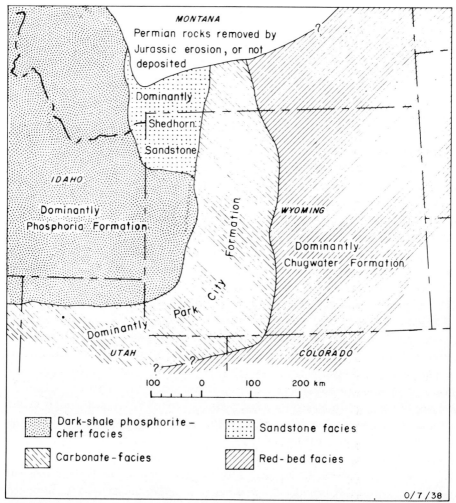

Fig. 3. Distribution of main sediment types and major rock units in the Western Phosphate Field. (After Sheldon, 1963. Courtesy of U.S. Geol. Surv., Washington.)

and then to compare that to a maximum in the Permian (a period of about 40 m.y.) is rather misleading. Bushinski (1969b) disputes that there are any worldwide maxima; he suggests that phosphate accumulates in response to localized phenomena.

Although there is considerable doubt about the existence of worldwide peaks in phosphate deposition there is no doubt that phosphorites have been deposited in extensive phosphogenic provinces at particular times. Some of these provinces are evident from Fig. 1. They include:

(1) the Late Precambrian province of central and southeast Asia;

(2) the Cambrian province of central and southeast Asia, extending into northern Australia;

(3) the Permian province of North America;

(4) the Jurassic-Lower Cretaceous eastern European province;

(5) the Upper Cretaceous-Eocene Tethyan province of the Middle East and North Africa, extending into West Africa and the northern part of South America;

(6) the Miocene province of southeastern North America.

These provinces extend for several thousand kilometres; their original extent is uncertain owing to the questionable nature of some (particularly Palaeozoic and older) continental reconstructions. There are also commonly several different types of phosphorite deposits within a single province. Consequently, although the common factor of abundant phosphate may be present throughout, the genetic processes that concentrated the phosphate in the sediments vary from one deposit to the next.

Phosphate-rich sediments are present on modern continental shelves (Fig. 1) off southwest Africa (Summerhayes et al., 1973), northwest Africa (Tooms and Summerhayes, 1968; Summerhayes et al., 1972) the southeastern United States (Pevear and Pilkey, 1966), southern California (Dietz et al., 1942; d'Anglejan, 1967; Pasho, 1972), northern South America (Veeh et al., 1973), eastern Australia (Von der Borch, 1970; Marshall, 1971), and eastern New Zealand (Reed and Hornibrook, 1952). Most contain Tertiary fossils; initially these were considered to be reworked from older units but uranium series dating by Kolodny (1969) and Kolodny and Kaplan (1970) indicated that none of these deposits were less than one million years old. However, Baturin et al. (1972) and Veeh et al. (1973) have shown that two phosphorites are forming at the present day on the southwest African and Peruvian shelves. Both these localities will be discussed in detail later, but it is important to note at this stage that these two occurrences are on the shelf or the upper slope adjacent to arid regions and in areas with a high organic productivity.

TYPES OF PHOSPHATE DEPOSITS

No two phosphate deposits are precisely the same, but nevertheless a number of common features may be used as the basis for a classification scheme. Bates (1960) has suggested a descriptive phosphorite classification into: (a) dark compact and fine grained; interbedded with mudstone or limestone; (b) light coloured nodular beds in a sandy matrix; (c) residual. However, the most widely used 3-fold classification is:

(1) Geosynclinal or West-coast type (e.g., the Western Phosphate Field of the United States).

(2) Platform or East-coast type (e.g., the North Carolina deposits).

(3) Weathered or residual type (e.g., the brown rock deposits of Tennessee).

An additional category of "foredeep" has also been suggested (Delegation of the Soviet Union, 1968); the Sayan deposit of central Asia is regarded as an example of this type. However, the foredeep type would seem to be merely a particular type of geosynclinal deposit.

The difficulty with this classification is that deposits commonly have characteristics of more than one type. In addition, there are genetic implications in the terms, which are undesirable in many instances. For this reason, perhaps the non-genetic terms "West-coast" and "East-coast" are preferable if they are taken to mean "Phosphoria-type" and "North Carolina-type" deposits. The palaeogeographic use of west and east is, however, totally untenable. In addition the use of terms such as eugeosyncline and miogeosyncline have somewhat uncertain status (see Wyllie, 1973) in view of our new understanding of global tectonics. However, as these terms are in general used in the classification of phosphate deposits they will be used here. The characteristics of the three major types of deposits will now be considered briefly.

"Geosynclinal" phosphorites

Two types of geosynclinal deposits are distinguished: eugeosynclinal and miogeosyn-clinal. The eugeosynclinal deposits tend to be relatively small and are commonly associated with thick volcanogenic sequences. They are generally uneconomic although those of eastern Sayan and central Tien-Shan in central Asia contain up to 200 million tonnes of medium-grade ore.

The miogeosynclinal deposits are of much greater importance economically, with ore reserves in the order of billions of tonnes. Deposits such as those of Karatau in the U.S.S.R. and the Western Phosphate Field of the U.S.A. are important examples of this type of deposit. These deposits are characterized by a common association with chert, fine organic-rich argillaceous sediments, and carbonates (particularly dolomite). The phosphorites tend to be pelletal and commonly extend over hundreds to thousands of square kilometres, with a high P_2O_5 content throughout. Severe folding and faulting of the deposits is common.

"Platform" phosphorites

As implied by the name, these phosphorites are generally on, or bordering, cratons. Deposits commonly occur as rich discrete pockets covering tens to hundreds of square kilometres, and several metres thick, such as the Pamlico Sound deposit of North Carolina or the Mishash deposits of Israel. Alternatively they occur as thin low-grade nodular deposits covering many thousands of square kilometres as in the Mesozoic deposits of the Moscow basin of U.S.S.R. or the Ordovician deposits of central Australia. Both types of platform deposits are commonly associated with terrigenous sediments such as quartz siltstone and sandstone or with carbonates. Glauconite is abundant in some deposits; phosphatized coquinas are common in others (e.g., the Baltic deposits) shallow-water features such as cross-bedding and scour structures are present in some. The main differences between the geosynclinal and platform-type phosphorites are summarized in Table I. Despite all these differences, it is perhaps necessary to stress again the difficulty in

TABLE I

Comparison of phosphate deposits

Feature	Geosynclinal or West-coast type	Platform or East-coast type
1. Phosphorite type	generally pelletal; minor oolitic	pelletal, nodular, and non-pelletal
2. Matrix to pellets	argillaceous or siliceous	quartzose (sandy) or calcareous
3. Grade of the phosphorite	high grade	low grade
4. Nature of the deposit	thick extensive continuous beds	discontinuous beds
5. Fauna	pelagic	shallow-water
6. Inferred water depth	hundreds of metres	tens of metres
7. Sediment association	black shale-chert	carbonates, sands
8. Influence of syn-sedimentary structures	generally lacking	deposits commonly in synclines or the flanks of anticlines
9. Tectonics	strongly folded	gently folded

placing some deposits into one or other of these categories. The Cambrian phosphate deposits of northern Australia have attributes of both, such as an abundance of chert interbeds, but also features such as coquinas and cross-bedding are common.

Weathered and residual phosphorites

Post-depositional modification of phosphate-bearing sediments is a feature of many deposits. This is particularly the case with platform (East-coast) deposits which commonly have never been buried by more than a few hundred metres of sediment, and in many instances have been subjected to weathering for prolonged periods. Concentration of phosphate can occur as a result of chemical or mechanical weathering. Chemical weathering may produce a high-grade phosphorite by the leaching-out of a more soluble (generally calcareous) non-phosphatic matrix to leave a residual phosphorite such as the Tennessee brown rock deposits. Alternatively, the phosphate goes into solution and is then reprecipitated within the weathering profile; the Tennessee white rock deposits are an example of this type (Collette, 1968). In some cases the phosphate-rich solutions phosphatize pre-existing carbonate rocks. The processes of solution, redeposition, and replacement commonly occur in the same deposit.

Mechanical reworking of phosphorite commonly follows chemical leaching which either removes the matrix completely or alternatively makes it softer and thus more readily reworked. Probably the best known example of a reworked deposit is the Pliocene Bone Valley Formation of Florida in which the phosphatic material is derived from the Miocene Hawthorn Formation. Reworked deposits of this type are commonly pebbly and nodular and are generally mixed with coarse cross-bedded quartzose sands. They are typically lenticular, and ·infill depressions in the underlying unit. Where the phosphorite has been derived from a calcareous unit the erosion surface at the top of the carbonate may be karst-like.

PETROLOGY OF PHOSPHORITES

Most phosphorites are composed of collophane, a cryptocrystalline carbonate-fluorapatite. Some phosphorites are made up predominantly of pellets of crandallite (an aluminium phosphate) but this is believed to be a secondary weathering product after collophane. The form of the collophane making up phosphorites is highly varied and several authors have discussed their morphology in detail (Bushinski, 1935; Weaver, 1955; Emigh, 1958; Gulbrandsen, 1960; Mabie and Hess, 1964; Trueman, 1971; Cook, 1972). Many classification schemes have been suggested, but marine phosphorites have three basic forms: (1) phosphatic nodules (Fig. 4); (2) phosphatic grains and pellets (Fig. 5); (3) fine-grained non-pelletal (predominantly clay-size) structureless phosphorite (Figs. 6,7).

Although this is a grain-size classification scheme there are believed to be significant differences in the genesis of these three types. The boundary between a phosphatic pellet and a phosphatic nodule may conveniently be taken as 2 mm, which corresponds to the sand/gravel boundary.

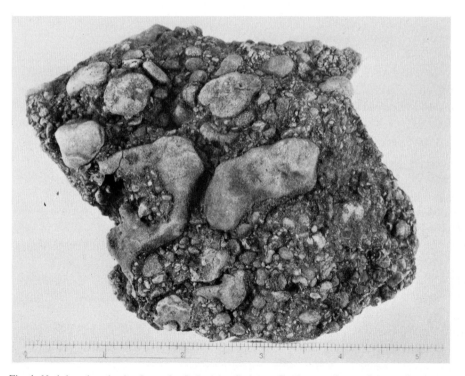

Fig. 4. Nodular phosphorite from the Ordovician Stairway Sandstone of central Australia. Scale at the base of the sample is marked in 1-inch (2.54-cm) intervals.

Fig. 5. Pelletal phosphorite from the Cambrian Beetle Creek Formation, northwest Queensland. The darker bands are chert; note the microtroughs infilled with fine pelletal collophane.

Phosphatic nodules

Phosphate nodules range up to several centimetres in diameter; they have a character-istically irregular external surface with many re-entrant faces (Fig. 4). Some of the larger nodules are flat; others grade into pavement-like and encrusting forms. Iron-rich or man-

Fig. 6. Finely bedded non-pelletal phosphorite from the Late Precambrian Areyonga Formation of central Australia. The darker patches are rounded clasts of chert.

Fig. 7. Structureless collophane (phoscrete) from Georgina Basin of northwest Queensland. The dark patch near the margin of the sample is due to manganiferous and ferruginous staining.

ganese-rich coatings are common, and a glazed, polished appearance is typical of many of the nodular phosphorites described from the present-day continental shelves (Murray and Renard, 1891; Dietz et al., 1942; Von der Borch, 1970; Pasho, 1972).

The internal structure of nodules is rather variable. Some are comparatively homogeneous and are composed predominantly of structureless collophane or alternatively silt- and clay-size terrigenous material in a collophane matrix. Others are layered, and some concentrically banded which has been ascribed to accretion or post-depositional weathering. Many nodules are composed of smaller nodules or angular fragments, and have a conglomeratic or brecciated texture. Phosphatic grains and pellets are common in many nodules; Pasho (1972) found that nodules from off southern California contain, on average, 12% pellets. Sharks' teeth and other fossil fragments are present in some nodules, and some exhibit infaunal burrowing.

Nodular phosphorites are most abundant in platform-type deposits such as those of the Moscow basin, and in residual deposits such as those of the Bone Valley Formation of Florida. Phosphatic nodules are also a relict feature of many disconformity and unconformity surfaces.

Phosphatic grains and pellets

Phosphatic pellets are generally well rounded, with a spherical to ellipsoidal form. Where the phosphatic material is angular, as is the case with some phosphatized fossil fragments, then the term grain is perhaps preferable to pellet. Inclusions in phosphate pellets may include silt-size detrital grains, clay minerals, fossils and fossil fragments, glauconite, pyrite, and organic matter. The abundant organic matter commonly imparts a black or dark brown color to unweathered pellets. Pelletal phosphorites are abundant in both geosynclinal and platform deposits (Fig. 5). The most comprehensive classification of pelletal phosphorites is by Mabie and Hess (1964) who describe more than thirty different textures in phosphate ores of the Western Phosphate Field. A modified version of their classification is used here.

Ovule. This is the commonest type of pellet in most phosphorites; more than 70% of all the phosphatic material in the Meade Peak Member of the Phosphoria Formation is ovular. Pellets of this type have a round or subround outline and generally show no internal structure (Fig. 8). In some instances, weathering may produce a pseudo-oolitic

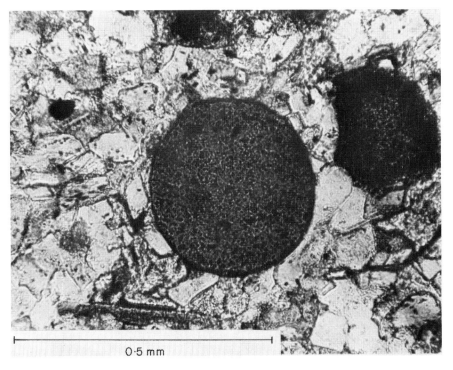

0·5 mm

Fig. 8. Phosphatic ovule (dark) in a light-coloured silty matrix. Sample from the Ordovician Stairway Sandstone of central Australia.

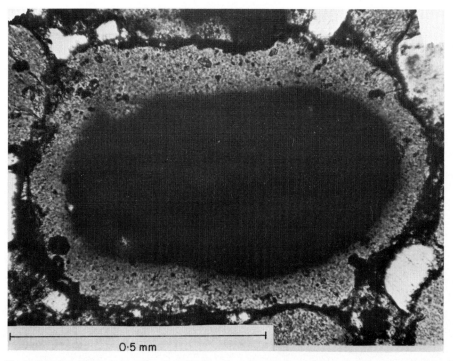

Fig. 9. Pseudo-oolitic ovule with a rim of light-coloured collophane from where organic carbon has been removed by oxidation.

appearance due to the marginal leaching of dark organic material (Fig. 9). The pellets of the Phosphoria Formation range in size from $-1\ \phi$ to $5\ \phi$ and have a mean diameter of about $1\ \phi$.

Nucleated pellet. This pellet type consists of a nucleus of a single fossil fragment or detrital grain, around which precipitation of phosphatic material has taken place (Fig. 10). This appears to be a comparatively rare pellet type in most deposits. In some nucleated pellets "ghosts" of fossil fragments may represent nucleus material which has been phosphatized.

Polynucleated pellet. As implied by the name, the nucleus of this pellet type consists of two or more detrital grains or fossil fragments. Many of these pellets form in much the same way as the nucleated pellets except that the pellet formed around a multiple nucleus. Others are believed to be of intraclastic origin as there are abundant detrital grains scattered throughout the pellet. They probably formed when a lamina cemented by the interstitial precipitation of phosphate became torn up and rounded to give a pelletal form.

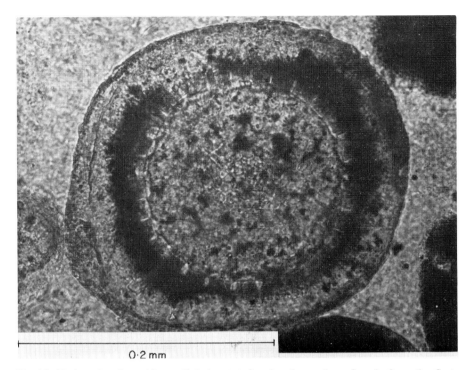

Fig. 10. Nucleated pellet with a radiolarian test forming the nucleus. Sample from the Cretaceous deposits of Khourigba, Morocco.

Compound pellet. This pellet is composed of two or more pellets or fragments of pellets. An intraclastic origin is indicated where pellets are broken. Commonly the pellets appear to have been cemented together; further accretion then occurred in the form of an outer skin around the multiple pellet (Fig. 11). This type of pellet can perhaps be compared with grapestone in calcareous sediment. In the Permian phosphorites of the western United States this type of pellet forms less than 2% of the total phosphatic components.

Oolith. Oolitic pellets are concentrically banded throughout; elongate included particles such as sponge spicules or mica flakes are concentrically aligned (Fig. 12). Ooliths are rarer in phosphorites than is commonly realized; in the Phosphoria phosphorites, ooliths represent only 3% of the total phosphate fraction. Ooliths may form by a "snowball" effect: gentle agitation of pellets resulting in rolling and the incorporation of phosphatic and other material in the outer skin of the pellet.

Phosphatic fossil fragments. Phosphatized fossil fragments (or in some cases, fragments of originally phosphatic shells) form a significant proportion of some deposits. The Ordo-

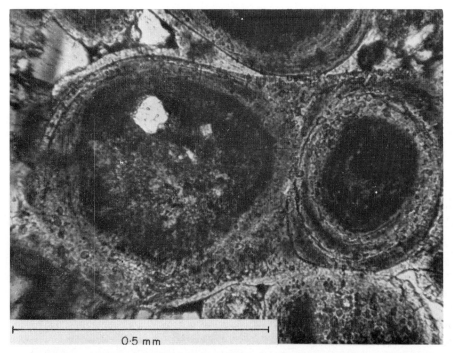

0·5 mm

Fig. 11. Compound pellet from the Permian Meade Peak Member of the Phosphoria Formation.

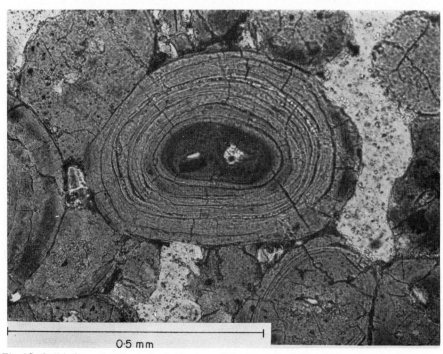

0·5 mm

Fig. 12. Oolith from the Meade Peak Member of the Phosphoria Formation, showing well developed concentric banding.

vician platform phosphorites of the Baltic region, for instance, are composed primarily of a phosphatic granular coquina mainly of phosphatic brachiopod shells (Delegation of the Soviet Union, 1968). Some of the phosphorite layers in the Cambrian deposits of north-eastern Australia are composed of pellets of rounded phosphatized fragments of pelmato-zoans (De Keyser and Cook, 1972). Some units, such as the Fish Scale Marker Bed of the Permian Meade Peak Member, comprise a fossil hash in which there is little or no rounding of the phosphatic bone and shell fragments.

Non-pelletal phosphate

This rock consists essentially of dense light-coloured structureless collophane; some forms are bedded (Fig. 6), others are encrusting on siliceous or calcareous sediments. Features such as veins and encrustations of iron and manganese oxides are common in some forms (Fig. 6). A variety of terms have been coined to describe this type of occur-rence: Freas (1964), and Freas and Riggs (1968) suggested the term "microsphorite"; Trueman (1971) used the term "collophane mudstone". The writer (Cook, 1972) has suggested the term "phospholutite" (analogous to calcilutite) to describe primary de-posits of this type and the term "phoscrete" (analogous to calcrete) for secondary phos-phatic deposits of supergene origin. An excellent petrological description of non-pelletal phosphorites is given by Trueman (1971) who makes the observation that this variety of phosphorite is relatively more abundant in Precambrian than in Phanerozoic deposits. In the Phanerozoic, it is more abundant in the platform than the geosynclinal-type deposits.

There are at least two major types of non-pelletal phosphorites, the primary and the secondary deposits. The primary deposits are laminated to thinly bedded, and contain included silt- and clay-size terrigenous material and rare phosphate pellets. In places they are interbedded with pelletal phosphorites. Riggs (1967) discussed phosphorites of this type (microsphorite) from the Noralyn Mine of central Florida and describes abundant evidence of burrowing by organisms and the development of penecontemporaneous brec-cias. He found most deposits were on ancient topographic mounds, and considers that the depositional environment was intertidal. Howard and Cooney (1974) have also described primary non-pelletal phosphorite (collophane mudstone) from the Cambrian D-Tree de-posit of the Georgina Basin. These phosphorites are also laminated to thin-bedded and contain terrigenous non-phosphatic material; interbeds of coquinite are present and some botryoidal surfaces may be of algal origin. In thin section there is little or no internal structure, but examination of material from the Lady Annie deposits by scanning elec-tron microscopy has shown that the phosphatic material occurs as fine acicular crystals, radially arranged in places, with no evidence of abrasion of any of the apatite crystallites.

The non-pelletal phosphorites of secondary origin are similar to (and in some instances indistinguishable from) those of primary origin. Staining by iron and manganese, the highly irregular nature of the laminations, and the presence of solution features such as stylolites and geodes, are common. De Keyser and Cook (1972) used the term "phoscrete" for this phosphorite in the Georgina basin and considered that the majority of such deposits were the result of supergene enrichment and replacement, much of it of Cainozoic age. More recent work by Howard and Cooney (1974) has shown that most of these deposits are of Cambrian age and they suggest the term "hardrock phosphorite". Thin sections commonly show no distinguishing features whatsoever, but in some places a replacement origin is indicated by pseudomorphs after dolomite or replaced algal remains. Such evidence is lacking in some units and the rock is composed primarily of coarse hexagonal apatite crystals with no replacement textures. This type of phosphorite may be a supergene precipitate or in some instances an early precipitate, interstitial precipitation having taken place below the sediment/water interface.

GEOCHEMISTRY OF PHOSPHORITES

Most phosphorites are composed of cryptocrystalline carbonate-fluorapatite, which may be represented by the formula $Ca_5(PO_4)_3$ (F, CO_3). In common with other members of the apatite group of minerals many substitutions are possible in carbonate-fluorapatite. This topic has been the subject of a large number of publications; excellent reviews are given by Jaffe (1951), and McConnell (1973). Gulbrandsen (1966), Smith and Lehr (1966), and Tooms et al. (1969) discuss the geochemistry of phosphorites in particular.

Substitutions of both the simple and the coupled type are possible for Ca, P (or PO_4), and F. As phosphorites are seldom (if ever) composed of pure carbonate fluorapatite, some of the suggested substitutions are difficult to prove or disprove. Some of these substitutions are potentially of economic interest; because many trace elements are present in higher than normal concentrations in phosphates (Table II) eventually uranium and rare earths and perhaps other trace elements may be extracted on a commercial scale from phosphorite. Substitution for Ca^{2+} in the apatite lattice is particularly common; rare earths (RE^{3+}) are known to readily substitute for Ca^{2+}. The ionic radius of Na^+ is also similar to that of Ca^{2+} and consequently it too is readily admitted into the lattice. Both Gulbrandsen (1966) and Smirnov (1958) have found high sodium values in phosphorites. Other substitutions which have been suggested for calcium include Sr^{2+}, K^+, Mg^{2+}, Ba^{2+}, Al^{3+}, Fe^{2+} and Mn^{2+}.

Substitution of uranium in the apatite lattice has been studied in some detail by Altschuler et al. (1958) and Sheldon (1959) because of the potential that phosphorites have as a source of uranium (Tooms et al., 1969, record an average content of 190 p.p.m. of uranium in phosphorite). The actual location of the uranium ion is somewhat uncertain; some capture of U^{4+} (radius of 0.97 Å) by Ca^{2+} (radius of 0.99 Å) may reasonably be expected. However, McConnell (1973) points out that both U^{4+} and U^{6+} are present in phosphorites and suggests that substitution of UO_4^{2-} may take place, comparable with the substitution of AlO_4^{5-} in apatite. Other substitutions in the phosphate ion which have been suggested include ionic forms of vanadium, arsenic, silicon (either as a coupled Si-S

TABLE II

Trace element concentrations in phosphorites

	(1)	(2)	(3)
Ag	3		4
As	40	21	
B		16	
Ba	100		210
Co		3	6
Cr	1000	285	140
Cu	100	22	48
I		24	
La	300		100
Li			6
Mn	30	428	479
Mo	30	19	4
Ni	100	13	27
Pb			39
Rb			8
Sb	7		
Sc	10		
Se	10	3	
Sn			2
Sr	1000	1900	354
Ti		476	243
U	90	190	78
V	300	167	116
Y	300		610
Zn	300	90	144
Zr	30		

(1) = Phosphoria Formation averages (Gulbrandsen, 1966, table 3); (2) = worldwide phosphorite averages after Tooms et al. (1969, table 1); (3) = Georgina basin averages for pelletal phosphorites (after Cook, 1972, table 3).

substitution for P, or alternatively as coupled Si-P and Na-Ca substitutions), manganese, and chromium. McConnell and Foreman (1966) have also suggested that in some circumstances the H_4O_4 group (tetrahedral hydroxyls) will substitute for the $(PO_4)^{3-}$ ion.

Substitution for fluorine is an important feature of sedimentary apatites. Deer et al. (1962) assert: "Fluorine chlorine and hydroxyl ions can mutually replace each other to form the almost pure end members fluorapatite chlorapatite and hydroxylapatite and it appears probable that there is a complete isomorphous series in natural apatites." In fact, the hydroxylapatite unit cell is slightly larger (and less stable) than fluorapatite; a natural primary precipitate of hydroxylapatite (such as bone) is rapidly converted to fluorapatite in an open system. Despite the fact that the marine environment in which phosphorites normally form has a considerable excess of Cl^- ions over F^- ions (the ratio is in the order of 8000 : 1), chlorapatite is seldom, if ever, formed in the marine environment. This may be because of the structural difficulty in substituting Cl$^-$ with a radius of 1.81 Å into the comparatively restricted position in the hexagonal channel normally occupied by F$^-$, with an ionic radius of 1.36 Å.

The location of carbonate in the apatite lattice has been the subject of much discussion. Hendricks (1952) and Carlstrom (1955) claimed that the carbonate is present outside the apatite lattice, as adsorbed cryptocrystalline or amorphous calcite. However, more recent work by Ames (1959), McConnell (1960), and Kolodny and Kaplan (1970) clearly indicates that the carbonate is within the lattice. The nature of this lattice substitution has still not been finally settled, but the most plausible suggestion is perhaps that made by Gulbrandsen et al. (1966), of a CO_3-F substitution for PO_4. This would seem to be a reasonable way of achieving substitution of a trigonal for a tetragonal complex.

In addition to substitution of elements directly into the apatite structure a further mode of occurrence is either by adsorption or the formation of metallic complexes with the abundant organic material which is commonly associated with phosphorites. Tooms et al. (1969, p. 65) conclude: "The ability of organisms to concentrate minor elements from seawater is not particularly effective in causing major differences to arise between elemental abundances in phosphorites and those in seawater." They do not, however, offer any compelling evidence in support of this statement. Conversely there is a considerable amount of data (Krauskopf, 1955; Trudinger, 1974, this volume) indicating that organisms are indeed able to concentrate some trace-elements to a very high degree. Gulbrandsen (1966) concludes from his work on the Phosphoria phosphorites that several elements such as arsenic and antimony are associated with the organic material in phosphorite. Thus, although phosphorites undoubtedly show some marked elemental concentrations, the location of many of these elements is still uncertain.

A geochemical question remaining is the nature of the organic matter in the phosphorites. This is important not only because of the influence it may have on the trace element composition of the phosphorites but also because phosphorites constitute potential source rocks for petroleum. Both McKelvey (1959) and Barbat (1967) have suggested that some of the world's major oil fields have phosphatic source rocks. Work by Powell et al. (1974) has shown that although phosphorites commonly do not have an excessively high concentration of organic matter, a very considerable proportion of this organic matter is in the form of readily extractable hydrocarbons, and consequently phosphorites do constitute potentially important petroleum source rocks.

THE GENESIS OF PHOSPHORITES

Four fundamental questions may be asked about all sedimentary phosphate deposits: (1) What was the source of the phosphate? (2) Was the collophane an organic or an inorganic precipitate? (3) Was the collophane a primary deposit or was it formed by post-depositional phosphatization of pre-existing sediments? (4) What were the depositional conditions under which phosphorites formed? Some of these questions are of course interrelated.

(1) In the marine environment, above-average concentrates of phosphate can occur in association with: (a) volcanic exhalations; (b) estuarine waters; (c) cold surface currents; and (d) upwelling currents. Although biological production might be regarded as an additional source of phosphate it is not considered as such here; high biological production is merely a result of a pre-existing abundance of phosphate (and other nutrients) and as such is the result rather than the cause of high phosphorous concentrations in seawater.

A volcanogenic origin has been suggested for a number of deposits. Mansfield (1940) considered that fluorine played a vital role in the precipitation of phosphate and suggested that there is a correlation between times of volcanism (when fluorine-rich gases are common) and phosphate deposition. Bidaut (1953) also attributes the Dinantian phosphorites of the Pyrenees to the action of submarine fumeroles rich in fluorine. However, as pointed out by Kazakov (1950) there is in fact no fluorine problem, for the amount of fluorine in seawater is very much greater (in proportion to PO_4) than is needed for carbonate fluorapatite. Rooney and Kerr (1967) found that the zeolite clinoptilolite is ubiquitous in the phosphorites of North Carolina. They conclude from this that volcanism played a major role in the formation of these deposits and suggest that: "Ash falls of long duration killed large numbers of marine organism whose subsequent decay contributed phosphate." However, as pointed out by Cathcart (1968) clinoptilolite is a comparatively minor component, forming only 0–5% of the total sediment. Consequently, there is no compelling evidence to indicate a significant volcanic association in any of the major sedimentary phosphate deposits.

Rivers are known to carry abundant phosphate in solution and consequently are capable of directly supplying much of the phosphate present in phosphorites. Pevear (1966) has suggested that the Cenozoic phosphorites of the eastern United States are of estuarine origin. Bushinski (1964, 1969b) considers that one large river was capable of supplying all the phosphate present in the Phosphoria Formation. Such a river would build up a large delta and Bushinski suggests that the Shedhorn Sandstone (Fig. 3) is a fluviatile sand. The Shedhorn Sandstone is, however, a blanket-type body of clean well-sorted sandstone which appears to have few affinities with most deltaic sediments; it is considered by Sheldon et al. (1967) to be the result of the build-up of offshore bars and barrier islands. Recent investigations by Cook and Mayo (1974) into the distribution of phosphorus in the water and sediments of a tropical estuary have shown that the phosphate concentration in estuarine waters is not necessarily the most important factor. A greater degree of phosphatization of sediments occurs in areas of very low phosphate concentration in the surface water with a slow rate of sedimentation, than in areas of very high phosphate concentration characterized by rapid sedimentation. This points out the major difficulty in postulating an estuarine source for the phosphate in phosphorites, namely, that there is generally a high rate of sedimentation in estuaries and that this will in most cases produce nothing more than a very slightly phosphatic mud or sand. The organic geochemistry of several phosphorites of wide geographic distribution and ranging in age from Precambrian to Cenozoic was examined by Powell et al. (1974). They found evidence (from the odd-even distribution of the n-alkanes) of land-plant material being the dominant organic component in only the North Carolina deposit. They conclude from this, that there was little to support an estuarine origin for most of the phosphorites they examined. An estuarine source is conceivable only in circumstances where the great bulk of the river sediment is prevented from reaching the estuary. It is unlikely that these conditions operated throughout an extensive phosphogenic province such as the Tethyan Late Cretaceous-Eocene province.

Cold oceanic currents, on the other hand, affect the phosphate abundance of oceanic zones over considerable distances at the present time. Presumably they occurred in the past though perhaps to a greater or lesser degree, depending on the size of the polar ice caps and ocean/continent configuration. In many areas, the distribution and productivity of cold currents cannot be divorced from the presence of upwelling areas. Sheldon (1964) has shown that virtually all important phosphorites were deposited within 40 degrees north or south of the palaeoequator and within this longitudinal range most cold currents are associated with coastal upwelling. Coastal upwelling may occur in response to sea-ward-moving surface water (divergent upwelling) or the movement of a current over a topographic high (dynamic upwelling). Freas and Eckstrom (1968) have summarized the conditions conducive to upwelling as follows:

"(1) In situations where ocean currents flow parallel or offshore and are enhanced by strong prevailing winds blowing in the same direction.

(2) In situations where ocean currents flow up onto a positive submarine topographic feature.

(3) In the belts of trade winds at low latitudes between $0°$ and $25°$.

(4) Along the north and west coasts in the northern hemisphere, and the south and west coasts in the southern hemisphere at latitudes between $0°$ and $25°$.

(5) Along coasts of land masses with dry climates.

(6) Along the coasts in the belt of westerlies approximately between $20°$ and $40°$.

(7) In large ocean basins with unrestricted circulations and open connection to polar seas."

As a result of one or more of these conditions cold deep water, rich in phosphate and other nutrients, is brought to the surface. There is strong evidence particularly from the sedimentary facies distribution pattern to suggest that phosphorites of the west coast type such as those of the Phosphoria Formation (Fig. 13) and the Lesser Karatau are associated with large-scale divergent upwelling. Other deposits such as those of Florida and some of the Middle East deposits are clearly associated with topographic highs which are likely to have produced dynamic upwelling. McKelvey et al. (1959) have shown that the mechanism of upwelling is more than adequate to produce the very considerable

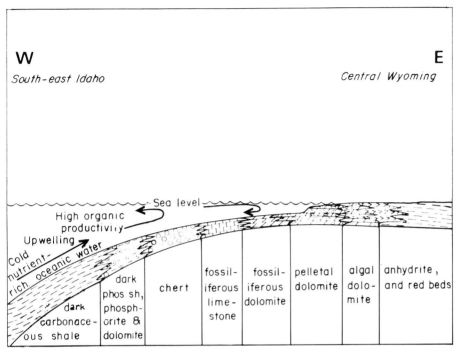

W South-east Idaho

E Central Wyoming

Fig. 13. Schematic representation of the sedimentation pattern in the Permian Phosphoria sea. (Diagram after Sheldon, 1963. Courtesy of U.S. Geol. Surv., Washington.)

amount of phosphate in phosphorites. Thus, there are reasonable grounds for regarding upwelling as being the major source of phosphate for many deposits. The greatest difficulty in applying the upwelling hypothesis is for deposits which are obviously of very shallow water origin with a maximum water depth of a few tens of metres. Some such deposits may owe their origin primarily to a fluviatile or estuarine source, but these deposits are likely to be of comparatively small areal extent. Small-scale, dynamic upwelling can occur in very shallow depths provided the current is sufficiently strong, though it is likely to be a very much less potent source of nutrients than deep upwelling currents. Entrainment of bottom waters by seaward-flowing surface waters in estuaries can induce localized upwelling and this mechanism could possibly also act as a further source of phosphate in very shallow seas. Phosphate-rich water upwelling on the edge of the shelf and then being swept across that shelf, may be an additional process by which nutrient-abundant conditions can prevail in shallow water.

(2) The question of whether phosphate is incorporated by chemical or biochemical precipitation has not been considered so far. Early workers such as Murray and Renard

(1891), and Mansfield (1918) concluded from the abundance of organic remains in many phosphorites that they were biogenic precipitates. This was disputed by Kazakov (1937) who proposed a model for inorganic precipitation. He suggested that phosphate precipitation will occur in areas of cold upwelling currents; as these currents ascend, the temperature increases, the partial pressure of CO_2 decreases, and there is a commensurate rise in pH. As phosphate solubility varies inversely with pH, this increase of pH and CO_2 results first in the precipitation of calcite and then apatite. He considered that the precipitation occurs at depths of 50–200 m and that it would not take place within the photosynthetic zone, where any available phosphate would be taken up by phytoplankton. This hypothesis has been widely accepted and successfully applied to explain sedimentary associations in many phosphate deposits. McKelvey et al. (1953) used a modified version of Kazakov's hypothesis to explain the juxtaposition of various sedimentary units in the Phosphoria Formation (Fig. 13); they suggested however that calcite is not precipitated before apatite, as proposed by Kazakov, but after.

Experimental work by Roberson (1966) indicates that seawater in general is supersaturated with phosphate and consequently precipitation should occur quite readily. Smirnov et al. (1962), on the other hand, considered from their experimental work that seawater is slightly undersaturated, but still concluded that removal of CO_2 will precipitate apatite. In recent years, however, increasing doubts have been expressed as to the relevance of these essentially inorganic reactions to a natural system in which there is a prolific biota. For instance, apatitic precipitates analogous to a calcareous "whiting", have not been proved in areas of upwelling. Gulbrandsen and Robertson (1973), describe a milky white turbidity in the area of high productivity around the Andaman Islands, but no mineralogical identification of this suspension was made. Smirnov et al. (1962) also concluded from their work that the diffusion of CO_2 from upwelling seawater is too slow to produce a significant amount of apatite as an inorganic precipitate. In addition, Bushinski (1966) makes the elementary but important point that any phosphate precipitate would be so fine-grained (as shown by experimental studies) that there would be little possibility of it settling onto the sea floor in areas in which there is any current activity. This view is echoed by Senin (1970) who also notes that if the phosphate was a fine inorganic precipitate it would be associated with the fine pelitic sediments of the shelf, whereas he found the highest phosphate concentrations in the sandy sediments. Senin concludes that the Recent phosphorites off southwest Africa are of biochemical origin because of "...the high biological productivity of this region, the extraordinarily high concentrations [of organic carbon] for bottom sediments... the significant coprolite content, the high concentrations of P in certain biogene sediments". Clearly, in upwelling areas, phytoplankton are likely to be an important biochemical agent. However, Breger (1911) considered the possibility of bacteria as the agent and McConnell (1965) has suggested that enzymes may play an important role. The role of microorganisms as concentrators of phosphate is discussed in some detail by Trudinger (this volume) and also by Gulbrandsen (1969). There is no doubt that phytoplankton can concentrate phosphate to a very high degree, but incorporation of phytoplankton in sediments would produce nothing more than a slightly phosphatic organic-rich sediment, and therefore decay and other forms of post-depositional modification are required before a phosphorite can result.

(*3*) This then brings us to the question of whether the collophane is in fact primary or secondary in origin. Some phosphatic material in phosphorites is obviously of primary origin, such as the rounded fragments of inarticulate brachiopods which make up much of the Ordovician phosphorites of the Baltic region. Other fragments though now phosphatic were originally calcareous; phosphatized pelmatozoan fragments are a common component of some of the Georgina basin phosphorites. If the inorganic hypothesis of Kazakov is accepted, then pellets and nodules may have formed by accretion of apatite particles as the pellet was rolled by bottom currents. Pellets are also commonly considered to be of faecal origin. Senin (1970) reports that faecal pellets are abundant in phosphatic sediments off southwest Africa, and it is probable that they are equally abundant in many ancient deposits. However, most faecal pellets are originally only slightly phosphatic and would have to undergo further phosphatization after deposition, to give the high phosphate concentrations found in them now.

Because of the similarity between phosphatic and calcitic or aragonitic ooliths, Emigh (1958, 1967) suggests that the Phosphoria and many other pelletal phosphorites had calcareous precursors. Most phosphorites are not, however, oolitic; they are ovular, and the pellets show no indication of calcitic parent material. Cook (1970) has shown that diagenetic phosphatization, calcitization, and silicification will occur readily, probably in response to changes of pH. It follows then that phosphatization can take place at or below the sediment/water interface irrespective of whether the sediment is calcareous or siliceous. Jitts (1959) has shown that bottom muds are capable of adsorbing considerable quantities of phosphate. Poncet (1964) has evidence to indicate that phosphatic pellets and nodules in Ordovician sediments in western France are the product of phosphatization of clay pellets. Bushinski (1964) also considers that the phosphatization of mud-size material is important, but he suggests that this phosphatization occurs in situ in the muds and that subsequently the material not cemented by collophane is winnowed out. Cook (1967, 1972) similarly found that winnowing was an important process for upgrading Ordovician sediments in the Amadeus basin from a slightly phosphatic mud or sand to a phosphorite. Relict bedding is present in some of these Ordovician pellets; such pellets presumably formed by the breaking-up of phosphatic beds, and subsequent abrasion of the clasts to form pellets. The writer has also found that poorly-phosphatic mudstones adjacent to rich phosphorites in the Phosphoria Formation commonly contain small patches of collophane which have not been abraded. Thus, there is evidence from ancient sediments that some of the phosphate pellets are the result of diagenetic processes; conversely, there is little evidence of direct precipitation.

Important information on the origin of phosphorites has been obtained as a result of investigations into the Recent phosphorites off southwest Africa by Baturin (1969, 1971), Senin (1970), and Romankevich and Baturin (1972). They have shown that precipitation of (and probably replacement by) apatite is taking place at the present day, below the sediment/water interface. Initially the apatite is in the form of soft pellets and nodules of gel-like calcium phosphate incorporating phosphatic particles. As lithification proceeds there is a further increase in the phosphate content of the pellets and nodules. Further upgrading occurs as a result of mechanical reworking of these sediments. Baturin (1969) considers that the phosphate concentration in seawater off southwest Africa is insufficient for there to be any significant inorganic precipitation of apatite. In the interstitial waters, on the other hand, phosphate concentrations are ten to a hundred times greater than those in seawater. The writer (Cook, 1974) obtained similar results for sediments in the Timor trough where P_2O_5 values of up to 26 p.p.m. are present in interstitial waters. In this case, one of the primary controls of phosphate solubility appears to be alkalinity (Fig. 14) rather than pH. This in turn is in part the result of the abundance of organic matter, but other factors may also be important in controlling interstitial alkalinity. Thus, there is now considerable evidence to indicate that collophane may be precipitated below the sediment/water interface, where phosphorus-rich interstitial fluids will phosphatize siliceous oozes, terrigenous clays, fossil fragments, coprolites, and calcareous sediments.

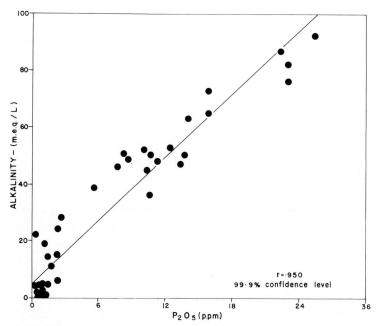

Fig. 14. Plot to show the positive correlation of P_2O_5 content of interstitial waters with alkalinity in Deep-Sea Drilling Project, site 262, Timor trough.

So far most of the discussion has been concerned with nodular and pelletal phos-phorites, but many of the same chemical or biochemical processes operate in the forma-tion of non-pelletal phosphorites. Pseudomorphs of fine collophane after dolomite have been observed by Trueman (1971) and Cook (1972) and it is evident in such cases that the phosphorite is a replacement product. Observations on the Georgina basin phos-phorites using scanning electron microscopy indicate that the apatite crystallites are morphologically different in the non-pelletal and pelletal forms. There are also indications that subaerial supergene processes may have been important in the precipitation of some non-pelletal collophane. Whether precipitation is from very shallow surface waters, or from interstitial waters, is uncertain although interstitial precipitation is considered more probable.

(4) It is known that phosphorites are formed predominantly under marine conditions, but their location on the sea floor, the water depth, and the physicochemical conditions of their depositional environment are somewhat uncertain. Kazakov (1937) considered that phosphorites form at water depths of 50–200 m. McKelvey et al. (1953) subse-quently suggested that phosphorites form at water depths of 200–1000 m. Krumbein and Garrels (1952) consider that the pH of the environment is of major importance, precipita-tion of apatite occurring within the pH range of 7.1–7.8; Eh on the other hand is regarded as being of little or no significance. Despite this, the abundance of organic material in most pelletal phosphorite suggests a reducing environment. This may, how-ever, only indicate a negative Eh below or just at the sediment/water interface; the overlying waters could conceivably have still been quite strongly oxidizing. In general, phosphorites are believed to have been deposited under conditions of near-normal marine salinity. Areas flanking the region of phosphate deposition, however, were commonly hypersaline. The phosphorites of the Phosphoria Formation grade laterally into car-bonates of the Park City Formation, then red beds and evaporites of the Chugwater Formation (Fig. 3, 13).

The modern phosphorites off southwest Africa are being deposited on the inner shelf in water depths of 50–150 m, which is within the euphotic zone. Senin (1970) found that this depth corresponds closely to the change in the water column (and the bottom sediments) from oxidizing to reducing. Romankevich and Baturin (1972) record redox conditions down to −233 mV in the sediments; therefore, anaerobic conditions obviously predominate there. Flanking these phosphorites is the arid hinterland of the Namib coastal desert where saline coastal lagoons are common, a situation apparently analogous to, for instance, the landward equivalents of the Phosphoria Formation. Similarly, the phosphorites of the Peruvian shelf have an arid hinterland (the Sechura desert). Baturin (1971) notes that several sea-level changes have occurred during the Quaternary and that considerable reworking of shelf sediments has taken place. As a consequence of the removal of fine material the phosphorites have been upgraded on both the Peruvian and southwest African shelves. Little information is available on the Peruvian phosphorites to date although again they are situated in an area characterized by strong upwelling and extremely high organic productivity. Veeh et al. (1973) note that the phosphorites occur at water depths ranging from 100 to 400 m. They also point out that the phosphorites are confined to two narrow bands corresponding to the upper and lower boundaries of an oxygen minimum layer. Sediments of this portion of the shelf are strongly anoxic.

Many of the features of the depositional environment evident in modern phosphorites may be found in ancient deposits. Most phosphorites probably formed in shelf environments at water depths considerably less than 500 m. Conditions within the water column were conducive to the development of a prolific biota, but were strongly reducing at or just below the sediment/water interface. Subsequent mechanical reworking of sediments was a most important feature in the upgrading of phosphatic sediments to phosphorites. Such reworking may have occurred in response to the influx of bottom currents or to relative change in sea level. Eustatic changes of sea level can result from the growth or contraction of icecaps such as have occurred during the Quaternary glacial period. Bushinski (1969a) discusses the possibility of an association between phosphatic sequences and tillites. He concludes that few of the "tillites" are in fact of glacial origin. Even some of the undoubted glacial deposits (e.g., those of northwest Queensland described by De Keyser, 1972) which underlie phosphatic sequences are in fact separated by extensive time breaks so that the association is more apparent than real. Nevertheless, glacial epochs are likely to have been times with wide fluctuations of sea level resulting in extensive reworking of shelf sediments. In addition, upwelling is likely to have been more intense. Consequently, it is possible that glacial epochs may have been a preferred time for the formation of some phosphate deposits.

No extensive non-pelletal phosphorites are known to be forming at the present day; consequently their depositional environment is less certain. The Cambrian non-pelletal deposits of the Georgina basin have many features which indicated very shallow water and even subaerial conditions (Cook, 1972; Howard and Cooney, 1974; Howard and Perrino, 1974). The closest comparison which may be drawn with this type of environment in the Cenozoic is the formation of phoscretes as a result of lateritic weathering, and the formation of phosphorites by the phosphatization of coral and other material by phosphate-rich groundwaters derived from guano deposits. Thus, the comparison of ancient with modern phosphorite is not entirely satisfactory as it seems that some ancient phosphorites have formed in much shallower water than that presently prevailing in modern phosphogenic environments. It is unlikely, however, that any major phosphate deposits have formed in waters much deeper than those off southwest Africa and Peru, i.e., approximately 500 m.

CONCLUSIONS

(1) Phosphorites range in age from Precambrian to Recent and are widespread. No two

occurrences are precisely the same but nevertheless a number of common features are evident which may be used as the basis for a three-fold lithogenetic classification into "geosynclinal", "platform", and weathered or residual deposits.

(2) Phosphorites have a varied petrography comprising phosphate nodules, grains, pellets, and non-pelletal (clay-size) material. Ooliths are not nearly so abundant as is commonly supposed. Most pellets are ovular. Some pellets are believed to be of intraclastic origin and it is evident that winnowing and reworking are a common feature of many ancient phosphorites. Nodules are common in platform deposits. Non-pelletal phosphorites (microsphorite, etc.) are common in the platform and residual deposits.

(3) Most phosphorites are composed of collophane-cryptocrystalline carbonate-fluorapatite. Lattice substitution of many trace elements in the apatite is common, but the nature of some substitutions is uncertain.

(4) Association with areas of oceanic upwelling is believed to be an important feature of ancient and modern phosphorites, but extensive revision to the original upwelling hypothesis of Kazakov is necessary as there is no evidence of inorganic precipitation of apatite during upwelling.

(5) The genesis of non-pelletal phosphorites (phospholutite, collophane mudstone, microsphorite, and phoscrete) is only poorly understood. Some may be comparatively deep subaqueous replacement deposits which have never undergone reworking. Most are believed to be the product of very shallow-water or subaerial environments, and are either replacement deposits (particularly replacement of dolomite) or interstitial supergene collophane precipitates.

(6) Knowledge of modern and ancient phosphorites indicates the following six-stage genetic scheme to account for the formation of nodular and pelletal phosphorites:

(a) Influx of nutrient-rich water, generally by upwelling, into a shallow-marine region (maximum water depth 500 m, but commonly considerably less) with a slow rate of terrigenous deposition, and often a warm arid climate.

(b) Development of a prolific biota.

(c) Formation of anoxic organic-rich bottom sediments; loss of C, N, and H from dead organisms occurs either before or immediately after burial.

(d) Interstitial waters rich in phosphorus form below the sediment/water interface by leaching of phosphate from organic remains as a consequence of low pH and high alkalinity in the sediments.

(e) Localized patches of apatite develop by phosphatization of sediments in the presence of phosphate-rich pore waters or in some instances by direct precipitation of apatite from the pore waters. Diagenetic phosphatization will take place whether the sediments are clayey, siliceous, or calcareous. Phosphatized faecal pellets are a common feature of some deposits.

(f) Reworking of sediments occurs in response to changes of current pattern or relative sea level. The coarser patches of phosphatized sediment remain as a lag deposit and the finer matrix is winnowed out, resulting in extensive upgrading of the phosphatic sediments into a high-grade phosphorite.

REFERENCES

Altschuler, Z.S., Clarke, R.S. and Young, E.J., 1958. Geochemistry of uranium in apatite and phosphorite. *U.S. Geol. Surv., Prof. Pap.*, 314-D; 45–90.

Ames, L.L. Jr., 1959. The genesis of carbonate apatites. *Econ. Geol.*, 54: 829–841.

Barbat, W.N., 1967. Crude-oil correlations and their role in exploration *Am. Assoc. Petrol. Geol., Bull.*, 51: 1255–1292.

Bates, R.L., 1960. *Geology of the Industrial Rocks and Minerals.* Harper, New York, N.Y.

Baturin, G.N., 1969. Authigenic phosphate concretions in Recent sediments of the southwest African shelf (Transl.). *Dokl. Akad. Nauk S.S.R.*, 189: 1359–1362.

Baturin, G.N., 1971. Stages of phosphorite formation on the ocean floor. *Nature (Phys. Sci.)*, 232 (29): 61–62.

Baturin, G.N., Merkulova, K.I. and Chalov, P.I., 1972. Radiometric evidence of recent formation of phosphatic nodules in marine shelf sediments. *Mar. Geol.*, 10: 37–41.

Bidaut, H., 1953. Note préliminaire sur mode de formation possible des phosphates dinantiens des Pyrénées. *Int. Geol. Congr., 19th Sess.*, 11: 185–190.

Boujo, A., 1968. Nouvelles données sur le Crétace et l'Eocène phosphate du gîsement des Gantour. *Notes Serv. Géol. Maroc.*, 28: 7–16.

Breger, D.L., 1911. Origin of Lander oil and western phosphate. *Mining Eng. World*, 35: 631–633.

British Sulphur Corporation, 1971. *World Survey of Phosphate Deposits*. Br. Sulphur Corp., London, 3rd ed., 180 pp.

Bushinski, G.I., 1935. Structure and origin of the phosphorites of the U.S.S.R. *J. Sediment. Petrol.*, 5: 81–92.

Bushinski, G.I., 1964. On the shallow-water origin of phosphorite sediments. In: M.L.J.U. van Straaten (Editor), *Deltaic and Shallow Marine Deposits*. Elsevier, Amsterdam, pp. 62–70.

Bushinski, G.I., 1966. *The Origin of Marine Phosphorites. Lithology and Mineral Resources.* Consultants Bureau, New York, N.Y., pp. 292–311.

Bushinski, G.I., 1969a. Old phosphorites of Asia and their genesis. (Translation from Russian by *Israel Progr. Sci. Transl., Jerusalem.*)

Bushinski, G.I., 1969b. Phosphoria Formation. *Akad. Nauk S.S.S.R., Trans.*, 210: 103 pp. (in Russian).

Caldwell, A.B., 1968. Lee Creek open pit mine and fertilizer plants. *Eng. Mining J.*, 17: 3–29.

Carlstrom, D., 1955. X-ray crystallographic studies on apatites and calcified structures. *Acta Radiol.*, Suppl. 121.

Cathcart, J.B., 1968. Florida-type phosphorite deposits of the United States: origin and techniques for prospecting. *U.N. Mineral Resour. Develop. Ser.*, 32: 178–186.

Collette, W.J., 1968. Tennessee phosphate deposits United States of America. *U.N. Mineral Resour. Develop. Ser.*, 32: 201–207.

Cook, P.J., 1967. Winnowing an important process in the concentration of the Stairway Sandstone (Ordovician) phosphorites of central Australia. *J. Sediment. Petrol.*, 37: 818–828.

Cook, P.J., 1970. Repeated diagenetic calcitization, phosphatization and silification in the Phosphoria Formation. *Bull. Geol. Soc. Am.*, 81: 2107–2116.

Cook, P.J., 1972a. Sedimentological studies on the Stairway Sandstone of central Australia. *Bur. Mineral. Resour. Aust., Bull.*, 95.

Cook, P.J., 1972b. Petrology and geochemistry of the phosphate deposits of northwest Queensland, Australia. *Econ. Geol.*, 67: 1193–1213.

Cook, P.J., 1974. Geochemistry and diagenesis of interstitial fluids and associated calcareous oozes. Deep Sea Drilling Project, leg 27, site 262, Timor trough. In: J.R. Heirtzler and co-workers, *Initial Reports of the Deep Sea Drilling Project*, XXVII. U.S. Govt. Printing Office, Washington, D.C. (in press).

Cook, P.J. and Mayo, W., 1974. Geochemistry of a tropical estuary (Broad Sound, Queensland). *Bur. Mineral. Resour. Aust., Bull.* (in prep.).

D'Anglejan, B.F., 1967. Origin of marine phosphorites off Baja California, Mexico. *Mar. Geol.*, 5: 15–44.

Deans, T., 1966. Economic mineralogy of African carbonatites. In: O.F. Tuttle and J. Gittins (Editors), *Carbonatites*. Interscience, New York, N.Y., pp. 385–413.

Deans, T., 1968. Exploration for apatite deposits associated with carbonatites and pyroxenites. *U.N. Mineral Resour. Develop. Ser.*, 32: 109–119.

Deer, W.A., Howie, R.A. and Zussmann, J.L., 1962. *Rock Forming Minerals, 5*. Wiley, New York, N.Y., pp. 323–338.

De Keyser, F., 1972. Proterozoic tillite at Duchess, northwest Queensland. *Bur. Mineral. Resour. Aust., Bull.*, 125: 1–6.

De Keyser, F. and Cook, P.J., 1972. Geology of the Middle Cambrian phosphorites and associated sediments of northwest Queensland. *Bur. Mineral. Resour. Aust., Bull.*, 138.

Delegation of the Soviet Union, 1968. Geotectonic distribution of sedimentary phosphorite deposits in the U.S.S.R. *U.N. Mineral. Resour. Develop. Ser.*, 32: 136–138.

Dietz, R.S., Emery, K.O. and Shepard, F.P., 1942. Phosphorite deposits on the sea floor of southern California. *Bull. Geol. Soc. Am.*, 53: 815–848.

Emigh, G.D., 1958. Petrography, mineralogy and origin of phosphate pellets in the Phosphoria Formation. *Idaho Bur. Mining Geol., Pamphl.*, 114: 60 pp.

Emigh, G.D., 1967. Petrology and origin of phosphorites. In: L.A. Hales (Editor), *Anatomy of the Western Phosphate Field – Intermount. Assoc. Geol., 15th Ann. Field Conf.*, pp. 103–114.

Fiveg, M.P., 1937. The apatite deposits of the Khibinian tundras. *Inst. Fertilizers Insectofungicides U.S.S.R., Trans.*, 142: 8–21.

Freas, D.H., 1964. Stratigraphy and sedimentation of phosphorite in the central Florida phosphate district. (Abstr.) *Econ. Geol.*, 59: 1619.

Freas, D.H. and Eckstrom, C.L., 1968. Areas of potential upwelling and phosphorite deposition during Tertiary, Mesozoic and late Paleozoic time. *U.N. Mineral Resour. Develop. Ser.* 32: 228–238.

Freas, D.H. and Riggs, S.R., 1968. Environment of phosphorite deposition in the central Florida phosphate district. *Conf. Ind. Minerals, 4th, Univ. Texas, Austin, 1968:* 117–128

Gulbrandsen, R.A., 1960. Petrology of the Meade Peak Phosphatic Shale Member of the Phosphoria Formation at Coal Canyon, Wyoming, *U.S. Geol. Surv., Bull.*, 1111-C: 71–146.

Gulbrandsen, R.A., 1966. Chemical composition of phosphorites in the Phosphoria Formation. *Geochim. Cosmochim. Acta*, 30: 769–778.

Gulbrandsen, R.A., 1969. Physical and chemical factors in the formation of marine apatite. *Econ. Geol.*, 64: 365–382.

Gulbrandsen, R.A. and Roberson, E.E., 1973. Inorganic phosphorus in seawater. In: *Environmental Phosphorus Handbook*. Wiley, New York, N.Y., pp. 117–140.

Gulbrandsen, R.A., Kramer, J.R., Beatty, L.B. and Mays, R.E., 1966. Carbonate-bearing apatite from Faraday township, Ontario, Canada. *Am. Mineralogist*, 51: 819–824.

Hendricks, S.B., 1952. Comments on the crystal chemistry of bone. *Fourth Conf. Metabolic Interrelations*, pp. 135–212.

Howard, P.F. and Cooney, A.M., 1974. The geology of the D Tree phosphate deposit, northwest Queensland. In: *Mineral Deposits of Australia*. Aust. Inst. Mining Metall. (in press).

Howard, P.F. and Perrino, F.A., 1974. The Geology of the Wonarah phosphate deposit, Northern Territory. In: *Mineral Deposits of Australia*. Aust. Inst. Mining Metall. (in press).

Jaffe, E.B., 1951. Abstracts of the literature on syntheses of apatites and some related phosphates. *U.S. Geol. Surv., Circ.* 135.

Jitts, H.R., 1959. The absorption of phosphate by estuarine bottom deposits. *Aust. J. Mar. Freshwater Res.*, 10: 7–21.

Kazakov, A.V., 1937. The phosphorite facies and the genesis of phosphorites. *Int. Geol. Congr., 17th Sess.*, pp. 95–113.

Kazakov, A.V., 1950. The fluorapatite system of equilibrium in the conditions of formation of sedimentary rocks. *Akad. Nauk. S.S.S.R. Geol. Ser.*, 144 (40): 1–21.

Kolodny, Y., 1969. Are marine phosphorites forming today? *Nature*, 244: 1017–1019.

Kolodny, Y. and Kaplan, I.R., 1970. Uranium isotopes in seafloor phosphorites. *Geochim. Cosmochim. Acta*, 34: 3–24.

Krauskopf, K.B., 1955. Sedimentary deposits of rare metals. *Econ. Geol.*, 50: 411–463.

Krumbein, W.C. and Garrels, R.M., 1950. Origin and classification of chemical sediments in terms of pH and oxidation-reduction potentials. *J. Geol.* 60: 1–33.

Love, J.D., 1964. Uraniferous phosphatic lake beds of Eocene age in intermontane basins of Wyoming and Utah. *U.S. Geol. Surv., Prof. Pap.,* 474-E: 1–66.

Mabie, C.P. and Hess, H.D., 1964. Petrographic study and classification of western phosphate ores. *U.S. Bur. Mines, Rep. Inv.,* p. 6468.

Mansfield, G.R., 1918. The origin of the western phosphates of the United States. *Am. J. Sci., 4 Ser.,* 46: 591–598.

Mansfield, G.R., 1940. The role of fluorine in phosphate deposition. *Am. J. Sci.,* 238: 863–879.

Marshall, J.F., 1971. Phosphatic sediments on the eastern Australian upper continent slope. *Bur. Mineral. Resour. Aust., Rec.* 1971/59 (unpublished).

McConnell, D., 1960. The crystal chemistry of dahllite. *Am. Mineralogist,* 45: 209–211.

McConnell, D., 1965. Precipitation of phosphates in sea-water. *Econ. Geol.,* 60(5): 1059–1062.

McConnell, D., 1973. *Apatite.* Springer, Berlin.

McConnell, D. and Foreman, D.W., 1966. The properties and structure of $Ca_{10}(PO_4)_6(OH)_2$ and its relation to tin (11) apatite. *Can. Mineralogist,* 8 (4): 431–436.

McKelvey, V.E., 1959. Relation of upwelling marine waters to phosphorite and oil. (Abstr.) *Bull. Geol. Soc. Am.,* 70: 1783.

McKelvey, V.E., Swanson, R.W. and Sheldon, R.P., 1953. The Permian phosphorite deposits of the Western United States. *Int. Geol. Congr., 19th Sess.,* 11: 45–65.

McKelvey, V.E., Williams, J.S., Sheldon, R.P., Cressman, E.R. and Cheney, T.M., 1959. The Phosphoria, Park City and Shedhorn formations in the Western Phosphate Field, *U.S. Geol. Surv., Prof. Pap.,* 313-A.

Murray, J. and Renard, A.F., 1891. *Scientific Results, H.M.S. "Challenger", Deep-Sea Deposits,* pp. 391–400.

Pasho, D.W., 1972. Character and origin of marine phosphorites. *U.S. Geol. Surv., Rep.,* USG-Geol., 72-5.

Pevear, D.R., 1966. The estuarine formation of United States Atlantic coastal plain phosphorite. *Econ. Geol.,* 61: 251–256.

Pevear, D.R. and Pilkey, O.H., 1966. Phosphorite in Georgia's continental shelf sediments. *Bull. Geol. Soc. Am.,* 77: 849–858.

Poncet, J., 1964. Couches intraformationelles à galets primitivement mons dans l'Ordovicien moyen de la region de Caen. In: L.M.J.U. van Straaten (Editor), *Deltaic and Shallow Marine Deposits.* Elsevier, Amsterdam, pp. 330–335.

Powell, T.G., Cook, P.J. and McKirdy, D., 1974. Organic geochemistry of phosphorites: relevance to petroleum genesis. *Am. Assoc. Pet. Geol., Bull.,* in press.

Reed, J.J. and Hornibrook, N.D., 1952. Sediments from Chatham Rise. *N. Z. J. Sci.,* 34: 173–189.

Riggs, S.R., 1967. *Phosphorite Stratigraphy, Sedimentation and Petrology of the Noralyn Mine, Central Florida Phosphate District.* Thesis. Univ. Montana, 267 pp. (unpublished).

Roberson, C.E., 1966. Solubility inplications of apatite in seawater. Geological Survey Research 1966. *U.S. Geol. Surv., Prof. Pap.,* 550-D: D178–D185.

Romankevich, Y.A. and Baturin, G.N., 1972. Composition of the organic matter in phosphorites from the continental shelf off southwest Africa (Engl. transl.). *Geokhimiya,* 6: 719–726.

Rooney, T.P. and Kerr, P.F., 1967. Mineralogical nature and origin of phosphorite, Beaufort county, North Carolina. *Bull. Geol. Soc. Am.,* 78: 731–748.

Russell, R.T. and Trueman, N.A., 1971. The geology of the Duchess phosphate deposits, northwest Queensland, Australia. *Econ. Geol.,* 66: 1186–1214.

Senin, Y.M., 1970. *Phosphorus in Bottom Sediments of the Southwest African Shelf.* Lithology and Mineral Resources Consultants Bureau, New York, N.Y., pp. 8–20.

Sheldon, R.P., 1959. Geochemistry of uranium in phosphorites and black shales of the Phosphoria Formation. *U.S. Geol. Surv., Bull.,* 1084-D: 83–113.

Sheldon, R.P., 1963. Physical stratigraphy and mineral resources of Permian rocks in western Wyoming. *U.S. Geol. Surv., Prof. Pap.,* 313-B: 49–273.

Sheldon, R.P., 1964. Palaeolatitudinal and palaeogeographic distribution of phosphorite. *U.S. Geol. Surv., Prof. Pap.*, 501-C: 106–113.

Sheldon, R.P., Maughan, E.K. and Cressman, E.R., 1967. Sedimentation of rocks of Leonard (Permian) age in Wyoming and adjacent states. *Intermount. Assoc. Geol., 15th Ann. Field Conf.*, pp. 1–13.

Smirnov, A.I., 1958. The problem of the genesis of phosphorites (Engl. transl.). *Akad. Sci. S.S.R. (Geochem.)*, 119: 53–56.

Smirnov, A.I., Ivnitskaya, R.B. and Zalavina, T.P., 1962. Experimental data on the possibility of chemical precipitation of phosphates from seawater. In: *Geology of Phosphorite Deposits*. Gosgortekhizdat, Moscow. (In Russian.)

Smith, J.P. and Lehr, J.R., 1966. An X-ray investigation of carbonate apatites. *J. Agric. Food Chem.*, 14: 342–349.

Strakhov, N.M., 1969. *Principles of Lithogenesis, 2*. Consultants Bureau, New York, N.Y., pp. 235–261.

Summerhayes, C.P., Nutter, A.H. and Tooms, J.S., 1972. The distribution and origin of phosphate in sediments off northwest Africa. *Sediment. Geol.*, 8: 3–28.

Summerhayes, C.P., Birch, G.F., Rogers, J. and Dingle, R.V., 1973. Phosphate in sediments off southwestern Africa. *Nature*, 243: 509–511.

Swanson, R.W., 1967. The Phosphoria, Park City and Shedhorn formations in Western Phosphate Field. In: L.A. Hale (Editor), *Anatomy of the Western Phosphate Field – Guide to the 15th Ann. Field Conf. Intermount. Assoc. Geol.*, pp. 15–33.

Tooms, J.S. and Summerhayes, C.P., 1968. Phosphatic rocks from the northwest African continental shelf. *Nature*, 218: 1241–1242.

Tooms, J.S., Summerhayes, C.P. and Cronan, D.S.L., 1969. Geochemistry of marine phosphate and manganese deposits. *Oceanogr. Mar. Biol. Ann. Rev.*, 7: 49–100.

Trueman, N.A., 1971. A petrological study of some sedimentary phosphorite deposits. *Aust. Mineral. Develop. Lab., Bull.*, 11: 1–72.

Veeh, H.H., Burnett, W.C. and Soutar, A., 1973. Contemporary phosphorites on the continental margin of Peru. *Science*, 181: 844–845.

Von der Borch, C.C., 1970. Phosphatic concretions and nodules from the upper continental slope, northern New South Wales. *J. Geol. Soc. Aust.*, 16: 755–759.

Weaver, C.E., 1955. Mineralogy and petrology of the rocks near the Quadrant-Phosphoria boundary in southwest Montana. *J. Sediment. Petrol.*

White, W.C. and Warin, O.N., 1964. A survey of phosphate deposits in the southwest Pacific and Australian waters. *Bur. Mineral. Resour. Aust., Bull.*, 69: 173 pp.

Wyllie, P.J., 1973. *The Dynamic Earth*. Wiley, New York, N.Y., 416 pp.

REFERENCES INDEX (PART II)

(Numbers in parentheses refer to volume numbers)

Aanerud, S., (6): 84, 122
Aarnio, B., (7): 343, 344, 378, 389
Adamides, N.G., (6): 26, 50
Adams, G.I., see Bain, H.G. et al.
Adams, S.S., Curtis, H.S. and Hafen, P.L.,
  (7): 121, 152
Addison, C.C., see McKnight, E.T. et al.
Adelberg, E.A., see Stanier, R.V. et al.
Adler, H.H., (7): 92, 119, 124, 152
Agar, W.M., see Fowler, G.M. et al.
Agassiz, A., (7): 297, 331
Aguilar, A., see Ruiz, C. et al.
Aguirre, L. and Mehech, S., (7): 455,
  470
Ahlburg, J., (7): 275, 276, 290
Ahlfeld, F., (7): 501
Aitken, J.D., (5): 75, 100
Aitken, J.D., MacQueen, R.W. and Usher,
  J.L., (5): 44, 100
Aitken, T., see Ewing, M. et al.
Albers, J.P. and Robertson, J.F., (6): 48, 50
Albers, J.P., see Kinkel, A.R. et al.
Albrecht, F., (7): 290
Aldrich, H.R., (7): 193, 197
Alexandrov, E.A., (7): 165, 191, 192, 193,
  194, 197, 204, 248
Al-Hasani, N. and Mostler, H., (5): 27, 30
Al-Kufaishi, F.A.M., see Ineson, P.R. and
  Al-Kufaishi, F.A.M.
Allchurch, P.D., Brook, W.A., Marshall, A.E.
  and Reynolds, D.G., (6): 212, 214
Allen, J.R.L., (7): 99, 100, 105, 152
Allsopp, H.L., Burger, A.J. and Van Zyl, C.,
  (5): 270, 313
Allsopp, H.L., Erlank, A.J. and Horning, G.,
  (5): 296, 313
Alto, K.R., (5): 45, 100
Altschuler, Z.S., Clarke, R.S. and Young,
  E.J., (7): 520, 532
Ames Jr., L.L., (7): 522, 532
Amos, A.C., see Matulich, A. et al.

Amin Singgih, P., see De Groot, A.J. et al.
Ampilogov, I.F., (7): 413, 470
Amstutz, G.C., (5): 14, 30; (6): 27, 50, 449,
  454; (7): 275, 284, 285, 286, 287, 290
Amstutz, G.C. and Bernard, A.J., (3): 337;
  (7): 290
Amstutz, G.C. and Bubenicek, L., (6): 482,
  491; (7): 215, 248
Anandalwas, M.A., see Narayanswami, S. et al.
Andermann, G., (7): 321, 331
Anderson, C.A., (5): 100; (6): 22, 36, 50
Anderson, C.A. and Creasey, S.C., (6):
  158, 181, 183, 214
Anderson, C.A. and Nash, J.T., (6): 81,
  122, 158, 159, 200, 214
Anderson, C.A., Blacet, P.M., Silver, L.T.
  and Stern, T.W., (6): 158, 214
Anderson, D.C., (7): 144, 152
Anderson, G.M., (6): 202, 214
Anderson, G.M., see Nriagu, J.D. and
  Anderson, G.M.
Anderson, J.M., see Ney, C.S. et al.
Anderson, R.N. and Halunen, A.J., (6):
  43, 50
Andrews, J.E., (7): 301, 304, 331
Andrews, J.E. and Meylan, M.A., (7):
  300, 301, 302, 304, 331
Andruschenko, P.F. and Skornyakova,
  I.S., (7): 362, 389
Angel, F. and Trojer, F., (5): 26, 30
Angel, F. and Weiss, P., (5): 26, 31
Angelkov, K., (6): 31, 50
Anger, G., (6): 105, 108, 111, 122; (7):
  284, 290
Anger, G. and Eisbein, P., (6): 105, 108,
  111, 122
Anger, G., Nielsen, H., Puchelt, H. and
  Ricke, W., (6): 22, 50, 579, 583
Anger, G., Borchert, H., Gies, H.,
  Lehmann, F. and Rieck, K., (7):
  497, 501

Angermeier, H.O., (7): 477, 483, 484, 501
Anhaeusser, C.R., (5): 259, 270, 282, 313
Anhaeusser, C.R. and Button, A., (5): 293,
    297, 313
Anhaeusser, C.R. and Lenthall, D.H., (5):
    286, 313
Anhaeusser, C.R., Mason, R., Viljoen, M.J.
    and Viljoen, R.P., (5): 259, 308, 313
Antweiler, J.C., see Cannon, R.S. et al.
Aoki, K., Sato, K., Takeuchi, T. and Tatsumi,
    T., (6): 209, 214
Archbold, N.L., see Shawe, D.R. et al.
Arkhangelskaya, V.V., see Volfson, F.I.
    and Arkhangelskaya, V.V.
Armstrong, G.C., (5): 267, 313
Arnold, M., Maucher, A. and Saupé, F.,
    (7): 494, 501
Arrhenius, G., (7): 302, 317, 331, 362, 389
Arrhenius, G. and Bonatti, E., (7): 312, 331
Arrhenius, G., Mero, J. and Korkisch, J.,
    (7): 312, 331
Arrhenius, G., see Greenslate, J.L. et al.
Asbury, B.C., (6): 189, 193, 215
Asbury, B.C. and Scott, S.D., (6): 189, 215
Ashley, P.M., (6): 63, 68, 75
Ashley, P.M., Chenhall, B.E., Cremer, P.L. and
    Irving, A.J., (6): 63, 75
Ashwill, W.R., see Laverty, R.A. et al.
Aubouin, J., (7): 237, 248, 259, 260, 287,
    290
Audley-Charles, M.G., (7): 297, 304, 331,
    436, 470
Aumento, F., Lawrence, D.E. and Plant, A.G.,
    (7): 304, 331, 440, 470
Austin, S.R., (7): 118, 152
Austin, S.R., see King, J.W. and Austin, S.R.
Ayres, D.E., (7): 221, 248

Baadsgaard, H., see Burwash, R.A. et al.
    see also Greig, J.A. et al.
        Mukherjee, A.C. et al.
Baas Becking, L.G.M. and Moore, D., (6):
    433, 443; (7): 120, 152
Baas Becking, L.G.M., Kaplan, I.R. and
    Moore, D., (7): 330, 331, 387, 389
Bachinski, D., see Kanehira, K. and
    Bachinski, D.
Bächtiger, K., (5): 16, 31
Back, W., see Hanshaw, B.B. et al.

Bäcker, H. and Richter, H., (7): 229, 240,
    248
Bacon, W.R., (5): 89, 100
Bahnemann, K.P., (5): 293, 313
Bailes, A.H., (6): 153, 155, 164, 165, 172,
    215
Bailey, E.H., Irwin, W.P. and Jones, D.L.,
    (7): 449, 470
Bailey, L.W., (5): 142, 154
Bailey, R.V., (7): 152
Bailey, S.M., see Wagman, D.D. et al.
Bain, G.W., (6): 158, 215
Bain, H.G., Van Hise, C.R. and Adams,
    G.I., (6): 463, 491
Baird, D.M., (5): 124, 127, 131, 154
Baird, D.M. and Snelgrove, A.K., (5): 127,
    155
Baker, A.A., Duncan, D.C. and Hunt, C.B.,
    (7): 440, 470
Baker, W.E., (6): 435, 443
Bakun, N.N., Volodin, R.N. and Krendelev,
    F.P., (6): 14, 17, 18
Balkwill, H.R., see Price, R.A. et al.
Bancroft, J.A. and Pelletier, R.A., (6):
    350
Bancroft, W.L., see Price, P. and Bancroft, W.L.
Baragar, W.R.A., (6): 25, 50
Baragar, W.R.A. and Goodwin, A.M., (6): 45,
    50, 171, 215
Baragar, W.R.A., see Dimroth, E. et al.
    see also Irvine, T.N. and Baragar, W.R.A.
Barbat, W.N., (7): 522, 532
Barbosa, A.L.M. and Grossi Sad, J.H., (7):
    169, 170, 187, 188, 197
Barghoorn, E.S. and Tyler, S.A., (7): 179,
    183, 197
Barnes, H.L., see Crerar, D.A. and Barnes,
    H.L.
    see also Scott, S.D. and Barnes, H.L.
Barnes, J., see White, D.E. et al.
Barnes, V.E., (6): 407, 443
Bartel, A.J., see Rosholt, J.N. and Bartel, A.J.
Barten, K.S. and Shaw, J.L., (7): 304, 332
Barth, V., (7): 287, 290
Barthel, F.H., (7): 89, 119, 152
Bartlett, J.H., (7): 341, 344, 389
Barton Jr., P.B., (6): 437, 443, 486, 491, 531
Barton Jr., P.B. and Toulmin, P., III, (6): 90,
    122

Basden, H., (6): 60, 75
Basden, H., see Markham, N.L. and Basden, H.
Bastille, R.A., see Park, W.C. and Bastille, R.A.
Bastin, E.S., (6): 467, 486, 491
Bateman, A.M., (6): 350
Bateman, J.D., (6): 165, 215
Bates, R.L., (7): 532
Bathurst, R.G.C., (7): 204, 205, 217, 220, 248
Baturin, G.N., (7): 528, 529, 532
Baturin, G.N., Merkulova, K.I. and Chalov, P.I., (7): 509, 532
Baturin, G.N., see Romankevich, Ye.A. and Baturin, G.N.
Bauld, J., see Walter, M.R. et al.
Baumann, A., Richter, H. and Schoell, M., (7): 229, 240, 248
Baumann, L., (5): 250, 254; (6): 400, 402
Baumann, L. and Rösler, H.J., (6): 400, 402
Baumann, L. and Werner, C.D., (6): 400, 403
Baumann, L., see Rösler, H.J. and Baumann, L.
Bayley, R.W. and James, H.L., (7): 170, 179, 198, 204, 220, 248
Bazilevskaya, Y.S., see Shterenberg, L.Y. et al.
Beales, F.W. and Jackson, S.A., (6): 450, 454
Beales, F.W. and Oldershaw, A.E., (6): 540, 583
Beales, F.W. and Onazick, E.P., (6): 454, 529, 531
Beales, F.W., Carracedo, J.C. and Strangway, D.W., (6): 451, 452, 454
Beales, F.W., see Jackson, S.A. and Beales, F.W.
Beall Jr., A.O., (6): 417, 443
Beals, H.L., (7): 342, 389
Beane, R.E., (6): 202, 215
Bear, L.M., (6): 33, 34, 44, 50
Beardsley, K.M., see Robie, R.A. et al.
Beath, O.A., see Trelease, S.F. and Beath, O.A.
Becker, R.H. and Clayton, R.N., (7): 191, 198, 229, 248
Beckinsale, R.D., see Spooner, E.T.C. et al.
Behr, S.H., (5): 268, 313
Behre Jr., C.H., see Brokaw, A.L. et al.
Behrend, F., (7): 277, 290
Behrens, W.W., see Meadows, D.H. et al.
Beiersdorf, H., see Heye, D. and Beiersdorf, H.
Belik, G.D., (5): 94, 100

Bell, C.K., see Coats, C.J.A. et al.
Bell, J.D., see Mitchell, A.H. and Bell, J.D.
Bell, R.T., (5): 44, 100
Bell, R.T. and Hofmann, H.J., (7): 239, 248
Belova, I.V., see Strakhov, N.M. et al.
Belyea, H.R., see Douglas, R.J.W. et al.
Bender, M.L., (7): 382, 389
Bender, M.L., Ku, T.L. and Broecker, W.S., (7): 303, 323, 332
Benedict, P.C., Wiid, D. de N., Cornelissen, A.K. and Staff, (5): 268, 313
Bennet, E.M., (6): 537, 572, 573, 575, 583
Bennett, R.A. and Rose Jr., W.I., (6): 144, 215
Bennett, R.H., see Keller, G.H. and Bennett, R.H.
Benson, D.G., (5): 140, 155
Berezowski, M., (6): 188, 189, 215
Berg, G., (6): 103, 113, 122
Berg, H.C., Jones, D.L. and Richter, D.H., (5): 47, 48, 49, 51, 101
Bergeron, R., (7): 209, 248
Bergeron, R., see Dimroth, E. et al.
Bergstøl, S. and Vokes, F.M., (6): 122
Berka, L.H., see Masterton, W.W. and Berka, L.H.
Berker, L.V. and Marshall, L.G., (7): 238, 248
Bernard, A.J., (5): 5, 11, 31; (6): 218, 449, 454
Bernard, A.J. and Samama, J.C., (6): 2, 18
Bernard, A.J. and Soler, E., (6): 29, 34, 50
Bernard, A.J., see Amstutz, G.C. and Bernard, A.J.
Bernard, H.A. and Major Jr., C.F., (7): 100, 104, 152
Bernard, H.A., Major Jr., C.F., Parrott, B.S. and LeBlanc Sr., R.J., (7): 100, 152
Berner, R.A., (7): 92, 120, 121, 124, 150, 152, 227, 229, 240, 248, 357, 373, 385, 389
Bertine, K.K. and Turekian, K.K., (7): 323, 332
Bertine, K.K., see Kharkar, D.P. et al.
Besnus, Y., Bronner, G., Mosser, C. and Oksengorn, S., (7): 204, 235, 248
Betekhtin, A.G., (7): 413, 414, 459, 470
Bethke, P.M., see Robie, R.A. et al.

Brusca, C., Dessau, G., Jensen, M.L. and
    Perna, G., (5): 11, 31
Bubela, B., see Lambert, I.B. and Bubela, B.
Bubenicek, L., see Amstutz, G.C. and
    Bubenicek, L.
Buchan, R., see Coats, C.J.A. et al.
Buchanan, J.Y., (7): 343, 389
Buck, K.L., see Cannon, R.S. et al.
Buckley, E.R. and Buehler, H.A., (6):
    470, 491
Buddington, A.F. and Chapin, Th., (5):
    47, 101
Buehler, H.A., see Buckley, E.R. and
    Buehler, H.A.
Bugge, C., (6): 104, 107, 122
Bunce, E.T., see Pimm, A.C. et al.
Buol, S.W., see Collins, J.F. and Buol, S.W.
Burchard, E.F., (7): 501
Burger, A.J. and Coertze, F.J., (5): 259, 314
Burger, A.J., see Allsopp, H.L. et al.
Burnett, W.C., see Veeh, H.H. et al.
Burnham, C.W., Holloway, J.R. and Davis,
    N.F., (6): 37, 50
Burnol, L., see Bouladon, J. et al.
Burns, R.G., (7): 317, 321, 332, 389
Burns, R.G. and Brown, B.A., (7): 308,
    316, 317, 326, 332
Burns, R.G. and Burns, (7): 389
Burns, R.G. and Fuerstenau, D.W., (7): 307,
    332, 370
Burns, R.G. and Fyfe, W.S., (7): 321, 332
Burroughs, R.H., see Pimm, A.C. et al.
Bursill, C., Luyt, J.F.M. and Urie, J.G.,
    (5): 298, 314
Burst, J.E., (7): 214, 248
Burwash, R.A., Baadsgaard, H. and Peterman,
    Z.E., (5): 42, 55, 69, 101
Buser, W. and Grutter, A., (7): 315, 332,
    361, 362, 389
Bush, F., see Evans, G. et al.
Bush, P.R., (6): 450, 455
Bushinski, G.I., (7): 506, 508, 512, 523,
    526, 527, 530, 532
Butcher, N.J.D. and Ford, T.D., (5): 162,
    193
Butler, G.P., (6): 420, 421, 422, 433, 434,
    443
Butler, R.D., (6): 531
Button, A., (5): 261, 274, 275, 278, 307,
    314

Button, A., see Anhaeusser, C.R. and
    Button, A.
    see also Minnitt, R.C.A. et al.
Butuzova, G.Y., (7): 277, 291
Byers, A.R., Kirkland, S.S.T. and Pearson,
    W.J., (6): 156, 157, 215
Byrne, B., Downing, D. and Romer, D., (5):
    244, 246, 248, 254
Byrne Jr., R.H., see Kester, D.R. and Byrne Jr.,
    R.H.

Čadek, J., see Sattran, V. and Čadek, J.
Cahen, L., Delhal, J., Deutsch, S.,
    Grogler, N., Ledent, D. and
    Pasteels, P., (6): 227, 235, 238, 350
Caia, J., (6): 14, 18, 19
Caldwell, A.B., (7): 532
Callahan, W.A., (6): 484, 491
Callahan, W.H., (6): 449, 455, 496, 501,
    502, 504, 505, 506, 507, 531, 532
Callender, E., (7): 302, 332, 342, 344,
    346, 349, 351, 362, 364, 365, 374,
    379, 380, 381, 382, 390
Callender, E., Bowser, C.J. and Rossmann, R.,
    (7): 362, 364, 367, 376, 377, 390
Callender, E., see Bowser, C.J. et al.
    see also Edgington, D. and Callender, E.
               Robbins, J.A. and Callender, E.
               Rossmann, R. and Callender, E.
               Rossmann, R. et al.
Calvert, S.E. and Price, N.B., (7): 302, 332, 343,
    355, 356, 358, 365, 367, 382, 390,
    407, 414, 470
Calvert, S.E., see Price, N.B. and Calvert, S.E.
Cameron, D.E. and Romer, D., (5): 244, 245,
    246, 254
Cameron, E.N., see Sorem, R.K. and Cameron,
    E.N.
Campana, B., (7): 161, 198
Campbell, A.B., see Hobbs, S.W. et al.
Campbell, F.H.A., see Coats, C.J.A. et al.
Campbell, N., (6): 466, 491
Campbell, N. and Irvine, W.T., (5): 85, 92,
    101
Campbell, R.B., (5): 41, 42, 101
Campbell, R.B. and Tipper, H.W., (5): 101
Campbell, R.B., see Wheeler, J.O. et al.
Canaval, R., (5): 23, 31
Canavan, F., (5): 52, 101
Cann, J.R., (6): 27, 50, 119, 122

Churkin Jr., M., (5): 39, 47, 48, 101

Cilliers, J.J. le R., (5): 280, 281, 314

Cilliers, J.J. le R. and Genis, J.H., (5): 280, 281, 314

Cissarz, A., (6): 394, 403; (7): 268, 275, 276, 281, 282, 291

Clar, E., (5): 5, 26, 31

Clark, B.R. and Kelly, W.C., (6): 184, 215, 507, 511, 532

Clark, B.R., see Salmon, B.C. et al.

Clark, G.J., see Mathias, B.V. and Clark, G.J.
    see also Mathias, B.V. et al.

Clark, G.R., see Derry, D.R. et al.

Clark, L.A., (5): 58, 59, 101; (6): 205, 215

Clark, L.A., see Coats, C.J.A. et al.
    see also Tatsumi, T. and Clark, L.A.

Clark Jr., S.P., see Toulmin, P., III and Clark Jr., S.P.

Clarke, R.S., see Altschuler, Z.S. et al.

Claxton, C., see Brown, M.C. et al.

Clayton, R.N., Friedman, I., Graf, D.L., Mayeda, T.K., Meents, W.F. and Shimp, N.F., (6): 485, 492

Clayton, R.N., see Becker, R.H. and Clayton, R.N.

Cloud, P.E., (7): 166, 183, 184, 194, 195, 198, 211, 236, 239, 249

Cloud Jr., P.E. and Semikhatow, M.A., (7): 210, 244, 249

Cloutier, J.P., see Sauvé, P. et al.

Clowes, R.M., see Kanasewich, E.R. et al.

Clutten, J.M., see Rijken, J.H.A. and Clutten, J.M.

Coates, J., (5): 62, 101

Coats, C.J.A., Clark, L.A., Buchan, R. and Brummer, J.J., (6): 156, 157, 164, 180, 181, 189, 190, 215

Coats, C.J.A., Quirke Jr., T.T., Bell, C.K., Cranstone, D.A. and Campbell, F.H.A., (6): 153, 156, 180, 181, 215

Cochrane, G.W. and Edwards, A.B., (7): 204, 214, 221, 246

Coelho, I.S., see Dorr, J.V.N. et al.

Coertze, F.J., see Burger, A.J. and Coertze, F.J.

Coetzee, C.B., (5): 287, 288, 308, 314

Coetzee, F., (5): 267, 314; (7): 66, 75, 87

Coffin, R.C., (7): 119, 153

Colbert, E.H., see Kay, M. and Colbert, E.H.

Cole, G.A.J., (5): 232, 234, 239, 254

Coleman, J. and Gagliano, S.M., (6): 416, 443

Coleman, J.M., (7): 92, 99, 100, 112, 153

Coleman, J.M., see Ho, C. and Coleman, J.M.

Coleman, L.C., (6): 156, 215

Coleman, R.G., (6): 56, 75

Coleman, R.G., see Garrels, R.M. et al.

Coleman, R.J., (6): 21, 31, 50

Collette, W.J., (7): 511, 532

Colley, H. and Rice, C.M., (6): 25, 50

Collins, B.I., (6): 435, 443

Collins, J.F. and Buol, S.W., (7): 384, 390 399, 403, 470

Conary, S.D., see Ewing, M. et al.

Constantinou, G. and Govett, G.J.S., (5): 124, 151, 155; (6): 33, 50, 81, 123, 581, 583

Cook, D.G., see Price, R.A. et al.

Cook, H.E., (7): 306, 332

Cook, P.J., (7): 512, 519, 521, 527, 528, 529, 530, 532

Cook, P.J. and Mayo, W., (7): 523, 532

Cook, P.J., see De Keyser, F. and Cook, P.J.
    see also Powell, T.G. et al.

Cooke, D.L. and Moorhouse, W.W., (7): 239, 249

Coomer, P. and Ford, T.D., (5): 176, 193

Cooney, A.M., see Howard, P.F. and Cooney, A.M.

Cooper, J.A. and Richards, J.R., (5): 68, 70, 102

Cooper, J.R., (5): 124, 155

Cope, F.W., (5): 162, 163, 193

Corbett, J.A., Lambert, I.B. and Scott, K.M., (6): 553, 555, 559, 565, 566, 583

Corliss, J.B., (6): 35, 36, 49, 51

Cornelissen, A.K., see Benedict, P.C. et al.

Cornelius, H.P. and Plöchinger, B., (5): 29, 31

Cornwall, H.R., see Phillips, C.H. et al.

Correns, C.W., (6): 391, 403

Côté, R., see Dimroth, E. et al.

Cotton, R.E., (6): 545, 550, 565, 583

Courtois, C., (7): 204, 249

Cousins, C.A., (7): 65, 74, 87

Craig, H., (5): 70, 102, 288, 314

Craig, J.R. and Kullerud, G., (6): 196, 215

DeGrace, J.R., see Kennedy, M.J. and
    DeGrace, J.R.
De Groot, A.J., Zschuppe, K.H., De Bruin, M.,
    Houtman, J.P.W. and Amin Singgih,
    P., (7): 373, 390
De Huff, G.L., see Hewett, D.F. et al.
Deike, R.G., see Hanshaw, B.B. et al.
De Jager, D.H., (5): 308, 314
De Jager, D.H. and Simpson, W., (5): 307,
    314
De Jager, D.H. and Von Backström, J.W.,
    (5): 308, 314
De Keyser, F., (7): 530, 533
De Keyser, F. and Cook, P.J., (7): 519, 533
De Kock, W.P., (7): 70, 75, 87
De Kun, N., (7): 450, 470
Delach, M.N., see Horn, D.R. et al.
Delevaux, M.H., see Cannon Jr., R.S. et al.
    see also Heyl, A.V. et al.
            Stavey, J.S. et al.
Delhal, J., see Cahen, L. et al.
Delibrias, G., see Lalou, C. et al.
De Llarena, J.G., (5): 26, 31
Denckewitz, R., (7): 291
Denckmann, (7): 275, 276
Denis, T.C., see Dresser, J.A. and
    Denis, T.C.
Denison, R.E., Hetherington, E.A. and
    Otto, J.B., (6): 457, 492
Denson, N.M. and Gill, J.R., (7): 153
De Preez, J.W., (5): 299, 314
Déprez, D. and Soler, E., (7): 447, 448,
    471
De Quervain, F., see Hügi, Th. et al.
Derby, O.A., (7): 198, 415, 471
Dercout, J., (5): 102
De Rosen-Spence, A., (6): 198, 201, 216
De Rosen-Spence, A., see Spence, C.D.
    and de Rosen-Spence, A.F.
Derrick, G.M., see Plumb, K.A. and
    Derrick, G.M.
Derry, D.R., Clark, G.R. and Gillatt, N.,
    (5): 245, 251, 254; (6): 452, 455;
    (7): 281, 282, 291
Desai, A.A., see Hagni, R.D. and Desai, A.A.
Descarreaux, J., (6): 24, 25, 45, 51, 144,
    187, 216
Deschow, E.W.C., (5): 140, 155
Dessau, G., see Brusca, C. et al.
    see also Jensen, M.L. and Dessau, G.

De Swardt, A.M.J., (6): 351
Deutsch, L., see Cahen, L. et al.
De Villiers, J., (7): 431, 434, 471
De Villiers, J., see Martin, H. et al.
De Villiers, J.E., (5): 266, 270, 271, 301,
    302, 304, 314; (7): 434, 435, 471
De Villiers, P.R., (5): 279, 302, 303, 314;
    (7): 431, 433, 434, 471
De Waal, S.A. and Herzberg, W., (5): 268,
    314
Dewey, H., (5): 184, 186, 187, 193
Dewey, H. and Eastwood, T., (5): 212, 228
Dewey, J.F. and Bird, J.M., (5): 113, 115,
    116, 124, 155
Dewey, J.F., see Bird, J.M. and Dewey, J.F.
    see also Upadhyay, H.D. et al.
Dickson, F.W., see Bischoff, J.L. and
    Dickson, F.W.
Dickson, T.W., (6): 63, 75
Dickson, W.L., see Strong, D.F. et al.
Di Colbertaldo, D., see Brigo, L. and
    Di Colbertaldo, D.
Dietrich, R.V., Hobbs Jr., C.R.B. and
    Lowry, L.D., (7): 215, 241, 249
Dietz, R.A., (7): 300, 333
Dietz, R.S. and Holden, J.C., (7): 95, 107,
    111, 153
Dietz, R.S., Emery, K.O. and Shepard, F.P.,
    (7): 509, 514, 533
Dill Jr., D.B., see Lea, E.R. and Dill Jr., D.B.
Dimroth, E., (7): 169, 179, 191, 198, 205,
    209, 211, 214, 236, 238, 239, 244,
    245, 246, 250
Dimroth, E. and Chauvel, J.J., (7): 181, 206,
    209, 210, 211, 213, 214, 215, 216,
    217, 218, 219, 220, 221, 222, 223,
    224, 225, 236, 244, 245, 246, 247,
    250
Dimroth, E. and Dressler, B., (7): 211, 244,
    250
Dimroth, E., Baragar, W.R.A., Bergeron, R.
    and Jackson, G.D., (7): 236, 238,
    239, 250
Dimroth, E., Rocheleau, M., Boivin, P.,
    Larousche, M. and Côté, R., (7):
    235, 250
Dimroth, E., see Chauvel, J.J. and Dimroth, E.
Dingess, P.R., see Brockie, D.C. et al.
Dingle, R.V., see Summerhayes, C.P. et al.

Goble, R.J., see Morton, R.D. et al.
Goebel, E.D., Thompson, T.L., Waugh, T.C. and
    Mueller, L.C., (6): 487, 492
Goldberg, E.D., (7): 297, 321, 325, 334, 357,
    370, 380, 391
Goldberg, E.D., see Liss, P.S. et al.
Goldich, S.S., (7): 163, 164, 199, 239, 251
Goldich, S.S., see Lepp, J. and Goldich, S.S.
Goldstein Jr., A., see Flawn, P.T. et al.
Gondi, J., see Irvine, W.T. et al.
Goodchild, J.G., (5): 203, 227
Goodell, H.G., Meylan, M.A. and Grant, B.,
    (7): 301, 304, 305, 334
Goodell, H.G., see Fleischer, R.L. et al.
Goodschild, J.H., (7): 192, 199
Goodwin, A.M., (5): 283, 315; (6): 142, 144,
    146, 168, 169, 171, 199, 216; (7): 158,
    166, 167, 168, 175, 179, 191, 192, 194,
    199, 206, 208, 209, 221, 222, 223, 229,
    230, 235, 237, 241, 246, 251, 292
Goodwin, A.M. and Ridler, R.H., (6): 133,
    142, 143, 144, 145, 146, 173, 174,
    184, 201, 208, 216; (7): 251
Goodwin, A.M. and Shklanka, R., (7): 166,
    199
Goodwin, A.M., see Baragar, W.R.A. and
    Goodwin, A.M.
Gorham, E. and Swaine, D.J., (7): 343, 344,
    349, 351, 352, 356, 357, 358, 386, 391
Gorshkov, (7): 276
Gossens, P.J., (6): 17, 19
Goto, K., see Okamoto, G. et al.
Gott, G.B. and Hill, J.W., (6): 487, 492
Gotte, W., see Brause, H. et al.
Götz, H., (7): 292
Gough, D., (5): 213, 214, 217, 229
Gough, J.W., (5): 182, 193
Gould, H.R. and McFarlan Jr., (6): 418, 444
Gould, W., Smith, R.B., Metzger, S.P. and
    Melancon, P.E., (7): 92, 154
Govett, G.J.S., (7): 235, 251
Govett, G.J.S. and Pantazis, Th.M., (6):
    29, 44, 45, 51
Govett, G.J.S., see Constantinou, G. and
    Govett, G.J.S.
Govett, G.S., (7): 163, 199
Gräbe, R., (7): 263, 275, 276, 292
Grad, H., see Protić, M. et al.
Grad, K., see Drovenik, F. et al.

Graf, D.L., see Clayton, R.N. et al.
Graf Jr., J.L. and Skinner, B.J., (6): 216
Grafenauer, S., (7): 493, 501
Graham, F., (6): 452, 455
Granger, H.C. and Warren, C.G., (7): 149, 150,
    154
Granger, H.C., Santos, E.S., Dean, B.G. and
    Moore, F.B., (7): 125, 128, 154
Granger, H.C., see Dooley Jr., J.R. et al.
    see also Waters, A.C. and Granger, H.C.
Grant, J.B., (7): 309, 334
Grawe, O.R., see Hagni, R.D. and Grawe, O.R.
Gray, A., (6): 351
Green, D.A., (6): 411, 444
Green, G.R., see Jago, J.B. et al.
    see also Williams, E. et al.
Green, G.W., (5): 183, 184, 186, 187, 188, 193
Green, G.W. and Welch, F.B., (5): 184, 185,
    193
Green, L.H. and Roddick, J.A., (5): 44, 103
Green, M.E., see Whyte, R.J. and Green, M.E.
Greenslate, J.L., Frazer, J.Z. and Arrhenius,
    G., (7): 314, 335
Greenwood, W.R., see Reid, R.R. et al.
Gregory, F.E., see Fowler, G.M. et al.
Gregory, J.W., (6): 351
Greig, J.A., Baadsgaard, H., Cumming,
    G.L., Folinsbee, R.E., Krouse, H.R.,
    Ohmoto, H., Sasaki, A. and Smejkal,
    V., (5): 245, 249, 250, 251, 253, 254
Gressus, C.L., see Lalou, C. et al.
Griffin, P.H., (7): 341, 342, 344, 391
Griffith, R.J., (5): 239, 254
Griffiths, J.R., see Solomon, M. and
    Griffiths, J.R.
Griggs, A.B., see Hobbs, S.W. et al.
Griggs, R.E., (7): 292
Grigor'ev, D.P., (5): 237, 254
Grill, E.V., Murray, J.W. and MacDonald,
    R.D., (7): 367, 391
Grill, R., see Lechner, K. et al.
Grimes, D.J., see Harrison, J.E. and
    Grimes, D.J.
Grintal, E.F., (6): 14, 19
Grip, E., (6): 19
Grip, E. and Frietsch, R., (6): 92, 95, 123
Grant, B., see Goodell, H.G. et al.
Grogan, R.M. and Bradbury, J.C., (5):
    294, 315

Hill, W.T., see Hoagland, A.D. et al.
see also Winslow, K.R. and Hill, W.T.
Hilpert, L.S., (7): 142, 154
Hilpert, L.S., see Fischer, R.P. and
Hilpert, L.S.
Hinterlechner, K., (5): 24, 32
Hirayama, H., see Ohtagaki, T. et al.
Hirst, D.M., see Dunham, K.C. and Hirst,
D.M.
Hirst, J.A., (6): 31, 51
Hitchen, C.S., (5): 217, 229
Ho, C. and Coleman, J.M., (7): 229, 240, 251
Hoagland, A.D., (6): 532
Hoagland, A.D., Hill, W.T. and Fulweiler, R.E.,
(6): 533
Hoagland, A.D., see Crawford, J. and
Hoagland, A.D.
see also Gilbert, R.C. and Hoagland, A.D.
Hobbs, S.W., Griggs, A.B., Wallace, R.E.
and Campbell, A.B., (5): 58, 103
Hobbs, W.H., (6): 217
Hobbs Jr., C.R.B., see Dietrich, R.V. et al.
Hodder, R.W. and Hollister, V.F., (6): 55, 76
Hodder, R.W., see Hutchinson, R.W. and
Hodder, R.W.
Hodge, B.L., see Dunham, K.C. et al.
Hodge, H.J., (6): 205, 217
Hofmann, H.J., (7): 207, 209, 210, 211,
244, 251, 440, 472
Hofmann, H.J., see Bell, R.T. and
Hofmann, H.J.
Hoffmann, W., (6): 393, 404
Holden, J.C., see Dietz, R.S. and Holden, J.C.
Höll, R., (5): 3, 5, 19, 20, 24, 25, 27, 28,
32; (7): 477, 478, 485, 490, 491, 502
Höll, R. and Maucher, A., (5): 5, 19, 20, 23,
26, 27, 32; (7): 477, 489, 491, 502
Höll, R., Maucher, A. and Westenberger, H.,
(5): 5, 20, 32; (7): 491, 492, 502
Höll, R., see Cunningham, W.B. et al.
see also Maucher, A. and Höll, R.
Holland, H.D., (7): 193, 194, 195, 199, 238,
239, 251
Hollingworth, S.E., see Trotter, F.M. et al.
Hollister, C.D. and Heezen, B.C., (7): 301, 335
Hollister, C.D., Johnson, D.A. and Lonsdale,
P.F., (7): 301, 335
Hollister, C.D., see Heezen, B.C. and
Hollister, C.D.
see also MacDonald, K.C. and
Hollister, C.D.

Hollister, V.F., see Hodder, R.W. and
Hollister, V.F.
Holloway, J.R., see Burnham, C.W. et al.
Holtrop, J.F., (7): 416, 472
Holubec, J., (6): 145, 217
Holzer, H., (5): 33
Holzner, H., see Lechner, K. et al.
Homma, H., see Tokunaga, M. and Homma, H.
Honnorez, J., Honnorez-Guerstein, B., Valette,
J. and Wauschkuhn, A., (6): 200, 217
Honnorez, J., see Bonatti, E. et al.
Honnorez-Guerstein, B., see Bonnorez, J. et al.
Horen, A., see Dorr II, J.V.N. et al.
see also Straczek, J.A. et al.
Horikoshi, E., (5): 152, 156; (6): 26, 30, 36,
51, 81, 82, 83, 123, 209, 217; (7): 239,
251
Horikoshi, E. and Sato, T., (6): 210, 217
Horikoshi, E., see Matsukuma, T. and
Horikoshi, E.
Horn, B.M., see Horn, D.R. et al.
Horn, D., see Ewing, M. et al.
Horn, D.R., (7): 297, 298, 304, 335
Horn, D.R., Delach, M.N. and Horn, B.M., (7):
298, 312, 335, 367, 391
Horn, D.R., Horn, B.M. and Delach, M.N.,
(7): 297, 298, 299, 304, 305, 312,
335
Horn, D.R., Ewing, M., Horn, B.M. and
Delach, M.N., (7): 298, 301, 335
Hornibrook, N.D., see Reed, J.J. and
Hornibrook, N.D.
Horning, G., see Allsopp, H.L. et al.
Horsfield, E.L., see Shirley, J. and Horsfield,
E.L.
Hough, J.L., (7): 190, 191, 194, 199, 235,
251
Houston, R.S., (7): 142, 154
Houtman, J.P.W., see De Groot, A.J. et al.
Howard, P.F. and Cooney, A.M., (7): 519,
520, 530, 533
Howard, P.F. and Perrino, F.A., (7): 530,
533
Howell, J.E., (7): 236, 251
Howie, R.A., see Deer, W.A. et al.
Howkins, J.B. and Martin, P.L., (6): 190, 217
Howland, A.L., see Garrels, R.M. et al.
Hsü, K.J. and Schneider, J., (6): 433, 444
Hsü, K.J. and Siegenthaler, C., (6): 434, 436,
444

Hubbard, N.J., see Kay, M. et al.
Huber, N.K., (7): 190, 192, 199
Hubred, G.L., (7): 304, 309, 335
Hudson, D.R., see Ewers, W.E. and Hudson,
    D.R.
Hudson, F.S., see Taliaferro, N.L. and
    Hudson, F.S.
Hudson, R.G.S., (5): 206, 228
Huebner, J.S., (7): 408, 409, 448, 449, 472
Huffman, G.G., (6): 466, 492
Hughes, C.J., (5): 112, 156
Hughes, C.J. and Brückner, W.D., (5): 112, 156
Hügi, Th., (5): 16, 33
Hügi, Th., Köppel, V., de Quervain, F. and
    Rickenbach, E., (5): 16, 33
Hull, E., Cruise, R.J. and Hatch, F., (5): 235,
    254
Hummel, (7): 276
Hunt, C.B., see Baker, A.A. et al.
Hunt, G., (5): 55, 103
Hunt, G.H., (6): 166, 217
Hunter, D.R., (5): 270, 272, 315
Hurd, D.C., (7): 312, 313, 335
Hutchinson, R.W., (5): 103, 283, 315; (6):
    21, 24, 48, 51, 55, 75, 152, 179,
    183, 188, 213, 214, 217, 580, 581,
    584
Hutchinson, R.W. and Hodder, R.W., (6): 31,
    51, 55, 58, 76
Hutchinson, R.W. and Searle, D.L., (5): 124,
    151, 156; (6): 26, 51, 81, 124
Hutchinson, R.W., Ridler, R.H. and Suffel,
    G.G., (6): 174, 201, 202, 217
Hutchinson, R.W., see Suffel, G.G. et al.

Iijima, A., (6): 33, 41, 51
Iijima, A. and Hay, R.L., (6): 542, 584
Iliev, Z., see Zhelyaskova-Panajotova, M. et al.
Ineson, P.R., (5): 177, 193, 202, 203, 217,
    227, 229
Ineson, P.R. and Al-Kufaishi, F.A.M., (5):
    169, 172, 193
Ineson, P.R. and Mitchell, J.G., (5): 176, 177,
    194, 217, 218, 219, 229, 243, 253,
    254
Ineson, P.R., Richardson, R.T. and Wood, G.H.,
    (5): 168, 182, 194
Ineson, P.R., see Dunham, K.C. et al.
    see also Ford, T.D. and Ineson, P.R.
Inostrantsev, A.A., (7): 343, 391

Ireland, H.A., (6): 460, 492
Irrinki, R.R., see Davies, J.L. et al.
Irvine, R., see Murray, J. and Irvine, R.
Irving, H. and Williams, R.J.P., (7): 369, 391
Irvine, T.N. and Baragar, W.R.A., (6): 171,
    217
Irvine, W.T., Gondi, J. and Sullivan Mine
    Geological Staff, (5): 66, 103
Irvine, W.T., see Campbell, N. and
    Irvine, W.T.
Irving, A.J., see Ashley, P.M. et al.
Irving, H. and Williams, R.J.P., (7): 369, 391
Irwin, W.P., see Bailey, E.H. et al.
    see also Jones, D.L. et al.
Ishihara, S., (6): 208, 217, 579, 584
Issajeva, A.B., (7): 481, 502
Ivanov, M.V., see Kuznetsov, S.I. et al.
Ivanov, S.N., (5): 237, 254
Ivnitskaya, R.B., see Smirnov, A.I. et al.
Ixer, R.A., (5): 169, 194

Jackson, E.J., see Langton, G. and Jackson,
    E.J.
Jackson, G.C.A., (6): 351
Jackson, G.D., see Dimroth, E. et al.
Jackson, S.A. and Beales, F.W., (6): 450,
    455, 529, 531, 533, 569, 584
Jackson, S.A., see Beales, F.W. and Jackson,
    S.A.
    see also Billings, G.K. et al.
Jacobs, I.S., see Fleischer, R.L. et al.
Jacobsen, J.B.E., (5): 291, 296, 315
Jacobsen, W., (5): 296, 315
Jaffe, E.B., (7): 520, 533
Jago, J.B., Reid, K.O., Quilty, P.G., Green,
    G.R. and Daily, B., (6): 32, 51
Jakeš, P. and White, A.J.R., (6): 24, 51, 118,
    120, 124
James, H.L., (5): 274, 282, 288, 315; (7):
    159, 163, 174, 175, 176, 181, 182,
    184, 185, 186, 187, 190, 194, 199,
    203, 204, 209, 217, 225, 226, 227,
    228, 230, 238, 252
James, H.L., and Sims, P.K., (7): 190, 199
James, H.L., see Bayley, R.W. and James, H.L.
Jankovic, S., (7): 281, 282, 292, 493, 502
Jedwab, J., (7): 297, 335, 336
Jeletzky, J.A., and Tipper, H.W., (5): 51, 103
Jenkins, S.R., (7): 384, 391

Lahusen, L., (5): 23, 24, 33; (7): 489, 490, 502

Lal, D., see Bhat, S.G. et al.
    see also Krishnaswamy, S. and Lal, D.

Lalou, C. and Brichet, E., (7): 324, 336

Lalou, C., Brichet, E. and Gressus, C.L., (7): 324, 336

Lalou, C., Brichet, E. and Ranque, D., (7): 324, 336

Lalou, C., Delibrias, G., Brichet, E. and Labeyrie, J., (7): 324, 336

Lamarche, R.Y., (5): 115, 127, 156

Lamarche, R.Y., see St. Julien, P. and Lamarche, R.Y.

Lambert, I.B., (6): 55, 58, 64, 76, 566, 569, 572, 584

Lambert, I.B. and Bubela, B., (6): 566, 584

Lambert, I.B. and Sato, T., (6): 36, 41, 42, 52, 579, 584

Lambert, I.B. and Scott, K.M., (6): 553, 555, 559, 560, 565, 566, 568, 584

Lambert, I.B., see Corbett, J.A. et al.
    see also Ferguson, J. and Lambert, I.B.
        Trudinger, P.A. et al.

Lamphere, M.A., see Dalrymple, G.B. and Lamphere, M.A.

Landergren, S., (7): 297, 336, 343, 392

Landmesser, C.W. and Morgenstein, M.E., (7): 304, 336

Landstrom, E., see Robbins, J.A. et al.

Lang, R., (6): 390, 392, 404

Lange, H., (7): 293

Lange, H., see Rösler, H.J. and Lange, H.

Langer, M., (6): 404

Langer, M., see Erzberger, R. et al.
    see also Rentzsch, J. and Langer, M.

Langton, G. and Jackson, E.J., (5): 270, 316

Lapwood, E.R., (6): 36, 37, 39, 41, 52

Larouche, M., see Dimroth, E. et al.

Larsen, K.G., (6): 466, 493

Larsen 3rd, E.S., see Garrels, R.M. et al.

Latulippe, M., (6): 200, 218

Laughton, A.S., (7): 304, 337

Laugier, R., (7): 214, 252

Laurence, R.A., (6): 533

Laurence, R.A., see Brokaw, A.L. et al.

Laverty, R.A., Ashwill, W.R., Chenoweth, W.L. and Norton, D.L., (7): 119, 155

Lawrence, D.E., see Aumento, F. et al.

Lawrence, L.J., (6): 31, 52

Lea, E.R. and Dill Jr., D.B., (6): 141, 171 181, 189, 218, 448, 455

Lea, E.R. and Rancourt, G., (5): 140, 156

Lebedev, L.M. and Nikitina, I.B., (6): 202, 218

LeBlanc Sr., B.S., see Bernard, H.A. et al.

Lechner, K. and Plöchinger, B., (5): 29, 33

Lechner, K., Holzner, H., Ruttner, A. and Grill, R., (5): 33

LeCouteur, P., (5): 53, 63, 64, 68, 69, 70, 71, 72, 77, 80, 82, 104

Ledent, D., see Cahen, L. et al.

Lee, W., (6): 487, 493

Leech, G.B., (5): 64, 104; (6): 166, 207, 218

Leech, G.B. and Wanless, R.K., (5): 44, 55, 63, 68, 104; (6): 166, 167, 218

Lees, A., (5): 234, 254

Legierski, J. and Sattran, V., (5): 250, 254

Lehman, E., (7): 276, 286, 287, 288, 289, 293

Lehman, F., see Anger, G. et al.

Lehnert-Thiel, K., (5): 24, 33

Lehr, J.R., see Smith, J.P. and Lehr, J.R.

Leith, C.K., (7): 183, 200

Leith, C.K., see Van Hise, C.R. and Leith, C.K.

Leitmeier, H., (5): 26, 33

Leitmeier, H. and Siegl, W., (5): 26, 33

Lemoalle, J. and Dupont, B., (7): 240, 241, 252

Lenthall, D.H., see Anhaeusser, C.R. and Lenthall, D.H.

Leonard, A.B., see Swineford, A. et al.

Leonard, J.D., see Rashid, M.A. and Leonard, J.D.

Leone, R.O., see Ensign, C.O. et al.

Leonhard, A., see Schmidt, A. and Leonhard, A.

Leopold, L.B., Wolman, M.G. and Miller, J.P., (6): 155

Lepp, H. and Goldich, S., (7): 163, 190, 192, 200, 203, 204, 238, 239, 252

Le Roex, H.D., see Söhnge, P.G. et al.

LeRoux, N.W., see Temple, K.L. and LeRoux, N.W.

Lesko, I., (5): 26, 33

Levinson, A.A., (7): 364, 392

Lewis, B.R., Forward, P.S. and Roberts, J.B., (6): 576, 584

Lewis, G.N. and Randall, M., (7): 328, 337

Li, Y.H., Bischoff, J.L. and Mathieu, G., (7): 302, 337, 381 382, 392

Noddack, J. and Noddack, W., (6): 394, 404
Noddack, W., see Noddack, J. and Noddack, W.
Norman, G.W.H. and McCue, J., (5): 89, 105
Normark, W.R., see Lonsdale, P.F. et al.
Norris, A.W., see Douglas, R.J.W. and Norris, A.W.
Northcote, K.E. and Muller, J.E., (5): 91, 95, 105
Norton, D.L., see Laverty, R.A. et al.
Novokhatskiy, I.P., (7): 458, 459, 473
Nowlan, J.P. and Wright, J.D., (5): 147, 157
Nriagu, J.D. and Anderson, G.M., (6): 450, 456, 570, 571
Nriagu, J.P., (7): 357, 392
Nussmann, D.G., (7): 351, 352, 358, 392
Nutter, A.H., see Summerhayes, C.P. et al.

Obradovich, J.D. and Peterman, Z.E., (5): 44, 55, 105
O'Brien, M.V., (5): 234, 235, 236, 247, 255
Odell, J.H., see Snyder, F.G. and Odell, J.H.
Oder, C.R.L. and Miller, H.W., (6): 500, 533
Oder, C.R.L. and Ricketts, J.E., (6): 514, 533
O'Driscoll, C.F., see Strong, D.F. et al.
Oelsner, O., (6): 404
Oertel, G. and Curtis, C.D., (7): 215, 216, 229, 253
Oertel, G., see Curtis, C.D. et al.
Oftedahl, C., (5): 85, 105, 152, 157; (6): 104, 108, 111, 117, 125, 199, 219; (7): 275, 284, 289, 293
Ohashi, R., (5): 288, 316
Ohle, E.L., (6): 16, 19, 529, 533
Ohle Jr., E.L. and Brown, J.S., (6): 465, 493, 533
Ohmoto, H., (6): 563, 564, 584
Ohmoto, H. and Rye, R.O., (6): 36, 42, 47, 52
Ohmoto, H., see Greig, J.A. et al.
Ohtagaki, T., Tsukada, Y., Hirayama, H., Fujioka, H. and Miyoshi, T., (6): 42, 52
Ohtagaki, T., see Sato, T. et al.
Okamoto, G., Okura, T. and Goto, K., (7): 200
Oksengorn, S., see Besnus, Y. et al.
Okura, T., see Okamoto, G. et al.
Olausson, E. and Uusitalo, S., (7): 325, 338

Oldershaw, A.E., (7): 218, 253
Oldershaw, A.E., see Beales, F.W. and Oldershaw, A.E.
Olson, E.C., (6): 445
Olson, P.E. and Fyles, J.T., (5): 105
Omenetto, P., (5): 11, 34
Onazick, E.P., see Beales, F.W. and Onazick, E.P.
O'Neil, J.R., see White, D.E. et al.
Onions, C.T., (7): 5, 27
Ore, H.T., (7): 99, 100, 101, 155
Oriel, S.S., Myers, D.A. and Crosby, E.J., (6): 410, 445
O'Rourke, J.E., (7): 164, 174, 200
Orville, P.M., (6): 165, 219
Osaki, S., see Sakai, H. et al.
Ostic, R.G., Russell, R.D. and Stanton, R.L., (6): 575, 578, 585
Otgonsuren, O., Perelygin, V.P. and Flerov, G.N., (7): 297, 338
Otto, J.B., see Denison, R.E. et al.
Ovenshine, J.T., see Jones, D.L. et al.
Oversby, V.M., (5): 250, 255
Owen, B.B., see Harned, H.S. and Owen, B.B.
Owens Jr., M.F., see McKnight, E.T. et al.

Packham, G.H., (6): 25, 30, 52, 63, 76
Packham, G.M., (6): 64, 76
Padget, P., see Kullerud, G. et al.
Page, N.J., (6): 90, 105, 108, 114, 116, 125
Pagson, (6): 67
Paknomova, A.S., see Klenova, M.J. and Paknomova, A.S.
Palmer, R.A., see McCormick, J.E. et al.
Paltridge, I.M., (6): 352
Panella, G., (7): 211, 253
Pantazis, Th.M., see Govett, G.J.S. and Pantazis, Th.M.
Panteleyev, A., see Ney, C.S. et al.
        see also Sutherland Brown, A. et al.
Papenfus, J.A., (5): 268, 316
Papezik, V.S., (5): 113, 157
Paproth, E., see Dvorak, J. and Paproth, E.
Parak, T., (6): 52
Park, C.F., (7): 443, 473
Park, C.F. and MacDiarmid, R.A., (5): 277, 290, 293, 316
Park, W.C. and Bastille, R.A., (5): 144, 157
Park, W.C. and Schot, E.K., (7): 217, 253
Parker, V.B., see Wagman, D.D. et al.

Ruitenberg, A.A., Chandra, J. and Ruitenberg, G., (5): 122, 123, 158

Ruitenberg, A.A., Venugopal, D.V. and Giles, P.S., (5): 118, 121, 122, 158

Ruitenberg, A.A., Giles, P.S., Venugopal, D.V. and McCutcheon, S.R., (5): 112, 158

Ruitenberg, G., see Ruitenberg, A.A. et al.

Ruiz, C., Aguilar, A., Egert, E., Espinosa, W., Peebles, F., Quezada, R. and Serrano, M., (6): 17, 19

Runcorn, S.K., (7): 162, 201

Russell, H.D., see Willemse, J. et al.

Russell, M.J., (5): 252, 255

Russell, R.D., see Ostic, R.G. et al.

Russell, R.E., see Mathias, B.V. et al.

Russell, R.T. and Trueman, N.A., (7): 534

Rust, B.R., see Williams, P.F. and Rust, B.R.

Rust, G.W., (6): 430, 445

Ruttner, A., see Lechner, K. et al.

Ryan, B.D. and Blenkinsop, J., (5): 67, 106

Ryan, P.J., (5): 264, 317

Rydell, H., see Bonatti, E. et al.

Rydzewski, A., (6): 405

Rye, D.M., see Williams, N. and Rye, D.M.

Rye, R.O., see Ohmoto, H. and Rye, R.O.
see also Pinckney, D.M. and Rye, R.O.

Ryzhenko, B.N., see Khodakovskiy, I.L. et al.

Saadallah, A.A., see Hagni, R.D. and Saadallah, A.A.

Saager, R., (5): 267, 317; (6): 93, 94, 96, 105, 108, 111, 125

Saager, R. and Esselaar, P.A., (7): 66, 71, 88

Saager, R., see Köppel, V.H. and Saager, R.
see also Viljoen, R.P. et al.

Sackett, W.M., (7): 323, 339

Sadler, H.E. and Wyatt, R.J., (5): 162, 194

Sahama, T.G., see Rankama, K. and Sahama, T.G.

Sahli, E.W., (5): 284, 317

Sainfeld, P., see Bouladon, J. et al.

Sakai, H., Osaki, S. and Tsukagishi, M., (6): 212, 220

Sakai, H., see Kanehira, K. et al.
see also Kobayashi, K. et al.

Sakamoto, T., (7): 190, 192, 194, 201, 235, 253

Sakrison, H.C., (6): 187, 208, 212, 220

Salmon, B.C., Clark, B.R. and Kelly, W.C., (6): 184, 220

Samama, J.C., (6): 2, 9, 17, 20; (7): 145, 156

Samama, J.C., see Bernard, A. and Samama, J.C.

Samsoni, Z., see Szalay, A. and Samsoni, Z.

Sandberger, F., (7): 275, 276, 294

Sander, B., (5): 10, 34; (7): 217, 253

Sanders, J.E., see Friedman, G.M. and Sanders, J.E.

Sangster, D.F., (5): 73, 74, 75, 81, 82, 106, 140, 158; (6): 21, 22, 24, 30, 31, 33, 39, 47, 52, 81, 83, 125, 129, 131, 156, 169, 220, 448, 453, 454, 456, 581, 585; (7): 229, 241, 253

Santos, E.S., see Granger, H.C. et al.

Sapotnitskii, A.A., see Perfilér, B.V. et al.

Sapozhnikov, D.G., (7): 397, 414, 441, 459, 474

Sarjeant, W.A.S., see Ford, T.D. and Sarjeant, W.A.S.

Sarkar, B., (7): 214, 253

Sarkar, S.N., (7): 422, 474

Sasaki, A., (6): 212, 220

Sasaki, A., see Greig, J.A. et al.
see also Kanehira, K. et al.
Sato, K. and Sasaki, A.

Sato, K. and Sasaki, A., (6): 47, 52

Sato, K., Slawson, S.F. and Kanasewich, E.R., (6): 47, 52

Sato, K., see Aoki, K. et al.

Sato, T., (6): 36, 42, 53

Sato, T., Tanimura, S. and Ohtagaki, T., (6): 30, 32, 34, 41, 53

Sato, T., see Lambert, I.B. and Sato, T.
see also Horikoshi, E. and Sato, T.

Sattran, V. and Čadek, J., (5): 240, 241 255

Sattran, V., see Legierski, J. and Sattran, V.

Saupé, F., (7): 490, 494, 495, 502, 503

Saupé, F., see Arnold, M. et al.
see also Maucher, A. and Saupé, F.

Sauvé, P., Cloutier, J.P. and Genois, G., (5): 115, 127, 128, 134, 135, 158

Savage, W.H.D., see Van Rensburg, W.C.J. et al.

Sawkins, F.J., (5): 106, 180, 194, 204, 228; (6): 31, 53, 55, 58, 76, 119, 125, 479, 493

Sawkins, F.J. and Petersen, U., (6): 55, 76

Saxby, J.D., (6): 555, 562, 573, 585

Sayles, F.L. and Bischoff, J.L., (7): 366

Scarpelli, W., (7): 416, 474

Sweeney, R.E., see Kaplan, I.R. et al.
Swett, K., (6): 542, 585
Swiegers, J.U., (5): 292, 317
Swift, W.H., (5): 296, 317
Swineford, A., Leonard, A.B. and Frye, D.C.,
    (7): 209, 210, 254
Szalay, A. and Samsoni, Z., (7): 142, 156

Takabatake, A., (7): 444, 475
Takahashi, T. and Suga, K., (6): 42, 53
Takeuchi, T., see Aoki, K. et al.
Talbot, C.J., (5): 309, 317
Talbott, L.W., see Woodward, L.A. et al.
Taliaferro, N.L. and Hudson, F.S., (7):
    449, 475
Tammam, A.O., see Franklin, J.M. et al.
Tan, F.C., see Perry Jr., E.C. and Tan, F.C.
    see also Perry Jr., E.C. et al.
Tan, L.P., (6): 21, 53
Tanatar, J., (7): 194, 201
Tanimura, S., see Sato, T. et al.
Tarling, D.H., (6): 55, 77, 437, 445; (7):
    303, 339
Tarr, W.A., (6): 1, 20
Tatsumi, T., (5): 107; (6): 208, 212, 221;
    (7): 294
Tatsumi, T. and Clark, L.A., (6): 30, 53
Tatsumi, T. and Watanabe, T., (5): 93, 107,
    152, 158, 237, 255; (6): 35, 53, 211,
    221
Tatsumi, T., Sekine, Y. and Kanehira, K.,
    (7): 294
Tatsumi, T., see Aoki, K. et al.
    see also Kanehira, K. and Tatsumi, T.
Taupitz, K.C., (5): 5, 35; (6): 456
Taupitz, K.C., see Cunningham, W.B. et al.
Tauson, L.V., Kozlov, V.D. and Kuzmin,
    M.I., (6): 17, 20
Taylor, D., see Riley, J.P. and Taylor, D.
Taylor, G.C., (5): 46, 107
Taylor, G.C. and Stott, D.F., (5): 44, 107
Taylor, G.C., Macqueen, R.W. and Thompson,
    R.I., (5): 81, 107
Taylor, G.C., see Macqueen, R.W. and Taylor,
    G.C.
Taylor, G.H., (6): 571, 585
Taylor, G.R., (6): 25, 44, 53
Taylor Jr., H.P., (6): 44, 54, 485, 494
Tchaikovsky, V.K., see Rakhmanov, V.P.
    and Tchaikovsky, V.K.

Temple, K.L. and Le Roux, N.W., (6):
    434, 445
Templeman-Kluit, D.J., (5): 80, 107; (6):
    192, 221
Terasmae, J., (7): 342, 393
Thiel, J.M., see McKnight, E.T. et al.
Thienhaus, R., (7): 186, 201
Thomas, H.H., see Kinkel Jr., A.R. et al.
Thomas, R.L., see Cronan, D.S. and
    Thomas, R.L.
Thomas, R.L., see Damiani, V. et al.
Thompson, G., Shido, F. and Miyashiro,
    A., (6): 45, 54
Thompson, I.S., (5): 244, 245, 256
Thompson, J.B., (7): 182, 201
Thompson, J.B., see Zen, E-an et al.
Thompson, M.E., see Garrels, R.M. and
    Thompson, M.E.
Thompson, R.I., (5): 81, 107
Thompson, R.I., see Taylor, G.C. et al.
Thompson, T.L., see Goebel, E.D. et al.
Thomson, J.E., (6): 145, 221
Thormann, W., see Gundlach, H. and
    Thormann, W.
Thorndike, E., see Ewing, M. et al.
Thurlow, J.C., Swanson, E.A. and
    Strong, D.F., (5): 154; (6): 29, 54
Tikhomirova, E.S., see Strakhov, N.M. et al.
Timms, P.D. and Marshall, D., (6): 160, 221
Timofeieva, M.W., see Egorov, E.W.
    and Timofeieva, M.W.
Tipper, H.W., see Campbell, R.B. and Tipper,
    H.W.
    see also Jeletzky, J.A. and Tipper, H.W.
Tischendorf, G., (6): 387, 405
Tischendorf, G. and Ungethüm, H., (6): 395,
    405
Tixeront, M., (6): 13, 20
Toens, P.D., (5): 274, 317
Tokunaga, M. and Honma, H., (6): 37, 54,
    202, 221
Tollmann, A., (5): 35
Tollon, F., see Dandurand, J.L. et al.
Tomasson, J. and Kristmannsdottir, H.,
    (5): 122, 158
Tooms, J.S. and Summerhayes, C.P., (7):
    509, 535
Tooms, J.S., Summerhayes, C.P. and Cronan,
    D.S.L., (7): 520, 521, 522, 535

SUBJECT INDEX (PART II)

(Numbers in parentheses refer to volume numbers)

Abitibi belt, Ontario, (6): 24, 25, 141–146,
   153, 161, 173, 201
Absorption, (6): 342, 529
–, equilibrium, (7): 142
– of gold, (7): 18, 60
–, uranium, (7): 143
Abyssal environment, (6): 56
– –, tholeiitic basalt, (6): 56, 60, 68
Acadian orogeny, Northern Appalachians, (5):
   112, 117, 130, 136, 142, 144, 152, 153
Acidic igneous rocks, (6): 29, 32, 71, 74, 96,
   117, 155, 168, 169, 172, 173, 188, 209,
   211, 307, 390, 578
– – –, acid vs. basic rocks, (7): 86
– – – of Canadian Cordillera, (5): 96, 97,
   98
– – – of Eastern Alps, (5): 2, 3, 4
– – –, associated with Hg–Sb–W deposits,
   (7): 477, 499–501
– – – of Ireland, (5): 235
– – – of Lake district, England, (5): 219
– – – of Lahn–Dill-type deposits, (7): 275
– – – of Northern Appalachians, (5): 112,
   115, 119, 127–144, 146, 148–151
– – –, ores in acid host-rocks, (5): 90–92,
   93, 115
– – – in origin of ancient Mn-deposits, (7)
   441, 447, 452–456, 458, 460
– – – of Pacific orogen, (5): 47, 89
– – – as source of SiO$_2$, (7): 192
– – –, part of source model, (7): 9
– – – of South Africa, (5): 259, 261, 282–
   284, 289, 290, 294; (7): 8, 20, 44, 67,
   85–87
– – – of U.S.A. Western States, (7): 95
– – –, see also Felsic igneous rocks
Actualistic principle
– –, applied to Lahn–Dill-type ores, (7):
   256, 274, 270–281, 290
– –, – – Precambrian cherty Iron Forma-

tions, (7): 157, 158, 189, 190, 230, 231,
   235, 238
– –, see also Comparative studies
Adsorption, (7): 325, 329, 361, 364, 370, 374,
   386, 388, 397, 403, 495, 522, 527
– in concentrating metals, (6): 384–389, 434,
   435, 529, 569
– in Kupferschiefer genesis, (6): 381, 382,
   384, 391
–, Noll's Law, (6): 382
Aeolian environment, (6): 417
– – of Zambian copper belt, (6): 227, 228,
   244, 250, 255, 275, 276, 284, 286,
   298–300, 302, 303, 307, 308, 313,
   319–321, 324, 329–331, 334, 335,
   344, 346
Aeromagnetic maps, (6): 460
Ages, absolute, (6): 156, 158, 400, 537, 575,
   576, 578
–, – and relative, (6): 2, 11, 21, 22, 31, 32,
   48, 82, 116, 129, 152
– of ancient Mn-deposits, (7): 395, 398–403,
   414, 416, 417, 419, 423, 427–429, 431,
   435–440, 443, 456, 460
– of Columbian orogen, (5): 55, 63
– of deep-sea Mn-nodules, (7): 300–301, 303,
   435
–, differences of greenstones, (7): 9, 86
– of dikes and sills in Witwatersrand, (7): 46
–, distribution of major magmatic and metamorphic events, (7): 165
– of freshwater Mn-deposits, (7): 345, 435
– of Hg–Sb–W deposits, (7): 478–480, 482,
   483, 485–487, 489–491, 493, 499
– of Ireland, (5): 235, 237, 250
– of Lake district, England, (5): 217, 218
– of Mendip Hills, (5): 187, 190
–, metamorphic, (7): 165
– of Mississippi Valley-type deposits, (6):
   449, 451, 468, 513, 514, 529

– – of carbonate rocks, (6): 500
– – of deep-sea Mn-nodules, (7): 304
– –, elements, (7): 145
– – in geochemical cell (roll), (7): 127
– – of fresh-water Mn-deposits, (7): 345, 380
– –, gold, (7): 8
– –, heavy minerals, (7): 19, 78
– –, limonite, (6): 512
– –, manganese, (6): 512
– –, of phosphorite-type, (7): 509–511, 514, 531
– –, see also Clays
– –, see also Lag deposits
Resistivity against weathering, (6): 1, 4
Reworking, (6): 4, 6, 82, 83, 168, 172, 242, 342, 345, 399, 416, 428; (7): 8, 16, 19, 21, 27, 29, 46, 48, 52, 54, 58, 63, 73, 77, 106, 112, 146, 171, 176, 179, 263
– of Hg–Sb–W deposits, (7): 478, 496,
– of Lahn–Dill-type deposits, (7): 264–266, 268, 272
– of phosphate deposits, (7): 509, 511, 514, 516, 528–531
– of Precambrian Iron Formations, (7): 171, 176, 179, 205, 208
– of sulphides, sphalerite and dolomite, (6): 451
–, see also Mobilization
–, see also Remobilization
Rhodesian copper belt, (5): 297
– – –, see also Zambian copper belt
Rhodochrosite, (5): 303
Rhodonite, (5): 29
Rhyolite, (5): 10, 49, 52, 88, 91, 109, 114, 117, 118, 122, 130, 131, 135, 136, 140, 142, 144, 146, 150, 259, 283, 284; (6): 22, 24–26, 29–32, 36, 44, 47, 71–73, 118, 119, 144, 146, 149, 152, 158, 168, 169, 171, 173, 185, 186, 194, 209, 457, 537; (7): 44, 45, 142, 168, 442, 452, 453
Rhythmicity, see Cycles and cyclicity
Riebeckite, (7): 203, 222
Rifts, (6): 57, 59, 61, 64, 71, 206, 207
–, see also Metallogenesis and metallogeny
–, see also Plate tectonics
Rio Tinto deposits, Spain, (6): 23, 34, 42; (7): 447
– – –, associated Mn-deposits, (7): 447, 448
Rises and ridges, see Paleogeography and paleotopography
River water

– –, supply of metal and organics in fresh-water Mn-deposits, (7): 371–377, 397
Roan deposits, Zambian copper belt, (6): 285–297, 326, 332, 333, 337, 339, 341, 346, 347
– – –, cross-section, (6): 279, 295, 296
Roll (uranium cell), (7): 92, 98, 114–146
–, see also Geochemical cell (roll)
–, see also Western States-type deposits
Roseberry deposit, Australia, (6): 22, 27–30, 44, 45
– –, spacing, (6): 35
Rote Fäule
– – of Kupferschiefer deposit, (6): 363, 368–371, 376, 379, 382, 393–395, 397–401
Rubidium/strontium method and ages, (5): 67–68; (6): 156, 235, 238, 267, 576; (7): 32
Rutile, (5): 146, 268, 270

Sabkha environments and deposits
– – – –, Cu-deposits, (6): 407–443
– – – – of Zambian copper belt deposits, (6): 319, 335, 349
Salinity, (5): 178, 179, 202, 204, 224, 280, 281; (6): 9, 202, 203, 284, 410, 422, 538, 540, 568; (7): 169, 191, 192, 214, 225, 277, 330, 405, 529
–, saline fluids, (6): 9, 11, 202, 203, 207, 284, 299, 410, 485
– of sea water, (6): 42
–, types of salinity-temperature solutions, (6): 203–205
–, see also Brines
–, see also Evaporites
–, see also Fluid inclusions
–, see also Volcanic–exhalative processes and deposits
Salmo-type Pb–Zn ores, (5): 74–76
– – – vs. Shuswap-type ore, (5): 76
Salt deposits, (5): 306
Salton Sea hydrothermal system, (5): 70, 71, 288; (6): 202, 437, 440; (7): 277–281, 285
Sandstones and sandstone-ore host-rocks, (6): 1–18,
– – – – of ancient Mn-deposits, (7): 423–430, 440, 451, 453, 455, 456, 458
– – – – of Canadian Cordillera, (5): 99
– – – – of Columbian orogen, (5): 41, 45, 56, 78
– – – – with copper, Ireland, (5): 239